TMap® Next

TMap® Next

for result-driven testing

Tim Koomen
Leo van der Aalst
Bart Broekman
Michiel Vroon

UTN Publishers, 's-Hertogenbosch

This book is a full translation of the the Dutch book
TMap Next, voor resultaatgericht testen, 2006, ISBN 90-72194-79-9

Translation: V V H business translations, Utrecht (NL)

UTN Publishers
Willem van Oranjelaan 5
5211 CN 's-Hertogenbosch
The Netherlands
www.utn.nl

ISBN(10) 90-72194-80-2
ISBN(13) 9789072194800

Preface

Foreword to TMap Next, by Rex Black

By the 1980s, Fred Brooks and Barry Boehm had explained that the costs and risks associated with bugs are high and increase as projects progress. In the 1980s, Boris Beizer and Bill Hetzel added another essential insight: testing, done properly, must be influenced by, and influence, risk.

Come the 1990s, leading test professionals were striving mightily to put these insights into action. How do we integrate testing into the entire lifecycle to reduce cost and schedule impacts of bugs? How do we use risk to determine the extent and sequence of testing? How can we report test results in terms of risks mitigated and not mitigated? How can we help project teams make rational decisions regarding the optimal amount of time and energy to expend on testing?

I was one of those test professionals. So were the authors of this book, Tim Koomen, Leo van der Aalst, Bart Broekman, Michiel Vroon, and Rob Baarda. In this book, as in my own books, you can see where that synthesis has taken us. And it has taken us a long way.

As you read this book, comprehensive and comprehensible, pause to remember that it was only ten years ago that test professionals were struggling to understand and implement a complete, consistent approach to testing that managed product quality risks and delivered demonstrable business value. Now, test professionals have a number of fully articulated strategies such as those in this book and my own books which we can use to ensure that we are solving the right testing problems.

In this book, you'll find practical ideas for business driven test management and product risk analysis. These two concepts are so central to testing, yet so often ignored and misunderstood. How does testing serve the needs of the organization and project? What are the risks associated with the system under test that can and should be mitigated through testing? These may seem like obvious questions, yet all too often test teams don't know the answers, or, worse yet, they "know" the *wrong answers*. Getting the right answers to these questions is foundational to a good test effort, and serves to set the direction.

As essential as this direction-setting, foundation-laying material is, there is a lot more to this book than just a means to get the starting point right. Indeed, the authors promise a "full description of the total test process," an explanation of the entire TMap method, from start to finish, and they deliver.

Let me mention a few high points.

The chapter summarizing test design techniques is alone a good reason to have this book close at hand if you work as a test engineer. The discussion on bug management is a fine one. There is a wide-ranging discussion of estimation techniques. There is an intelligent discussion of test metrics, one that doesn't make the all-too-frequent mistake of starting with fancy Excel graphs and tables, but rather by discussing what kind of information that management needs from us as testers.

Pick a random spot in this book and you'll find something interesting. Whether you are in the first days or the final days of a test effort, you'll find pertinent ideas in this book. Like my own books, this book was obviously written to sit on your desk, ready to serve as a helpful guide on a regular basis, not to collect dust on your bookshelf.

I have in the past complained that as testers we have not built on the foundations of our profession as well as our brothers and sisters in programming. In fact, this has been a key driver for me as an author of testing books. Similarly, Tim, Leo, Bart, Michiel, and Rob have done a fine job of summarizing in this book a number of foundational concepts in software testing. For that reason, I recommend that this book join the set of ready references available to you as together we practice and improve our profession of software testing.

Rex Black, October 2006
Author of *Managing the Testing Process, Critical Testing Processes, Foundations of Software Testing,* and *Pragmatic Software Testing*
President of Rex Black Consulting Services, Inc.
President of the International Software Testing Qualifications Board

Foreword by Luc-François Salvador

It is a great privilege for me to recommend TMap Next to you as a member of the continued growing group of people who are professionally involved in improving the quality of a wide range of business processes.

Test Management Approach (TMap) was published in 1996 as a revolutionary management approach for structured testing. Within a few years, TMap was adopted worldwide by companies searching for a structured way to improve their information systems. The objective is to preserve their business processes and market image from damage.
Today TMap has become the de facto world standard for structured testing.

In the meantime, information technology is developing with an astonishing speed. The complexity of chains of information systems supporting the business is increasing rapidly. Defect tolerance is decreasing at the same speed. Experience gained by practice in the area of software testing and the knowledge of IT issues acquired over the years in professional testing are brought together in this complete update: TMap Next.

This impressive book is an absolute **must** for the modern business manager, IT manager, and Testing expert. Not only will TMap Next inform you as a manager of how to take advantage of the latest developments in the testing profession, but also, even more importantly, assist you in improving the quality of IT incorporated in your current business processes.

Without hesitation I can say this to the reader – if you practice what you read in this book the dream of predictable software engineering to realize business value is indeed attainable by your organization.

Luc-François Salvador
CEO Sogeti SA
Paris

Foreword by the authors

Introducing a completely revised and updated TMap

Ten years after the first (Dutch) book; five years after the second version; and three years after the English translation, we started with a large-scale renewal of the method at the end of 2005. The result is this new book.

We published this completely new version for several reasons:
- Over time many people have asked us to update the method and suggested ideas.
- In 2006, most organisations recognize the importance of testing and are focusing more on the duration, quantity and objects of testing.
- In the previous version, testing was described as an autonomous process in the (waterfall) development of new information systems. Current IT trends are much more broadly based: more maintenance than new development, many package implementations and iterative and agile system development. While the method evolved along with practice, the book did not. In this new version, testing is presented as a much more integral part of the big picture.
- In many organisations testing is more part of mainstream activities instead of purely as a project-based activity. A variety of line organisation are possible, including complete test factories, each with their specific pros and cons. The literature devotes little attention to this aspect.
- And perhaps most importantly: testing should be perceived much more as an economic activity within IT. Time and costs, but the benefits as well, must be made clear to the client. With this information, he or she can manage test work on the basis of the required quantity of time and costs versus the benefits: insight into quality and risks, confidence in the product, and project (management) information. This part of TMap is BDTM, Business Driven Test Management, and represents the main motive of the method.

We faced a number of challenges while revising the method. The suggested revisions sometimes conflicted heavily with the awareness that many organisations are already using TMap to their full satisfaction and are not very happy about changing their methods. We therefore decided to leave the main components of TMap intact, but incorporate the necessary revisions to the details. We proceeded with the greatest possible care. For you, as our reader, this means that you will recognise many things. We preserved the outline of the process descriptions on the basis of phases, with various activities per phase, and the attention devoted to techniques, organisation and infrastructure. We made several supplemental changes to these elements.

The main changes are:
- BDTM has been traced through the process as a motive to offer the client as many management options for testing as possible.
- The performance of a product risk analysis is described in detail.
- We have included various estimating techniques for testing.
- The management activity has been expanded considerably.
- Setting up and managing the infrastructure has become a separate phase, and we added the new role of test infrastructure coordinator.
- The description of the test design techniques has been improved significantly and updated. The techniques are now related to various coverage types.
- Several supporting processes, such as the permanent test organisation, but also the selection and implementation of tools and management of test environments, are discussed.
- Test types for regression, usability, performance, portability and security testing have been added.
- The method is described in a much wider context than simply new development in a waterfall programme.
- The entire book has been enriched with tips, more detailed information, and practical examples (more than 400).

The new TMap can be summarised by four essential points:
- It is based on a business driven test management approach that enables the client to manage the test process on rational and economic grounds.
- It provides a full description of the total test process.
- TMap contains a complete 'tool set', i.e. technique descriptions, checklists, procedures, and so on.
- It is an adaptive method that can be applied in a versatile manner, making it suitable for all test situations in most development environments, such as new development, maintenance, waterfall / iterative / agile development, customised or package software.

TMap offers the tester and the test manager guidelines to deliver results for the client.

Since the request for renewal came from both Dutch-speaking countries and other countries, the book is published concurrently in both Dutch and English.

We created this new edition without involvement from the original authors, Martin Pol, Ruud Teunissen and Erik van Veenendaal. We are still highly appreciative of their pioneering work in creating a complete test method. TMap would not be what it is without them.

Clearly a large group of people assisted in the creation of this book. Their contributions range from suggesting ideas, sharing experiences and experience products and reviewing chapters, to helping us establish the required preconditions. Whatever their contribution, it proved vital to the quality we achieved. We would like to take this opportunity to thank them. While aware of the risk of forgetting one or more of our valued contributors, we would still like to list their names here.

We first thank the external reviewers who invested their great knowledge, time and attention to reviewing this work. These are:
Jan Blaas (KPN)
Jan Boerman (ICTRO, Ministry of Justice)
Jarmila Bökkerink-Scheerova (Philips)
Heidi Driessen (Rabobank)
Bart Dooms (Acerta, Belgium)
Ed van der Geest (SNS Bank)
Erwin Kleinveld (Rabobank)
Sander Koopman (Fortis Bank)
Ine Lutterman (Interpay)
Marco Maggi (Ministry of Agriculture, Nature and Food quality)
Benjamin Makkes van der Deijl (PGGM)
Jan Mellema (CIP Police)
Remco Möhringer (Reaal Insurance)
Paul van der Molen (Cordares)
Brian Taylor (FortisBank)
Ubel van Tergouw (UWV)
Sylvia Verschueren (ABN AMRO)
Hans Vedder (Friesland Bank)
Dennis van Velzen (AFAS ERP Software BV)

Naturally our big group of Sogeti colleagues proved immensely helpful. Their contributions vary from membership of the sounding board group to reviewing, contributing ideas and even complete texts:
Richard Ammerlaan, Eric Begeer, Paul Bentvelzen, John Bloedjes, Martin Blokpoel, Hester Blom, Martin Boomgaardt, Raoul Gisbers, Frank Goorhuis, Guy Holtus, Bart Hooft van Iddekinge, André Huikeshoven, Marco Jansen van Doorn, Ralph Klomp, Rob Kuijt as guest author of chapter 7, Peter van Lint, Dominic Maes (Sogeti Belgium), Willem-Jan van der Meer, Henk Meeuwisse, Gerrit Mudde, Guido Nelissen, Bert Noorman, André van Pelt, Elisabeth Reitsma, Ewald Rooderijs, Rob Smit, Gert Stad, Marc Valkier, Thomas Veltman, Johan Vink, Ben Visser, Harm de Vries, expertise group for usability (Kinga Visser, Gina Utama, Ronald Oomen, Wolter van Popta, Robin Klein, Thomas Veltman, Mans Scholten, Mark Schut, Martien Adema, Jeroen Bultje)

Our Sogeti USA colleagues Craig Mayer, Camille Tetta Costanzo and Dan Hannigan reviewed the English language chapters in little time and, where necessary, suggested improvements.

This work would not have been impossible without the support of the Software Control management team. We would like to express our thanks to Wim van Uden and Mark Paap in particular. Their appreciation and interest proved a huge stimulus.

We worked on the book with great enthusiasm. Whether you are an experienced TMap user or an inexperienced tester, we hope this work offers you a clear story on how to best set up the test process in all its aspects and inspire you with many ideas, detailed information and tips. We are proud of the result and hope you, our reader, will agree.

Tim Koomen
Leo van der Aalst
Bart Broekman
Michiel Vroon
Rob Baarda (project leader and editor)

Rotterdam, October 2006

Recommendations

"The quality of our IT is essential for our business operations. New releases may not disrupt the business processes, they must be faultless. To demonstrate this quality of IT and to give assurance to the business good and structured test processes are very important. This requires a fruitful cooperation between business and IT-department. I would like to stress the importance of Business Driven Test Management as explained in this book. We are implementing BDTM now step-by-step. The TMap method is an important tool for our test processes and we are glad that we as Fortis have contributed to this new version of the book."
Gert Heslenfeld,
Sectormanager IS / Accountmanager Information Services,
Fortis Insurance, The Netherlands

"TMap Next, is definitely a must read for test organizations using TPI Model for Test Process Improvement and/or TMap approach to testing. At the same time, the book is not dependent on understanding of these models, and is a useful resource for organizations implementing risk based test strategy in their organizations.. The process, techniques and tools described in this book will enable a test professional to better balance the test cost with the benefits provided by testing, thus making it easier to get management buy in for the test project."
Ruku Tekchandani
SW Validation CoP Program Manager
Intel Corporation, United States of America

"In many organisations all over the world TMap is the standard for testing for many years. The experiences gained using TMap over all these years and the new approaches in software development are the motivators to update TMap and to write this book. For instance, product risk analysis and business driven test management are added to TMap as well as use case testing and exploratory testing. The "new" TMap standard is very useful to solve the testing problems of today and tomorrow."
Prof. Dr. Andreas Spillner
University of Applied Sciences Bremen
Member of the German Testing Board (SIGIST)
Germany

"This is testing in a book. If you need to implement the practice of testing, this is a tool that is essential. Tim Koomen and colleagues have taken a great and popular book, TMap®, and have improved it in its updating – TMap Next highlights testing as an economic activity within IT and, the new emphasis on Business Driven Test Management empowers the business to get the economic and other benefits from IT that they have only dreamed of until now. This book will become a classic on software testing."

Wayne Mallinson and Peter Sage
Communications and Technical Directors respectively – Test and Data Services (Pty) Ltd
Founder and current Chairman respectively – CSSA Special Interest Group in Software Testing (SIGiST)
Gauteng South Africa

"TMap contains practical, proven ideas and methods for a risk based testing approach. The updated TMap is an important read for anyone endeavoring to understand how business driven test management fits within the context of the end-to-end process of business driven development."

Dr. Daniel Sabbah
General Manager, IBM Rational Software
United States of America

"The Ministry of Agriculture, Nature and Food Quality spends a lot of money each year to maintenance, package implementations and development of software. Standardisation at all disciplines in the software lifecycle is necessary to manage these processes. In the lifecycle, testing is becoming more important from a quality and cost perspective. That is why the Ministry has chosen for a standard method and a permanent test organisation. It is good to see this standard TMap evolving, not only adapting to the fast technological developments, but, with Business Driven Test Management, also answering to the increasing demands of clients. "

Pieter C.A. Arends
Manager Project management, Consultancy & Test services
Member of the board of IT-operations
Ministry of Agriculture, Nature and Food Quality The Netherlands

"I like this book because of it being a detailed recipe for how to organize, plan, execute and control testing. Most techniques are explained in detail, with lots of examples. Especially useful are the chapters about handling risk, and the one about test case design. The latter one is great for system and acceptance testing, while most other literature concentrates on lower level testing."
Hans Schaefer
Independent test consultant
Leader of the Norwegian Testing Board (SIGIST)

"TMap is one of the important instruments to assure the quality of our IT products. That is why REAAL Insurances has gladly contributed to the part on development testing in TMap Next."
Nico Jongerius
Member of the board/CIO of REAAL Insurances
The Netherlands

"TMap is for testing what ITIL is for operational processes. This book is a comprehensive yet highly accessible guide for both test managers and test professionals. It is truly a meaningful help to anyone who's involved in the testing business; whether you have one or more specific questions, or if you are in search of a whole testing framework or well targeted process improvements."
Wim Waterinckx
process manager testing
KBC Group
Belgium

"TMap is the most thorough to help organise testing in large IT companies".
Dorothy Graham, Grove Consultants
Great Britain

"I've been a heavy user of TMap since the availability of the book in English. I have utilized TMap for testing process communication, competence development and expanding the "skill-toolbox" of my testers in Nokia. The basic framework is very similar, but it is now much more useful because of the explicit support for wider selection of contexts.
I like the clarity of the big picture of test design: how test planning includes risk-based test strategy that links to test types, and how eventually various test design techniques provide the right depth for testing at expected coverage. As a bonus the framework suits well to expanding with your own techniques and test types."
Erkki Pöyhönen
TietoEnator Quality Assurance Competence Center, previously with Nokia
Finland

"As the quality assurance was moving from a project issue to an issue for the company board our test organisation needed to unify and structure the test process. TMap Next follows the projects phases and has as a logical toolbox. This helped us to complement our existing test process to meet the company board's timescale. TMap Next also gave us useful information how to handle people, tools, infrastructure and the organisation that in many ways has influenced the organisation of the test centre at the Swedish Tax Agency."
Henrik Rylander
Head of Test Centre
Test Unit
The Swedish Tax Agency
Sweden

Contents

PROCESSES

1   Introduction

TMap is Sogeti's prominent Test Management approach to the structured testing of information systems. The approach is described generically, since the specific makeup of this, the best fitting test approach, depends on the situation in which it is applied.
TMap can be summarised in four essentials:
1. TMap is based on a business driven test management approach.
2. TMap describes a structured test approach.
3. TMap contains a complete tool box.
4. TMap is an adaptive test method.

The first mentioned essential is directly related to the fact that the importance of the IT-business case (the justification of a project) for organisations is continuously growing. For testing this means the choices on what risks to cover with testing, what results are to be delivered and how much time and money to spend need to be made based on rational and economic grounds. This is why TMap has developed the business driven test management approach, which can be seen as the 'leading thread' of the structured TMap test process.

By describing a structured test process (essential 2) and giving a complete tool box, TMap answers the classic questions what/when, how, what with and who. With the description of test process use has been made of the TMap life cycle model: a development cycle related description of the test cycle. The life cycle model describes *what/when* should be carried out.

Besides this, to be able to execute the test process properly, several issues in the field of infrastructure (*what with*), techniques (*how*) and organisation (*who*) should be implemented. TMap provides a lot of applicable information in the shape of examples, checklists, technique descriptions, procedures, test organisation structures and test environment/tools (essential 3).

Furthermore, TMap has a flexible design so that it can be applied to several system development situations: i.e. new development as well as maintenance of information systems, development in-house or a purchased package and with outsourcing of (parts of) the testing (essential 4).

In this chapter, a sequential overview is given of how TMap became a standard approach to structured testing, the reasons for a new version of TMap, the key points of TMap and a number of suggestions concerning which chapters are of interest to which target groups.

1.1   The history of TMap

In the international testing world, TMap is a familiar concept, as this approach to testing has been in existence for some time. While it is not necessary to know the history of TMap in order to understand or apply the approach, this section invites you to take a glimpse behind the scenes.

Standard approach to structured testing

This book was preceded by the Dutch book "*Testen volgens TMap*" (= Testing according to TMap) in 1995 and "*Software Testing*" [a guide to the TMap approach] in 2002 (both books by Pol, Teunissen and Van Veenendaal)[1]. The books turned out to be, and still are, bestsellers. TMap has evolved over recent years to become a standard for testing information systems. It is currently applied in hundreds of companies and organisations, including many banks, insurance companies, pension funds and government organisations. The fact that TMap is seen to be a prominent standard approach to structured testing is demonstrated by facts as, for example, suppliers of test tools advertising with the words "applicable in combination with the TMap techniques"; test professionals who ensure that TMap experience is prominent on their CV or, increasingly, that they are TMap-certificated; recruitment advertisements in which test professionals with knowledge of TMap are sought, and independent training institutions that provide TMap courses. It is also worth mentioning the publication in a leading Dutch IT-magazine "Computable" of 30 September 2005, showing TMap to be the most-requested competence! Ahead of Java, ITIL and Unix, for example.

Moreover, its use is growing fast in other market segments, such as in the embedded software industry. Since testing in this industry differs from testing in the administrative world, another TMap concept-based book has been written especially for this [Broekman, 2003].

The strength of TMap

The strength of TMap can largely be attributed to the considerable practical experience that is the basis for the method. This experience comes from hundreds of professional testers in as many projects over the last twenty years! The aim of this book is to be a valuable aid in coping with most, if not all, challenges in the area of testing now and in the near future. The disadvantage of a book is that the content, by definition, is static, while in the field of IT new insights, system development methods, etc., are created with great regularity.

It would be commercially irresponsible to compile and publish a new version the TMap book with every new development in IT. To enable TMap to keep

---

[1] Up-to-date information about the translations in other languages can be found at www.tmap.net

up with current developments, an expansion mechanism is created. An expansion describes the way TMap has to be applied in a new development. Recent expansions, in the form of white papers, are included in the book *TMap Test Topics* [Koomen, 2005]. To keep the TMap users updated about the new expansions, different means of communication are used. For example, the large number of presentations and workshops that are given at test conferences, the popular TMap Test Topics sessions (in which current test themes are presented) and the many articles in the various specialist publications. All of this makes TMap what it is now: "A complete test approach, with which any organisation can successfully take on any test challenge, now and in the future!"

Tip

Take a look at www.tmap.net. You will find there, among other things:
• downloads (including white papers for expansions, checklists, test-design techniques and a glossary)
• published TMap articles
• TMap newsletters (if you wish to receive these automatically, you can register for this on the site).

1.2 TMap evolves in step

"Why then a new version of TMap," you may ask, "Was there something wrong with the previous version?" No, however, since it appeared on the market, various new developments have taken place both in IT and testing. And in order to keep TMap as complete and up to date as possible, these have been incorporated in the new version. This concerns developments such as the increasing importance of IT to organisations and a number of innovations in the area of system development. Besides this, the tester appears to be better served by a test approach written as a guide, rather than as a testing manual. An explanation of this is given in the following sections.

Increasing importance of IT to organisations

Since the end of the nineties, the use of software or information technology in general, has become increasingly important to organisations, so that IT projects are more often initiated and managed from within a user organisation. This is prompted by the following developments:

■ Cost reductions of IT development and management
  IT is required to be cheaper and the business case (the 'why' in combination with costs and profits) formulated more clearly.
■ Growing automation of business processes

More and more business processes within organisations are either automated or strongly dependent on other automated processes.

- Quicker deployment of automation
  With the growth of automation, IT has grown from being a company support resource to one that differentiates the company from the competition. This means that the flexibility and speed with which this resource can be deployed is of crucial importance in beating the competition.
- Quality of automation is becoming more important (see the practical example "Consequences of software failures"). The fact that IT end users currently make sure they have their say, combined with the fact that CEO's, CFO's and CIO's are made personally responsible for the accuracy of the company's financial information leads to (renewed) interest in quality of IT.

These four aspects are summed up as "more for less, faster and better". A consequence of this is that IT projects are becoming increasingly dynamic and chaotic in nature. This can put great pressure on the testers and increase the relative share of testing within IT. In order to make the test process manageable and to keep it that way, the "business driven test management" (BDTM) approach was developed for TMap, and has been incorporated in this book. With this, the creation of a test strategy is directly related to the risks. It enables the client to make responsible, risk-based choices in the test process. By making these choices, the client has significant influence on the timeline and the costs of the test process.

Real-world examples

Consequences of software failures
Because IT has become more important within organisations, the impact of any software problems is increased.
Some examples are:
- Revenue loss
- Brand/reputation loss
- Compensation claims
- Productivity loss.

The fact that this can involve considerable losses is demonstrated by the following real-world examples:
- A sporting goods manufacturer suffered a 24% drop in turnover (€100 million) in a single quarter because of software faults in the stock administration. In the days that followed, after the company had announced that they had problems with the software, the share value decreased by more than 20%.
- Through a fault in their encryption software, a financial advisory organisation displayed their customers' social security numbers and passwords in legible text on

their website. This caused distress among the customers and led to a sizeable loss of business.
- After a pharmaceutical wholesale company had gone bankrupt, the parent company submitted a claim for damages of €500 million to the software supplier, claiming that the 'enterprise software' had been faulty.

Innovations in the system development area

The test principles on which TMap is based, came into being in the eighties, and, of course, they relate to the system development methods of that time. Nowadays, these methods are often referred to as 'waterfall' methods. Their most important characteristic is the purely sequential execution of the various development activities. Besides that there is a growing interest in other methods. The most important characteristic of the new generation of system development methods is incremental or iterative development, with the test process increasingly being integrated in the development process. Dynamic Systems Development Methodology® (DSDM), Rational Unified Process® (RUP), Rapid Application Development (RAD) and the Agile approach are examples of this.

Since, in the course of various activities, testing touches on the chosen system development method, it is inevitable that a test approach like TMap should evolve in step with changes in the area of system development. How to apply TMap in certain situations is often already laid down in the previously mentioned expansions. The key points of the expansions have now been integrated in this new version of TMap, so that the book again provides a current and as complete as possible overview of how TMap can be applied in a variety of situations.

Test approach guide

The previously mentioned two developments, i.e. the increasing importance of IT within organisations and the innovations in system development, indicate the increased dynamic of the various development and test environments. In a situation like this, a manual is often seen as being too rigid. Furthermore, it appears that testing is increasingly being carried out by a broader public with a wide range of competencies, so that there is now a greater need for more comprehensive descriptions of how specific TMap activities can be carried out. A consequence of this for the description of the test approach is that it needs to be written more as a guide than a manual, taking the reader 'by the hand'.

The version of TMap now before you has been entirely revised in response to the developments mentioned and to the many requests for amendments and amplifications to the book.

In short, this version of TMap *offers the tester a guide to delivering results to the client.*

1.3   What TMap offers

But what exactly does TMap now offer – what can you do with it? You will find the answer to that question in this section, in which a general overview is given of the assistance that TMap can supply and where TMap can be applied. In the rest of the book, this is gone into in more detail and much attention is paid to the way in which TMap can be applied in various situations.

1.3.1   Where TMap helps

In order to assist the tester in his work, TMap explains how to carry out certain activities, or how these are supported by TMap. This concerns help with:
- the translation of the client's requirements into a concrete test approach and management of the execution
- assisting the test manager, test coordinator and/or tester to deal with the various IT development approaches, each from within their own areas of responsibility
- the execution of, among other things:
  - a product risk analysis
  - a test strategy
  - a (non-)functional test
- the organisation of testers in e.g. an existing test organisation or in flexible project teams
- the setting up and the management of test infrastructure for the current and other projects
- the creation of test designs and the use of various test design techniques
- the preparation, specification and execution of the tests, described as processes within the TMap processes
- the execution of the test activities with real-world examples, tips and also detailed explanations of certain aspects
- the reporting of the test results from the perspective of the client
- supplying information in connection with the project result
- considering the test process as much as possible from the exterior vantage point, by answering, for example, practical questions (what does testing actually deliver?) and making use of general project information
- selecting the right test dialogue partner for specific clients:
  - a test manager views the testing from a wider perspective (focusing on the environment) and is therefore a suitable contact for clients at management level

- a test coordinator focuses mainly on the internal test process and will therefore often be the contact for e.g. project leaders
- a tester is task-focused and will concern himself mainly with the design and execution of the test cases.

1.3.2   Where TMap can be applied

These days, the IT development approach is extremely variable. TMap addresses this directly and first defines the following possibilities of applying TMap:

- where there is either a demand-supplier relationship (e.g. outsourcing) between client, developer and tester (each with their own responsibilities), or a collective interactive approach
- with iterative, incremental, waterfall and agile approaches
- with new development, maintenance and migration of information systems
- in situations with combinations of development approaches, such as in-house, reuse-based, use of standard packages and assembling of purchased modules, all within a single IT architecture
- with coverage of non-functional requirements of the information system in the test approach
- in situations where much attention has to be paid to the communication process and associated skills.

Tip

The implementation or improvement of a test approach is not something that can be done casually. Among other things, it requires knowledge of the current test maturity of an organisation and of the environment in which the testing is to be implemented or improved. It should also be clear why there is a need for certain test aspects to be improved. It often seems difficult in practice to determine what steps should be taken in which sequence in order to implement or improve the testing. The "Test Process Improvement" model [Koomen, 1999] is a popular model of step-by-step implementation and improvement of a test approach.

1.4   Reading guide and the most important changes

If you are reading this book,[2] the chances are that you want an answer to a specific (test) question. If you don't wish to read the whole book, the following description of its structure and the reading guide should lead you to the answer quickly.

To notice all the differences compared with the last version, the whole book should be read. Most of the text has been re-written and the book contains more than 400 new ideas, tips and examples. We can however, imagine that an experienced TMap user would quickly like to find the changes made. Therefore we have added a section that refers to the chapters, sections and subjects which have undergone major, important changes (section 1.4.3).

1.4.1   Structure of the book

The book has three parts: general, processes and components.

The general part describes the framework and importance of testing. Besides giving the history and evolution of TMap, it also describes what TMap has to offer, providing a summary overview.

The processes part describes the test processes, including the master test plan (managing the total test process), acceptance and system testing and development testing. Also described in this part are the associated supporting processes (including the permanent test organisation and the organisation and management of test environments).

The components part describes a number of components that can be used independently (including quality characteristics and test roles) or as an aid in the processes (including product risk analysis and test design techniques). For a complete overview of these components, refer to table 1.1 "Reading suggestions" in the next section.

At various places in the book, definitions, practical examples, tips and more detailed explanations are provided. These can be recognised by title and a box or a grey background.

---

[2] For the sake of readability of the book, the use of he/she has not been included. However, where reference is made to 'he', it should be understood that 'she' is emphatically also intended.

1.4.2 Reading guide

The main target group of this book is those who are directly involved in the test process. A test team can use the book as a guide for carrying out the test activities. For those who operate further on from the primary test process, such as clients, end users and EDP auditors, the book offers good insight into professional testing. To this end, some chapters have been included on the background and organisation of testing.

"TMap Next" is not a book that asks to be read from cover to cover. Depending on your involvement in testing, chapters can be read carefully, scanned quickly, or even skipped altogether. The requirement for, or interest in, the various chapters will vary per target group. As an aid to choosing the chapters that are of interest in connection with certain questions or target groups, reading suggestions have been provided (table 1.1). On the next page we distinguish some possible questions and target groups:

A. You are requested to set up the testing of an application and to manage its execution (test managers, test coordinators, etc.)
B. You are requested to test an application (testers, developers, users and system administrators)
C. You are requested to assess the quality of a test with associated processes and products (EDP auditors and quality assurance employees)
D. You are responsible for the IT department or are the owner of an application and wish to have professional testing carried out (development and test process clients and relevant line management)
E. With your training background, you are interested in the testing profession (students and tutors of information technology/business economics)
F. You are responsible for HRM within the organisation and you are recruiting testers (personnel & organisation employees).

Chapter		A	B	C	D	E	F
General							
Ch01	Introduction	√	√	√	√	√	√
Ch02	Framework and importance of testing	√	√	√	√	√	√
Ch03	The essentials of TMap	√	√	√	√	√	√
Processes							
Ch04	Introduction to the processes	√	√	√	√	√	
Ch05	Master test plan, managing the total test process	√		√	√	√	
Ch06	Acceptance and system tests	√	√	√	√	√	
Ch07	Development tests	√	√	√			
Ch08	Supporting processes	√			√		√
Components							
Ch09	Product risk analysis	√					
Ch10	Quality characteristics and test types	√	√				
Ch11	Estimation techniques	√					
Ch12	Defects management	√	√				
Ch13	Metrics	√					
Ch14	Test design techniques		√			√	
Ch15	Evaluation techniques	√	√				
Ch16	Test roles	√					√

Table 1.1: Reading suggestions

Table key: √, the relevant target group is advised to study the chapter well. The other chapters are optional reading (this is certainly recommended to group E).

1.4.3 The most important changes

The changes within TMap have been integrated with all the chapters of the book. It is therefore almost impossible to pinpoint those exact places in the book that have been changed. We are convinced that an experienced TMap user can fathom the most important changes without reading the entire book. For them we have drawn up the list below referring to all chapters, sections and subjects that have undergone important changes:

- TMap is divided in four essentials. Chapter 3 gives a full description of this subject. It also contains an overview of business driven test management.
- A full description of implementing a product risk analysis is given in chapter 9.
- Business driven test management and the product risk analysis have a great influence on, amongst others, understanding the testing assignment, strategy, estimation and planning. See chapter 5 and 6.
- Control phase of the total test process and the Control phase for acceptance and system testing have become separate phases (separated from the Planning phase). See sections 5.3 and 6.3.
- The Setting up and maintaining infrastructure phase is new. See section 6.4.
- The Planning phase and the Control phase (of the total test process) mainly describe the test management activities. To be able to see all the changes (shifts) the activity diagrams in chapters 5 and 6 should be looked at.
- Chapter 11 contains a great number of new estimation techniques.
- A new 'look' on development testing is described in chapter 7.
- Besides the test process chapters we now have a chapter that contains supporting processes. This chapter 8 goes further into subjects such as: test policy, permanent test organisation, test environments, test tools and the test professional.
- In chapter 14, mainly in the first three sections, a new angle can be found on coverage, basic techniques and test design techniques.
- The test design techniques decision table test and data combination test have been altered. New techniques are use case test and exploratory testing. Besides these four techniques section 14.4 describes a further seven techniques.
- The set of test types have been extended with testing of regression, usability, performance, portability and security in section 10.3.

2 Framework and importance of testing

This chapter provides an introduction to testing in general and focuses on structured testing. No specific (prior) knowledge of TMap is required in order to understand this. In sequence, an explanation is given of: what is understood by testing, why testing is necessary (and what it delivers), what the role of testing is and what structured testing involves.

In chapter 3 "The essentials of TMap", a description is given of a structured testing approach using TMap.

2.1 What is testing?

While many definitions of the concept of testing exist, one way or another they all contain comparable aspects. Each of the definitions centres on the comparison of the test object against a standard (e.g. expectation, correct operation, requirement). With this, it is important to know exactly what you are going to test (the test object), against what you are going to compare it to (the test basis) and how you are going to test it (the test methods and techniques).

The International Standardisation Organisation (ISO) and the International Electrotechnical Commission (IEC) apply the following definition [ISO/IEC, 1991]:

Definition

Testing is a technical operation that consists of the determination of one or more characteristics of a given product, process or service according to a specified procedure.

Testing supplies insight in the difference between the actual and the required status of an object. Where quality is roughly to be described as 'meeting the requirements and expectations', testing delivers information on the quality. It provides insight into, for example, the risks that are involved in accepting lesser quality. For that is the main aim of testing. Testing is one of the means of detection used within a quality control system. It is related to reviewing, simulation, inspection, auditing, desk-checking, walkthrough, etc. The various instruments of detection are spread across the groups of evaluation and testing[1]:

---

[1] The theory also refers to verification and validation. Verification involves the evaluation of (part of) a system to determine whether the products of a development phase meet the conditions that were set at the beginning of that phase. Validation is understood to mean determining whether the products of the system development meet the user needs and requirements. [IEEE, 1998]

- Evaluation: assessment of interim products.
- Testing: assessment of the end products.

Put bluntly, the main aim of testing is to find defects: testing aims to bring to light the lack in quality, which reveals itself in defects. Put formally: it aims to establish the difference between the product and the previously set requirements. Put positively: it aims to create faith in the product.

The level of product quality bears a relationship to the risks that an organisation takes when these products are put into operation. Therefore, in this book we define testing, according to TMap, as follows:

Definition
Testing is a process that provides insight into, and advice on, quality and the related risks.

Advice on the quality of what? Before an answer to this can be given, the concept of quality requires further explanation. What, in fact, is quality?

Definition
The totality of features and characteristics of a product or service that bear on its ability to satisfy stated or implied needs [ISO, 1994].

In aiming to convert 'implied needs' into 'stated needs' we soon discover the difficulty of subjecting the quality of an information system to discussion. The language for discussing quality is lacking. However, since 1977, when McCall [McCall, 1977] came up with the proposal to divide the concept of quality into a number of different properties, the so-called quality characteristics, much progress has been made in this area.

Definition
A quality characteristic describes a property of an information system.

A well-known set of quality characteristics was issued by the ISO and IEC [ISO 9126-1, 1999]. In addition, organisations often create their own variation of the above set. For TMap, a set of quality characteristics specifically suited to testing has been compiled, and these are listed and explained in chapter 10, "Quality characteristics and test types". This set is the one that is used within the framework of this book.

What, then, is the answer to the question: "Advice on the quality of what?" Since, where quality is concerned, the issue is usually the correct operation of the software, testing can be summed up as being seen by many to mean:

establishing that the software functions correctly. While this may be a good answer in certain cases, it should be realised that testing is more than that. Apart from the software, other test objects exist, the quality of which can be established. That which is tested, and upon which quality recommendations are subsequently given, is referred to as a test object.

Definition

The test object is the information system (or part thereof) to be tested.

A test object consists of hardware, system software, application software, organisation, procedures, documentation or implementation. Advising on the quality of these can involve – apart from functionality – quality characteristics such as security, user friendliness, performance, maintainability, portability and testability.

Pitfalls

In practice, it is by no means clear to everyone what testing is and what could or should be tested. Here are a few examples of what testing is *not*:

- Testing is not a matter of releasing or accepting something. Testing supplies advice on the quality. The decision as regards release is up to others (stakeholders), usually the commissioner of the test.
- Testing is not a post-development phase. It covers a series of activities that should be carried out in parallel to development.
- Testing is something other than the implementation of an information system. Test results are rather more inclined to hinder the implementation plans. And it is important to have these – often closely related - activities well accommodated organisationally.
- Testing is not intended initially to establish whether the correct functionality has been implemented, but to play an important part in establishing whether the required functionality has been implemented. While the test should of course not be discounted, the judgement of whether the right solution has been specified is another issue.
- Testing is not cheap. However, a good, timely executed test will have a positive influence on the development process and a qualitatively better system can be delivered, so that fewer disruptions will occur during production. Boehm demonstrated long ago that the reworking of defects costs increasing effort, time and money in proportion to the length of time between the first moment of their existence and the moment of their detection [Boehm, 1981]. See also "What does testing deliver?" in the next section.
- Testing is not training for operation and management. Because a test process generally lends itself very well to this purpose, this aspect is often too easily included as a secondary request. Solid agreements should see

to it that both the test and the training will be qualitatively adequate. A budget and time should be made exclusively available for the training, and agreements made as regards priorities, since at certain times choices will have to be made.

It is the task of the test manager, among others, to see that these pitfalls are avoided and to make it clear to the client exactly what testing involves.

2.2   Why test?

In chapter 1 "Introduction", it is explained that IT has been increasing in importance to organisations since the end of the nineties. But with this, many organisations are plagued by projects getting out of hand in terms of both budget and time, owing to software defects during the operation of the developed information systems. This shows that organisations are accepting, or having to accept, systems without having real insight into their quality. In many cases, too, there is a lack of good management information upon release. This often results in big risks to the company operations: high reworking costs, productivity loss, brand/reputation loss, compensation claims and loss of competitiveness through late availability of the new product (revenue loss) may be the consequences.

Before an information system goes into production, the organisation will have to ask itself explicitly whether all requirements are met. Have all the parts and aspects of the system been explored in sufficient depth? Besides the functionality, have checks been carried out on, for example, the effectivity, performance and security aspects? Or, as ISO puts it: has it been established whether the product possesses the characteristics and features necessary to meet the stated or (even more difficult) implied needs? What is self-evidently implied to one may be a revelation to another.

Have all the errors been reworked, and have any new errors been introduced in the course of reworking them? Can the company operations depend on this system? Does the system really provide the reliable solution to the information issue for which it was designed?

The real question is: what risks are we taking and what measures have been taken to reduce those risks. In order to avoid obtaining answers to these crucial questions only at the operational phase, a good, reliable testing process is required. That demands a structured test approach, organisation and infrastructure, with which continuous insight may be obtained in a controlled manner into the status of the system and the risks involved.

What does testing deliver?

While a structured test approach is considered to be of great importance, the question "What do you think of the test process?" is generally answered with "Expensive!" This response can seldom be quantified, since it is often a gut reaction, unsupported by figures. Testing is expensive. Yes, that is true if you only look at the test costs and disregard the test benefits. Test costs are based on, among other things:

- the costs of the test infrastructure
- the hours worked by the testers and their fees.

Test benefits are [Black, 2002]:

- The prevention of (high) reworking costs and consequential damage to the production situation, thanks to defects being found during testing and rectified within the system development process. Examples of consequential damage are: revenue loss, brand/reputation loss, compensation claims and productivity loss.
- The prevention of damage in production, thanks to errors being found during testing, and, while not being solved, being flagged as 'known errors'.
- Having/gaining faith in the product.
- Facilitating good project management through the supply of (progress and quality) information.

If there is a way of expressing test benefits in money, the answer to the question "What does testing deliver" may be, from a test-economic perspective:

Test Yield = Test Benefits − Test Costs

Although this appears to be a simple calculation, in practice it is very difficult to estimate how much damage would have been caused by failures that were found during testing, had they occurred at the production stage. And anyway, how do you translate, for example, potential loss of image into money? In the literature, some attempts have nevertheless been made at making this calculation (e.g.: [Aalst, 1999]).

However, it remains difficult to establish exactly what having faith in the quality of a product, or gaining (progressive) information really delivers. Despite that, within the world of testing there are more and more tips and tricks to be found that make it possible to observe one or more of the following defects and to operate accordingly:

- too much testing is carried out, so that the costs of finding a defect during testing no longer offset the damage that this defect would potentially cause if it occurred in production
- too little testing is done, so that more issues occur in production and the

reworking costs of these are proportionately higher than the test costs would have been to find the defects during testing
- testing is carried out ineffectively, so that the test investment is not recouped.

2.3   The role of testing

This section explains both the significance and role of certain test concepts in their environment. Spread across the following subjects, the associated concepts are explained:
- Testing and quality management
- Testing: how and by whom
- Test and system development process
- Test levels and responsibilities
- Test types

2.3.1   Testing and quality management

Quality was, is and remains a challenge within the IT industry (see also examples in section 1.2 "TMap evolves in step"). Testing is not the sole solution to this. After all, quality has to be built in, not tested in! Testing is *the* instrument that can provide insight into the quality of information systems, so that test results – provided that they are accurately interpreted – deliver a contribution to the improvement of the quality of information systems. Testing should be embedded in a system of measures in order to arrive at quality. In other words, testing should be embedded in the quality management of the organisation.

The definition of quality as expressed by the ISO strongly hints at its elusiveness. What is clearly implied to one is anything but to another. Implicitness is very much subjective. An important aspect of quality management is therefore the minimisation of implied requirements, by converting them into specified requirements and making visible to what degree the specified requirements are met. The structural improvement of quality should take place top-down. To this end, measures should be taken to establish those requirements and to render the development process manageable.

Definition

Quality assurance covers all the planned and systematic activities necessary to provide adequate confidence that a product or service meets the requirements for quality [ISO, 1994].

These measures should lead to a situation whereby:

- there are measurement points and units that provide an indication of the quality of the processes (standardisation)
- it is clear to the individual employee which requirements his work must meet and also that he can evaluate them on the basis of the above-mentioned standards
- it is possible for an independent party to evaluate the products/services on the basis of the above-mentioned standards
- the management can trace the causes of weaknesses in products or services, and consider how they can be prevented in future.

These measures may be divided into preventive, detective and corrective measures:

- Preventive measures are aimed at preventing a lack in quality. They can be, for example, documentation standards, methods, techniques, training, etc.
- Detective measures are aimed at discovering a lack of quality, for example by evaluation (including inspections, reviews, walkthroughs) and testing.
- Corrective measures are aimed at rectifying the lack of quality, such as the reworking of defects that have been exposed by means of testing.

It is of essential importance that the various measures are cohesive. Testing is not an independent activity; it is only a small cog in the quality management wheel. It is only one of the forms of quality control that can be employed. Quality control is in turn only one of the activities aimed at guaranteeing quality. And quality assurance is, in the end, only one dimension of quality management.

2.3.2 Testing: how and by whom

Testing often attracts little attention until the moment the test is about to begin. Then suddenly a large number of interested parties ask the test manager about the status. This section demonstrates, however, that testing is more than just the execution of tests. We then explain the ways of testing and by whom the testing can be carried out.

There is more to testing

Testing is more than a matter of taking measurements – crucially, it involves the right planning and preparation. Testing is the tip of the iceberg, the bigger part of which is hidden from view (see figure 2.1 "The iceberg").

Figure 2.1: The iceberg

In this analogy, the actual execution of the tests is the visible part, but on average, it only covers 40% of the test activities. The other activities – planning and preparation – take up on average 20% and 40% of the testing effort respectively. This part is not usually recognised as such by the organisation, while in fact it is where the biggest benefit, not least regarding time, is to be gained. And, significantly, by carrying out these activities as much as possible in advance of the actual test execution, the testing is on the critical path of the system development programme as briefly as possible. It is even possible, because of technical developments (test automation), to see a decreasing line in the percentage of test execution compared with preparation and planning.

Ways of testing

There are various ways of testing (in this case, executing tests). For example, is the testing being done by running the software or by static analysis? And is a characteristic of the system being tested using test cases specially designed for it, or precisely not? A number of ways of testing are:
- Dynamic explicit testing
- Dynamic implicit testing
- Static testing

Dynamic explicit testing

With dynamic explicit testing, the test cases are explicitly designed to obtain information on the relevant quality characteristic. With the execution of the test, or the running of software, the actual result is compared against the expected result in order to determine whether the system is behaving according to requirements. This is the most usual way of testing.

Dynamic implicit testing

During dynamic testing, information can also be gleaned concerning other quality characteristics, for which no explicit test cases have been designed. This is called dynamic implicit testing. Judgements can be made, for example, on the user-friendliness or performance of a system based on experience gained without the specific test cases being present. This can be planned if there has been a prior agreement to provide findings on it, but it can also take place without being planned. For example, if crashes occur regularly during the testing. In that case, a judgement can be made concerning the reliability of the system.

Static testing

With static testing, the end products are assessed without software being run. This test usually consists of the inspection of documentation, such as security procedures, training, manuals, etc., and is often supported by checklists.

Who tests?

Anyone can do testing. Who actually does the testing is partly determined by the role or responsibility held by someone at a given time. This often concerns representatives from development, users and/or management departments. Besides these, testing is carried out by professional testers, who are trained in testing and who often bring a different perspective to testing. Where, for example, a developer wants to demonstrate that the software works well ("Surely I'm capable of programming?"), the test professional will go in search of defects in the software. Moreover, a test professional is involved full-time in testing, while the aforementioned department representatives in many cases carry out the testing as a side issue. In practice, the mix of well-trained test professionals and representatives from the various departments leads to fruitful interaction, with one being strong in testing knowledge and the other contributing much subject or system knowledge.

2.3.3   Test and system development process

The test and system development processes are closely intertwined. One delivers the products, which are evaluated and tested by the other. A common way of visualising the relationship between these processes is the so-called V model. A widely held misunderstanding is that the V model is suited only for a waterfall method. But that misrepresents the intention behind the model. It is also eminently usable with an iterative and incremental system development method. Therefore, with such a method, a V model can be drawn, for example, for each increment. Many situations are conceivable that influence the shape and the specific parts of the V model.

A few situations are shown in the box below: "Influences on the V model". With the help of the V model, the correlation between test basis, evaluation and testing (test levels) is explained in this and the following subsection.

In more detail

Influences on the V model

The form and specific parts of a V model can vary through, for example:
• The place of the testing within the system development approach.
  ○ Using a waterfall development method with characteristics including: construction of the system in one go, phased with clear transfer points, often a lengthy cyclical process (SDM, among others).
  ○ Using an incremental and iterative development method with the following possible characteristics: constructing the system in parts, phased with clear transfer points; short cyclical process (DSDM and RUP, among others).
  ○ Using an agile development method characterised by the four principles: individuals and interaction over processes and tools, working software over extensive system documentation, user's input over contract negotiation, reacting to changes over following a plan (extreme programming and SCRUM, among others).
• The place of testing within the life cycle of the information system.
  ○ Are we looking at new development or the maintenance of a system?
  ○ Does this involve the conversion or migration of a system?
• A self-developed system, a purchased package, purchased components, or distributed systems.
• The situation whereby (parts of) the system development and/or (parts of) the testing are outsourced (outsourcing and off-/near shoring, among other things).

Left side of the V model

In figure 2.2 "V model (the left side)" the left-hand side shows the phases in which the system is built or converted from wish, legislation, policy, opportunity and/or problem into the realised solution. In this case, the left-hand side shows the concepts of requirements, functional and technical designs and realisation. While the exact naming of these concepts is dependent on the selected development method, it is not required in order to indicate the relationship between the system development and test process at a general level.

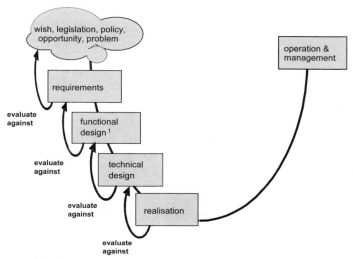

Figure 2.2: V model (the left side)

Evaluation

During the system development process, various interim products are developed. Depending on the selected method, these take a particular form, content and relationship with each other and can be tested on these.

Definition

Evaluation is assessing the interim products in the system development process.

In the V model, the left-hand side shows which interim products can be evaluated (against each other). In evaluation, the result can be compared with:

■ The preceding interim product
For example, is the functional design consistent with the technical design?
■ The requirements from the succeeding phase
For example, can the builder realise the given design unambiguously and are the specifications testable?
■ Other interim products at the same level
For example, is the functional design consistent internally and with functional designs related to it?
■ The agreed product standard
For example, are there use cases present?

■ The expectations of the client (see box "Realised requirements")
  Is the interim product still consistent with the expectations of the
  acceptors?

With this, various techniques are available for the evaluation: reviews,
inspections and walkthroughs (see also chapter 15 "Evaluation techniques").

In more detail

Realised requirements
What about the trajectory of wish, legislation, etc., to product? Will, for example, all the
requirements be realised, or will something be lost along the way? A survey carried
out by the Standish Group unfortunately shows a less than encouraging picture. The
findings of the survey (figure 2.3 "Realised requirements"), in which the percentage
of realised requirements was determined, shows that, of the original defined
requirements, only 42% to 67% are actually realised by the project [The Standish
Group, 2003].

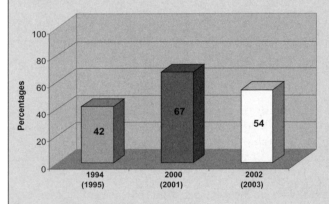

Figure 2.3: Realised requirements

Besides normal evaluation results (the finding of defects) a well-organised and
executed evaluation process can deliver a contribution to a higher realisation
percentage in respect of the original defined requirements.

2.3.4   Test levels and responsibilities

In a system development phase, a separation can be made between the
responsibilities of client, user, manager and system administrator on the
one hand and system developer and supplier on the other. In the context
of testing, the first group is collectively known as the accepting (requesting)
party and the second group as the supplying party. Other concepts that are

also mentioned in this connection are the demand and supply organisations. At a general level, there are two possible aims in testing:

- The supplying party demonstrates that what should be supplied actually is supplied.
- The accepting party establishes whether what has been requested has actually been received and whether they can do with the product what they want to/need to do.

Right side of the V model

In figure 2.4 "V model (the right side), a horizontal dotted line indicates this (formal) separation. In practice, the separation is less concrete and system developers will be called in for the information analysis and the setting up of the specifications, and will also supply support with the acceptance test. The expertise of users and administrators will also be employed in the building activities. It is important to define the various responsibilities clearly. This certainly applies to the testing. Who acts as the client of a test, who accepts it, who wants advice on the quality and who will test what, and when?

Testing takes place at the right-hand side of the V model. With this, a distinction is often made within the supplying party between testing by the developer and testing by the project/supplier:

- Testing by developer
  For example, by a programmer, technical designer or engineer.
- Testing by project/supplier
  For example, by a project or supplier of software or package supplier, or maintenance organisation.

In practice, this distinction in (test) responsibilities is translated into the grouping of test activities into test levels.

Definition

A test level is a group of test activities that are managed and executed collectively.

For every phase of construction, there are one or more test levels. A misconception in this is that the test level rectangles in the V model are seen as phases of the system development process. However, these represent the test execution (the measuring phase) of a test level.

Figure 2.4 "V model (the right side)" places the development and system tests under the responsibility of the supplying party and the acceptance tests under the responsibility of the accepting party:

- Development tests
  Tests in which the developing party demonstrates that the product meets
  the technical specifications, among other things.
- System tests
  Tests in which the supplying party demonstrates that the product meets
  the functional and non-functional specifications and the technical design,
  among other things.
- Acceptance tests
  Tests in which the accepting party establishes that the product meets
  expectations, among other things.

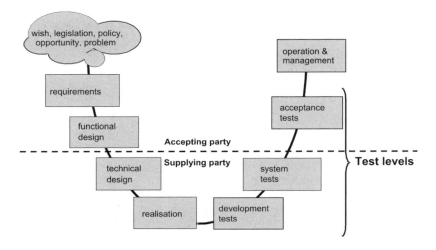

Figure 2.4: V model (the right side)

Although test level is a much-used concept, in practice people often have
difficulty in substantiating it. It does not appear to be possible to designate *the*
test level set. Even within one company, it is often impossible to define one set
that should be used in every project.

In this book, we refer to the three test levels mentioned. In incidental cases,
in order to describe a certain case appropriately, these test levels are further
subdivided. In chapter 4 "Introduction to the processes", the set of test levels
used by TMap are specified more closely.

As mentioned previously, there is no such thing as one standard set of test
levels. This is simply because it strongly depends on the organisation, the
project and even the individual. But of course, there are some indications
available for arriving at a relevant test level categorisation in a particular

situation. You can see these indications in chapter 5 "Master test plan, managing the total test process".

Test basis and test levels

A test level is aimed at demonstrating the degree to which the product meets certain expectations, requirements, functional specifications or technical specifications. System documentation is often used here for reference. In certain situations, usually in cases of migration operations, the current production system may also serve for reference. If there is little, no, or only obsolete system documentation available, the knowledge of, for example, the end users and product owners may be used for reference. There are many sources of information that can be used for reference in testing. The general term for this is 'test basis'.

Definition

The test basis is the information that defines the required system behaviour.

This is used as a basis for creating test cases. In the event that a test basis can only be changed via the formal change procedure, this is referred to as a 'fixed test basis'.

Figure 2.5 "V model (test basis)" uses arrows with the text "Input for" to indicate which information sources can be used in which test level as a basis in order to derive test cases. From the model it also appears that it is possible that the same test basis is being used in two test levels. This often happens when there are two different parties carrying out a test according to their individual responsibilities. In the illustrated model, a functional design is used as test basis by the supplying party to demonstrate to the accepting party, for example, that the system complies with this design. However, the accepting party uses the same functional design as a test basis in order to check whether the system supplied actually complies with this design.

It is obvious that in such a situation, there is a chance of duplicate testing being carried out. This can be a conscious and perfectly valid decision, but it can be equally justifiable to combine certain test levels. In chapter 5 "Master test plan, managing the total test process", you will find a number of indications for making selections in this.

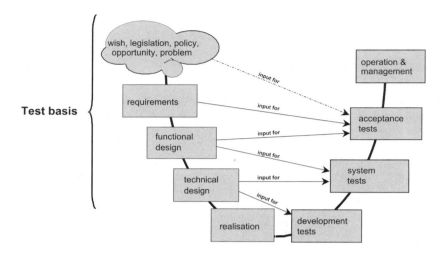

Figure 2.5: V model (test basis)

2.3.5 Test types

During the testing of a system, various types of properties can be looked at
- the so-called quality characteristics. Examples of these are functionality,
performance and continuity.

At detail level, it may be, however, that a certain quality characteristic is too
general, making this difficult to maintain in practice. The quality characteristic
should then be cast in a form that is easier for the tester to use. In the example
of functionality, risks are conceivable in the area of interfaces, in- and output
validations, relationship checks, or just the processing. With performance we
could look to load and/or stress risks. And in the example of continuity, there
is the matter of the importance of backup, restore and/or failover facilities.
This commonly used form of quality characteristics is called the "test type".

> **Definition**
> A test type is a group of test activities with the intention of checking the information
> system in respect of a number of correlated (part aspects of) quality characteristics.

On the website www.tmap.net, you will find a list of a number of common test
types. This list is not exhaustive and will vary from test project to test project,
and from organisation to organisation.

A strange fish among these is the "regression" test type: a test type was, after all, intended to provide detailed information on the specific risks with regard to the relevant quality characteristics, while regression, on the contrary, is a rather general term and in fact cites a specific risk in itself.

Definition

Regression is the phenomenon that the quality of a system deteriorates as a whole as a result of individual amendments.

Definition

A regression test is aimed at verifying that all the unchanged parts of a system still function correctly after the implementation of a change.

Often, the establishment of whether a regression has taken place is an aim in itself. It is therefore better to pay some attention to it here, where the distribution of quality characteristics across test levels is being considered in general terms.

When filling in the detail, thought could be given to what is meant by "correct functioning" in the above definition. Does this concern, for example, functionality, performance or failover facilities? In fact, all the quality characteristics and test types can be part of a regression test.

How test types are used within TMap is explained in chapters 6 "Acceptance tests and system tests" and 10 "Quality characteristics and test types".

2.4 What is structured testing?

In practice, it seems that testing is still being carried out in an unstructured manner in many projects. This section, besides citing a number of disadvantages of unstructured testing and advantages of structured testing, also cites a few characteristics of the structured approach.

Disadvantages of unstructured testing

Unstructured testing is typified by a disorderly situation, in which it is impossible to predict the test effort, to execute tests feasibly or to measure results effectively. This is often referred to as 'ad hoc testing'. Such an approach employs no quality criteria in order to, for example, determine and prioritise risks and test activities. Neither is a test-design technique employed for the creation of test cases. Some of the findings that have resulted from the various studies of structured and unstructured testing are:

- Time pressures owing to:
  - absence of a good test plan and budgeting method
  - absence of an approach in which it is stated which test activities are to be carried out in which phase, and by whom
  - absence of solid agreements on terms and procedures for delivery and reworking of the applications.
- No insight in or ability to supply advice on the quality of the system due to:
  - absence of a risk strategy
  - absence of a test strategy
  - test design techniques not being used, therefore both quality and quantity of the test cases are inadequate.
- Inefficiency and ineffectiveness owing to:
  - lack of coordination between the various test parties, so that objects are potentially tested more than once, or even worse: not tested at all
  - lack of agreements in the area of configuration and change management for both test and system development products
  - the incorrect or non-use of the – often available – testing tools
  - lack of prioritisation, so that less important parts are often tested before more risk-related parts.

Advantages of a structured testing approach

So what are the advantages, then, of structured testing? A simple, but correct, answer to that is that in a structured approach, the aforementioned disadvantages are absent. Or, put positively, a structured testing approach offers the following advantages:

- it can be used in any situation, regardless of who the client is or which system development approach is used
- it delivers insight into, and advice on, any risks in respect of the quality of the tested system
- it finds defects at an early stage
- it prevents defects
- the testing is on the critical path of the total development as briefly as possible, so that the total lead time of the development is shortened
- the test products (e.g. test cases) are reusable
- the test process is comprehensible and manageable.

Features of the structured testing approach

What does the structured testing approach look like? Many different forms are conceivable. In chapter 3 "The essentials of TMap" and the subsequent chapters, the specific TMap form of this is given.

In general, it can be said that a structured testing approach is typified by:

- Providing a structure, so that it is clear exactly *what*, by *whom*, *when* and in *what sequence* has to be done.
- Covering the full scope and describing the complete range of relevant aspects.
- Providing concrete footholds, so that the wheel needn't be reinvented repeatedly.
- Managing test activities in the context of time, money and quality.

3   The essentials of TMap

This chapter describes the specific TMap content of a structured test approach. The content can be summarised in four essentials.

The four essentials of TMap
1.   TMap is based on a business driven test management (BDTM) approach.
2.   TMap describes a structured test process.
3.   TMap contains a complete tool box.
4.   TMap is an adaptive test method.

The first essential can be related directly to the fact that the business case of IT is becoming ever more important to organisations. The BDTM approach provides content that addresses this fact in TMap and can therefore be seen as the 'leading thread' of the structured TMap test process (essential 2). The TMap life cycle model is used in the description of the test process. Furthermore various aspects in the field of infrastructure, techniques and organisation must be set up to execute the test process correctly. TMap provides a lot of practical applicable information on this, in the form of e.g. examples, checklists, technique descriptions, procedures, test organisation structures, test environments and test tools (essential 3). TMap also has a flexible setup so that it can be implemented in different system development situations: both for new development and maintenance of a system, for a self-developed system or an acquired package, and for outsourcing (parts of) the testing process. In other words, TMap is an adaptive method (essential 4).

In figure 3.1 "TMap model of essentials", the left triangle symbolises BDTM, the triangle at the bottom the tool box, the parallelogram the structured test process, and the 'circle' TMap's adaptiveness.

Figure 3.1: TMap model of essentials

3.1   Business driven explained

The key to testing is that tests are executed on the basis of test cases, checklists and the like. But what kind of tests are they? To ensure the tests' usefulness, they must be set up to test *those* characteristics and parts of a test object that represents a risk if it does not function adequately in production later on. This means that various considerations have already been made before test execution can begin. In other words, some thought has already been given to which parts of the test object need not be tested, and which must be tested and how and with what coverage. So what determines this? Why not test all parts of the test object as thoroughly as possible? If an organisation possessed unlimited resources, one option might indeed be to test everything as thoroughly as possible. But naturally, in real life an organisation rarely has the resources to actually do this, which means that choices must be made in what is tested and how thoroughly. Such choices depend on the risks that an organisation thinks it will incur, the available quantities of time and money, and the result the organisation wishes to achieve. The fact that the choices are based on risks, result, time and cost is called business driven and constitutes the basis for the BDTM approach. To understand and apply the BDTM approach, we first explain the concept of the "business case".

Business case as determining factor

IT projects must be approach increasingly from a purely economic perspective. The theory of IT governance controls projects on the basis of four aspects: result, risk, time and cost. For instance, it might be a more attractive investment for an organisation to start a high-risk project that potentially yields a high result than a project with very low risks where the benefits barely exceed the costs.

Normally, a business case is at the basis of an IT project. There are various definitions of business case, including the project-oriented one below according to [PRINCE2, 2002].

Definition

The business case provides the justification for the project and answers the questions: why do we do this project, which investments are needed, what does the client wish to achieve with the result?

During the project, the business case is verified at predefined points in time to ensure that the eventual results remain valid for the client. TMap supports the justification of IT, translating it to the activity of testing. TMap assumes that a project approach based on a business case complies with the following characteristics:

- The approach focuses on achieving a predefined result.
- The total project to achieve this result is realised within the available (lead) time.
- The project to achieve this result is realised at a cost in balance with the benefits the organisation hopes to achieve.
- The risks during commissioning are known and as small as possible. All of this within the framework set by the abovementioned characteristics.

The four IT governance aspects described above can be found in these characteristics.

For the successful execution of a project, it is important that the test process is aligned with the business case. The relationship between the business case and the test process is made via the business driven test management approach. In other words, with this approach, the business case characteristics can be 'translated' to the test process.

Characteristics of a business driven test management approach

Often test plans and reports fail to appeal to the client. The reason being that in the past the tester virtually always made decisions from an IT perspective. The test process was internally oriented and filled with test and IT jargon. This made it difficult to communicate with a non-IT client, such as a user department, even though this is extremely important.

TMap devotes explicit attention to communication due to the business driven test management approach.[1] BDTM starts from the principle that the selected test approach must enable the client to control the test process and (help) determine the test approach. This gives the testing an economic character. The required information to make this possible is delivered from the test process.

BDTM has the following specific properties:
- The total test effort is related to the risks of the system to be tested for the organisation. The deployment of people, resources and budget thereby focuses on those parts of the system that are most important to the organisation. In TMap, the test strategy in combination with the estimated effort is the instrument to divide the test effort over system parts. This provides insight into the extent to which risks are covered, or not.
- The estimated effort and planning for the test process are related to the

---

[1] Please note that BDTM is not an entirely accurate name. The word "business" suggests that it is intended exclusively for the link with the user departments, while testers clearly often still deal exclusively with IT departments. In this book, however, the general name BDTM is used.

defined test strategy. If changes are implemented that have an impact on the thoroughness of testing for the various system parts or systems, this is translated immediately to a change in the estimate and/or planning. The organisation thus is ensured of an adequate view of the required budget, lead time and relationship with the test strategy at all times.

■ At various moments in the testing programme, the client is involved in making choices. The advantage is that the test process matches the wishes and requirements – and therefore the expectations – of the organisation as adequately as possible. Moreover, BDTM provides handholds to visualise the consequences of future and past choices explicitly.

The steps in the business driven test management approach

To understand the BDTM approach, it is important to keep an eye on the final objective. Which is to provide a quality assessment and risk recommendation about the system. Since not everything can ever be tested, a correct assessment can only be realised by dividing the test effort, in terms of time and money, as adequately as possible over parts and characteristics of the system to be tested. The steps of BDTM focus on this (see figure 3.2):

1. Formulating the assignment and gathering test goals.
   In consultation with the client, the test manager formulates the assignment, taking account of the four BDTM aspects: result, risk, time and cost.

   The test manager gathers the test objectives to determine the desired results of testing for the client. A test goal is a goal for testing relevant to the client and other acceptants, often formulated in terms of IT-supported business processes, realised user requirements or use cases, critical success factors, change proposals or defined risks (i.e., the risks to be covered).

2. Determining the risk class for each combination of characteristic and object part.
   When multiple test levels are involved, it is determined in a plan which test levels must be set up (master test plan). It is often already determined on the basis of a product risk analysis[2] what must be tested (object parts) and what must be investigated (characteristics).

---

[2] A product risk analysis (PRA) aims to ensure that the various stakeholders and test manager achieve a joint view of the more and less high-risk parts/characteristics of the system. The focus in the PRA is on the product risks, i.e. what is the risk to the organisation if the product does not have the expected quality?

If only one test level is involved, or if no or an overall product risk analysis was performed at the master test plan level, a (possibly supplementary) product risk analysis is performed within the relevant test level.

The eventual result (whether it is arrived at immediately or after one or more supplementary analyses) is a risk table defining a risk class related to the test goals and the relevant characteristic per object part ("Master test plan risk table").
A table then provides a guideline for the relative depth of testing per combination of characteristic/object part and test level ("Master test plan strategy table").

Now an *iterative process* emerges:
3. Determining whether a combination of characteristic and object part must be tested thoroughly or lightly.
   To determine the thoroughness of testing, the risk class per object part determined in the previous step is used as a starting point. Initially, the following applies: the greater the risk, the more thorough the required testing. The result is recorded in a strategy table per test level ("Test plan strategy table").

4. An overall estimate is then made for the test and a planning set up. This is communicated with the client and other stakeholders and, depending on their views, adjusted as necessary. In this case, steps 3 and 4 are executed once again. This emphatic gives the client control of the test process, enabling him to manage based on the balance between result and risk on the one hand and time and cost on the other.

End of iteration.

5. Allocating test techniques to the combinations of characteristic and object part.
   When the client and stakeholders agree on the estimate and the planning, the test manager completes a "Test design table". In here, the decisions concerning thorough and less thorough testing are translated to concrete statements about the targeted coverage. He then allocates test techniques to the combinations of characteristic and object part. The available test basis, among other things, is taken into account. These techniques are used to design and execute the test cases (and/or checklists) at a later stage. This is where the primary test process starts.

6. Throughout the test process, the test manager provides the client and other stakeholders with adequate insight into and control options over:
   • the progress of the test process

- the quality and risks of the test object
- the quality of the test process.

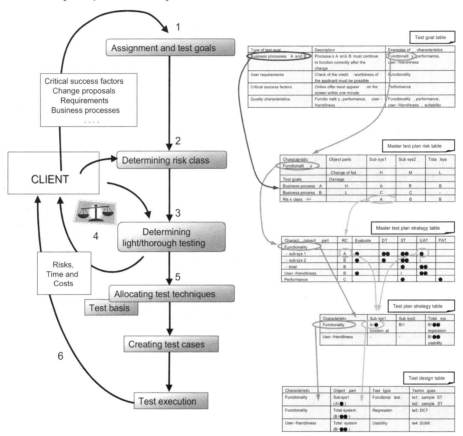

Figure 3.2: BDTM steps

In summary, the advantages of the BDTM approach are:
- The client having control over the process.
- The test manager communicates and reports in the terminology of the client with information that is useful in the client's context. E.g. by reporting in terms of test goals (such as business processes) instead of object parts and characteristics.
- At the master test plan level, detailing can be as intensive as required or possible. This may enable expending less effort on performing a product risk analysis or creating a test strategy for the separate test levels, or even to skip these steps (explanation of master test plan in subsequent section).

3.2   Structured test process

This section describes the phasing and activities in the following TMap processes:

- Master test plan, managing the total test process
- Acceptance and system tests
- Development tests.

Master test plan and other TMap processes

When the test manager, after consultation with the receiving parties, decides what will be tested for each test level, chances are that in the total picture of testing, certain matters will be tested twice unnecessarily. Or that certain aspects are ignored. The method should therefore be vice versa. A test manager, in consultation with the client and other stakeholders, makes a total overview of the distribution across test levels as to what must be tested when and with what thoroughness. The aim is to detect the most important defects as early and economically as possible. This agreement is defined in the so-called master test plan (MTP). This plan constitutes the basis for the test plans for the separate test levels. In addition to this content-based alignment, other types of alignment are: ensuring uniformity in processes (e.g. the defect procedure and testware management), availability and management of the test environment and tools, and optimal division of resources (both people and means) across the test levels.

This means that in addition to test levels like acceptance, system and development tests, the master test plan also plays an important part in TMap. Both for the master test plan and the test levels, it is important to set up a good process for creating plans and preparing, executing and managing activities.

While the goals of the acceptance and system tests differ, these test levels are not described separately, but as one single process. This was decided because the activities in both test levels are virtually the same and separate process descriptions would therefore have (too) much overlap.

In addition to these processes, the process "Supporting processes" has been defined because it is more efficient to organise certain aspects/support centrally than per project. This involves supporting processes for the following subjects:

- Test policy
- Permanent test organisation
- Test environments
- Test tools
- Test professional.

The supporting processes are discussed in relevant places as part of the complete tool box (see section 3.3).

3.2.1   Process: master test plan, managing the total test process

The master test plan provides insight into the various test and evaluation levels to be used, in such a way that the total test process is optimised. It is a management tool for the underlying test levels.

The process "Master test plan, managing the total test process" is split up into two phases: the Planning phase of the total test process and the Control phase of the total test process.

Planning phase of the total test process

The author of the MTP, often the test manager formulates the assignment, taking into account the four BDTM aspects of result, risks, time and cost, in consultation with the client. The test manager then works on the upcoming programme by having discussions with stakeholders and consulting information sources, such as documentation. In parallel, the test manager further elaborates the assignment and determines its scope in consultation with the client. In this phase, the first four steps of BDTM are executed: performing a PRA, establishing a test strategy, estimate and planning (see figure 3.2 "BDTM steps").

Further activities in the creation of the plan are: the test manager defines the products that must be delivered by the test levels and makes a proposal as to the setup of the test organisation, centrally and overall per test level. The test manager aligns the infrastructure requirements of the test levels in order to deploy the – often scarce – test infrastructure as efficiently as possible. Test management can also be set up in part at the master test plan level. This can be achieved both by defining central procedures and standards for management and by the central management of certain aspects. Both options aim to prevent reinventing the wheel in the various test levels. The main risks threatening the test process are listed, and possible measures are proposed to manage these risks. As his last step, the test manager submits the master test plan to the client for approval.

Control phase of the total test process

The aim of this activity is controlling the test process, infrastructure and test products at the overall level to provide continuous insight into the progress and quality of the total test process and the quality of the test object.

Conformable to the frequency and form defined in the test plan, reports are made on the quality of the test object and the progress and quality of the test process. From the very first test activities, the testers develop a view of that quality. It is important that this is reported in every stage of the test process. The client receives periodical reports, and ad-hoc reports on request, on the condition of the system. Such reporting and adjustment are a vital part of the BDTM approach (BDTM step 6) and take place at both the level of the master test plan and that of the test level (figure 3.3 "Control and test processes").

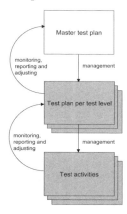

Figure 3.3: Control and test processes

3.2.2   Process: acceptance and system tests

The acceptance test and system test are considered as autonomous processes to be organised. They have their own test plan, their own budget, and often their own test environment to. They are processes running parallel to the development process, which must be started while the functional specifications are created. The TMap life cycle model is used both in the creation of the test plan and in the execution of the other activities in the test process.

Life cycle model
Like a system development process, a test process consists of a number of different activities. A test life cycle model is necessary to structure the various activities and their mutual order and dependencies. The life cycle model is a generic model. It can be applied to all test levels and test types and used in parallel with the life cycle models for system development. In the TMap life cycle model, the test activities are divided across seven phases: Planning, Control, Setting up and maintaining infrastructure, Preparation, Specification, Execution and Completion (see figure 3.4 "TMap life cycle model"). Each phase is split up into a number of activities.

Using a test life cycle model enables the organisation to keep an overview during the test process. By recording *what* has to be done *when, how, with what, where,* by *whom,* etc the claims to and the relationships with other aspects like techniques, infrastructure and organisation are made automatically.

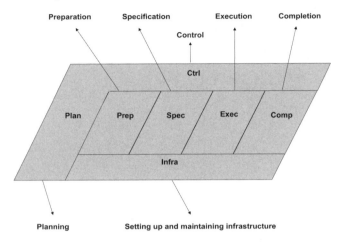

Figure 3.4: TMap life cycle model

The critical path and the shape of the life cycle model

If we were to compare the test process with an iceberg, only the Execution phase would be 'visible'. This means that only the Execution phase should be on the 'critical path' of a project. All activities in the other phases can be done either before or after.

The form of the life cycle model (parallelogram) shows that the test phases do not have to be executed strictly sequentially.

Test life cycle model relationships

The relationship between the TMap test life cycle and system development life cycle depends on the system development method used and the relevant test level. However, two 'fixed' relationships can be indicated. The start of the Preparation phase has a relationship with the moment at which the test basis becomes available; the start of the Execution phase has a relationship with the moment at which the test object becomes available.

Planning phase

The activities to be executed in the Planning phase create the basis for a manageable and high-quality test process. It is therefore important to start this phase as quickly as possible. The planning phase is an important test phase but is almost always underestimated. Often, the framework for a certain test level is are already defined at the overall level in a master test plan. In this case, the detailed elaboration occurs in this phase.

After the test assignment has been finalised, an overall introduction to the test basis, subject matter and organisation (of the project) is made. It is impossible to test the system completely. Most organisations do not have the time and money for that. This is why the test strategy, estimate and planning are determined according to a risk analysis process (BDTM steps 1 through 4), of course always in consultation with the client. It is then determined which test techniques must be used (BDTM step 5). The objective is to realise the best achievable coverage at the right place within the defined BDTM frameworks. The first steps in setting up the test organisation and test infrastructure are also made. These activities are executed and laid down in the test plan for the relevant test level at the beginning of the test process.

Control phase

The primary test process is rarely executed according to plan. As such, the execution of the test plan also has to be monitored and adjusted, if necessary. This is done in the Control phase. The aim of the activities in this phase is to control and report on the test process in an optimal manner, such that the client has adequate insight into and control over the progress and quality of the test process and quality of the test object.

The test manager and/or administrator manage the test process, infrastructure and test products. Based on these data, the test manager analyses possible trends. He also ensures that he keeps well informed of the developments beyond testing, such as delays in development, upcoming big change proposals, and project adjustment. If necessary, the test manager proposes specific control measures to the client.

Information is the main product of testing. To this end, the test manager creates different kinds of reports for the various target groups, taking account of the BDTM aspects of result, risks, time and cost (BDTM step 6).

Setting up and maintaining infrastructure phase

The Setting up and maintaining infrastructure phase aims to care for the required test infrastructure and resources. A distinction is made between test environments, test tools and workplaces.

Setting up and maintaining the infrastructure represents a specific expertise. Testers generally have limited knowledge in this respect, but are highly dependent on it. No test can be executed without an infrastructure. All responsibilities in relation to setting up and maintaining infrastructure are therefore usually assigned to a separate management department. In a testing programme, therefore, the team will have to collaborate closely with these other parties that may be external to the organisation. This means that test managers are in a situation in which they do not have control over the setup and maintenance of the infrastructure, but depend on it. This makes the setup and maintenance of the infrastructure an important area of concern for the test manager. It is a separate phase in the TMap life cycle model to maintain focus on it during the test. This phase runs in parallel to the Preparation, Specification, Execution and Completion phases. Dependencies with activities in other TMap test phases exist for some Setting up and maintaining infrastructure activities.

Preparation phase

The testability review of the test basis is done in the Preparation phase. The ultimate goal of this phase is to have access to a test basis of adequate quality to design the tests, which has been agreed with the client of the test.

Furthermore an early testability review of the test basis improves quality and prevents potential costly mistakes. This is because the development team works on developing the new information system on the basis of system documentation (which is part of the test basis). This documentation may contain errors that can cause a lot of – often costly – correction work if they are not detected in a timely manner. The earlier an error is found in a development process, the easier (and cheaper) it can be repaired.

Specification phase

The Specification phase specifies the required tests and starting situation(s). The aim is to prepare as much as possible so that tests can be executed as quickly as possible when the developers deliver the test object. This phase starts once the testability review of the test basis is completed successfully. The test specification runs in parallel to, and in the shadow of, the realisation of the software.

Execution phase

The aim of the Execution phase is to gain insight into the quality of the test object by executing the agreed tests.

The actual execution of the test starts when the test object, or a separately testable part of the test object, is delivered. The test object is first checked for completeness. It is then installed in the test environment to assess whether it functions as required. This is achieved by executing a first test, the so-called pretest. This is an overall test to examine whether the information system to be tested, in combination with the test infrastructure, has sufficient quality for extensive testing. The central starting point is prepared if this is the case. The test can be executed on the basis of the test scripts created in the Specification phase. In this case, the starting point must be prepared for the test scripts that are to be executed. The test results are verified during execution. The differences between the predicted and actual results are registered, often in the form of a defects report.

Completion phase

The structured test approach of TMap can yield many benefits in the repeatability of the process. It allows products to be reused in subsequent tests if they comply with certain requirements. This may speed up certain activities. Products may be tangible things like test cases or test environments (testware), but also non-tangible things like experience (process evaluation).

When preserving the testware, a selection is made from the often large quantities of testware. Testware means, among other things, the test cases, test scripts and description of the test infrastructure. During the test process, an attempt was made to keep the test cases in line with the test basis and the developed system. If this was not (entirely) successful, the selected test cases are first updated in the Completion phase before the testware is preserved. The advantage of preserving testware this way is that it can be upgraded with limited effort when the system is changed to execute a (regression) test, for instance. There is therefore no need to design a completely new test.

The test process is also evaluated in this phase. The aim is to learn from the experiences gained and to apply these lessons learned in a new test, if any. It also serves as input for the final report, which the test manager creates in the Control phase.

3.2.3   Process: development tests

Development testing is understood to mean testing using knowledge of the technical implementation of the system. This starts with testing the first/smallest parts of the system: routines, units, programs, modules, objects, etc. After it has been established that the most elementary parts of the system are of acceptable quality, the larger parts of the system are subjected to integral testing. The emphasis here is on data throughput and the interfacing between e.g. the units up to the subsystem level.

Place of development tests

The development tests are an integral part of the development work executed by the developer. They are not organised as an autonomous process for an independent team. Despite that, a number of different activities for the development test process, with their mutual order and dependencies, can be identified and described with the aid of the TMap life cycle model. The detailed elaboration may vary per project or organisation and depends, among other things, on the development method used and the availability of certain quality measures.

An important quality measure is the concept of the agreed quality. To this end, the expectations of the client in relation to the craftsmanship and product quality must be made explicit during the planning to set up development testing. Examples of other quality measures are: test driven development, pair programming, code review, continuous integration, and the application integrator approach.

Differences between development and system/acceptance tests

The development test requires its 'own' approach that provides adequate elaboration of the differences between the development test and system/ acceptance test as described below:
- Contrary to the system and acceptance tests, development tests cannot be organised as autonomous processes for more or less independent teams.
- Development testing uses knowledge of the technical implementation of the system, thereby detecting another type of defects than system and acceptance tests.
- In the development test, the person detecting the defects is often the same as the one who solves the defects.
- The perspective of development testing is that all detected defects are solved before the software is handed over.
- It is the first testing activity, which means that all defects are still in the product.
- Usually, the developers themselves execute development tests.

3.3   Complete tool box

TMap supports the correct execution of the structured test process with a complete tool box. The tool box focuses on working with the following subjects:
- Techniques: *how* it is tested
- Infrastructure: *where* and *with what* it is tested
- Organisation: *who* does the testing

The various tools are described in more detail in TMap at the moment they can be used. With the tool box, the tester possesses a great number of options to meet the test challenge successfully.

3.3.1   Techniques

Many techniques can be used in the test process. A test technique is a combination of actions to produce a test product in a universal manner.

TMap provides techniques for the following (see figure 3.5):
- Test estimation
- Defect management
- Creating metrics
- Product risk analysis
- Test design
- Product evaluation.

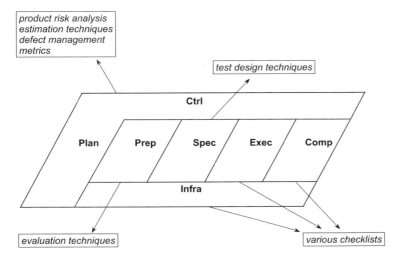

Figure 3.5: Test techniques

TMap also offers various checklists and overviews that can be used as a tool during the preparation and/or execution of certain activities.

The (groups of) test techniques are summarised in the following sections.

Test estimation

Estimates can be made at a number of different levels. The various estimation levels are shown in the figure below.

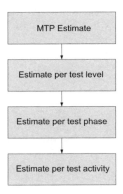

Figure 3.6: Estimation levels

Independent of the level, creating an estimate consists of the following generic steps:
1. Inventory the available material that can serve as a basis for the estimate.
2. Select (a number of) estimating techniques.
3. Determine the definitive estimate.
4. Present the outcome.

Choosing the estimating techniques in particular is a step requiring experience. You can select from several estimating techniques:
■ Estimation based on ratios. Here, the test effort is generally measured against the development effort, e.g. in percentage ratios.
■ Estimation based on test object size.
■ Estimation using a 'Work Breakdown Structure'.
■ Proportionate estimation based on the total test budget.
■ Estimation on the basis of extrapolating experience figures from the beginning of the testing programme.
■ Estimation on the basis of size and strategy using TMap's test point analysis (TPA).

Furthermore, TMap provides a technique to create an evaluation estimate.

Defect management

A defect is an observed difference between the expectation or prediction and the actual outcome. While the administration and monitoring of the defects is factually a project matter and not one of the testers, testers are usually very closely involved. A good administration must be able to monitor the lifecycle of a defect and provide various overviews. These overviews are used, among other things, to make well-founded quality statements.

Creating metrics

The definition, maintenance and use of metrics is important to the test process because it enables the test manager an answer, supported by facts, to questions like:
- What about the quality of the test object?
- What about the progress of the test process?

A structured approach to realise a set of test metrics is using the Goal-Question-Metric (GQM) method. In addition to describing the GQM method, TMap gives instructions to set up a practical test metrics starter set. It also provides a checklist that can be useful to make pronouncements on the quality of the object to be tested and the quality of the test process.

Product risk analysis

A product risk analysis (PRA) is analysing the product to be tested with the aim of achieving a shared view, among the test manager and other stakeholders, of the more or less risky characteristics and components of the product to be tested so that the thoroughness of testing can be agreed upon. The focus in PRA is on the product risks, i.e. what is the risk to the organisation if the product does not have the expected quality?

The result of the PRA constitutes the basis for the subsequent decisions in strategy as to light, thorough or non testing of a characteristic (e.g. a quality characteristic) or object part (component) of the product to be tested.

Test design

A test design technique is a standardised method to derive, from a specific test basis, test cases that realise a specific coverage. The implementation of test design techniques and their definition in the test specifications have several advantages:
- It provides a well-founded elaboration of the test strategy: the agreed coverage in the agreed place.
- It is a more effective way to detect defects than e.g. ad-hoc test cases.
- The tests are reproducible because the order and content of the test execution are described in detail.

- The standardised method ensures that the test process is independent of the individual who specifies and executes the test cases.
- The standardised method ensures that the test specifications are transferable and maintainable.
- It becomes easier to plan and manage the test process because the processes of test specification and execution can be split up into clearly definable blocks.

Test design techniques exist in many variants and combinations. The test design techniques described in TMap constitute a varied set with which most organisations can get to work immediately. TMap describes the following coverage types and test design techniques.

- Coverage types
  paths, decision points, equivalence classes, pair-wise testing, orthogonal arrays, limit value analysis, CRUD, operational and load profiles, right and fault paths, and checklists
- Test design techniques
  decision table test, data combination test, elementary comparison test, error guessing, exploratory testing, data cycle test, process cycle test, real-life test, semantic test, syntactic test, and use case test.

Product evaluation

TMap describes and uses the following evaluation techniques:

- Inspection
  In addition to determining whether the solution is adequately processed, an inspection focuses primarily on achieving consensus on the quality of a product.
- Review
  A review focuses primarily on finding courses for a solution on the basis of the knowledge and competencies of the reviewers, and on finding and correcting defects.
- Walkthrough
  A walkthrough is a method by which the author explains the contents of a product during a meeting. Several objectives are possible:
  - Bringing all participants to the same starting point, e.g. in preparation for a review or inspection process
  - Transfer of information, e.g. to developers and testers to help them in their programming and test design work, respectively
  - Asking the participants for additional information
  - Letting the participants choose from the alternatives proposed by the author.

Various checklists and overviews

TMap offers a great variety of checklists that will constitute a welcome addition to the tester when executing certain activities. For instance, there are checklists that can be used as support in taking stock of the assignment, determining the test facilities, determining the test project risks, establishing the test strategy, the evaluation of the test process, taking interviews, and determining whether adequate information is available to use a specific test design technique. TMap also offers other tools, such as an overview matrix of automated tools per TMap activity, a test type overview, and criteria to select a tool.

These tools and many more can be found on and downloaded from www.tmap.net.

3.3.2 Infrastructure

Test environments, test tools and workplaces are necessary to execute tests.

Test environments

A fitting test environment is necessary for dynamic testing of a test object (running software). A test environment is a system of components, such as hardware and software, interfaces, environmental data, management tools and processes, in which a test is executed. The degree to which it can be established in how far the test object complies with the requirements determines whether a test environment is successful. The setup and composition of a test environment therefore depend on the objective of the test. However, a series of generic requirements with which a test environment must comply to guarantee reliable test execution can be formulated. In addition to being representative, manageable and flexible, it must also guarantee the continuity of test execution.

Setting up and managing the test environment represents an expertise of which testers generally have no knowledge. This is why a separate department – outside the project – is generally responsible for setting up and managing the test environment.

Test tools

To execute the tests efficiently, tools in the form of test tools are necessary. A test tool is an automated instrument that provides support to one or more test activities, such as planning and control, test specification, and test execution. The use of tools can have the following advantages:

- Increased productivity
- Higher testing quality
- Increased work enjoyment
- Extension of test options.

The test tools are classified in four groups:
- Tools for planning and managing the test
- Tools for designing the test
- Tools for executing the test
- Tools for debugging and analysing the code.

Workplaces

One of the aspects that is often forgotten in testing, is the availability of a workplace where testers can do their job under good conditions, effectively and efficiently. This means office setup in the broadest sense since the testers must also be able to do their work under good conditions. The workplace is therefore more than just office space and a PC. Matters such as access passes, power supply and facilities to have lunch must be arranged. At first sight, the workplace for a tester does not differ much from the regular workplace. But appearances can be deceptive. What is tested is often new to the organisation and the workplace. Testers may have to deal with the situation that their workplace is not yet prepared for the new software. For example, testers often require separate authorisations. They must, for instance, be able to install the new software on their local PC. This may also be necessary for the use of certain test tools.

3.3.3   Organisation

Test processes that are not adequately organised usually have disastrous results. The involvement of many different disciplines (see figure 3.7), conflicting interests, unpredictability, complex management tasks, lack of experience (figures), and time pressure make setting up and managing the test organisation a complex task. On the one hand there is the organisation in the test team where everyone must have their tasks and responsibilities. On the other, the test team must be an integral part of the project organisation.

A test organisation can be seen as the creation of effective relationships between test functions, test facilities and test activities to issue good quality advice in time.

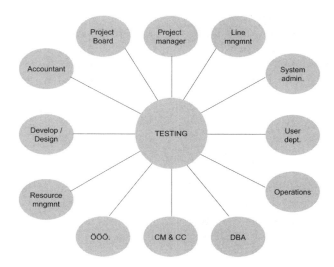

Figure 3.7: The many disciplines involved

The organisation of structured testing requires attention for the following fields:
- Test policy
- Permanent test organisation
- Test organisation in projects
- Test professional
- Test roles.

Test policy

The test policy describes how an organisation deals with the people, resources and methods involved in the test process in the various situations. Since testing is one of the tools to ensure quality, the test policy will have to be in line with the other policy measures and initiatives in relation to quality management. We recommend making sure that the test policy is in line with the strategic, tactical and operational policy of the organisation.

Permanent test organisation

A permanent test organisation, contrary to project-based testing, does not elaborate a specific element of the test process on a per project basis, but across all projects. Reasons to create such an organisation are, among other things, the improved leverage of scarce expertise, standardisation of test products, limiting the test project start-up time, continuous improvement of the test process, consolidation of experiences, and prior insight into the test costs and lead time.

Test organisation in projects

At the start of a test project, the roles, tasks, authorisations and responsibilities for the test project are defined. This can be done for the total test process (i.e. across all test levels), or for one specific test level. The relationship between the specified roles, the separate test levels, and the relationships with the other stakeholders in the system development process are then determined and laid down. The test manager must not forget to establish the relationship with a test or quality department, if any.

How this is all set up specifically depends heavily on the organisation type selected for the test work. The choice depends on the test level, project and organisation. The test manager can sometimes – but not always – influence this decision. Roughly, the following organisation types can be distinguished:
- Testing as an autonomous activity in a project
- Testing integrated in a project
- Testing as an autonomous line organisation
- Testing integrated in a line organisation.

Test professional

A great variety of expertise is required for a tester to be able to function well in the discipline of testing. A tester must have knowledge in the field of the subject matter, the infrastructure (test environment, development platform, test tools) and testing itself. What are a tester's characteristics, in other words, what properties must a person have to be an ideal tester? While many can be listed, the tester must at least:
- have verbal and written communication skills
- be able to work accurately and have analytical skills
- be convincing and persevering
- be factual and have a positively critical attitude
- be creative.

Test roles

The execution of test activities in a project or in the line requires that the tasks are defined and that the executor of the tasks has the right knowledge and competencies.

Roles and positions can be distinguished in this respect. A role is the description of one or more tasks with the required knowledge and competencies. There are roles that match positions one-on-one. There are also roles that do not exist as a position.

Differences and similarities between roles and positions:

- A role aims at fulfilling tasks for the test project or permanent test organisation.
- A position focuses on the employee and his place in the career cube.
- They share the tasks to be executed and the required knowledge competencies.

3.4   Adaptive and complete method

TMap is an approach that can be applied in all test situations and in combination with any system development method. It offers the tester a range of elements for his test, such as test design techniques, test infrastructure, test strategy, phasing, test organisation, test tools, etc. Depending on the situation, the tester selects the TMap elements that he will deploy. There are situations in which only a limited number of elements need to be used; but in others he will have to use the whole range of elements. This makes TMap an adaptive method, which in this context is defined as:

Definition

Adaptive is the ability to split up an element into sub-elements that, in a different combination, result in a new, valuable element for the specific situation.

The adaptiveness of TMap is not focused on a specific aspect of the method, but is embedded throughout the method. Adaptiveness is more than just being able to respond to the changing environment. It is also being able to leverage the change to the benefit of testing. This means that TMap can be used in every situation *and* that TMap can be used in a changing situation. In the course of projects and testing, changes may occur that have an impact on earlier agreements. TMap offers the elements to deal with such changes.

TMap's adaptiveness can be summarised in four adaptiveness properties:

- *Respond* to changes
- *(Re)use* products and processes
- *Learn* from experiences
- *Try* before use

These properties are explained in further detail below.

3.4.1   Respond to changes

Adaptiveness starts with determining the changes and responding to them. In TMap, this happens from the very beginning in the earliest activities of the (master) test plan. When determining and taking stock of the assignment, obtaining insight into the environment in which the test is executed and establishing possible changes play a major part. This is precisely where the basis is created for the further elaboration and implementation of the method. Which test levels, test types, phases, and tools are used and how? But it is not limited to these activities. The test strategy and associated planning are defined in close consultation with the client. If the test strategy and derived estimate and planning are not acceptable to the client, the plan is adapted. This emphatic gives the client control of the test process, enabling him to manage based on the balance between result and risk on the one hand and time and cost on the other. Such feedback is provided throughout the testing programme, and in the control phase, the test manager may also decide to adapt certain aspects of the test plan in consultation with the client.

3.4.2   (Re)use products and processes

Being able to use products and processes quickly is a requirement for adaptiveness. TMap offers this possibility, among other things thanks to the large quantity of tools included in the form of test design techniques, checklists, templates, etc. These can be found in the book and on www.tmap. net.
In addition to use, reuse plays an important part. The emphasis in this respect lies in the Completion phase, where the activities are defined to identify what can be reused and how it can be optimally preserved. TMap offers various forms of a permanent test organisation for the organisational anchoring of the reuse of products and processes.

3.4.3   Learn from experience

As a method, TMap offers the space to learn and apply what was used. Therefore the activity evaluating the test process is incorporated into the test process. An other important instrument is the use of metrics. For the test process, metrics on the quality of the test object and the progress and quality of the test process are extremely important. They are used to manage the test process, justify the test recommendations, and compare systems or test processes. Metrics are also important to improve the test process through assessing the consequences of certain improvement measures.

3.4.4   Try before use

TMap offers room to try something before it is actually used. The main instruments here are the activities relating to the intake. The intake of the test basis (using a testability review), of the test infrastructure, and of the test object allow one to try first before actually using.

Implementing TMap does not mean that everything in the book should be used without question. Another form of trying before using is therefore 'customising' TMap to fit a specific situation. A selection can be made from all of the TMap elements to achieve this. After the approach, customised to the situation, has been tried out ('pilot'), it can be rolled out in the organisation.

For many situations, 'customising' TMap has already been done. The specific TMap approach for a certain situation (known under the name 'expansion') can be found on www.tmap.net and in the TMap Test Topics book [Koomen, 2005].

4 Introduction to the processes

4.1 Structure and contents of the process chapters

This chapter provides an introduction to chapters 5, 6, 7 and 8. Testing is normally organised into a number of test levels, with each test level having a specific goal, e.g. establishing whether a component is working properly or that the quality of a system is adequate to take into production. In outline, TMap distinguishes the following groups of test levels:
• Development tests
• System tests
• Acceptance tests.

These groups of test levels often comprise several individual test levels. For example, the functional, user and production acceptance tests are well-known acceptance test levels. While this book predominantly refers to the concepts of development tests, system tests and acceptance tests, in some cases more detail is necessary. In such a situation, a permanent set of test levels in TMap is drawn upon (Figure 4.1 "TMap test levels"). Therefore, this is not *the* set, but simply one of several. Individual organisations often have their own self-defined set of test levels. In this book, TMap maintains mainly one particular set of test levels to avoid possible confusion on test levels and in order to facilitate a consistent description of the test approach.

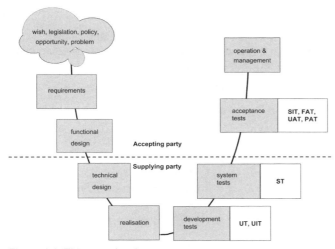

Figure 4.1: TMap test levels

Below is an overview and a brief description of the TMap test levels. With this, an organisation can independently lay down a relationship with the test levels it uses.

Definition

- **Unit test (UT)**
  A unit test is a test carried out in the development environment by the developer, with the aim of demonstrating that a unit meets the requirements defined in the technical specifications.
- **Unit integration test (UIT)**
  A unit integration test is a test carried out by the developer in the development environment, with the aim of demonstrating that a logical group of units meets the requirements defined in the technical specifications.
- **System test (ST)**
  A system test is a test carried out by the supplier in a (manageable) laboratory environment, with the aim of demonstrating that the developed system, or parts of it, meet with the functional and non-functional specifications and the technical design.
- **System integration test (SIT)**
  A system integration test is a test carried out by the future user(s) in an optimally simulated production environment, with the aim of demonstrating that (sub)system interface agreements have been met, correctly interpreted and correctly implemented.
- **Functional acceptance test (FAT)**
  The functional acceptance test is a test carried out by the future user(s) in an optimally simulated production environment, with the aim of demonstrating that the developed system meets the functional requirements.
- **Users acceptance test (UAT)**
  The users acceptance test is a test carried out by the future user(s) in an optimally simulated production environment, with the aim of demonstrating that the developed system meets the requirements of the users.
- **Production acceptance test (PAT)**
  The production acceptance test is a test carried out by the future administrator(s) in an optimally simulated production environment, with the aim of demonstrating that the developed system meets the requirements set by system management.

The test levels should be mutually coordinated. This is done by creating a master test plan and managing the overall test process.

In respect of both the master test plan and the test levels, it is important to organise a satisfactory process for the planning, preparation, execution and management of activities. In both cases, these processes are aimed at the testing of a particular software product (administrative system or embedded software, self-built or package). These processes can be applied in a test project or in a test from within a line department, for example a maintenance test of a new release.

Organisations also often set up line support for testing, independent of a specific test or specific test object. Forms of general support are anything from a department with test advisers who support the individual test projects, a resource pool of testers that the projects can draw on, all the way up to complete test factories. More specific forms of support from the organisational line are the selection and management of test tools and the setup and management of test environments. These support activities, too, can be seen and organised as processes.

In the following chapters, the processes below are described (Figure 4.2, "TMap processes"):
- Master test plan, managing the total test process (Chapter 5)
- Acceptance and system tests (Chapter 6)
- Development tests (Chapter 7)
- Supporting processes (Chapter 8).

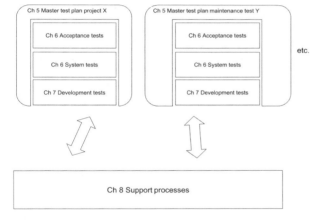

Figure 4.2: TMap processes

The sequence of the chapters is chronological: first, the master test plan is created, then the plans for the acceptance test and system test, and during – or shortly before – coding, the plans for the development tests are created. The support processes do not have a clear-cut beginning or end, but should be seen more as continuous processes.

It is perhaps noteworthy that the acceptance and system test levels are not described separately, but as a single process. This has been decided because the activities in both test levels are more or less similar and separate process descriptions would therefore involve too much overlap. Both the acceptance test and the system test can in fact be considered (and therefore organised) as separate processes. They have their own test plan, their own budget and often also their own test environment in which the test is executed. They are processes that run in parallel with the development process and that should start during the creation of the functional specifications.

The activities for the creation and management of a master test plan also bear many similarities with the creation and management of an acceptance or system test plan. However, mainly because of the higher level of perspective of the master test plan which contains, as it were, the other test plans, the activities do diverge on a significant number of points. This warrants a separate chapter. The chapter is set up in such a way that all activities are included, but the descriptive and explanatory texts mainly focus on the specific aspects of master test planning and control of the overall test process. The basic explanation and many tips are included with the descriptions of acceptance and system tests in sections 6.2 "Planning Phase" and 6.3 "Control Phase". This has been decided upon for a number of reasons:
- To maintain the chronological sequence in the chapters
- It is expected that Chapter 6 will be more often and more thoroughly read and used than Chapter 5
- The test manager of a master test plan will normally have followed the career path of test manager for an acceptance or system test and will be familiar with this.

The reader is therefore advised to read sections 6.2 and 6.3 before starting on Chapter 5.

4.2   Chapters 5, 6 and 7: the TMap phases

The processes and underlying activities in Chapters 5, 6 and 7 are described on the basis of the TMap phases. In Chapter 5, those handled are Planning and Control. Chapters 6 and 7 discuss the complete TMap life cycle model. This is a generic model that inventories the various activities, setting out their sequence and mutual dependencies. In the TMap life cycle model, the test activities are distributed across seven phases. These are Planning, Control, Setting up & Maintaining Infrastructure, Preparation, Specification, Execution and Completion.

In Chapters 5 and 6, the phases, processes and activities are described in detail. The phasing is described below concerning the processes in connection with, consecutively, the master test plan (managing the total test process), the acceptance test and the system test:

Per *phase*, it is indicated what the aim of the phase is, the context, the preconditions under which it is carried out, the significant roles and responsibilities and the activities that constitute the phase. A brief description of the method of operation is also included.

Per *activity*, it is indicated what the goal is, what method of operation is used and what products are delivered. Where applicable, it is shown how test techniques and test tools play a part.

For an overview of the chapters 5 and 6 processes, phases and activities, please see the inner cover.

Chapter 7 contains a brief description of the phases and activities required for development tests. This chapter is more in the manner of supplying the broad picture and makes comparisons with the other test levels. It is less of a "How to" chapter than 5 and 6. The target readership is mainly:

- The developers/development testers looking for ideas
- The test adviser who is asked to support the (organisation of) development testing
- The test manager for the overall test process who has to coordinate the development tests with the other test levels
- The line or project manager of developers, who is interested in improving the management of the quality of the software produced and who wishes to know how to achieve this.

4.3 Chapter 8: supporting processes

Chapters 5, 6 and 7 discuss the test processes that operate according to the life cycle model of TMap and how this is organised for the testing of a system or package. The last process chapter discusses support processes at organisational level. This breaks down into a number of separate topics:

- Test policy
  An organisation formulates a test policy stating how the people, resources and methods in connection with the test processes are to be dealt with. This also determines the central support to be set up.
- Permanent test organisation
  There are various forms of permanent test organisation, such as an advisory group, a resource pool of testers or a "test factory". This is explained comprehensively, including the possible services, and a general process model of such an organisation is provided, with a brief explanation of the process of setting up a test organisation.
- Test environments
  The organisation and management of the test environment is often placed with a separate department, outside of the project. Various aspects of test environments are explained, including a number of processes that need to

be well organised in order to guarantee a manageable test environment. The organisation and management of test environments as a service is also discussed.

- Test tools

  Test tools are often purchased and managed at organisation level. The individual test projects can/should then use these tools. The subject of test tools is discussed in general, including the process of implementing a test tool.

- Test professionals

  In many organisations, the test projects are manned from within a department or pool of testers, or external testers are hired. Requirements must be set in respect of a tester. The prospect of a career path, including training, should be embedded in the standard HRM process in order to attract and retain testers for the organisation.

5 Master test plan, managing the total test process

5.1 Introduction

Section 2.3 "The role of testing" already discussed the fact that testing software (information system, package implementation or embedded software) is usually organised with a number of test levels. Each test level has a specific aim, e.g. establishing the correct functioning of a component or a system's adequate quality for production. When the test manager of each test level, in consultation with his direct clients, decides what will be tested, chances are that in the total picture of testing, certain matters will be tested twice unnecessarily, or that to the contrary specific issues are forgotten. The method should be vice versa: based on the total overview a test manager, in consultation with the client and other stakeholders, makes a division as to which test level tests what and when (and with what intensity), fitting within the implemented development or maintenance approach. The aim is to detect the most important defects as early and economically as possible. This agreement is laid down in the so-called master test plan (MTP). This plan constitutes the basis for the detailed test plans for the separate test levels.

In addition to the content-based alignment, there are other reasons to try and gear activities to one another: ensuring uniformity in processes (e.g. the defect procedure and testware management), availability and management of the test environment and tools, and optimal division of resources (both people and means) across the test levels.

In more detail

Master test plan self-evident?
While creating a master test plan may seem self-evident, it is not that easy in actual practice. Unfortunately, the test managers of the individual test levels are often expected to achieve alignment. While agreement can usually be reached at the level of milestones, it becomes more difficult when involving the scope and thoroughness of the various test levels. A project manager is generally unable to devote adequate attention to this, while the test manager of a separate test level does not have the right authorisations. Fortunately, the importance of tuning and maintaining alignment of the test levels is understood more and more often in system development. For instance, in IBM's system development method, Rational Unified Process®, the master test plan is a formalised product.

Creating a master test plan and managing the total test process requires a specific role: the test manager or overall test coordinator for the overall test process.

> **'Unnecessary double testing'**
> An important reason for a master test plan is preventing unnecessary double testing.
> The word 'unnecessary' is important in this context. As such, double tests are not a
> problem; often they cannot be avoided, and in some cases they are even mandatory.
> In a unit test, for instance, the same functionality will often be tested as in a system
> test, and various test cases will resemble each other. Part of the system test may also
> be repeated on purpose in the acceptance test, e.g. to check that everything works on
> the production-like infrastructure or within existing business processes. An example
> of 'unnecessary double' is when two test levels use a similar test design technique to
> derive and execute similar test cases.

This chapter discusses the management of the total test process based on the
BDTM philosophy, and is therefore not limited to creating the master test
plan. Coordination and adjustment is vital when executing the test plans.
Delayed deliveries, disappointing quality, or a lack of time or resources are
more of a rule than the exception in IT. The test manager of a test level must
then adjust the planned approach. Coordinating and managing the total test
process across the test levels must ensure that, despite individual adjustments
in various test levels, a coherent overall approach for testing continues to be
implemented. Adjustment in a test level may result in inefficiency in other test
levels, e.g. because the test object has insufficient quality when completing
the first test level. The test manager must notify others and propose or take
measures in consultation with the client and project management. The so-
called Deming wheel [Deming, 1992] can be distinguished in the management
and improvement mechanism used to this end: Plan something, Do it, Check
the result, and Act if necessary. See the figure on the next page.

This chapter is split up into the Planning phase (using a master test plan)
and the Control phase. An overview is given for each subject, after which
the activities are described in greater detail. We recommend that the reader
peruse sections 6.2 and 6.3, planning and managing system and acceptance
tests, before this chapter. Many of the issues and activities described therein
apply to this chapter as well.

In some cases, in particular for maintenance and outsourcing, large parts of
the master test plan are created with reuse in mind. This is the last variant
described in this chapter, the Generic Test Agreements (GTAs).

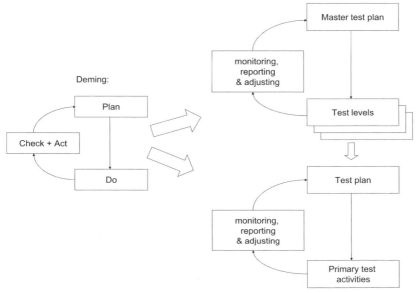

Figure 5.1: Management of master test plan and test levels

5.2   Planning phase of the total test process

Aim
Setting up the total test process by:
- Aligning the test levels
- Minimising overlaps or gaps in the test coverage
- Optimal distribution of available resources, e.g.
  - Testers
  - Infrastructure and tools
  - Technical or domain expertise
- Detecting the most important defects at the earliest possible stage
- Testing as early as possible on the critical path of the overall project
- Achieving uniformity in the test processes
- Laying down agreements with stakeholders
- Informing the client of the approach, planning, estimated effort, activities and deliverables in relation to the total test process.

The plan provides insight into the various test and evaluation levels to be used, in such a way that the total test process is optimised. All other test plans must be based on the master test plan. As such, the master test plan constitutes the management basis for the underlying test levels.

Context

A master test plan is necessary when multiple test levels are used. This is usually the case, both for new builds and maintenance or package implementation – either waterfall or iteratively.

In more detail

The type of system and/or development approach and/or test policy determine which forms of which test levels are best used. For iterative system development, for instance, a thorough acceptance test is less obvious. This is because the quality from the user perspective has already been tested in previous test levels. However, for package implementations there is a far greater emphasis on a thorough acceptance test. The risks here are focused on the implementation of the package in the organisation, a typical acceptance test aspect.

After determining which test levels there are or should be, it must be determined which of these test levels are to be included in the master test plan. In theory, all test levels and evaluation types (reviews, inspections) are eligible, but in practice usually the test levels for system and acceptance testing (see figure below) are aligned in the master test plan. Please refer to the figure below for some examples of the test levels that can be included in a master test plan.

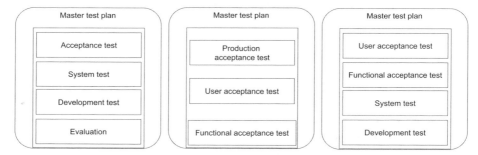

Figure 5.2 Examples of the fields of coverage of a master test plan

To align test and evaluation types in a master test plan, each test or evaluation level must provide insight into what it tests and doesn't test, and with what intensity. However, alignment becomes difficult or even impossible if such insight is not provided and, for instance, it is known for the development test that a programmer will test, but now how. If such insight can or will not be provided for a specific test level, it becomes very difficult to include it in the master test plan. The project and test management must change this. This goes even more if the master test plan is meant to prescribe what and how the individual test levels should test.

In more detail

Development tests and evaluation levels

Please note that it is important to include the development tests and evaluation levels in the master test plan, because this offers a range of opportunities to optimise the overall process. Both development tests and evaluations occur earlier on in the system development than the system and acceptance tests. As such they are able to detect defects earlier and closer to the source – for evaluations even before the defects are implemented in the software. This means that rework costs are lower and advice on the quality of the system can be provided at an earlier stage. Hence, it is clearly preferable to include the evaluation levels in the plan. To avoid using 'testing and evaluation' in this chapter, we only use the term 'testing'. This explicitly includes evaluation.

Alignment undesirable?

It is possible that the party responsible for a specific test level perceives the alignment as an undesirable influence on the part of other parties on its own test (whether rightly or wrongly). However, it is still useful to try including this test level in the master test plan because the master test plan may visualise, in an explicit manner, a double test of the same aspect or a missing test of an aspect. If, for instance, a third party develops and system tests the system - as often happens with outsourcing - there may not sometimes be sufficient opportunities to align the test levels in advance. The master test plan must then include the requirements defined for the test levels at the supplier. In addition to requirements concerning the required test strategy, these may also include the delivery of testware, test results and reports. The master test plan then also serves as a communication tool to this party.

The master test plan must be started early on in the system development process, so that as many test levels as possible can be included. 'Early' in this context may mean when creating the requirements, or even on initiation of the project. The later on in the process the master test plan is started, the fewer opportunities there are to optimise and align the test levels.

A master test plan can be created and executed regardless of the 'test maturity' of the relevant test levels, i.e. the quality of their test processes. If test maturity is low, however, the test manager must keep this in mind in drawing up the master test plan. He cannot set excessive demands for setup and management of the separate test levels.

A master test plan is created in the broader context of a process for system development or maintenance, or package implementation. Various other plans are also created, e.g. a Project Initiation Document (in the PRINCE2® project management method [PRINCE2, 2002]), the project or work plan, the configuration management plan, and a quality plan. The test manager must investigate which other plans there are, as well as the relationships between the master test plan and these plans. Examples:

- The estimated test effort in the master test plan serves as input for the project proposal in which a budget is requested.
- The test products are also included in the configuration management plan. The test manager must have influence on this to ensure that the test products can be managed according to his wishes.
- The testability review of the test basis can be done in the regular reviews. The quality plan must then provide for participation of the testers in the reviews.

Preconditions

The following matters must be known to start creating the master test plan:
- Aim and importance of the system or package for the organisation
- Global requirements
- The organisation of the development process
- Overall (delivery) planning
- Global system size (in function points or hours)
- The method for the system to be developed or maintained or the package to be implemented
- The client for the total test process

The unavailability of this information, e.g. because the development approach is not yet known, has negative consequences. In other words, the lead time or required effort to create the plan increase, or the quality and desired detail level of the plan are reduced. Furthermore, the organisation must be willing and able to make general arrangements in the field of testing.

Method of operation

As the author of the master test plan, the test manager supports the client in formulating a clear assignment taking account of the four BDTM aspects Result, Risks, Time and Costs (see section 3.1 "Business driven explained"), and records these in the plan. The test manager then works on the upcoming process by having discussions with stakeholders and consulting information sources, such as documentation. In parallel, the test manager further elaborates the assignment and determines its scope in consultation with the client. Together with the stakeholders a product risk analysis is performed to determine the required results of testing, and which parts and aspects of the system or package to be tested present higher or lower risks. This analysis represents the basis for the test strategy.

A process with iterative properties emerges. In the test strategy, it is determined which test levels must be set up, the aspects to be tested by the various test levels and with what thoroughness are established (the greater the risk, the more thorough testing). A rough estimate of the required effort is then created for the test levels and the overall test process, and a planning is established (the greater the risk, the earlier). This is aligned with the client and other stakeholders and, depending on their views, adjusted if necessary. In this case, the steps are executed once again. By conforming with BDTM, the client has an explicit level of control in relation to the test process.

Further steps in the creation of the plan are: the test manager defines the products that must be delivered by the test levels and makes a proposal as to the form of the test organisation, centrally and overall per test level. He aligns the infrastructure requirements of the test levels and defines the necessary test infrastructure. Test management can be set up in part at the master test plan level. This can be achieved by both defining central procedures and standards for management and the central management of e.g. defects and test products. Both options aim to prevent reinventing the wheel in the separate test levels. The main (project) risks threatening the test process are listed, and possible measures are proposed to manage these risks. As his last step, the test manager submits the master test plan to the client and any other stakeholders for approval.

While the activities in this subprocess are described successively, certain activities will be executed several times and/or in a different order in actual practice. When, for instance, the infrastructure required for a test cannot be delivered or is judged too costly, the test strategy may have to be adjusted.

Tips

(Too) early involvement?
The aim is for the test manager to be involved in the development process as early as possible to create the master test plan. This offers the most ample opportunities to correctly align the total tests. A disadvantage of such early involvement is that the test manager is sometimes involved so early on in the process that it might seem he does not have much to do after the master test plan. Designs have not yet been delivered, meaning that it is too early to specify test cases. In practice, except part-time deployment, there are a number of tasks that the test manager may take on in the process in consultation with the client:

• **Creating test plans for individual test levels**
• **Creating procedures and templates, setting up a defect administration.**
  The management approach described in the master test plan often requires expansion. The test manager is well placed to do this.
• **Organising reviews/inspections**
  This activity is often not assigned or allocated to the project manager who has (too) little time for it. The test manager is well placed to organise this activity, moderate sessions, etc.
• **Reviewing intermediate products**
  By participating in reviews of intermediate products from the perspective of testability, the quality of the intermediate products is increased and the test manager gains a lot of knowledge about the system to be tested. We should specifically mention reviewing whether relevant non-functional requirements, such as security and user-friendliness, have been specified and whether the requirements are adequately

SMART (Specific, Measurable, Acceptable, Realistic and Time-bound) defined.
- **Tasks relating to requirements, quality, configuration, change or risk management**
  If the test manager possesses the required knowledge, he may play a part in setting up or executing other, quality assurance-related project activities.
- **Increasing awareness of testing**
  Devote time to the awareness within the organisation and project of (the importance of) testing. Clarify the place of testing and the role of the test manager in the upcoming process. Creating a social network and emphatically claiming the test manager role strengthens the position of the test manager in the rest of the process.

Roles/responsibilities

The test manager, sometimes also known as overall test coordinator, is the role primarily responsible for creating the master test plan. In some cases, the role is combined to include quality assurance (QA) responsibilities, to integral test and QA manager.

Activities

Creating the master test plan consists of the following activities:
1. Establishing the assignment
2. Understanding the assignment
3. Analysing the product risks
4. Determining the test strategy
5. Estimating the effort
6. Determining the planning
7. Defining the test products
8. Defining the organisation
9. Defining the infrastructure
10. Organising the management
11. Determining the test project risks and countermeasures
12. Feedback and consolidation of the plan.

The diagram below shows the overall order of and dependencies between the various activities. All activities may be executed several times, because the results of one activity may require a review of the previous one. As mentioned in the method, steps 4, 5 and 6 have an explicitly iterative nature:

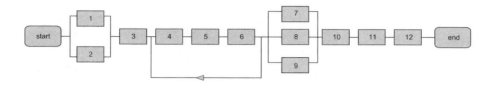

Figure 5.3: Creating the master test plan

5.2.1   Establishing the assignment

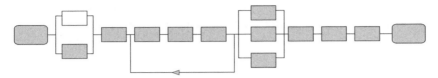

Aim
A test process starts with formulating the assignment, so that the aim, tasks, responsibilities and authorisations of testing are clear to all stakeholders.

Method of operation
Formulating the assignment is one of the vital parts in a test process. When establishing the assignment formulation in the master test plan, arrangements concerning the overall test process with the stakeholders (including the client) are made explicit. Expectations are mutually aligned. The assignment formulation in the master test plan constitutes the overall assignment for all underlying test levels. The assignment formulation of each test level must be in line with it.

An assignment formulation for a master test plan consists of the following components:
- Client
- Supplier
- Assignment
- Scope
- Preconditions and assumptions.

These components are explained in greater detail below:
Client
The party giving the assignment to create the master test plan and execute the tests. It is important for the test project to acknowledge the person issuing the assignment to execute the various tests. This can be the project manager, often employed by or appointed on behalf of the user organisation.
Supplier
The party responsible for creating the master test plan and/or the execution of the test assignment. This person is generally called the test manager or overall test coordinator.
Assignment
The test manager supports the client in the formulation of a concise assignment. It must describe the purpose of the test process and a clear delimitation of the assignment. The client is emphatically responsible for the assignment formulation.

Example 1:
The assignment to the test process covers the testing of all software (package and custom-made) that project XYZ will deliver. The scope of this project is described in section x.x. The software must be tested to the extent that a solid personnel administration with adequately converted data can be taken into production. The test process is split up into the test levels described in section y.y and set up in such a way that any risks can be identified in a timely manner. The aim is to issue a well-founded advice in relation to commissioning based on the insight into the quality of the system to be delivered.

Example 2:
The master test plan represents a supplement to the project plan XYZ. This plan is used for e.g. project delimitation, scope, planning, etc. The project's aim is to render workplace support to BDE compliant. In simple terms, this can be translated as:
• Making XYZ suitable for running under Windows/XP
• Organising access to workplace support via BDE.

The master test plan describes the relationship between test levels system test (ST), users acceptance test (UAT), and production acceptance test (PAT). The test activities in these test levels must be aligned as optimally as possible. This means that unnecessary, duplicate and/or non-testing of specific objects is prevented. The test strategy was created in consultation with the XYZ project leader and line manager Test & Support. The relationship between the test levels is described in general terms in the master test plan. The responsible party creates a separate detail test plan for each test level.

The overall test assignment is:
• Report whether, and if yes, which, risks <organisation> incurs when taking XYZ release 2006 1.5 into production on the basis of the tests executed within the selected test strategy.

Example 3:
Use the project 'Centralisation SYS-VS' as a pilot to evaluate the proposed new test approach for the components as defined in the scope. Remain within the framework of the PID (Project Initiation Document) until the integration and explicitly exclude the overall project (SYS release 3.0) for this plan. The project has already been determined planning-wise; the approach must be subject to this. Components in the plan can be applied if they add clear value to the direct, ongoing activities and agreement has been reached, such at the discretion of the project leader.

Example 4:
In the first phase of Chain Automation, several quality management measures – including test and evaluation activities – are organised. These activities must be executed in time and with insight into the desired quality on the part of all stakeholders.
The plan describes the arrangements between the partners in terms of the tests and

> evaluations that are executed and which parties are responsible. It is established what insights and reports will be delivered on the basis of which decisions can be made.

In addition to the primary assignment, the master test plan sometimes also contains a secondary assignment, e.g. improving the test processes of the relevant test levels, see example 3 above. A point of concern is that the test manager must include any additional time and resources in the planning and estimated effort.

Scope
This must describe the boundaries of the scope of testing. This specifically involves the scope of the test activities to be executed. It must include the following aspects (if applicable):
- system(s)
- conversions
- Administrative Organisation (AO) procedures
- Interfaces with surrounding systems (is the interface tested up to the other system or including the other system or even including the entire chain?).

Furthermore it is important to describe which aspects are outside the scope of testing. In addition to these aspects, you should also think of:
- system changes not included in the project (e.g. hardware changes in the mainframe platform)
- test activities that are executed by other parties
- reorganisations
- possible future projects with an impact on this project (in particular if other projects are not yet clear).

> **Tips**
> • Add an image that shows a visual representation of the scope by drawing a line around the in-scope systems, interfaces, AO, etc.
> • Do not exaggerate the list of aspects not included in the scope. This might seem highly defensive or even self-evident.

Preconditions
Preconditions are understood to mean conditions imposed on the test process by third parties, such as the client, the project or the users, within which the test process must operate.

Assumptions
These are external conditions or events that must occur to ensure the test process' success, but that cannot be controlled by the test process. In other words, these are the requirements of the test process vis-à-vis others.

Products
The assignment formulation as laid down in the master test plan.

Techniques
Not applicable.

Tools
Not applicable.

5.2.2   Understanding the assignment

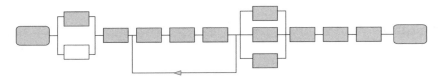

Aim
Obtaining insight into the (project) organisation, the objective and setup of the system development process, the system or package to be tested and the conditions with which it must comply, so that the other steps of planning can be controlled more adequately.

Method of operation
The method consists of the following sub-activities:
1.   Determining acceptants with acceptance criteria and other information providers (like quality assurance employees, domain experts, designers and system administrators)
2.   Studying the available documentation
3.   Taking interviews.

In practice, this activity is executed in parallel with the assignment formulation; it is also somewhat underestimated. This mainly means that the test manager talks to too few acceptants, while it is especially vital early on to assess the expectations correctly and 'issue feelers everywhere' as test manager. This is necessary for the adequate execution of subsequent activities in the Planning phase, as well as to control the total test process correctly in the future.

In relation to the similarly named activity in section 6.2.2, the following points of concern are especially important:
■   The number of acceptants and stakeholders for the total test process is much higher than for an individual test level and the moment is usually earlier on in the process, when expectations vary most. The test manager must obtain an adequate image of these expectations and the political situation. Where are the sensibilities? Where are the fields of tension? Is this project about time, money or quality? What is the underlying importance for the organisation? What is the position of the stakeholders in the project? What are their test goals?
■   The master test plan has relationships with various other plans in the development or maintenance process, as described earlier in the context of the master test plan (section 3.2). The test manager must inventory these relationships and elaborate them on the basis of the master test plan.

- When it comes to documentation and interviews, the test manager must devote special attention to collecting the test basis, since this is not defined as a separate activity for the master test plan.

Before starting the next activity – Analysing the Product Risks – the test manager provides feedback on the findings of this activity to the client for verification.

Products

This activity provides the components below of the master test plan. The plan must specify clearly that these aspects concern a preliminary inventory and that it will be elaborated, updated and detailed at a later stage, in the separate test levels.

- Acceptants and acceptance criteria
  The acceptants relevant to testing and their acceptance criteria.
- (Reference to) Test Basis
  Generally speaking not all product requirements are listed in the (master) test plan. A reference to (the) document(s) containing the requirements must suffice. It is important to include a version number, so that the version(s) of document(s) on which the test is based is clear to all parties at all times.
- Standards to be adhered to
  The standards used are listed here. In terms of testing, one might think of instructions from the line organisation Testing, TMap, the TPI model [Koomen, 1999] or test manuals. Development standards, document standards or quality standards that are (must be) respected can also be listed here.
- Documents related to the master test plan
  This is a list of the documents that have a relationship with the master test plan. For instance a Project Plan or Plan of Approach for the project, specific project or test planning documents, a specific or generic test method, an implementation plan, or other documents of importance.

Techniques

Checklist 'Understanding the assignment' (www.tmap.net).

Tools

Not applicable.

5.2.3   Analysing the product risks

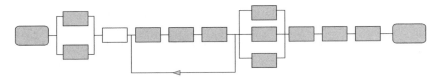

Aim
The stakeholders and test manager achieve a joint view of what the more and less risky parts and characteristics of the system are.

Method of operation
Testing is a measure to provide insight into the quality and the related product risks of a system or package when it is taken into production by an organisation.[2] Since there will never be an unlimited quantity of resources and time, it is important to determine in advance which system parts and characteristics require additional or less test effort. Well-justified choices have to be made in this context. One instrument to determine areas of concern for the test is executing a product risk analysis (PRA).

Executing a PRA consists of the following sub-activities:
1. Determining participants
2. Determining the PRA approach
3. Preparing session/interviews
4. Collecting and analysing product risks
5. Completeness check

These steps are described in detail in chapter 9 "Product Risk Analysis". It must be taken into account that a great number and variety of participants are involved in a master test plan, which means that the risk analysis may be less detailed. The participants are often acceptants, but also other information providers as discussed in section 5.2.2. For instance, test goals often differ and a division into object parts varies for technical management and users and is usually dependent on a characteristic. Functionality, for instance, has another division of the system into object parts than performance or security. Quality characteristics are often chosen for characteristics, but testable aspects can also be used – such as installability, multi-user, regression, etc. A possibility is that a PRA session may be combined with (part of) the subsequent activity, Determining the test strategy.

---

[2] Testing itself can never ensure that the damage when the system is taken into production is reduced. Based on the test results, defects and therefore potential damage are demonstrated. Based on this, it is determined to either make changes to the test object that eliminate or reduce the damage when it is taken into production, or not.

Products

The risk tables with the test goals and possible object parts with risk indications for each characteristic, managed separately and optionally laid down in the master test plan.

The PRA total overview with characteristics/object parts with risk class, defined in the master test plan.

Techniques

Product risk analysis (chapter 9)

Explanation of quality characteristics (chapter 10).

Tools

Not applicable.

5.2.4   Determining the test strategy

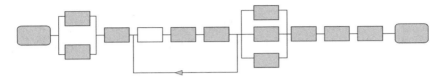

Aim

Based on the product risk analysis, deciding which characteristic/object part must be tested how thoroughly in which test level.

Method of operation

Determining a test strategy for a master test plan involves the following activities:

1. Determining test levels
2. Determining thoroughness of testing per characteristic/object part per test level

These activities are explained in greater detail below.

The product risk analysis and a first draft of the test strategy can often be combined in one single session. If this is impossible, the test manager creates a proposal for the test strategy after the product risk analysis, and discusses it with the client and several other stakeholders. A broadly supported result is achieved by creating a test strategy in consultation with these parties. This makes it easier to make effective decisions about the balance between thoroughness of testing, costs and time at a later stage.

1) Determining test levels

This involves the test levels to which the master test plan relates. Good arrangements must be made over the test levels to be distinguished and the parties responsible for executing each test level. Many organisations distinguish a unit test (UT), unit integration test (UIT), system test (ST), sometimes a functional acceptance test (FAT), a users acceptance test (UAT), and a production acceptance test (PAT). The UT, UIT and ST usually are the responsibility of the development organisation. The future user organisation is responsible for the FAT and UAT. The future (technical) system management organisation is responsible for the PAT. It is preferred that reviewing also be part of the master test plan - which is what many organisations are already doing. This is the case in particular in organisations that do not create a separate quality or review plan.

Many organisations have a standard classification of test levels. The test manager must examine in how far he must or can deviate from this. If the test levels have not yet been established or deviations are possible, in this step the test manager investigates the desired classification in test levels while taking account of the results of the product risk analysis.

When determining the test levels, arrangements are made about the aim and content of each test level.

In more detail

Considerations for test level classification

- **Development method used/selected**
  Various development methods each have their own testing requirements. This may be a consideration to simply adopt the test levels from such a method.

- **Organisation structure of the departments**
  If an organisation has a functional department structure (production, user, management departments, etc), you might consider letting each relevant department plan its tests, etc independently of the other departments. This occurs, for instance, with respect to the test levels production acceptance test, users acceptance test and/or functional acceptance test.

- **Separate responsibilities**
  A delivering party has other (test) responsibilities than the accepting party. Further divisions are often logical within these two parties. If, for instance, a production department is held responsible for the stable operation of a system, you might consider instituting the test level production acceptance test. It may be even more specific if this department is also responsible for a specific performance of the system, for instance. In this case, the test type performance test might be organised as a separate test level. Also when components or services from third parties are used, for instance in service oriented architectures, it is recommended to organise acceptance of these components or services as a separate test level.

- **Various stakeholders**
  If a stakeholder wants to be certain that his wishes/requirements are complied with, a separate test level can be defined to this end. For a package implementation, for instance, where the user is not convinced that the package contains all of the required functionalities. You might then define the test level functional (acceptance) test.

- **Risk level**
  In the event of high risks, a separate test level might be created to ensure adequate focus on risk testing. E.g. if a system has many (high-risk) interfaces, the test level system integration test may be a good addition. Or for instance when security or performance constitute great risks, you might consider organising these test types as a separate test level (security test, performance test).

- **Test and development maturity**
  If testing and development are insufficiently mature, it is often wise to refrain from combining or integrating test levels. In such a situation, the test levels system test (executed by the supplying party) and functional test (by the accepting party) are often defined separately. However, if maturity is high, these tests might be combined into a so-called combined test (CT), with the aims of both parties being maintained but the organisation and execution being combined.

- **Contractual agreements**
  In a demand-supply situation, a supplying party must comply with contractual agreements. This may mean that the party must demonstrate, in a system test, that specific requirements have been met, or that an Internet application cannot be hacked by means of a security test, or that a performance test demonstrates that the package has an acceptable response time when using production data. Especially when certification is involved (for smart cards, for security for web applications, for compliancy schemes like SOX), we recommend creating a separate test level for these issues.
- **Availability of infrastructure**
  Sometimes one is forced to review a certain test level classification because some test infrastructures simply have limited accessibility. For instance, a separate system integration test may be defined because an external party wants to make its test environment available on a limited basis during a certain period for executing tests ('test window').
- **Integration level**
  Generally, we could say that if the complexity of (the environment of) a system increases, you might consider splitting up the tests into multiple test levels to make and keep everything manageable. Furthermore, it may be impossible to test some quality characteristics until the system has reached a certain level of integrity. An example of this is performance. You would prefer to measure it as early on as possible, but often it cannot be realistically measured until the system is as good as complete. This might be a consideration to define a separate test level for this purpose.
- **Purchase or acceptance**
  To distinguish between purchase and acceptance, you could say that purchase is mainly about whether the defined requirements have been met as well as the obligation to pay (cf. the consideration contractual agreements). Acceptance, however, is mainly about the question: 'Can the organisation work with this?' In this case, requirements that are not described are also involved.

The following deviations occur regularly in practice:
- **End-to-end test**
  An end-to-end test requires alignment between various systems, parties, infrastructures, etc. In many organisations this is so complex, that the test is organised as a separate test level - system integration test - with its own test manager and testers.
- **Combined test**
  The system test and (functional) acceptance test usually have the same aim from the perspective of content, i.e. testing whether the system is functionally correct. The difference is the party responsible: supplier or client. From the perspective of efficiency, these test levels can be combined into one single combined test, on the condition that good agreements have been reached about tasks and responsibilities, management and verification of correct execution.
- **Security test, performance test, usability test**
  If a test level requires a highly specific test environment or expertise, it may be useful

to organise it as a separate test level with its own plan and organisation. Such tests are often outsourced for this reason.

- **Proof-of-concept test**
  In case of high uncertainty, i.e. when it is extremely difficult to assess the risks correctly, a so-called proof-of-concept test is sometimes set up. This test level often appears in large-scale migrations. The proof-of-concept test verifies whether the proposed project and/or development approach will work. This is done by building and testing a small (about 10%) but representative part of the system at an early stage. The results and experiences provide more certainty about the total process and help optimise everything.

Tips

- **Inflexible standard classification of test levels**
  As mentioned before, many organisations use a standard classification of test levels. Adapting this may require excessive energy or even be unfeasible. In these cases, the test manager should mould the tests to be executed into the existing test levels.
- **Order of test level execution**
  A classification into test levels does not necessarily mean the order of execution of tests. A planned performance test in a production acceptance test (PAT) can sometimes be executed very early on, possibly even before the users acceptance test or just after or even in parallel to the system test. In other words, even if the PAT is the last in a list of test levels, this does not mean it has to be executed last. This is determined when creating the planning (section 5.2.6) and also depends on the risks to be covered.

---

2) Determining thoroughness of testing per characteristic/object part per test level
After the test levels included in the scope of the master test plan are determined, the specified characteristics/object parts from the product risk analysis are allocated to the test levels. This results in alignment between the various test levels that are executed within the project. Clearly, the relevant responsibilities and authorisations must not be neglected in this context. Often a type of standard division can be used based on the aim of the test levels (primarily functionality for ST, suitability and user-friendliness for UAT, etc).

In more detail

As described earlier, evaluation can also be in the scope of the master test plan and therefore covered by the activity establishing the strategy. Only the documentation that is (formally) delivered can be evaluated. Such documentation may include: designs at all levels (requirements, use cases, functional design, process design, technical design, AO procedures), meeting reports, results of brainstorm sessions, etc.

First the characteristics and object parts from the PRA with their risk class (high, average, low) are set out against the test levels. It is then determined for each characteristic/object part combination how thoroughly it must be tested in which test level. A • symbol in a matrix shows whether a specific characteristic/object part is part of the test strategy of a test level. •• or even ••• shows that a relatively high level of attention must be devoted to the characteristic/object part in the relevant test level. Naturally a characteristic/ object part can be included in more than one test level, but the depth of testing usually differs. If test design techniques are used, results of previous test levels can be reviewed in e.g. the acceptance test. On the basis of this, less thorough testing may be required in that test level.

Characteristic/object part	RC	Evaluation	Developm test	ST	UAT	PAT
Functionality						
- subsys 1	A	•	••	••	••	
- subsys 2	B	•	•	••		
- total	C			•	•	
User-friendliness	B	•		I	••	
Performance						
- online	B			•		•
- batch	C					•
Security	A	•		S	•	•••
Suitability	B	•			•••	

Comments on the table above:

PRA-RC	Risk class (from PRA, where A=high risk, B=average risk, C=low risk)
Evaluation	Evaluation/review of the various intermediary products, such as requirements, functional design, technical design
Development test	Unit test + Unit integration test
ST	System Test
UAT	Users Acceptance Test
PAT	Production Acceptance Test
•	limited thoroughness of the dynamic test
••	medium thoroughness of the dynamic test
•••	high thoroughness of the dynamic test
S	Static testing
	Checking and examining products without executing the software
I	Implicit testing
	Including in another test type without creating specifically designed test cases.
<blank>	If a cell is bank, it means that the relevant test or evaluation level does not have to be concerned with the characteristic.

> **Tip**
>
> Determining the strategy is more than just the mechanical allocation of test thoroughness bullets based on the risk classes. Other aspects involved are:
> - Adequately classifying the test levels to be used
> - Performing evaluations/reviews, so that defects can be detected at an early stage when they can be reworked at relatively low cost
> - Refined delimitation of total testing and the individual test levels, so that the scope of each test level becomes clear
> - Non-testers have difficulty interpreting such tables. You should therefore add an explanation that can be understood by everyone (what is tested, at what depth/coverage ratio, how is overlap prevented, etc).

> **In more detail**
>
> **Overlap in tests**
> An important aim of allocating characteristics/object parts to test levels is to ensure that tests are not executed in duplicate or forgotten unintentionally. Clearly, in some situations, it can be decided to have multiple parties execute similar tests. This is useful, for instance, if a certain test aspects can be investigated from different perspectives. For instance the characteristic security can be included in the UAT and in the PAT. The UAT tests the authorisations, while the PAT looks at the technical functioning of the firewalls.
>
> **Increments**
> Developers work with increments, a sort of intermediate release, in iterative or agile system development. Each increment contains more functionality. The test manager can take this into account when determining the strategy by creating one overall master test plan strategy with the general testing approach, after which the separate test levels determine the strategy for each increment. Alternatively, the test manager determines a small (master test plan) strategy for each increment instead of one big one.

> **Tips**
>
> - In particular for functionality: a thoroughness of ••• for a test seems to suggest that, in this test level, the entire (sub)system must be tested at the greatest possible depth. This is not the case! The number of bullets indicates that heavier, similar or rather lighter testing than average is required. As such, it falls to the test manager of the test level in question to elaborate this further in the detailed test strategy.
> - When determining the strategy, the test manager must take the weighing of cost, time and required competencies into account as much as possible. If he knows that there is a very limited budget, or that the available people do not have experience

> with testing, he must refrain from proposing 'impossible' strategies such as very costly tests or very thorough test design techniques (to avoid many feedback cycles).
> • The starting point is that a test must be executed as early as possible in the system development process. This reduces the rework costs. Depending on the desired coverage of a risk, one might think of an early usability test in the development environment. However, not every characteristic can be tested at an early stage. E.g. testing suitability requires the presence of a (nearly) complete system.

Products
The test strategy, including explanation, laid down in the master test plan. Summary description per test level, with at least the aim of the test and person or department responsible.

Techniques
Determining the strategy (as described in this section)

Tools
Not applicable.

5.2.5   Estimating the effort

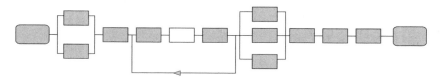

Aim
Estimating the required effort for the total test process based on the test strategy, so that the client can approve it or request adjustment.

Method of operation
Estimating the effort for the total test process is done early on in the project and is based on the test strategy. Often, not all knowledge of the test object is available at this point. As a consequence, the accuracy of the estimate is limited. The size and/or complexity of the test object may change during the project. Furthermore, the test environments and any test tools represent a (significant) cost item. It is important for the test manager to make it clear to the stakeholders that the estimate is based on a number of assumptions and therefore will have to be detailed – and possibly adapted – later on. A possible solution is to use margins to represent the initial estimate for a master test plan.

The estimate in the master test plan constitutes the framework for the estimates per test level (e.g. system test, users acceptance test, and production acceptance test).

In more detail

Estimation techniques
Choosing the estimating techniques in particular is a step requiring experience. There are various estimating techniques to help assess the required effort. The steps to create an estimate are described in chapter 11 "Estimation Techniques". An estimate for a master test plan can be made on the basis of:
• Ratio figures
• Test object size
• Work Breakdown Structure (WBS)
• Proportionate estimation
• Test point analysis (TPA)

To increase the reliability of the estimate, we strongly recommend using both the organisation's own experience figures and multiple estimating methods and techniques.

Products
The estimated effort for the total test process, including assumptions, laid down in the master test plan.

Techniques
Various estimating techniques, including Test Point Analysis (chapter 11)
Step by step plan for estimating the effort (section 11.1).

Tools
Planning and progress monitoring tool (spreadsheets for estimating the test effort and for Test Point Analysis are available at www.tmap.net).

5.2.6 Determining the planning

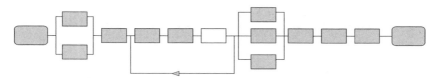

Aim
Creating the most reliable possible overall planning for all in-scope test levels, so that the client can take it into account or make adjustments. The principle of the planning is to find the most important defects first within the framework of the strategy and estimated effort.

Method of operation
Based on the planning of the system development process, the test strategy and estimated effort, an overall planning for the total test process is created. Factors observed while understanding the assignment, such a whether a time, money or quality-driven project is involved, have an impact on the planning. The start and end date and deliverables are specified for each test level. In the Planning phase of the various test levels, the detailed planning is elaborated. The overall planning must at least contain:
- Activities to be executed (at the phase level per test level)
- Relationships with and dependencies on other activities (in or out of the test process and between the various test levels)
- Time to be invested in each test level
- Required and available resources (people and infrastructure)
- Required and available lead time
- Deliverables.

If requested by the client, the financial consequences of the choices made must be visualised in a financial planning. Think of costs for (internal and external) personnel, training, workplaces, test environments and test tools.

The aim must be to ensure that the test execution activities for the various test levels match up or have a controlled overlap (overlap testing). When planning choices involving risks must be made for the sake of milestones, the test manager must report and explain this.

A quality-related aspect of planning is when a test level is completed. The test manager therefore has an important role in aligning the entry and exit criteria of the successive test levels. For an explanation of the relation between acceptance criteria and exit criteria, refer to section 6.2.7 "Determining the planning".

In more detail

Example of exit/acceptance criteria
In this example from practice, exit and acceptance criteria have high overlap.

The test approach and acceptance criteria are tuned with the stakeholders (see section x.y). Two levels of acceptance can be distinguished:
1) Acceptance of system XYZ by all stakeholders. This involves releasing the products for production.
2) Individual acceptance by the client(s) of each test level of the test level executed.

For level 1 acceptance, the test must be executed according to the agreed test strategy and the following guidelines are respected for any defects found:
The products of XYZ can be taken into production (are accepted) if:
- There are no category A defects.
- A patch or workaround is available for category B defects. The developer must also submit a planning reporting how and when the problem will be solved structurally.
- A document is available for category C defects, explaining how these non-critical defects are dealt with.

For level 2 acceptance, the test team (responsible for the relevant test level) will be discharged if the aims as defined globally in section y.z and further specified in detailed test plans, if any, are achieved. This is also a Go/No Go decision to start executing the following test level.

Feedback

The test manager provides feedback on the combination of the selected test strategy, estimated effort and planning to the client for approval or adjustment. The client can opt for better risk coverage in exchange for more test time and funds, or vice versa. The previous steps for Strategy, Estimating and Planning are repeated, if necessary. To facilitate communication, the test manager refers back to the original test goals.

Furthermore, he describes the use of tolerances in test execution with the client. These are boundaries within which the test manager does not have to ask the client for permission. Often a tolerance of 5% is used for the estimate, for instance.

Products

The overall planning for the total test process, laid down in the master test plan

Entry and exit criteria per test level

Strategy, estimated effort and planning with feedback from the client

Optional: Tolerances for strategy, estimated effort and planning.

Techniques
Not applicable.

Tools
Planning and progress monitoring tools
Workflow tool.

5.2.7   Defining the test products

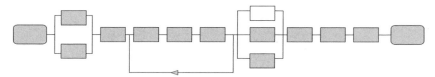

Aim
Defining the test products to be delivered at the master level and across the various test levels.

Method of operation
The activities that are executed to plan and control the total test process yield certain products, such as the master test plan and reports, but also procedures, instructions and project documentation (such as minutes of meetings). In consultation with the client and other stakeholders, the deliverables are determined. A choice can then be made in the master test plan as to which test levels must deliver which test products. These may be testware, such as test plans or test scripts or (automated) regression tests, i.e. products that are eligible for reuse, but also test documentation, like progress reports. In addition to specifying deliverables, this may also include standards with which the products must comply. Finally, the common use of tools for configuration and test management helps enforce a uniform operating method and facilitate subsequent management.

In more detail

Why at the master test plan level?
There are reasons to include the aligning of test products in the master test plan instead of leaving it to each individual test level:
• It forces test levels to use a uniform method, improving control of the total test process. This is a particularly important argument when external parties execute certain tests.
• It facilitates communication between test levels and overall test management.
• It increases the reusability of the products, not just within a test level but also across test levels.
• The uniform method makes it easier to switch people between test levels.

Products

A description of the deliverable test products (per test level and at the overall level), including standards, laid down in the master test plan
Templates for the various documents.

Techniques

Not applicable.

Tools

Testware management tool.

5.2.8   Defining the organisation

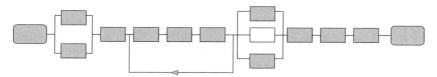

Aim
Defining the roles, tasks, authorisations and responsibilities applying for the total test process across the test levels.

Method of operation
The method consists of the following sub-activities:
1. Determining required roles
2. Allocating tasks, authorisations and responsibilities
3. Describing the organisation
4. Allocating staff
5. Establishing training and coaching requirements
6. Establishing consultation and reporting structures.

1) Determining required roles
To ensure good alignment between the various test levels, it is determined globally which test roles (see chapter 16 "Test Roles") must be distinguished and fulfilled. These are, in particular:
- Test management or test coordination
- Other types of management (on the master test plan level, think of e.g. management of the test infrastructure or the defects administration for all test levels)
- Support (on the master test plan level, think of e.g. test tool experts, a test method expert for all test levels, domain expert or developer).

On behalf of the resource claim, it is also determined roughly which test roles are required per test level. This is then elaborated further in the Planning phase for the relevant test levels.

2) Allocating tasks, authorisations and responsibilities
This shows the tasks and responsibilities per required role. Not yet at the level of the test levels (it is described in the detailed test plans), but at the overall level.

In more detail

Examples of tasks
• Creating the instructions for the products delivered by the various test levels

- Checking the enforcement of the instructions (internal reviews)
- Coordinating the various test activities comparable for the test levels, such as setting up and managing the technical infrastructure
- Creating guidelines for communication and reporting between the test levels, and the test process and the suppliers
- Setting up overall test method-related, technical and functional support
- Keeping the various test plans consistent
- Reporting on the overall test progress and quality of the test object
- Deployment/hiring of (extra) test personnel.

Manager or coordinator?

In practice, it is especially important to be clear about the responsibility of test management and coordination. In other words, when a certain test level becomes uncontrollable and the responsible test manager is not able to resolve the problem, does the (overall) test manager bear (final) responsibility or is his/her role more focused on coordination and advice? In the first case test manager is the proper term; in the second he is more of an overall test coordinator. In the first case, it means that the test manager must also have the associated authorisations. Think of e.g. his own budget and being able to take measures, such as deploying additional people or even replacing them. In the second case, the test coordinator's task involves coordinating the various tests, specifying and monitoring the test method, and informing and advising the project management on test progress and the quality of the tested system. In practice, where testing is often allocated to multiple parties we usually see overall test coordination. Test management is more likely when various test levels are allocated to one single party.

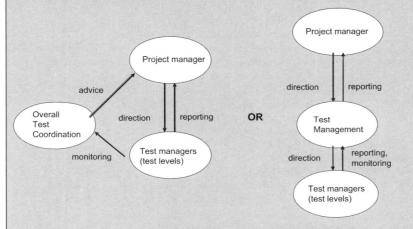

Figure 5.4, Possible responsibilities of test coordination or management

We should note that, in practice, a mix of management and overall coordination usually appears. For instance, the test manager directly controls one or more test levels (e.g. the ST and UAT) and coordinates others (e.g. development tests and the PAT). Creating the organisation chart can help clarify the situation.

3) Describing the organisation

The relationship between the specified roles, the separate test levels, and the relationships with the other stakeholders in the system development process must be determined and laid down. The organisation of testing is clearly part of the bigger (project) picture. In case of a project, one must not forget to define the relationship with a test or quality department, if any.

Testing must be organised, both at the overall level and the level of the test levels, within the framework of a master test plan. The following options are roughly distinguishable for a test level:

1. Testing as an **autonomous activity** or **integrated with other activities**
2. Either a **project** or **line organisation** is responsible for testing

As these choices depend on the test level, project and organisation, and little influence can be exerted on them at the master test plan level, we refer to section 6.2 "Planning phase" and section 8.3 "Permanent test organisation" for more information.

Another choice is to organise the overall management, control and support in a project or line organisation.

Example

The figure below shows an example of a fairly traditional organisation structure.

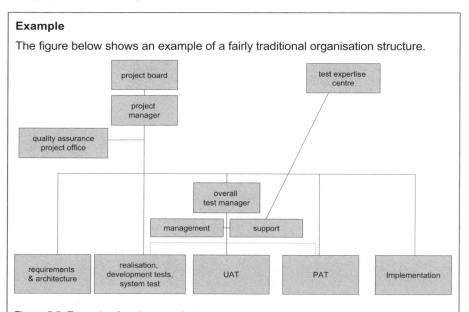

Figure 5.5: Example of testing organisation

This example is a mix of test management and test coordination. The test manager directly controls the UAT, but has no more than a coordinating task in relation to the other test levels, such as the development tests, the system test, and the PAT. Overall support and management for testing occurs under the flag of test management, with a relationship with the Testing line organisation, the test expertise centre, for the use of a generic approach, standards, templates and tools. The test manager is accountable to the project manager. The latter is responsible for the assumptions of the test process, such as the timely availability of personnel, resources, planning, and test basis. Naturally the project manager delegates a lot of the organisation work to the test manager. The project management maintains the relationship with the project client and the project board.

Upon request, advice on the quality is sometimes submitted directly to the project board and/or the client, periodically or when the tests are completed.

Another example of an organisation relates to a package implementation:

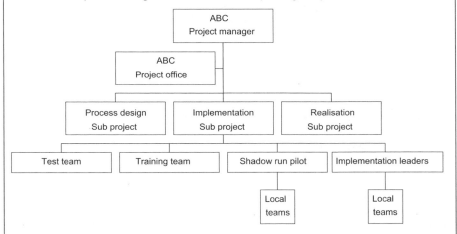

Figure 5.6: Example of testing organisation 2

The test team above has the following composition:

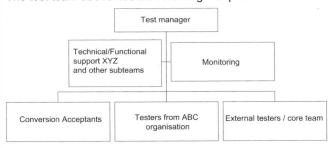

Figure 5.7: Example of test team organisation

A test team led by a test manager is established for testing. The test manager is responsible for the entire test process. The team has a flexible composition for the various activities, but has permanent core personnel. The test process is monitored by representatives of the accepting parties throughout the test process. These take part in the twice monthly monitoring meeting. The monitors have access to all documentation in the test process at all times. Thanks to the continuous monitoring, the test process can be adapted to the requirements of the monitoring party at an early stage if the monitors deem it necessary. Think, for instance, of requirements of the future system management organisation for testing authorisations and integration tests.

For maintenance, the test levels can be specified, as well as which persons, or which departments, are responsible for their elaboration and execution. Generally speaking it can be said that the user organisation is responsible for functional management and the (users) acceptance test, the processing organisation for technical management and the production acceptance test, and the maintenance organisation for application management and the unit/system test (see figure below).

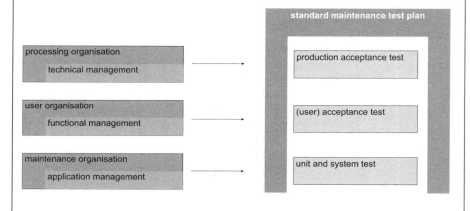

Figure 5.8: Departments in relation to test levels

In more detail

Iterative and agile system development

In these forms of system development, an important question is who is responsible for a test level. This is clear for unit and unit integration tests, but there are a number of options for the system and acceptance tests. The table below lists the most common test levels and their responsible parties.

Test level	Which party?
Unit test	Development (in team)
Unit integration test	Development (in team)
System test	Development (in team)
(Functional/users) acceptance test	User organisation (in or outside of team)
Production acceptance test	System management organisation (usually outside team)

'In or outside of team' means that a test can be executed within the project team, but that for some test levels, a separate test team outside the project team or even outside the organisation can be created to execute the test. For instance, the production acceptance test is usually executed outside the project team. This test requires specific (system management) expertise on the testers' part, plus a test environment that is as faithful to the production environment as possible. Often, both are available within the project on a limited basis.

The strong involvement of users with a decision-making mandate, and the collaboration within the team, make that the traditional wall between developers and users/ acceptants is much lower. In the course of the process, users provide continuous feedback on prototypes (by means of testing and evaluation), due to which the acceptance test can be a very 'thin' test. This will consist primarily of tests that could not be executed earlier, such as an end-to-end test. If the acceptance test is executed in the project, one may then also consider integrating it with the system test. The test team then comprises a mix of users, developers and professional testers.

Less logical is executing the acceptance test outside the project. This is not really in line with the principles of iterative development. The choice depends on the risks. If the organisation expects high risks, an acceptance test outside the team is more logical even though it is not in line with iterative principles. Examples of such risks are an insufficient decision-making mandate for users, that the project manager or developers seem to 'dominate' the users, or that the system is so critical that testing must occur in an adequately controlled, stable and production-like environment.

4) Allocating staff

After it has been established which test roles must be fulfilled in the test process, people are allocated to each role. Clearly, their availability and competencies in relation to the knowledge and competencies required for the relevant test roles are taken into account (see section 8.6 "Test professionals" and chapter 16, "Test Roles"). One person may fulfil multiple roles, which often happens in iterative development environments. In this case, you should be alert to conflicting responsibilities!

5) Establishing training and coaching requirements

The people involved in the test levels must have various types of knowledge, i.e. of testing, the business domain, and the system. At the overall level, organising training courses for people involved in the test levels must be taken into serious consideration. We also recommend informing the various parties indirectly involved in the test process, such as project or line management, about the importance of (structured) testing via a presentation.

6) Establishing consulting and reporting structures

Communication must occur with various parties from the total test process. It must be agreed with each party whether consultation and/or reporting will occur, and the aim and frequency thereof.

Consultation types
For consultation types, it is agreed who will be present and possibly what the standard agenda is.

Examples of consultation types for the test manager are:
- weekly meeting with all test managers and/or test coordinators
- weekly project meeting
- periodical steering group meeting.

Reports
Various forms of reporting are possible to different target groups and at various times. Depending on the report type, it is based on one or more of the four BDTM aspects Result, Risks, Time and Costs. The main reporting types are:
- progress report
- risk report
- release advice
- final report

The test manager determines, for each of the report types, who sends which report to whom, its content and detail level, and frequency. The test manager already determined which parties want/need to receive reports in the activity "Understanding the assignment". This is now detailed in consultation with the client. The report types and content are described in detail in section 6.3.3 "Reporting".

Examples are:
- Weekly report per test level on progress of testing and quality and risks of the test object, delivered by the test manager of a test level to the test manager and client and other stakeholders (such as the project consultation).
- Weekly summary/additional report on progress of testing and quality and risks of the test object, based on the above reports, delivered by the test manager to the client and other stakeholders (such as the project consultation).
- Periodical report on progress of testing and quality and risks of the test object, delivered by the test manager to the project board meeting.

In terms of content, the progress and quality report is most important because timely adjustment and control are possible on the basis of this information and advice. The data for this report are supplied by the (reports of the) test levels and by organising management at the overall level, see section 5.2.10 "Organising the management".

Products
A description of the test organisation, laid down in the master test plan.

Techniques
Not applicable.

Tools
Not applicable.

5.2.9   Defining the infrastructure

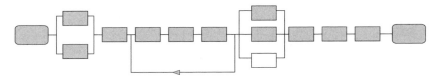

Aim

Determining the infrastructure required for the test process at an early stage, in particular the parts that must be set up for multiple test levels or have a relatively long order time.

Method of operation

The method consists of the following sub-activities:
1. Defining the test environment
2. Defining test tools
3. Defining the office setup
4. Establishing the infrastructure planning.

For a comprehensive description of test environments and tools, please refer to section 8.4 "Test environments" and section 8.5 "Test tools", respectively.

1) Defining the test environment
Every test level requires a test environment to execute the tests. This environment is roughly composed of the following components:
- Hardware
- Software
- Communication resources
- Facilities to create and use files
- Procedures

The environment must be composed and set up in such a way that it can be optimally determined, on the basis of the test results, in how far the test object complies with the defined requirements. The environment has a significant impact on the quality, lead time and costs of the test process.
To manage the environment correctly, it is therefore often separate from the development or production environment. Every test level has different requirements for the test environment. As a rule of thumb, the early tests – such as the development tests – have a greater need for a flexible environment that is easy to adapt. Later tests, such as the acceptance test, are more in need of stability and representativeness. Thus, the development tests are usually executed in the Development Environment, the system test in its own Test Environment, the acceptance tests in an Acceptance Environment,

just before the actual Production Environment. This is also called the DTAP model (section 8.4.5 "DTAP model").

Www.tmap.net contains a checklist that can be useful to establish the test environment.

When the test environments already exist, e.g. in a maintenance situation, they only need to be referred to and any required changes specified.

In more detail

While each test level can organise the detailed description of the environment it requires, there are reasons to start this at the master test plan level:
- Arranging, preparing and setting up a test environment often takes a lot of time, so it is best to start doing this at the earliest possible stage.
- An environment is (very) costly; not every test level has a budget for an environment of its own. In this case, limiting the number of test environments by sharing the environment with another test level may be an option. This requires good alignment and planning.
- The costs of the test environment must be included in the total estimated effort of the master test plan.
- Another option sometimes used is to turn the acceptance environment into the production environment after the test. The disadvantage is that, once the system is taken into production, there is no more environment for acceptance testing changes or new releases. This, too, can be decided on the basis of the master test plan.
- Often a test level is given one test environment by default. This does not take into account that a test level often tests a range of quality characteristics; the testing of each may have very different requirements for the environment. For instance, a performance test requires a production-like environment, but a user-friendliness test is perhaps better executed in a prototype-like environment, or in a usability lab with video cameras and transparent mirror walls. This requires early arrangement of the test environments.
- The execution of test levels is also perceived as sequential: "after the system test of version 0.5.2, this version can be transferred to the acceptance environment". Such sequential execution does not take adequate account of the need to execute tests as early as possible. For instance, the user-friendliness of the screens can be tested in the user acceptance test before the system test does a functional test of these screens. This can be done in the development environment or the acceptance environment, if the latter is available at this early stage. A conscious choice is then made between obtaining earlier test results and lower representativeness. Vice versa, the builders may assess performance as a high risk and wish to perform an (early) performance test. The production-like acceptance environment is most suitable to this end. This requires early and prior alignment.
- All these test levels and their environments may quickly result in a considerable number of test environments. The question is: who manages these environments? This can be done by a system management or infrastructure department, or a Testing line organisation. To ensure good communication, the managing party must have a

> (fixed) point of contact within the test process. This may be the test manager, but it
> is better to have a (test) infrastructure expert at the overall level in the test process.

2) Defining test tools
The required test tools are defined roughly. Test tools can provide support
for most test activities. The focus for the master test plan is on the tools that
can be used for multiple test levels. Examples are test management, capture
& playback, defects administration and simulation tools.

3) Defining the office setup
The office infrastructure (work spaces, meeting rooms, telephones, PCs,
network connections, office software, printers, etc) required for testing is
defined in outline. This means office setup in the broadest sense since the
testers must be able to do their work under good conditions. A checklist for
office setup can be found on www.tmap.net.

4) Establishing the infrastructure planning
For all of the required parts of the infrastructure, it is determined who is
responsible for their elaboration, selection and acquisition. Agreements are
recorded. An overall planning is also created with the times at which the
various facilities must be available.

Products
The description of the required infrastructure at the overall level, including
planning, laid down in the master test plan.

Techniques
Checklist "Office setup" (www.tmap.net)
Checklist "Test environment" (www.tmap.net).

Tools
Not applicable.

5.2.10　Organising the management

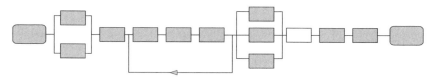

Aim
Laying down the manner in which the management of the test process, infrastructure, test products, and defects is organised. This can be achieved both by defining central standards for management and the central management of certain aspects. Both options aim to prevent reinventing the wheel in the separate test levels.

Method of operation
The method consists of the following sub-activities:
1. Defining test process management
2. Defining infrastructure management
3. Defining test product management
4. Defining the defects procedure.

At the master test plan level, standards can be defined for the separate test levels, supported by procedures, templates and tools (test management, planning and progress monitoring tools). Because this is virtually the same as when done at the level of test levels, we refer to section 6.2.12 "Organising the management" for a description of these sub-activities. This section only discusses the specific parts of setting up overall management.

In addition to the efficiency benefits, i.e. that the management procedures only have to be set up once and management tools can be shared between test levels, overall management has another big advantage: management uniformity results in improved control of the separate test levels by the test manager, in particular in the case of outsourcing or external party testing. Section 16.3 "Roles not described as a position" describes the following administrator roles for this: test project administrator, testware administrator and defects administrator.
Good management is also necessary when the test manager bears responsibility for the traceability of all tests: can it be demonstrated that everything that needs to be tested has actually been tested?

1) Defining test process management
Test process management focuses on managing the test process in terms of progress and quality and providing insight into the quality of the test object.

To this end, the following data must be identified, registered, administrated, stored and interpreted:
- Progress and use of budget and time
- Quality indicators
- Test statistics.

This information represents the basis for control and reporting by the test manager. The test manager of each test level is responsible for managing his own test process. The overall test manager ensures that this is done correctly. To this end, the test manager checks, randomly if necessary, the separate test levels (or orders checks) both for progress and quality of the test process. The latter can be achieved by e.g. asking the method test expert to check the traceability from test basis to test scripts to test results. The enforcement of instructions, approach and procedures can also be verified. If required, a separate report can be made on this aspect.

The progress data are derived from the data and reports of the individual test levels and by recording the data on the overall activities and products. Maintaining the same types of data for all test levels is therefore vital to the creation of overall statistics.

2) Defining infrastructure management
It is often useful to organise infrastructure management centrally, across the test levels.

In addition to the general management tasks described in section 6.2.12, such as backup and recovery, availability, version management and maintenance, the following tasks are specific to central management:
- Managing an environment and/or test tools shared by test levels
- Aligning the separate infrastructure planning schedules
- Acting as an intermediary between suppliers (system management department or the central test organisation) and clients (test levels) of the infrastructure. Central management can, for instance, define the delivery procedure.

3) Defining test product management
At the master test plan level, standards are defined for managing the test products of the separate test levels, supported by procedures, templates and tools. This facilitates the reusability of the products and communication on this subject. Sometimes, it is decided to handle this management centrally as well. We recommend using the standards for documentation and configuration management generally applicable within the system development process.

4) Defining the defects procedure

Because a defects procedure applies to the entire project and not to a separate test level, this procedure is best defined at the master test plan level instead of per separate test level. This also makes it possible to detect trends crossing the boundaries of test levels. Please refer to chapter 12 "Defects Management" for a description of the defects procedure.

Products

A description of the above-mentioned management processes, laid down in the master test plan.

Techniques

Not applicable.

Tools

Testware management tool
Defect management tool
Workflow tool
Planning and progress monitoring tool.

5.2.11   Determining test process risks (& countermeasures)

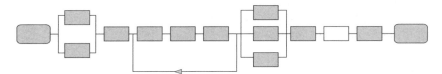

Aim

Explicitly specifying the risks for the total test process, improving the client's and other stakeholders' understanding of the risks for the test process and enabling them to take them into account in the management of the total process.

Method of operation

In executing previous activities, the test manager obtained a picture of the (im)possibilities for the test process, but also of threats and risks. The master test plan indicates, for each risk, whether, and if yes, which, countermeasures have been taken to cover or mitigate the detected risk. Think of preventative measures to avoid risks, but possibly also of detection measures to detect problems in time or corrective measures to solve the consequences.

In more detail

The risks may involve, among other things:
- **Not all relevant parties are involved**
  The PRA and therefore the test strategy may be incomplete because the input of these parties was missing. This also involves the risk that big changes in the system may be necessary at a later stage.
- **Continued discussions on the scope of the system**
  If the parties cannot agree on the scope of the system, it becomes difficult to create a reliable strategy, planning and budget for testing, thereby obstructing the test process.

Products

A description of the detected (test) process risks and possible countermeasures, laid down in the master test plan.

Techniques

Checklist "Test process risks" (www.tmap.net).

Tools

Not applicable.

5.2.12 Feedback and consolidation of the plan

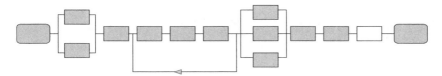

Aim
On the one hand, recording the results of all of the activities executed to date. On the other, obtaining approval from the client for the selected approach.

Method of operation
The method consists of the following sub-activities:
1. Creating the master test plan
2. Feedback on the master test plan
3. Consolidating the master test plan.

1) Creating the master test plan
The results of all of the activities executed so far are laid down in the master test plan. The master test plan contains at least the following chapters:
- Formulation of the assignment
- Test strategy, including Product Risk Analysis
- Approach (including aim, summary description, and exit criteria per test level)
- Organisation
- Infrastructure
- Management
- Threats, risks and countermeasures
- Overall estimated effort and planning.

2) Feedback on the master test plan
Feedback on the master test plan with the results of previous activities is given to the client and other stakeholders for approval or adjustment. This makes the planned test approach transparent and controllable, entirely in line with BDTM.

While many things can change, in practice we see that mainly the combination of chosen test strategy, estimated effort and planning is adjusted. By adapting the strategy (with the risk analysis not changing, in principle), the tests manager is able to allow the client to control based on the consideration between test effort versus test thoroughness and the associated risks. This results in a modified test strategy, where the elimination of test thoroughness is shown by ○ instead of ● (and extra test thoroughness by ●̲ instead of ●), e.g.:

Characteristic	PRA RC	Evaluation	Development test	ST	UAT	PAT
Functionality						
- subsys 1	A	●	● ○	●●●̲	●●	
...						

3) Consolidating the master test plan
After previous activity, the test manager must submit the master test plan to the client and other stakeholders for approval. The plan is now placed under configuration management as a formal test product. Furthermore a presentation, for instance to the project board and various stakeholders, can contribute to obtaining approval and, at least as important, support within the organisation.

Products
The master test plan

Techniques
Not applicable.

Tools
Not applicable.

5.3 Control phase of the total test process

Aim
Providing the client with adequate insight into *and* control options over:
- The progress of the test process
- The quality and risks of the test object
- The quality of the test process.

To this end, the test manager must control the total test process in an optimal manner and report on it.

Context
This activity relates to all test and evaluation levels involved in the master test plan, as already described in section 5.2 "Context". The testing may relate to new development, maintenance, migration, a package implementation, or a mix of these elements. The development approach may be waterfall, iterative, agile or a mix. Depending on the agreements reached, the test manager may have a managing, coordinating or simply observing role in relation to a test level.

Preconditions
This activity starts after the master test plan is created or once one or more of the relevant test and evaluation levels have started.

Method of operation
The test manager and administrator(s) execute the activities assigned to them in the master test plan. They manage the test process, infrastructure and test products, partly on the basis of the data supplied by the test levels. Based on this data, the test manager analyses possible trends. He also ensures that he is well informed of the developments beyond testing, such as delays in development, upcoming big change proposals and project adjustments. If necessary, he proposes specific control measures to the client.

Information is the main product of testing. To this end, the test manager creates different kinds of reports for the various target groups, taking account of the BDTM aspects of Result, Risks, Time and Costs.

Roles/responsibilities
The test manager or overall test coordinator is the role primarily responsible for (the coordination of) the management of the total test process.

Furthermore, certain roles may be created at the overall test level for management and support, both for the overall level and for the separate test levels.

Activities

Managing the total test process consists of the following activities:
1. Management
2. Monitoring
3. Reporting
4. Adjusting.

The diagram below shows the order of and dependencies between the various activities, with the arrow demonstrating that the activities are emphatically iterative:

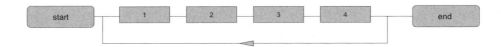

Figure 5.9: Control of the total test process

5.3.1 Management

Aim
Managing the test process, infrastructure and test products at the overall level to provide continuous insight into the progress and quality of the total test process and the quality of the test process.

Method
The management activity can be split up into two sub-activities:
- The following forms of management are executed in a way that conforms to the procedures established in the master test plan: Management of the test process, infrastructure management, test product management and defect management (see section 5.2.10 "Organising the management").
- The test levels are supported with and checked for the implementation of the overall management standards.

These activities are covered by the role of administrator or test manager as defined in section 5.2.8 "Defining the organisation". Section 16.3 "Roles not described as a position" describes in more detail the following administrator roles: test project administrator, testware administrator and defects administrator.

Products
A managed test process.

Techniques
Not applicable.

Tools
Defect management tool
Testware management tool
Workflow tool
Planning and progress monitoring tool.

5.3.2   Monitoring

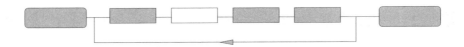

Aim

On the basis of internal managed data and external information, monitoring the total test process.

Method of operation

The main and most difficult task of the test manager is monitoring the execution of the master test plan. While described as a very instrumental activity in the section below, this is mainly a *communicative activity* with *employee, stakeholder and expectation management* that requires strong social and communication skills.

Generally speaking, the test levels described in the plan must be executed according to a specific time path and in a certain order. The test manager must be able to determine whether it is wise to start testing. Towards the end of test execution, the test manager must be able to answer the question whether it is wise to stop testing.

Practice has shown that deviations from the original plan often occur. Such deviations may have a cause both inside and outside the test process. Examples of the former are that specifying or executing test cases proceeds more slowly than expected (the testers are less productive than expected), or that certain test levels cannot begin testing according to the planning (due to an incorrect assessment beforehand). Examples of the latter are: inadequate quality of the test basis or test object, additional change proposals, or delays in design or development. The test manager must detect such events or trend as early on as possible. He can then take timely measures to correct a negative trend. This is nearly always better, more economical and faster.

The information for the events or trends is supplied from several sides:
- Internally managed data at the overall level
- Data supplied by (reports of) the test levels
- Information from outside the test process supplied by documentation like minutes or memos, but certainly also by spoken consultation, such as project meetings, bilateral consultations, stand-up meetings, etc.

The spoken source of information in particular underlines the importance of good (social) skills and external orientation on the part of the test manager.

On the basis of the data, the test manager analyses possible trends and tries to detect threats (or opportunities) in time. He executes the following steps to this end:
1. Analysing the event, estimating risks and defining countermeasures
2. Coordinating with the client and other stakeholders (optional, depending on tolerance)

These steps are described in detail in section 6.3.2 "Monitoring". The present section limits itself to explaining certain specific issues for the master test plan.

In more detail

Below you will find a few examples of common events with causes, consequences and countermeasures that the test manager can propose:

Event	A test level deviates from the planning
Possible causes	The causes may lie in the process before the test process. For instance lower quality of test basis/object, late delivery by design/building, test infrastructure not installed in time, installation of test object in test environment delayed (significantly). The cause may also lie in the test level itself. Think of inadequate resources, incorrect planning, or inadequate progress monitoring.
Consequences for the test process	Successive test levels may start later.
Possible countermeasures	• In iterative development in consultation with the developers: Limiting system functionality • Deploying extra test capacity • Successive test levels start in parallel with the ongoing test level, resulting in some inefficiency (two test levels detect the same defect) • It is decided to merge certain test levels or types, executing them together • Requesting additional budget • Reassessing overall test strategy, taking extra risk • Reassessing the project planning • ...

Event	A test level has no further time/resources to execute all required (re)tests
Possible causes	Here, too, the causes may lie outside the testing, cf. above. But internal causes are possible, too: inadequate planning and estimate, unexpected shortage of resources, insufficient productivity.
Consequences for the test process	• Successive test levels receive a test object of inadequate or uncertain quality • Successive test levels are delayed or must stop after inadequate testing • Backlog effect: the project seems to be continuing at full speed in a way that conforms with the plan, but an increasing backlog of incomplete work/inadequate quality emerges. Only in that case will the team stop to assess the situation and recognise the enormous quantity of rework and delays.
Possible countermeasures	• Deploying extra test capacity • Allowing a delay of the relevant test level, cf. above • Requesting additional budget • Reassessing overall test strategy, taking extra risk • Reassessing the project planning • …

Event	Uncertainty about the scope of the test levels
Possible causes	• Lack of information when creating the overall test strategy • Inadequate alignment when creating the overall test strategy • Progressive insight or changed functionality/scope of project makes new testable aspects clear
Consequences for the test process	• Certain aspects are not tested, or • Extra time/money/resources needed to test the aspect • Delays in planning
Possible countermeasures	• Realigning the scope of test levels, reassessing the overall test strategy • Deploying extra test capacity for the relevant test levels • Allowing a delay of the relevant test level, cf. above • Requesting additional budget • Reassessing the project planning • …

Event	Relatively large numbers of defects for certain characteristics or object parts in specific test levels
Possible causes	Depending on the cause: inadequate quality of test object or test basis
Consequences for the test process	• Extra time/money/resources needed for retesting and additional tests • Delays
Possible countermeasures	• Realignment, reassessing the overall test strategy • Recommending that prior test and evaluation activities be executed more thoroughly for the relevant characteristics/object parts • Deploying extra test capacity for the relevant test level • Allowing a delay of the relevant test level, cf. above • Planning additional tests in the following test level • Requesting additional budget • Reassessing the project planning • …

Note: The above tables serve as an example. They are intended to provide a single view, not a complete picture.

Products
Proposed control measures.

Techniques
Not applicable.

Tools
Defect management tool
Testware management tool
Workflow tool
Planning and progress monitoring tool.

5.3.3   Reporting

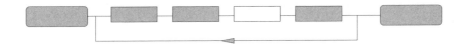

Aim

Creating reports to provide insight into both the quality of the test object and the progress and quality of the separate test levels and the total test process. These reports ensure that the client and other stakeholders can manage effectively based on the progress of the test process.

Method of operation

During the test project, the test manager creates various reports. In the master test plan, the chapter "Management" specifies the type and frequency of reporting. Periodical reports are made on the quality of the test object and the progress and quality of the test process. In addition to the periodical reports, the client or other stakeholders may request ad hoc reports. The most common example is the risk report to map the possible consequences of a threat or risk to the test process and propose countermeasures. Furthermore, a sudden request for an additional progress report may be made, e.g. as most up-to-date input for a project board or project management meeting. A release advice and final report are compiled at the end of the test process.

All this information provides the client, project manager and other stakeholders with insight into the degree to which:
- the intended result has been achieved
- the risks during commissioning are known and as small as possible within the framework of the defined preconditions
- this is done within the defined budget and proposed (lead) time.

In other words, these are the BDTM aspects of Result, Risks, Time and Costs. Providing insight means that the report must match the perception of its recipients.

The reports are based on the data as recorded that conforms with section 5.2.10 "Organising the management". The data are supplied mainly by the test levels.

> **Tip**
>
> The importance of tools emerges for reports. They help with the standard reports, but also and especially with ad hoc reports, where speed is of the essence. The test manager must therefore be able to handle the relevant tools (cf. below) well.

The main reports are:
- progress report
- risk report
- release advice
- final report.

These reports are described in detail in section 6.3.3 "Reporting".

The next page shows an example of (part of) a progress report, in which Result and Time are combined in a spreadsheet.

sheet	Status [application]
version	1.0
date	May 19 2006
author	B. Taylor / Stigter
application	[application]
test level	System / Acceptance

Project summary: internet site with applications enabling customers to make changes

Test infrastructure		
Development	available, no real test data	
System	available from 01-03-2006.	
Acceptance	The acceptance environment still needs to be set up. The first delivery will occur on 01-12-2006. Until that time, the business tests in the system test environment.	

Area of risk/concern	Test object + ID	Test unit	System test							User acceptance test + Production acceptance test					
			Test cases available? Y / N	Start ST	End ST	Tested?	Results OK/ NOK	Open defects	Total qty	Comments	Start UAT / PAT	End UAT / PAT	Tested?	Results OK/ NOK	Unresolved defects	Total qty	Comments
Functionality	**Internet front-end**														
		GU001	y	21-05-06	25-05-06	25%	n	10	1		3-06-06	7-06-06	0%	n		
		GU002	y	21-05-06	25-05-06	25%	n				3-06-06	7-06-06	0%	n		
		Navigation	y	21-05-06	25-05-06	25%	n				3-06-06	7-06-06	0%	n		
		Lay-out	y	11-05-06	25-05-06	85%	n	2,8	2		29-05-06	6-10-06	0%	n		
	[application] - AB														
		ABx01	y	11-05-06	25-05-06	100%	n				29-05-06	6-10-06	0%	n		
		ABx02	y	11-05-06	25-05-06	60%	n	2			29-05-06	6-10-06	0%	n		
		ABx02	y	11-05-06	25-05-06	60%	n	8			29-05-06	6-10-06	0%	n		
	Context Management System														
		CM001	y	01-05-06	15-05-06	100%	y				18-05-06	28-05-06	50%	n	4,5	2	
		CM002	y	01-05-06	15-05-06	100%	y				18-05-06	28-05-06	50%	n		
		DS4	y	01-05-06	15-05-06	60%	y			Not all tests executed, yet still moving to acceptance	19-05-06	28-05-06	50%	n	-1,5	
	Management Information														
		MI001	y	12-05-06	15-05-06	100%	y				19-05-06	1-06-06	0%	n	6	1	Due to lack of time, the project management decided to exclude this component from the UAT. This component was approved in ST.
		Report Y	y	12-05-06	15-05-06	100%	y				19-05-06	1-06-06	0%	n		
		Report Y	n	12-05-06	15-05-06	100%	y				19-05-06	1-06-06	0%	n	6	
Suitability	**Department**														
		AIx001	n/a				n/a				3-06-06	10-06-06	0%	n		
		AIx002	n/a				n/a				3-06-06	10-06-06	0%	n		
		Business process 1	n/a				n/a				3-06-06	10-06-06	0%	n		
		Business process 2	n/a				n/a				3-06-06	10-06-06	0%	n		
		Helpdesk procedure	n/a				n/a								
Usability	**Usability test**														
		US001	n	05-05-06	10-05-06	100%	y			Executed by an external agency based on the prototype and approved.			0%	n/a		
		External usability lab	n	05-05-06	10-05-06	100%	y						0%	n/a		
		US002	n	05-05-06	10-05-06	0%	n			Project management decided to not redcourse this test due to budget problems, instead extra attention is devoted to it in the internal training.				n/a		
		External usability lab														
Security	**Security tests**														
		SE001	n/a				n/a				3-06-06	7-06-06	0%	n		
		SE002	n/a				n/a				15-06-06	25-06-06	0%	n		
		Hacker test (external)	n/a				n/a				1-06-06	7-06-06	0%	n		
		Authorisations	n/a				n/a				3-06-06	7-06-06	0%	n		
		[application] - SSL														
		[application] - transactions - authorisation level 1														
Manageability	**Webserver**														
		WS001	n/a				n/a				18-05-06	7-06-06	60%	n	9	1	Defects were detected during the FAT, but not all employees register them. The picture is therefore incomplete.
		Procedure backup / restore database [application]	n/a				n/a				18-05-06	26-05-06	60%	n	9	
		WS002	n/a				n/a				3-06-06	7-06-06	0%	n		
		WS003	n/a				n/a				3-06-06	7-06-06	0%	n		
		Manageability Checklist														
		Fallback procedure														
Performance	**Performance test**														
		PE001	n/a				n/a				3-06-06	7-06-06	0%	n		
		Load test	n/a				n/a				3-06-06	7-06-06	0%	n		
		PE002	n/a				n/a				3-06-06	7-06-06	0%	n		
		Stress test														

Products

Reports (progress report, risk report, release advice, final report)
Experience data
Cost/benefit analysis.

Techniques

Checklist "Test process evaluation" (www.tmap.net)
Metrics (chapter 13).

Tools

Defect management tool
Testware management tool
Workflow tool
Planning and progress monitoring tool.

5.3.4   Adjusting

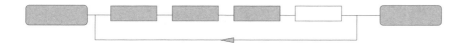

Aim
Adjusting the total test process (if necessary in consultation with the client).

Method of operation
When the measures proposed in section 5.3.2 "Monitoring" are reported and the client has approved and chosen one or more of the possible alternatives, the test manager can implement them. This involves the following steps:
1. Implementing measures and evaluating effectiveness
2. Adjusting products from the planning phase (optional, dependent on tolerance)
3. Feedback to the client.

In more detail

Adjusting the strategy
In many cases, the test strategy needs to be adjusted. A good reason to change the strategy is that certain tests yield far more or less defects than expected, or that the test process shows that the product risks were not estimated correctly or additional product risks are perceived. It may be decided to specify and execute extra tests or execute only part of planned tests or even eliminate them altogether. A less adequate reason to change the strategy is if one wishes to compensate delays in the rest of the development process in costs or time by means of reduced testing.

Using the established strategy as a basis, the test manager consults with the client about the changed risk assessment and which aspects require additional or reduced testing. By indicating what testing will be reduced in relation to the defined product risks, the test manager is able to report correctly on the possibly emerged higher risk that remains after the test.

The table below is a good example of a changed PRA and test strategy at the overall level.

Example:

Characteristic	RC	Evaluation	Developm test	ST	UAT	PAT
Functionality						
- subsys 1	A	●	●	●●○	●○	
- subsys 2	A (B)	●	●	●●		
- total	B (C)			●<u>●</u>	●	
User-friendliness	B	●			●○	
Performance						
- online	B			●		●
- batch	C					●
Security	B (A)	●			●	●●○
Suitability	B	●			●●○	

In this example, the allocated risk class for functionality has been increased for subsystem 2 and the total system. However, the test thoroughness in the system test and user acceptance test of subsystem 1 has become lighter (from 3 to 2 and from 2 to 1, symbolised by ○). However, the system test of the total system is intensified, from 1 to 2, symbolised by ●. It is clear that the risk increases and the test thoroughness drops. Naturally this requires an explanation as well as a correct risk assessment by the test manager on behalf of the client (not covered by this example).

The most common and expected changes relate to the planning. If replanning one test level has consequences for the planning of other test levels and project parts, all stakeholders are notified and, where necessary, their approval must be obtained.

Products
Control measures
Adjusted plan in the form of a new version or as a supplement to the original plan.

Techniques
Not applicable.

Tools
Workflow tool
Planning and progress monitoring tool.

5.4   Generic Test Agreements

The so-called Generic Test Agreements (GTAs) resemble a master test plan and sometimes even replace it. By default, the master test plan applies to one project. In many cases, such as in case of outsourcing, offshoring, maintenance or for programmes, the test process goes beyond a single project, however. The initial investment does not usually yield a return until subsequent releases of the system, i.e. during maintenance. To prevent new agreements on the what and how of testing having to be made for every release, these are stipulated in the GTA document. This contains the general agreements on e.g. the test process, standard strategy, estimating method, procedures, organisation, communication, documentation, etc. This makes it the overall approach for the setup and organisation of test processes that applies to (all) future releases. This is therefore not per project/release in which the alignment between test levels of that release is described. Based on the GTA, it is then decided whether to create, for each release, just a detailed master test plan, or a master test plan with separate test plans per test level, or only the separate test plans.

In addition to the above-mentioned situations, GTAs are also often made for iterative projects. For each increment, the test manager creates a master test plan or even the separate test plans directly.

Another benefit of GTAs emerges in unplanned (ad hoc) maintenance. Here, solving the production problem has the highest priority. While the consequence is that not all required steps in a structured test approach can be executed, GTAs are particularly indispensable in this context because they specify which test activities are vital in ad hoc maintenance and must always be executed. If a scaleable regression test set that is 'easily' adapted to the test strategy is also available, a qualitatively good test can be executed 'even' for ad hoc corrective maintenance.

GTAs are actually a sort of Service Level Agreement between the client and supplier. This in turn is a part of the contract, also containing e.g. agreements on timely delivery of capacity, response times, training new people, pricing, etc.

For each release or project, the test manager supplements the GTAs with information such as what will be tested, personnel and milestones, up to the level of detail of a master test plan. This makes the layout of a GTA document and a master test plan identical – the difference is in the content. Example: the section Milestones in a GTA describes how it must be specified; a master test plan describes the actual milestones for the specific project.

You can find the table of contents of a GTA document on www.tmap.net. Since the GTAs do not contain a planning or milestones, they do not formally represent a plan. GTAs are also known as GMTAs (Generic Master Test Agreements), MTV (Master Test Vision), and GMTP (Generic Master Test Plan or Generic Master Test Protocol).

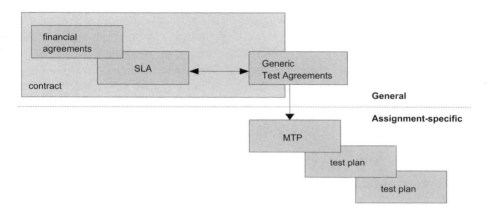

Figure 5.10: Relationship contract, GTA, master test plan (MTP), and test plans

6 Acceptance and system tests

6.1 Introduction

Acceptance test and system test

This chapter describes the TMap life cycle model, with the associated activities, for the test levels acceptance test and system test. Both can actually be considered (and therefore organised) as autonomous processes. They have their own test plan, their own budget, and often their own test environment to execute the test. They are processes running parallel to the development process, which must be started by preference while the functional specifications are being created.

As described in chapter 2 "Framework and importance of testing", a separation can be made in a development process between the client on the one hand and the supplier on the other. In the context of testing, the first group is summarised as the accepting (demanding) party and the second as the delivering party. Each of these parties has its own responsibility in testing. The supplier executes the system test to determine whether the system complies with the functional and technical specifications. This demonstrates that everything that needs to be delivered is actually being delivered. After the supplier has executed the system test, reworked the detected defects and subjected them to a retest with a positive result, the system is offered to the client for acceptance. The accepting party wants to determine, with the test, whether what has been asked for is actually being delivered and whether it can do with the product what it wants to/must do.

TMap life cycle model

The process of the acceptance and system tests consists of a number of different activities. The TMap life cycle model is used to map the various activities, with their mutual order and dependencies. It is a generic model and can be applied for both test levels. However, the acceptance test and the system test each give their own interpretation to the life cycle model. In the TMap life cycle model the test activities are divided over seven phases (see figure 6.1 "TMap life cycle model"). These are the phases Planning, Control, Setting up and maintaining infrastructure, Preparation, Specification, Execution and Completion.

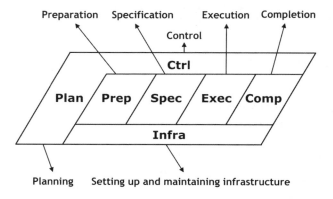

Figure 6.1: TMap life cycle model

In the Planning phase (section 6.2), the test manager formulates a coherent approach that is supported by the client to adequately execute the test assignment. This is laid down in the test plan. In the Control phase (section 6.3) the activities in the test plan are executed, monitored, and adjusted if necessary. The Setting up and maintaining infrastructure phase (section 6.4) aims to provide the required test infrastructure that is used in the various TMap phases and activities. The Preparation phase (section 6.5) aims to have access to a test basis, agreed with the client of the test, of adequate quality to design the test cases. The tests are specified in the Specification phase (section 6.6) and executed in the Execution phase (section 6.7). This provides insight into the quality of the test object. The test assignment is concluded in the Completion phase (section 6.8). This phase offers the opportunity to learn lessons from experiences gained in the project. Furthermore activities are executed to guarantee reuse of products.

The phases described above do not always have to be executed strictly sequentially. For instance, test cases for a part of the test may still be specified (Specification phase) while the test execution (Execution phase) has already begun for another part of the test. This is a situation that often occurs in projects in which there is phased delivery of software. We also recommend making preparations for the activities in the Completion phase as early as during the Specification phase. This phenomenon – where phases do not have to be executed sequentially - is expressed in the TMap life cycle model by the sloping lines between the phases. This results in the characteristic form of the model: the parallelogram.

In more detail

Retesting in the TMap life cycle model
The life cycle model also provides space for retesting. Retests occur when defects are detected while executing the test cases. If a retest must be prepared and executed, it may be necessary to go through some phases of the TMap life cycle model again. Depending on the situation, this may be limited to the Execution phase, e.g. if only defects in the software are to be solved. If defects in the test basis must be solved, it may be necessary to (re)plan the retest completely (in particular in the case of a extensive rework action of the test basis). The phases Preparation, Specification and Execution must then all be gone through again.

When the life cycle model is related to the system development life cycle, a number of relationships come to light. Figure 6.2 "Relationship between TMap life cycle and system development life cycle" shows an example of these relationships.

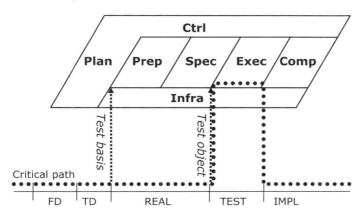

Figure 6.2: Relationship between TMap test life cycle and system development life cycle

The figure shows that the preparation phase of the TMap test life cycle can start when the test basis is delivered. The test basis is created in the system development phases FD (functional design) and/or TD (technical design). After these system development phases, the realisation of the test object begins (the system development phase REAL). The test (TEST) starts as soon as the test object is delivered. The next system development phase is the implementation phase (IMPL). This example demonstrates that only the TMap Execution phase is on the critical path of the project (the critical path is shown as a dotted line). All other test phases are executed in parallel to the other system development phases and, if ready in time, are not on the critical path.

TMap life cycle model in relation to development models
The TMap life cycle model can be applied within various system development models. It does not matter whether system development occurs on the basis of principles such as waterfall, iterative or increments. The reason is that every system development model has the system development phasing as shown in figure 6.2 "Relationship between TMap life cycle and system development life cycle". In iterative and incremental development (e.g. the RUP and DSDM methods), the first development phases in the model (FD, TD and REAL) must be seen as intermediary products. These are then tested (TEST) and integrated (INT). Figure 6.3 "Relationship TMap life cycle with increments" shows this schematically.

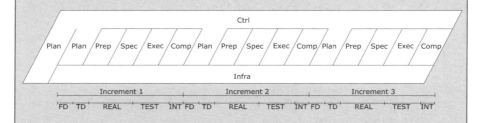

Figure 6.3: Relationship TMap life cycle with increments

At the project level, above all increments, the phases Planning, Control and Setting up and maintaining infrastructure are executed. The phases Planning, Preparation, Specification, Execution and Completion apply for every increment. The Planning phase in the increments is in close relationship to the master Control phase, hence the open link between the two. In view of the repetitive nature of iterative and incremental development, we must emphasise the repeatability of the tests. This can be achieved by e.g. the use of test tools and adequate testware management.

6.2 Planning phase

Aim

Formulating a cohesive and broadly supported approach with which the test assignment can be successfully executed. An important part of the planning phase is the creation of the test plan, for the purpose of informing the client and other stakeholders concerning the approach, schedule, budget, activities and the (end) products to be delivered in relation to the test process. If an overall master test plan exists, the test plan should be derived from it.

Context

All the steps of the planning phase should be gone through. The results are usually established in a separate test plan, if the test level is organised as a stand-alone activity. In some cases, particularly with iterative or agile development, the test level is integrated into the total process and the test plan is part of the project plan. The effort required to create the plan depends on what is already available. The presence of a master test plan, of Generic Test Agreements, or a Testing line organisation with instructions, templates and standards can make creating the test plan significantly easier, as it is easy to refer to them. In creating the test plan, the test manager should allow for the possible and the impossible. An important factor here is the existing "testing maturity", or the quality of the test process. If there is familiarity with test phasing, if test tools are available and the testers are using test design techniques, how are the management and reporting normally managed? If the testing is not very mature, the test manager cannot expect too much from the test process or the testers involved in it. This applies to a lesser extent to the maturity of the development or maintenance process that surrounds testing. If this is chaotic and unmanageable, it is probably inadvisable to invest in the "perfect" test process; a "reasonable" test process will suffice.

Preconditions

To be able to make a meaningful start on the creation of the test plan, the following points should be known:
- The client for the test level
- Aim and importance of the system or package to the organisation
- General requirements
- The organisation of the development, maintenance or implementation process
- The (delivery) plan for the system to be developed or maintained, or package to be implemented
- The method of developing or maintaining the system or implementing the package

- If there is a master test plan, it should be fixed and approved
- Insight into the development and production environment, so that the test environment can be defined.

If this information is not yet available, for example because the development approach is still unknown, it will have a negative effect on the lead time, the effort required for the creation of the plan, or on the quality and required degree of detail. Also required is the willingness and opportunity to agree on all kinds of aspects of the test process.

Method of operation

The test manager, as a rule, is the originator of the test plan. Ideally, a master test plan will be available. On this basis and in consultation with the client, he will formulate the assignment, making an allowance for the four BDTM (Business Driven Test Management) aspects of Result, Risks, Time and Costs (see section 3.1 "Business driven explained"). Subsequently, the test manager will prepare himself for the forthcoming phase by holding various discussions with stakeholders and consulting other sources of information, such as documentation. At the same time, he defines the assignment further in close co-operation with the client, and determines the scope of the test level.

In the event that, for the master test plan, a product risk analysis has not been executed, or if it is too general, a detailed analysis is carried out with the client and other stakeholders. This is done in order to establish the required results of the testing for the client (the *test goals*) and evaluate the risk level of the parts (*object parts*) and *characteristics* of the system or package to be tested. This analysis forms the basis of the test strategy and the process advances to an iterative stage. As part of the strategy based on the product risk analysis the tester determines the characteristics/object parts that should be tested, and with which test type and to which depth (the greater the risk, the greater the depth). Then the test costs are estimated in outline form and the test activities are planned (covering the biggest risks as early as possible). This is to be agreed on by the client and other stakeholders and, depending on their views, possibly revised. In that case, the steps are then gone through again. In accordance with BDTM, the client therefore has a clear understanding of the test process and can manage the balance of Time and Money versus Result and Risk. Subsequent to this, the test manager refines the strategy further by determining test units and translating the decisions about depth of testing into firm statements on which coverage is being aimed for. He then allocates *test techniques* to the characteristic/object part combinations, making allowance for the available test basis, resources and infrastructural provisions. Using these techniques, the test cases (and, for example, the checklists) are designed and executed at a later stage.

The figure below illustrates this.

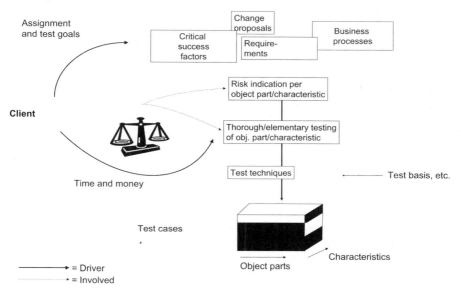

Figure 6.4: From assignment and test goals to test cases

Further steps in the plan formulation are that the test manager establishes the test basis, defines the test products and builds up the test organisation. The test manager also defines the required infrastructure. Test management is furnished with procedures and standards, supported as far as possible with tools. As a rule the elements available in the master test plan, Generic Test Agreements, the test policy or the Testing line organisation are used.

The most important risks that threaten the test process are cited, and possible measures are proposed for managing these risks. As a last step, the test manager has the test plan approved by the client. While the activities in this subprocess are described in sequence, in practice, certain activities will be done several times and/or in a different order. If, for example, certain infrastructure parts are required for a test and cannot be supplied, then the strategy may have to be adjusted.

Roles/responsibilities

The primary responsible role in the creation of the test plan is taken by the test manager, sometimes known as the test coordinator.

> **Test manager or test coordinator?**
> While in this section the term of test manager is consistently used to refer to the individual responsible for the test process, in practice it is also often a test coordinator who heads the system or acceptance test. The differences are more emotional and circumstantial than objective, but generally, the following is the case:
> - The more authorisations involved, the more the term of test manager is preferred
> - The greater the scope of the test, ditto
> - The greater the size of the test, ditto
> - If an overall test manager is managing the overall test process, test coordinator is preferred
> - If a test coordinator is coordinating the overall test process, test manager is preferred

Activities

The creation of the test plan involves the following activities:
1. Establishing the assignment
2. Understanding the assignment
3. Determining the test basis
4. Analysing the product risks
5. Determining the test strategy
6. Estimating the effort
7. Determining the planning
8. Allocating test units and test techniques
9. Defining the test products
10. Defining the organisation
11. Defining the infrastructure
12. Organising the management
13. Determining the test project risks and countermeasures
14. Feedback and consolidation of the plan.

The scheme below shows the sequence and the dependencies between the various activities. Every one of the activities may be gone through several times, as the result of an activity may mean a previous activity needs to be revised. As earlier indicated in the method of operation, the steps 5, 6 and 7 have an explicitly iterative character:

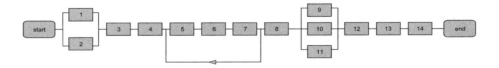

Figure 6.5: Creating the test plan

6.2.1   Establishing the assignment

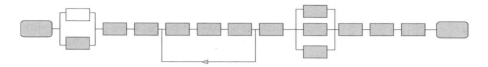

Aim

A system test or acceptance test starts with the formulation of the test assignment so that the aim, tasks and responsibilities of the test level are made clear to everyone involved.

Method of operation

By establishing the formulation of the assignment in the test plan, it is made clear to all the parties involved (including the client) what the test process is meant to deliver, and expectations are brought into line. The formulation of the test level should be compatible with the formulation of the assignment as set out in the master test plan.

A assignment formulation for a test plan consists of the following elements:
- Client
- Contractor
- Assignment
- Scope
- Preconditions and assumptions.

These parts are explained below:

Client
The party who has commissioned the creation of the test plan and the execution of the tests. It is important for the test level to acknowledge who has commissioned the execution of the test.

In more detail

In practice, we generally see the following possibilities for the various test levels:

System test	- Project manager from the supplier - Project manager /project leader for realisation
Functional acceptance test	- Project manager from client/accepters - Head of functional management
System integration test	- Project manager from client /accepters - Head of functional management
Users acceptance test	- Project manager from client /accepters - Head of users organisation
Production acceptance test	- Project manager from client /accepters - Head of system management

---

Contractor

Usually, a test manager or test coordinator is responsible for creating the test plan and executing the test assignment.

Assignment

This should be set up in consultation with the client and should indicate the aims and the scope of the testing.

In more detail

This would appear to be the obvious core of the activity – "Establishing the assignment". Despite the importance, in practice the formulation of the assignment is often somewhat abstract and generic, in terms of "providing a quality assessment" or "providing insight into risks". It is mainly in the scope, preconditions and assumptions (and later the strategy) that the total assignment is sharply defined.

Iterations

Iterative or agile system development delivers a large number of (interim) releases or prototypes for testing. It should be clear from the formulation of the assignment that such an interim release or prototype may not be assessed on every aspect of a forthcoming production system, but only on those aspects that are relevant to the interim release or prototype itself.

As test manager, you should ideally gain a feel for what the guiding principle of the project is in terms of BDTM. Is the client mainly concerned with Time or Costs, or is Result/Risk the driving force? This is no easy task, for the initial reaction ("our maximum budget is € …", and "the deadline of … is set in concrete") often seems crystal clear, but on further questioning is not always so ("… and if the system then only has ¾ of the functionality?"). Nevertheless, this insight will aid the test manager's understanding and facilitate later communication on the choices to be made. The sensitivity of this information means that it is not necessarily established in the plan.

Additionally, the test regularly involves secondary requests. The client should allocate budget and/or time available for these. Examples are:
- The creation of a *standard maintenance test plan*, to include all the reusable test aspects
- Training and coaching of the employees in testing
- Improvement and structuring of the test approach employed
- Implementation of a test tool
- The setup, use and maintenance of a scaleable regression test set (see section 6.6 "Specification phase")
- Supply of (automated) testware for the testing of subsequent releases.

In more detail

Usually, the client makes resources (people and means) available, or pays for them, for example, by hiring in people internally or externally. Payment usually takes place based on the number of hours. In certain cases, particularly in the case of outsourcing, when the testing is done by an external supplier, more creative agreements can be made. Below are some possible constructions that appear in practice:

- **Fixed-price**
  The supplier carries out the testing for a previously agreed fixed price. This usually includes a fixed number of retests. In the event of a breakdown in the test process owing to the client being unable to meet the set agreements, or if more (re)tests are necessary than were agreed, additional charges are applied. In the other cases, the risk is borne by the supplier
- **Fixed-price per test case**
  A variant on the above is that a fixed sum is agreed per test case to be specified and executed
- **Fixed-date**
  Similar to fixed-price, but with a fixed date of completion
- **Fixed-date, fixed-price**
  As above, with both a fixed price and a date of completion
- **Bonus malus**
  In addition to the above, agreements can be made with the intent of distributing the risk more satisfactorily among both parties. By doing this, the client pays the supplier by the hour with the understanding that there is a fixed date or fixed price. If the supplier requires fewer hours or less lead time, he is given a bonus in the form of more money. And an example of malus: if after X amount of time after going into production, critical faults arise, or if the timeline or hours are exceeded, the supplier gives a discount on the fees
- **Result sharing**
  An unconventional form is when the supplier is paid with a percentage of the profits from the new system. In this case, the system is an investment for both the client and the supplier, and both have every interest in a successful outcome. It will be obvious that this involves big risks (but also opportunities).

Scope of operation
The limits of the test operation should be indicated here. This should preferably be more specific than what is already stipulated in the master test plan. The following matters should be taken into consideration (where applicable):
- System(s)
- Conversions
- Administrative organisation (AO) procedures
- Quality characteristics (allocated in the master test plan)
- Interfaces with adjacent systems (is the interface being tested *up to* the other system or *up to and including*, or even to include the entire chain?)

In respect to changes, it is important to determine the parts of the above that are being considered. It is also important to indicate the issues that are outside of the scope of the testing. Besides those mentioned above, the following should be kept in mind:
- System changes that are not included in the project
- Test activities that are carried out by other test levels or parties
- Reorganisations
- Possible future projects that influence the current project (particularly if there is a lack of clarity concerning other projects).

Preconditions
Preconditions describe conditions set by third parties, such as the client, the project, managers or users with regard to the test process and within which the test process must operate.

Example:
- **Master test plan**
  The master test plan drives the setup and execution of the test level
- **Milestones**
  Often, as soon as the test assignment is issued, a number of milestones are established, such as the delivery date of the test basis, the test object, infrastructure and the date of going into production
- **Available resources**
  The client often sets limits to the available people, resources and budget
- **Norms and standards to be maintained**
  From within the (test) organisation or the master test plan, certain requirements may be set as regards method of operation, procedures, techniques, templates, etc.

Assumptions
These are external circumstances or events that must come about in order for the test process to succeed, but that are beyond the control of the test process. In other words, the requirements that the test process sets other parties.

> **For example:**
> - **Quality of preceding tests**
>   The preceding tests, e.g. development or system tests are carried out in the agreed manner
> - **Quality of test object**
>   The test object has the agreed entry quality. This should be established with the aid of so-called entry criteria, which overlap with (but are not necessarily the same as) the exit criteria of the preceding test
> - **Support to be supplied**
>   Within the test process there is a need for various forms of support, e.g. in respect of the test basis, test object, domain knowledge and/or infrastructure. This support may be required to a certain degree and/or for a certain period. Bear in mind, for example, the availability of developers for solving obstructive defects during the test execution. Usually, each test level has its own expertise. For instance, the users acceptance test will have little need of domain knowledge support, while the support needs will concern precisely the other types of expertise, such as technical or test-method support
> - **Changes in test basis and test object**
>   The test team should be involved in the implementation of changes. In most cases, this simply means following up the existing procedures within the system development process. For example, the test manager should participate in the Change Control Board in order to estimate the consequences of a change from the test point of view
> - **Delivery of the test object**
>   The development team delivers the test object in a number of different but efficiently testable parts, and takes responsibility for installation in the test environment
> - **Reaction time to defects**
>   How quickly should the project react to the finding of defects. Below is an example of such agreements:
>
> | Severity | Priority | Reaction time | Lead time |
> | --- | --- | --- | --- |
> | Test-obstructive | High | 1 hour | 4 hours |
> | Severe defect | High | 1 hour | 1 working day |
> | Regular defect | High | 1 working day | 2 working days |
> | Regular defect | Low | 1 working day | To be determined per defect |
> | Cosmetic defect | Low | 2 working days | To be determined per defect |

The test manager cannot make do with including these points in the plan and then assuming when the plan is accepted that all the points have been organised. On the contrary, he should first agree the points with the parties that own them, so that the points constitute set agreements and not surprises. It is advisable to mention in the plan, per assumption, for which stakeholder or parties these are intended.

For a checklist of possible preconditions and assumptions, please refer to www.tmap.net.

Products
The assignment formulation, established in the test plan.

Techniques
Checklist of preconditions and assumptions (www.tmap.net).

Tools
Not applicable.

6.2.2   Understanding the assignment

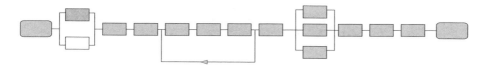

Aim
To obtain insight into the (project) organisation, the aim and purpose of the system development process, the system or package to be tested and the requirements to be met, so that better direction can be given to the other steps in the planning.

Method of operation
The method of operation covers the following activities:
1. Identifying accepters, using acceptance criteria and other information providers
2. Examining the available documentation
3. Conducting interviews

In practice, this activity is carried out in parallel with the formulation of the assignment. It is also somewhat underestimated. Specifically, the test manager may speak to too few stakeholders, although it is essential in the beginning to measure expectations adequately and, as test manager, to 'put the feelers out' in all directions. This is necessary in order to be able to carry out the following activities effectively and to manage the test process successfully in the future.

1) Identifying accepters, using acceptance criteria and other information providers
Usually the client is not the only stakeholder who has to accept the system; there are generally others, and it is important to clarify who these accepting parties are. This is done in consultation with the client. In practice, the test manager gets an opportunity here to discuss with stakeholders at a high level in the organisation (steering group members) and to interpret their opinions and expectations. Often there is no other opportunity for this, unless the test manager is in the (unfortunately) rare position of regularly participating in the steering group discussions. It is important to establish which accepters are to be provided with information directly or indirectly during the project by means of test reports. It should also be clear what requirements or acceptance criteria each accepter is proposing. These are the minimum qualitative requirements that the product must meet to make it satisfactory to the accepter. For the sake of clarity: the gathering of acceptance criteria is not the responsibility of the testers, but it is input into the setup of the test

process. Acceptance criteria can be very diverse. Some examples are:

- Qualitative criteria as regards product and generation process, e.g. the number of defects that may remain open
- Criteria as regards the environment, e.g. the infrastructure should be installed or the users should have followed a training course
- Criteria in the form of (the detailing of) requirements of the product, e.g. 'an order should be processed within X seconds'.

Not all the acceptance criteria are relevant to testing. The first example has a considerable overlap with the exit criteria for the test process discussed in section 6.2.7 'Determining the planning'. The second example is usually less important to testing, and the third example is a form of test basis.

In more detail

Acceptance criteria pitfall
This latter use of acceptance criteria contains a danger. In practice, the following sometimes happens: after establishing and freezing the requirements, users discover that they have additional requirements. They then formulate these requirements as acceptance criteria. In this way, acceptance criteria form the 'back door' for taking in even more requirements. This is not a good method of operation. The only correct way is to submit a change proposal to a Change Control Board.

Besides accepters, various other parties/individuals can supply the test process with relevant information. Bear in mind, for example:

In more detail

- The overall test manager, at coordinating level, for obtaining insight into the test assignment and what is expected of the test or the test manager
- The (representatives of the) client, for obtaining insight into the business aims and the 'culture' as well as the aims and strategic importance of the system
- The project manager or quality management employee, for obtaining insight into the steps and components of the development process and the correlations, with special focus on the (expected) place of testing in this
- The domain experts from the user organisation, for obtaining insight into the (required) functionality of the system
- The designers, for obtaining insight into the system functionality to be developed
- System administrators, for obtaining insight into the (future) production environment of the information system
- Testers, for obtaining insight into the test approach and test maturity of the organisation
- The suppliers of the test basis, the test object and the infrastructure, for guaranteeing coordination at an early stage among the various stakeholders.

2) Examining the available documentation

The documentation provided by the client is examined. For example:

In more detail

- Test documentation, such as the master test plan or a Generic Test Agreements document
- System documentation, such as stakeholder analyses, business or user requirements, or an information analysis, system requirements, functional and technical design
- Project documentation, such as the plan of approach for the system development process, organisational charts and responsibilities, the quality plan, review reports and a function-point analysis
- A description of the system development method, including the norms and standards
- A description of the test method applied, including the norms and standards
- Evaluations and points of learning from previous tests that may be relevant to the forthcoming test
- Contracts with suppliers

If the system development process relates to maintenance, then the availability and usability of existing testware is also investigated.

3) Conducting interviews

The various parties involved in the system development process are interviewed.

The test manager asks the stakeholders questions concerning, besides the general background of the system to be tested and the process to be followed:

- Their expectations about the results of the testing – what do they hope to see as the end result? This may relate to business processes supported by IT, realised user requirements or use cases, change proposals, critical success factors, cited risks (to be covered) but also, for example, that the new system should have at least exactly the same functionality as the old system (therefore no regression). These are referred to as the test goals. Do they fit with the test goals of the master test plan?

Definition

A test goal is a goal that, for the client, is relevant for testing, often formulated in terms of business processes supported by IT, realised user requirements or use cases, critical success factors, change proposals or cited risks to be covered.

- Does the interviewee have an idea of what the characteristics are (usually the quality characteristics) and object parts that operate in the above? Some people are able to answer this very well, but it may be too complex for others. The test manager has to estimate how much detail the discussion will allow

- What is the test basis, if any, that may or should be used later on as proof that the test was thorough enough?
- What is the risk estimate of the test goals and/or characteristics/object parts? A risk is defined here as the product of Damage x (Chance of defect x Frequency of use). Often the interviewee will only be able to mention particular aspects of a risk, such as the Damage, the Frequency of use *or* the Chance of a defect. That doesn't matter, for it can be expanded upon in the next step, the product risk analysis
- Does the stakeholder wish to be reported to, and if so, at what level? A point of focus here is that the number of types of reports should remain somewhat restricted for practical reasons. If necessary, the test manager should discuss this with the client.

It is also advisable where possible to consult those indirectly involved. For example, the EDP auditors, the implementation manager, the future maintenance organisation, etc.

> **Tip**
>
> Instead of individual interviews, a kick-off session could be organised with (a number of) the relevant parties. The advantage of this is that the various viewpoints help to arrive collectively at a clear picture. This often happens in particular when consultation is held to determine the (test) impact of change proposals.

The test manager feeds back the findings of this activity to the client for verification.

Products

This activity delivers the following parts of the test plan:

- Stakeholders and acceptance criteria
  The stakeholders relevant to the testing and their acceptance criteria
- Norms and standards
  The standards employed are cited here. As regards testing, these can involve instructions issuing from the Testing line organisation, the master test plan or generic test agreements, TMap, TPI or test manuals. Development standards, document standards or quality norms that have to be or will be followed are also possibilities
- Basis of the test plan
  Here the documents are mentioned that form the basis of this test plan. For example, a master test plan, project plan, specific project or test plans, a specific or a generic test method, generic test agreements, an implementation plan or other documents that are of importance.

Techniques

Checklist 'Understanding the assignment' (www.tmap.net).

Tools

Not applicable.

6.2.3   Determining the test basis

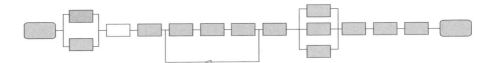

Aim

The unambiguous defining of the test basis, so that it is known at an early stage what the test object is to be compared against.

Method of operation

The method of operation covers the following subactivities:
1. Defining the test basis
2. Identifying the test basis

1) Defining the test basis
The test basis, or the gathering of all the written and unwritten requirements with which the test object should comply, can take various forms. Bear in mind, for example, requirements, acceptance criteria, functional designs, technical designs, user manuals, interviews, reports of meetings, legislation, but not forgetting the old system, a previous release of the system, a prototype or even a domain expert. The gathering of non-documented test basis in particular is difficult; further information on this is given in section 6.5 "Preparation Phase". It is important when determining the test basis to ensure that the non-functional requirements are also known, such as e.g. requirements in respect of performance or security.

> **In more detail**
>
> The individual test levels often make use of various sources for obtaining the product requirements, against which testing is carried out in the test level. For example, the acceptance test is often focused on requirements that are described at the level of, let's say, business processes, whereas in the unit testing it is checked whether the technical requirements pertaining to a specific unit have been met. The test basis will therefore not be the same for all the test levels.

Something to be kept in mind in respect of the test basis is that these requirements should be as concrete and measurable (testable) as possible to prevent misunderstandings. This is often not the case in practice. Where possible, it can already be observed at this stage, otherwise it will become apparent at the later stages of Preparation and Specification. It is also possible that, at a later stage, it will be discovered that a requirement is very difficult to test. In such cases, it is agreed with the client whether a simplified test is acceptable.

2) Identifying the test basis
Establish, as far as possible, the identification of the relevant test basis. Bear in mind the delivery date, version, status, etc.

Products
The test basis to be used, established in the test plan.

Techniques
Not applicable.

Tools
Not applicable.

6.2.4   Analysing the product risks

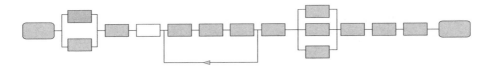

Aim
To have the participants and the test manager arrive at a common perspective about the parts and characteristics of the system based on the risk level.

Method of operation
Testing is a measure for obtaining insight into the quality and related product risks of a system or package when it is put into production by an organisation. Since time and resources are usually limited, it is important to determine the system parts or features that will require extra or less test effort early in the process. Practical choices must be made here. Performing a product risk analysis (PRA) will help determine the areas of focus for the test.

A PRA within the framework of a test level is optional: if the master test plan PRA has already been done in sufficient detail (i.e. at the level of characteristics and object parts), this step can be skipped. If there is no master test plan PRA, it must first be determined what the test goals are and what relationship they have with the characteristics/object parts that are to be tested in the relevant test level. This is done in a similar way to the PRA for the master test plan. If there is a master test plan PRA, but not at the level of object parts, then the PRA should be further refined.

The execution of a product risk analysis is divided into the following subactivities:
1. Determining the participants
2. Determining the PRA approach
3. Preparing sessions/interviews
4. Collecting and analysing product risks
5. Checking for completeness

In Chapter 9 "Product risk analysis", these steps are explained in detail.

> **Tips**
> - A point to note is that the PRA session, if relevant, may be combined with (a part of) the subsequent activity, 'Determining the test strategy'.
> - With a PRA for a test level, the challenge is to allow the test goals, characteristics and object parts to relate only to the scope of the test level. It is meaningless to recognise security as a big risk if this characteristic has already been assigned to another test level from within the master test plan.

Products

The risk tables with test goals and possible object parts per characteristic with risk indications, managed separately and optionally established in the test plan

The PRA overview of characteristics/object parts with risk class, established in the test plan.

Techniques

Product risk analysis (Chapter 9)
Explanation of quality characteristics (Chapter 10).

Tools

Not applicable.

6.2.5   Determining the test strategy

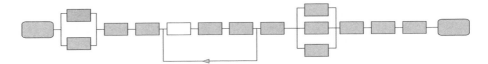

Aim
To decide, based on the insight into the risk levels associated with the object parts/characteristics of the system, on the test types to be used, and on the depth of testing for each (combination of) characteristic/object part of the system.

Method of operation
In defining the strategy for a test level, the choice is made about the test types and thoroughness of testing, i.e. the extent to which the combinations of characteristics and object parts are tested. This is dependent on the risk estimate from the PRA, or rather the degree to which the client wishes to cover these risks, and how much time/money he allocates for it.

To this end, the test manager makes a proposal for each combination of object part/characteristic in respect of the required test types and depth of testing.

Test types
In this, the test manager specifies what is to be tested out of a particular object part-combination. At its simplest, this is the test of a quality characteristic, e.g. a functionality test or performance test, but often it is possible, and necessary, to provide more insight. Other test types are associated with the quality characteristic functionality, e.g. the multi-user test, regression test or chain test. An overview of "Applied test types" is included at www.tmap.net.

In more detail

Traditionally, most attention is given to testing functionality. More and more other characteristics, like suitability, security, portability, performance and usability, are being tested. Specifically the Internet has made these characteristics of systems more important and full of risks. The characteristics can be tested using test design techniques or checklist, just like functionality. Besides that, other points of attention and ways to test are available. In section 10.3 "Test types" a description of some of these characteristics and related test types can be found.

Testing depth

As regards the depth of testing, a choice is made from the following possibilities:

●●●	Thorough dynamic testing
●●	Average dynamic testing
●	Light dynamic testing
S	Static testing
	Checking and inspecting products without software being run
I	Implicit testing
	Testing in conjunction with another test type without making explicit test cases; only observable defects are documented.
–	If there is nothing in a cell, this means that the relevant evaluation or test level can ignore the characteristic.

The result of this step is described below:

Example of ST					
Characteristic	**RC MTP**	**ST MTP**	**Subsys1**	**Subsys 2**	**Total sys**
Functionality	n/a	n/a	A/●●● functional, regression	B/●● functional, regression	C/● integration, multi-user
Performance online	B	●	-	-	C/● Random sample in ST environment
...					

RC MTP = Risk class assigned to the characteristic from within the master test plan
ST MTP = Depth of testing assigned to the test (in this case, the system test) from within the master test plan
n/a = not applicable, in the master test plan risk class and depth are not assigned to the characteristic, but to the combination object part/characteristic
A = High risk class
B = Average risk class
C = Low risk class
The risk classes are taken from the PRA of the master test plan or (in more detail) from the PRA of the test level itself.

The test manager then supplies this table with the necessary explanations. In the above example, a functional test is to be carried out for subsystems 1 and 2 in respect of the new and changed functionality, and a regression test in respect of the unchanged parts will be furnished. Following the separate testing of subsystems 1 and 2, the total system will be tested as regards integration aspects; a multi-user test will also take place. Performance will be tested in the non-representative ST environment for a limited number of situations.

UAT example

Characteristic	RC MTP	UAT MTP	Subsystem 1	Subsystem 2	Total sys
Functionality	n/a	n/a	A/●● Functional	B/-	C/● Regression
User friendliness	B	●●	C/I	-	B/●● Usability
Security	A	●			
- Authorisation matrix	B		-/S Authorisation test	-/S Authorisation test	B/●● Process test
- Application	C		-	-	C/● Penetration test
Suitability	B	●●●	B/● Scenario test	C/● Scenario test	A/●●● Process test
...					

In the above example, for subsystem 1 a functional test is performed again, using a number of the test cases from the ST, but in the AT environment. If several deliveries are made, a regression test on the total system takes place. A usability test in the own environment is carried out and in other tests an implicit test of user-friendliness is carried out. The authorisation matrix is evaluated as regards correct content for subsystems 1 and 2. Also, the business processes, or subprocesses, related to subsystems 1 and 2 are simulated by means of running user scenarios. Subsequently, the operation of the total system is tested in combination with the business processes. A light penetration test is also supplied.

An initial setup of the strategy is often possible in the PRA session or the PRA, and these steps of the Strategy definition can be combined. If this doesn't work, then the test manager makes a proposal.

A point to note is that when the MTP indicates a thoroughness of ●●● for a particular test level (e.g. ST) or a particular combination of characteristic/object part, this doesn't mean that, in the ST, the entire system, or the combination of characteristic/object part, should be tested in the greatest possible coverage, but that testing is required in greater depth than average. This should also be evident from the MTP notes.

Tips

- With iterative or agile system development, the test strategy should focus on regression tests in respect of the many interim releases (iterations, increments). Also, the test (strategy) should be restricted to the characteristics of the interim release and not formulate a strategy as if it concerns the final release. This appears easier than it is, for in the PRA the users provide their risk estimate on the basis of the expected final release. See also section 10.3 "Test types".
- At the setting up of the strategy, the test manager should make as much allowance as possible for the consideration of costs, time and skills required. If he knows that there is only a very limited budget or that the available people have no experience in testing, he should avoid proposing 'impossible' strategies, such as very expensive tests or very thorough test-design techniques (to prevent too may feedback cycles).
- It is advisable, when choosing between thorough and light testing of a characteristic/ object part, to make an immediate inventory of the test basis to be used, as the availability and degree of detail of the test basis can influence the budget and planning. Allowance can be made for this during these steps.

In more detail

Maintenance
The chance of defects is the principal difference between new-build and maintenance. The formulation of the changes as object part facilitates the strategy. Several variations are possible:
- A limited test, aimed only at the change
- A complete (re)testing of the function in which the change was made
- The testing of the correlation between the changed function and the functions directly surrounding it
- A test of the entire system.

Regression test
The regression test of the system as a whole is recognised as well. It focuses on the coherence between the changed and unchanged parts of the system, since this is where the chances of regression are the greatest. If the PRA for the new-build is available, the risk categories applied here to the characteristics/object parts can play a role in the composition of this regression test. A regression test may be carried out to a full or limited extent, depending on the risks and on the required test effort. It is very easy, with the aid of the scaleable regression test set (see section 6.6 "Specification Phase") to perform either a thorough or a light regression test. This makes for flexibility in the testing of later releases. For more information on regression testing, see section 10.3 "Test types".

Products

The test strategy, established in the test plan, with a brief description of the planned test types and an indication of the importance per characteristic/object part.

Techniques

Strategy determination (as described in this section).

Tools

Not applicable.

6.2.6   Estimating the effort

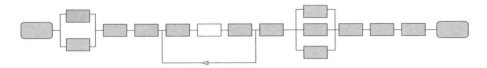

Aim

The estimation of the effort for the test level based on the test strategy, so that the client can accept it or request adjustments.

Method of operation

An estimate may already be set out in the master test plan for the test level. Nevertheless, this remains a necessary step. The test manager has to determine, on the basis of the strategy created, how many hours and possibly how much money will be required. If these exceed the margins of the allocation contained in the master test plan, the test manager should work with the test manager of the overall test process to resolve these discrepancies. Either the strategy or the estimate will need to be amended.

In practice, the number of test hours required almost always is a factor reflected in the estimate. Another, less apparent, part of the estimate is the financial part. How much do those hours cost? Do they involve internal or external resources or even outsourcing? What are the fees? But also: how much do the test environment, test tools and work stations cost? If the client requires it, the test manager also must create a financial budget.

Subsequently, within a test level, the time required for the various phases, such as Planning, Control, Setting up and maintaining infrastructure, Preparation, Specification, Execution and Completion is established. At the start of each test phase, the test manager estimates the effort for the separate test activities (see section 6.3.2 "Monitoring").

In more detail

Estimation techniques
The various estimation techniques and the steps involved in arriving at an estimate are described in Chapter 11 "Estimation Techniques". For a test plan, estimates can be made based on:
• Ratio figures
• Test object size
• Work Breakdown Structure (WBS)
• Proportionate estimation
• Test point analysis (TPA).
In order to increase the reliability of the estimate, you would be well advised to use

your own figures based on experience as well as other means and techniques of estimating.

Tips

- Sometimes a total budget is imposed by the client for testing. This has to be spread across the test phases and the characteristic/object part combinations. Some of the techniques described in Chapter 11 (Ratios and Work Breakdown Structure, in particular) provide assistance here. It should also be examined whether the budget is adequate. The following tips are useful, but much depends on the experience of the test manager:

  1) It is best to create an estimate by summing up the characteristic/depth-of-testing estimates (e.g. in PAT, a light performance test + a thorough security test = 120 + 200 hours = 320 hours).

  2) Another option is to evaluate the total budget using a rule-of-thumb summing up for test levels: 15% of the total project budget of 5,000 hours for the ST, 20% for the AT = 750 and 1,000 hours respectively.

  3) A third option is to employ a standard allocation formula for characteristics, established on the basis of a number of experiences. An example is to give Functionality, at risk category B, 70% of the total budget, at A, 80% and at C, 60%. You can also do this with a fixed number of hours, e.g. User-friendliness could be given 70 hours at category C, and up to 130 at category A (for an average system). This will make it easier to assess the real value of the individual estimates per test level /characteristic.

  4) Compare the allocated budget with the budgets and total hours spent in the course of comparable exercises in the past, both in the organisation itself and if possible in other, comparable, organisations.

  The estimate should be assessed for real value and should come out at around the level of the total assigned budget. Otherwise, adjustments will be necessary, by opting for a higher total budget, or testing fewer characteristics and/or testing in less depth.

  The figures used above are realistic examples. More information can be found in Chapter 11 "Estimation Techniques".

- A depth of testing level of ●●● for a characteristic in a particular test level (e.g. Functionality in the ST), means that the system should be tested in more depth than average, not that the entire system should be tested in the greatest possible depth. See also the comment under Test Strategy.
- The creation of an estimate for the test has a wide margin of uncertainty. It is important that the test manager make it clear to the stakeholders that the estimate is based on a number of assumptions and may therefore have to be revised later. A possible solution is the use of uncertainty margins. At the beginning of the test, the margin would be, for example, around 40%; at the start of the test execution this becomes around 25%, and somewhere in the middle it becomes around 10%.
- The link between estimate and depth of testing (using specific test techniques) is opaque. How much extra time does, for example, the application of the elementary comparison test require as against the data combination test? Few past figures are

available for this, and much is done on the basis of the test manager's experience and intuition.

- Various other factors (the quality of the testers, of the test object and test basis, test environment and test tools) can also exert significant influence on the estimate. These factors are either not known at the time the estimate is made or their effect on the estimate is very unclear. The test manager has to make assumptions here, and if necessary include them as assumptions in the plan, and most certainly should evaluate the assumptions as soon as possible.
- It is difficult to 'sell' the required maintenance test effort to management. A general 'testing image' problem is that testing costs too much in management's view. With testing during maintenance, that is reinforced by the fact that testing has a relatively big share in the maintenance effort – up to as much as 80%. This is partly because the total test costs consist of fixed and variable costs. Fixed costs refer to, for example, the effort required to prepare the test environment, or the execution of a 'standard' regression test; variable costs refer to, for example, the preparation and testing of implemented changes. With the testing of a small change, the percentage of fixed costs is high, since, irrespective of the size of the change, the environment must always be prepared and the regression test run. The greater the changes become, the more the fixed costs decrease in relative terms. For example, with the testing of a change, a 4-hour regression test is always run. If the testing of a change takes 8 hours in total, the fixed testing time amounts to 50% (4/8). If the testing of one or more changes takes a total of 40 hours, then this decreases to 10% (4/40). In general, the share of testing (fixed+variable) lies between 35% - 80% of all the maintenance activities. It is up to the test manager to make this clear to the client and to put the case for the importance (to the testing) of bigger, controlled releases, in which many changes are bundled, over the implementation of a constant procession of small changes.

Products
The estimate for the test level, in hours and optionally in money, supplied with assumptions used in this, established in the test plan.

Techniques
Various estimation techniques (Chapter 11)
Step-by-step plan for creating an estimate (Chapter 11).

Tools
Planning and progress monitoring tool (spreadsheets for estimating the effort and for Test Point Analysis are available at www.tmap.net).

6.2.7   Determining the planning

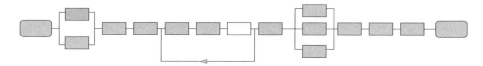

Aim

The creation of as reliable as possible a planning for the test level, so that the client can make allowance for this and can manage accordingly. The principle of the planning is to find the most significant defects (the finding of which belongs within the scope of the test level) first.

Method of operation

Based on the planning of the system development process and on the master test plan, a planning for the test level is created. The test manager indicates the start and end date per phase and the products to be delivered. The planning should cover at least:

- Activities to be carried out (at activity level per phase)
- Correlations with and dependencies on other activities (within or beyond the test level and between the various phases and other test levels)
- Time to be spent per phase
- Required and available resources (people and infrastructure)
- Required and available turnaround time
- Products to be delivered.

Depending on the client's requirements, the financial consequences of the choices made should be made visible in a financial planning. This means, for example, the setting out of the costs in terms of time for the (internal and external) personnel, training, workstations, test environment and test tools.

In more detail

In creating a planning, the following principles apply:
- The test strategy and estimated effort form the basis of the setup of the planning
- In a good planning, the characteristics/object parts designated as high risk are tested as early as possible
- With optimal planning, as far as possible only the test execution activities are carried out on the critical path of the project
- If there are no past figures available in respect of the number of retests, it is advisable to make allowance when creating a planning with one retest on average. Based on past experience, it can be decided to allow more or less time for retesting
- With maintenance, in particular, and with iterative or agile development phases, it is important to make allowance for the execution of regression tests

- When creating a planning, make allowance for the required time of third parties. For example, repair time for defects or time for preparing the test environment
- The transfer of the test object to, and installation in, the test environment often falls between two stools in planning, or rather between the planning of the development and testing activities. Particularly the first few times, this activity appears to cost significant amounts of time – days rather than hours. Make allowance for this
- Try to streamline the in- and outflow of personnel, so that peaks and troughs in staff levels are avoided.
- Further planning indications can be found in the IT classic [Brooks, 1975/1995].

Required information

In order to set up a planning based on the estimated effort, additional information is required concerning the following subjects:

- Available resources
  Worth noting here is that with the estimation of the effort, only limited allowance is made for the available resources. The calculation is made on the number of hours required. In combination with a deadline, this means that a certain number of resources is required for carrying out the planned tests. In practice, it is often the case that the number of available resources initially does not correspond with the required amount of resources. The test manager should make this clear and then discuss it with the client. Possible solutions are the hiring of temporary personnel, extending the timeline or adjusting the strategy
- Available timeline
  In practice, the available timeline is usually provided in the form of a deadline for the relevant phase
- Availability of resources, such as test environments and test tools
  When are these to be available for the activities? Do the test tools, for example, still have to be selected, purchased and set up?
- Dependencies between the various activities
  Activities that depend on other activities can only start after completion of those other activities and not in parallel with them
- Method of system development
  The test levels are planned depending on the way in which the system is developed. With a waterfall method, the phasing is different from that of an iterative process in which testing and development activities are parallel and sometimes executed integrally. The development test and system test as a rule have more to do with this than the acceptance test.
- Information on milestones in the development project
  This information is necessary in order to coordinate the test planning optimally with the planning of the rest of the project. This makes it possible to minimise the total timeline of the project.

The planning is reflected in, for example, a network planning or a bar chart, depending on the method used within the organisation. This book does not deal with planning techniques, because for the test process the test manager employs standard planning techniques that are not specific to testing.

Example of activities planning

TEST PHASE	Week number (2006)														Hours/FTE
	14	...	20	21	...	34	35	36	37	38	39	40	41	42	
Planning, Control and Setting up and maintaining infrastructure	X	X	X	X	X	X	X	X	X	X	X	X	X	X	2 FTE
Preparation and Specification	X	X	X	X	X	X	X								3,480 hours
Exec. FAT, FIT (functional integration test)								X	X	X	X				
Exec. CT (chain test)									X	X	X	X			3,480 hours
Exec. UAT									X	X	X	X			
Completion													X		
Reserve week													X		
Total:															2 FTE + 6,960 hours

Example of milestone planning

Milestone	Date	Owner
Delivery of definitive test basis	01-03-2006	SAP project leader
Delivery of test infrastructure	31-08-2006	SAP project leader
Delivery of test object	31-08-2006	SAP project leader
Completion of FAT, FIT, CIT, UAT test specifications	31-08-2006	Test coordinator
Completion of test execution	14-10-2006	Test coordinator
Delivery of testware	22-10-2006	Test coordinator
Delivery of Preliminary Release advice	15-10-2006	Test manager
Delivery of Release advice	22-10-2006	Test manager
Delivery of Test Report	22-10-2006	Test manager

Tip

When planning resources, indicate from which point it is no longer possible to accommodate imminent overrun by deploying extra people. Sometimes an environment is so complex or specific that an 'extra hand' will no longer gain time. It is not pleasant to have to explain this when the moment has already arrived and the project leader is already busily engaged in arranging extra people for the test team – even less so when those extra people are already being introduced to the team...

An aspect of planning related to quality is when a test level is ready and the test object can be transferred to the following test level or to production. In other words, what can the 'next' test level expect after the 'previous' test level is completed. In order to make these expectations explicit, requirements are set according to the result of the test level. In practice, these requirements are also known as exit criteria. With increasing outsourcing, it becomes more and more important to establish clear exit criteria to prevent the supplier from delivering inadequate quality.

In more detail

Exit criteria can relate, for example, to the number of issues in a particular risk category that may still be open, the way in which a certain risk is covered (e.g. all the system parts with the highest risk category have been tested using a formal test design technique), or the depth in which the requirements should have been tested. From within the master test plan, the exit criteria are applied to the test level. If that is not the case, or if there is no master test plan, the test manager should agree the criteria with the client.

The box below shows a number of concrete examples of exit criteria:

System X may only be transferred to the AT when the following conditions have been met:
• There are no more open defects in the category of "severe"
• There is a maximum of 4 open defects in the category "disrupting"
• The total number of open defects is no more than 20
• A workaround has been described for every open defect
• For every user functionality, at minimum, the correct paths have been tested and approved

System X may be transferred to the AT when it can be shown in writing that all the risks that were allocated to the ST in accordance with document Y have been tested in the agreed depth and by the agreed test method.

An important point of focus as regards the above-mentioned criteria is that clear definitions should be agreed by all the stakeholders of what a particular category of severity is and what is meant by 'agreed depth of testing and test method'. In practice, a lack of clarity here can lead to heated discussions.

Similarities and differences between acceptance and exit criteria
Another term for exit criteria that is used is 'acceptance criteria', as discussed in subsection 6.2.2. Besides the fact that acceptance criteria may be a broader term than exit criteria, another difference is that acceptance criteria come at the end, i.e. at acceptance, and exit criteria at the transfer from one test level to another, or to production. The figure below illustrates this.

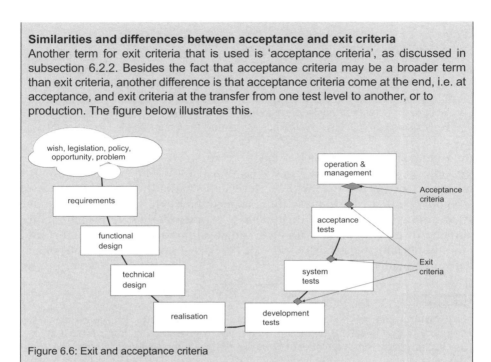

Figure 6.6: Exit and acceptance criteria

Tip

Suspend- and resume criteria
In some, particularly formally set up, tests, so-called suspend- and resume criteria may be defined in the plan. These criteria indicate under which circumstances the testing is temporarily suspended and then resumed. Examples of suspend criteria are that testing has to stop when a particular infrastructural component is not available, or if a test-blocking defect is found. A resume criterion may be that with the lifting of the suspend criterion the testing of the system part /function/component has to take place entirely anew.

Feedback

When the test manager has created a planning, this is the time to agree matters with the client. If the test strategy setup and subsequent estimate of required effort and planning are not acceptable, then these steps are repeated. With this, the client and test manager consider whether to test certain aspects in lesser depth, so that time and/or money is spared, but a higher level of risk is accepted, or the other way. To facilitate communication, the test manager refers here to the original test goals. Where a master test plan exists, the coordinating test manager is involved here, but the client makes the final choice.

An amended strategy is illustrated below, with less test depth indicated by ○ instead of ● and more test depth by **●**.

ST example

Characteristic	RC MTP	ST MTP	Subsystem 1	Subsystem 2	Total sys
Functionality	n/a	n/a	A/● ● ○ Functional, regression	B/● ○ Functional, regression	C/● Integration, multi-user
Performance online	B	●	-	-	C/● Random testing in ST environment
...					

UAT example

Characteristic	RC MTP	UAT MTP	Subsystem 1	Subsystem 2	Total sys
Functionality	n/a	n/a	A/● ○ Functional	B/-	C/● Regression
User friendliness	B	● ●	C/I		B/● ○ Usability
Security	A	●			
- Authorisation matrix	B		-/S Authorisation test	-/S Authorisation test	B/● ● Process test
- Application	C		-	-	C/● Penetration test
Suitability	B	● ● ●	B/● **●** Scenario test	C/● Scenario test	A/● ● ○ Process test
...					

The amended strategy leads to another estimated effort and planning, and also to an indication of bigger (or even smaller) product risks, translated into terms that are comprehensible to the client (referring back to the product risk analysis with test goals, characteristics and object parts).

In addition to the feedback on strategy, budget and planning, the test manager discusses with the client the use of tolerances in the execution of the test process. These are boundaries within which the test manager is not required to ask the client's permission. For example, a tolerance of 5% is often agreed for the budget. For the planning, it may be agreed that only deviations from project milestones will require discussion. With strategy tolerances, for example, the client's advance permission is not required for testing a characteristic/object part in one greater or lesser degree of depth.

Products

Planning for the test process
Exit criteria
Optional: tolerances for strategy, budget and planning
Optional: suspend and resume criteria
(above products are established in the test plan)
Strategy, budget and planning feedback to/from the client.

Techniques

Not applicable.

Tools

Workflow tool
Planning and progress monitoring tool.

6.2.8   Allocating test units and test techniques

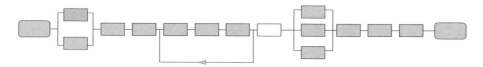

Aim
To finalize the test types and the thorough/light testing of characteristics/object parts based on the approved test strategy, budget and planning.

Method of operation
The method covers the following subactivities:
1. Determining test units
2. Allocating test techniques

This step requires information that is not always readily available in practice. In that case, the test manager will carry out this step in a general manner and bring in the details at a later stage, during the phase "Control".

1) Determining the test units
Within the strategy, the characteristics/object parts are allocated test types and a depth of testing. In some cases, a test type may be very extensive for a particular characteristic/object part. To facilitate the definition of manageable and executable activities, the test manager splits the object part further into 'test units'.

Definition

A test unit is a collection of processes, transactions and/or functions that are tested collectively.

The advantage of a test unit is that it forms a manageable unit (X hours in Y period) and as such, it is an important management mechanism for the test manager. Reasons for splitting a object part into test units are:
- The size of the object part is too big to be able to manage the testing of it effectively
- A particular piece of the object part requires a separate test approach with other test techniques, e.g. because the risk strongly deviates or because the nature of the part deviates from the rest (screen as against processing).

Since a test unit represents a unit of work, it is advisable for the test manager to coordinate this with the developer, so that a delivery unit corresponds with one or more test units and no half-test units are delivered.

2) Allocating test techniques
A subsequent step is that, per test type and based on the chosen depth of testing, one or more suitable test techniques are selected with which the test is to be specified and executed. If a object part is divided into test units, techniques are allocated per test unit. But how, then, do you select the suitable techniques? Chapter 14 "Test Design Techniques" covers a large number of test design techniques. Variations can be made on these, and there are other techniques, including those you create yourself. Checklists, too, can be used as a technique. This choice is, besides the choice of depth of testing, strongly dependent on a number of other aspects:

- Test basis
  Are the tests to be based on requirements; is the functional design written in pseudo-code or easily converted to it; are there state-transition diagrams or decision tables, or is it very informal with a lot of knowledge residing in the heads of the domain experts? Some techniques rely heavily on the availability of a certain form of described test basis, while with others the test basis may be an unstructured and poorly documented collection of information sources.
- Test type / quality characteristics
  What is to be tested? Some test design techniques are mainly suitable for testing the interaction (screens, reports, online) between system and user; others are more suitable for testing the relationship between the administrative organisation and the system, for testing performance or security, or for testing complex processing (calculations), and yet others are intended for testing the integration between functions and/ or data. Checklists are also often used for testing non-functional quality characteristics. All of these relate to the type of defects that can be found with the aid of the technique, e.g. incorrect input checks, incorrect processing or integration errors.
- What kind of variations should be covered, and to what degree?
  What depth of testing is required? This should be expressed in the definition of one or more forms of coverage and associated basic techniques (see also section 14.3 "Coverage types and basic techniques").
- Knowledge and expertise of the available testers
  Have the testers already been trained in the technique; are they experienced in it, or does the choice of a particular technique mean that the testers need to be trained and coached in it? Is the technique really suitable for the available testers? Users are normally not professional testers.
- Labour-intensiveness
  How labour-intensive are the selected techniques, and is this in proportion to the estimated amount of time? Sometimes other techniques should be chosen, with possibly different coverage, to remain within budget. If this means less thorough testing is to be carried out than was agreed, the client should, of course, be informed!

After covering the above aspects, the test manager makes a selection of techniques to be used. An example is set out below:

ST example

Characteristic	Object part	Test type	Techniques
Functionality	Subsystem 1 (A/● ●)	Functional test	tu1: DCoT tu2: SYN, SEM
Functionality	Subsystem 1 (A/● ●)	Regression test	tu3: selection from tu1 and tu2
Functionality	Subsystem 2 (B/●)	Functional test	tu4: Exploratory Testing tu5: SYN, SEM
Functionality	Subsystem 2 (B/●)	Regression test	tu6: selection from tu4 and tu5
Functionality	Total system (C/●)	Integration	tu7: DCyT
Functionality	Total system (C/●)	Multi-user	tu8: Exploratory Testing
Performance online	Total system (C/●)	Random test in ST environment	tu9: Error Guessing
…			

In more detail

In this example, the testing of subsystem 1 is spread across test units ("tu") 1 and 2; subsystem 2 consists of test units 4 and 5. Test unit 1, with many complex calculations, is nevertheless given rather an light technique, with the Data Combination Test (because the client opted for an average depth of testing), test unit 4 contains processing functionality and is allocated the (very free) "technique" of Exploratory Testing; test units 2 and 5 consist mainly of screens and are each given 2 techniques: the Syntactic and Semantic Test. The total system is then tested for coherence with the Data Cycle Test (test unit 7) and the multi-user aspect with Exploratory Testing (test unit 8). Later regression tests consist of a selection of previously created test cases (test units 3 and 6). Finally, a light Performance test is carried out using Error Guessing (test unit 9).

UAT example

Characteristic	Object part	Test type	Techniques
Functionality	Subsystem 1 (A/●)	Functional test	tu1: ST random test tu2: ST random test
Functionality	Total system (C/●)	Regression	tu3: DCoT
User-friendliness	Subsystem 1 (C/I)	User- friendliness	implicit in tu1 and tu2
User-friendliness	Total system (B/●)	Usability	tu4: SUMI
Security – auth.matrix	Subsystem 1 (-/S)	Authorisation test	tu5: Auth.matrix random test
Security – auth.matrix	Subsystem 2 (-/S)	Authorisation test	tu5: Auth.matrix random test
Security – auth.matrix	Total system (B/● ●)	Process test	tu7: SEM
Security - application	Total system (C/●)	Penetration test	tu8: Error Guessing
Suitability	Subsystem 1 (B/● ●)	Scenario test	tu9: PCT, test depth level 2
Suitability	Subsystem 2 (C/●)	Scenario test	tu10: PCT, test depth level 1
Suitability	Total system (A/● ●)	Process test	tu11: PCT, test depth level 2

In more detail

In this example, use is made in test units 1 and 2 of ST test cases. The regression test on the total system takes place with the light Data Combination Test. User-friendliness is implicitly tested simultaneously with test units 1 and 2 by evaluating the testers' impressions after completion. Thereafter, an explicit test takes place with the aid of the SUMI checklist (see also section 10.3.2 "Usability"). The authorisation matrix is first randomly checked for correct input, and then the authorisations are dynamically checked using the Semantic Test. A light penetration test takes place using Error Guessing, and Suitability is tested using the Process Cycle Test.

If the decision has been made to perform dynamic explicit testing, the table below can provide assistance in selecting the test design techniques to be employed. Per quality characteristic, the table provides various test design techniques that are suitable for testing the relevant characteristic. This table can also be found at www.tmap.net.

For the relevant quality characteristic, usable test design techniques are mentioned, making a distinction in respect of the thoroughness of the test. ● means light, ●● average, and ●●● thorough. The techniques mentioned should be seen as obvious choices and are intended to provide inspiration. The table is certainly not meant to be prescriptive – other choices of techniques are of course allowed.

Quality characteristic	Test design technique		
	● / light	●● / average	●●● / thorough
Manageability - installability	CKL	DCoT	DCoT
Effectivity	CKL	SEM	Penetration test
Usability	UCT	UCT PCT*	RLT
Continuity		RLT	RLT
Functionality - integration	DCoT	DCoT DCyT PCT*	DCoT
Functionality - detail	DCoT	DCoT ECT	DCoT + boundary value ECT + boundary value DTT
Functionality - validations	SYN	SYN SEM	
User-friendliness	SYN	SYN UCT* PCT*	Usability-test (if necessary in lab)
Infrastructure (suitability for)		RLT*	
Suitability	PCT test depth level 1 UCT*	PCT	PCT test depth level 3
Performance		RLT	
Portability	CKL Random sample functional tests Random sample environment combinations	Functional regression test Important environment combinations	All functional tests All the environment combinations
Efficiency		RLT	

Notes on the above table:

Abbreviations used:

*	If the technique is adapted to some extent, this can be used to test the relevant quality characteristic
DTT	Decision table test
CKL	Checklist
DCoT	Data combination test
DCyT	Data cycle test
ECT	Elementary comparison test
PCT	Process cycle test (test depth level = 2)
RLT	Real-life test

SEM   Semantic test
SYN   Syntactic test
UCT   Use case test

For a comprehensive description of these techniques, please refer to Chapter 14 "Test design techniques".

Concepts used

Environment combinations

In portability testing, it is examined whether the system will run in various environments. Environments can be made up of various things, such as hardware platform, database system, network, browser and operating system. If the system is required to run on 3 (versions of) operating systems, under 4 browsers (or browser versions), this runs to 3 x 4 = 12 *environment combinations* to be tested.

Penetration test

The penetration test is aimed at finding holes in the security of the system. This test is usually carried out by an 'ethical hacker'.

Portability – functional tests

In order to test portability, testing random samples of the functional tests – in increasing depth – can be carried out in a particular environment, the regression test or all the test cases.

Usability test

A test in which the users can simulate business processes and try out the system. By observing the users during the test, conclusions can be drawn concerning the quality of the test object. A specially arranged and controlled environment that includes video cameras and a room with two-way mirror for the observers is known as a usability lab.

See also section 10.3 "Test types".

In more detail

Test design techniques are actually first linked to test types and then to quality characteristics. In the absence of an unambiguous set of test types, a direct link to quality characteristics is selected.

The techniques of Exploratory Testing and Error Guessing do not appear in the above table. The reason for this is that these techniques can be used for all quality characteristics. Exploratory Testing is any form of testing with the tester making his test design during the execution of the test. The information obtained in the course of testing is used to design new and improved test cases. Error Guessing means that testers test the system in an unstructured way. For a description of Exploratory Testing and Error Guessing, refer to section 14.4 "A basic set of test design techniques".

Since it is impossible to establish all possible test situations in test cases, Exploratory Testing and Error Guessing are valuable techniques for carrying out supplementary testing. It is advisable to allow a limited amount of time during each test period for these techniques.

If a cell is left empty and no obvious techniques have been cited, then Error Guessing or Exploratory Testing can be applied. If relevant techniques have been cited, such as with Functionality validations with in-depth coverage, then aforesaid techniques can be used as a basis. These techniques can often be executed with a deeper-level variant, or several techniques can be selected.

Tip

Much uncertainty
In some cases, there is much uncertainty as to where the risks lie. This makes it difficult to determine a good strategy and to choose the right techniques. There are two possible solutions to this:
- Exploratory testing, because this has the flexibility to zoom in as necessary during the test execution on where the risk areas appear to be
- Employing the "onion" model. With this, somewhat general tests are specified in advance, but time and budget are planned for creating additional and targeted deeper-level tests during the test execution as the areas of risk become clearer. The testing thus progresses to a deeper layer each time.

Products
Categorisation of test units with allocation of test techniques.

Techniques
Not applicable.

Tools
Workflow tool.

6.2.9   Defining the test products

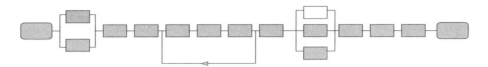

Aim
The clear definition of the test products to be delivered.

Method of operation
The activities that are carried out for the purposes of planning, execution and managing the test process deliver certain products, such as the test plan and reports, test cases and test scripts, but also procedures, instructions and project documentation, such as consultation notes. In consultation with the client and other stakeholders, it is determined what products are to be delivered. If there is a master test plan, this will also define test products to be delivered. This may concern testware, such as test plans, test scripts or automated regression tests – products, therefore, that are eligible for reuse, but which also may define test documentation, such as progress reports.

> **Tip**
> The use of tools for configuration or test management helps to produce a uniform method.

We distinguish the following test products:
- Testware

> **Definition**
> Testware is all the test documentation produced in the course of the test process that can be used for maintenance purposes and that should therefore be transferable and maintainable.

In retests or regression testing, existing testware is often used. Testware covers, for example:
- Test plan(s)
  Include both master test plans and other test plans
- Logical test specifications
  The logical specifications contain the logical description of the test cases
- Physical test specifications
  The physical test specifications contain the physical description of the test cases and the test scripts. Physical means that the test cases are

executable and checkable. The physical test cases are converted from the logical test cases. A test script contains the physical test cases placed in the most efficient order of execution.

- Traceability matrix (or cross-reference matrix)
  A matrix in which the link is indicated between the test basis (requirements, functional specifications, etc.) and the actual test cases. The situations to be tested from the test basis are shown vertically and the test cases horizontally. See also Traceability in section 6.2.12 "Organising the management"
- Test input files
  The test input files created on the basis of the test scripts should contain a (brief) description of the following:
  ○ Aim
  ○ The "physical" name
  ○ Date created
  ○ Brief description of the content
  ○ The file type and other relevant features
  ○ Reference to the test scripts.
- Basic documentation
  A description of the test environment, test tools, test organisation and underlying databases
- Test execution dossier
  The test execution dossier consists of:
  ○ Test results (logging of executed tests and test cases) and reports
  ○ Test execution (optional)
    The "material evidence" of the executed tests can consist of screen dumps, print output and output files. After completion of the test, the tester delivers the produced output to the administrator. The test documentation to be delivered from the output contains:
    - Reference to the "physical" name
    - Date of creation
    - Brief description of the content
    - File type and other relevant features
    - Reference to the test script.
  ○ Information on the defects and the changes
  ○ Transfer and version documentation.

■ Other test (project) documentation
During the test process, various documents are received or created that are not meant for reuse, such as:
- Project plans
- Reports of the discussions (with lists of decisions and activities)
- Correspondence, both on paper and electronic (e-mail)
- Memos
- (Project) standards and guidelines

- Test, review and audit reports
- Reports on progress and quality
- Etc.

By means of a brief description, the content and the aim of the various products or documents are indicated. Besides listing the products to be delivered, norms and standards can also be supplied and reference made to templates.

Products
A description of the test products to be delivered including norms and standards and any reference to templates, established in the test plan.

Techniques
Not applicable.

Tools
Testware management tool.

6.2.10 Defining the organisation

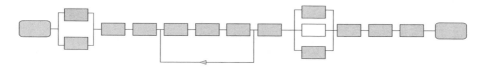

Aim

To define the roles, tasks, authorisations and responsibilities that are applicable to the test level.

Method of operation

The method covers the following subactivities:
1. Determining necessary roles
2. Delegating tasks, authorisations and responsibilities
3. Establishing the organisation
4. Allocating personnel
5. Establishing training and coaching needs
6. Establishing communication structures and reporting lines.

1) Determining necessary roles
In order to facilitate the activities in the test process, the test manager determines which test roles are required and how they are to be filled (see section 8.6 "Test professionals" and Chapter 16 "Test roles"). These will include, for example:
- Test management or test coordination
- Test team leading
- Tester
- Management (test process, test products, defects)
- Intermediary
- Support (domain knowledge, system knowledge, test environment, test tools or test method).

Make as much use here as possible of the roles set out at coordinating level.

2) Delegating tasks, authorisations and responsibilities
The tasks and responsibilities are set out here per required role.

In more detail

Examples of tasks (with the most likely role shown in parenthesis)
• Creating and maintaining the test plan (test manager)
• Directing the execution of, monitoring and adjusting the test activities (test manager)

> • Carrying out a testability review on the test basis (tester)
> • Designing tests based on user information (tester)
> • Specifying test cases and test scripts (tester)
> • Executing tests (tester)
> • Organising automated test execution (test-tool specialist, test-tool programmer)
> • Organising the technical infrastructure and the management of this (test infrastructure coordinator)
> • Organising methodical, technical and functional support (test manager)
> • Reporting on the test progress and quality of the test object (test manager)
> • Supporting users in creating test cases (specifically for iterative development) (tester)

3) Establishing the organisation

The correlations between the roles mentioned and the relationships with the other stakeholders within the system development process have to be determined and established. The organisation of the test level naturally forms part of a bigger whole. If the whole is a project, the test manager should also establish a relationship with the test or quality department, if any.

For the organisation of a test level, the possibilities can largely be defined as follows:
1. Testing as an **independent activity** or **integrated with other activities**
2. Testing placed within a **project** or in a **line organisation**
These choices are dependent on the test level, project and organisation. Sometimes, but by no means always, the test manager can exert influence on this. For a broader explanation of testing in a line organisation, refer to section 8.3 "Permanent test organisation".

	independent activity	integrated
project organisation	acceptance test, traditional system test	development tests, system test in agile environment
line organisation	testing factory	maintenance process

Figure 6.7: Organisational divisions with examples

Below are the most significant organisational forms with a few examples briefly mentioned. The descriptions and advantages are emphatically meant as a general indication; there are often exceptions in practice.

In more detail

Testing as an independent activity in a project

Within the project, a team is responsible for organising and executing the test. The testers within the team as a rule have a lot of test knowledge, together with – depending on the test level – a mix of system and organisational knowledge.

Advantages:
- Good accessibility to knowledge of the system
- Good coordination among users, developers and testers
- Knowledge and skills of testers are easily discernible
- Focus on an aim, therefore more manageable
- Independent assessment of the quality of the test object.

Testing integrated within a project

Within the project, testers, users and developers work in the same team. There are often several teams in action. The tester is responsible within his team for the organisation and execution of the test. The tester, as a rule, has a lot of technical knowledge of the system and architecture.

Advantages:
- Excellent knowledge of the application and architecture
- Close co-operation among users, developers and testers
- Very short lines of communication
- Focus on an aim, therefore more manageable

Testing as an independent line organisation

A separate department or organisation has testing – both the organisation and execution – as its primary task. Projects or other line departments issue a certain test instruction to this department/organisation. Test knowledge is dominant.

Advantages:
- Knowledge and skills of testers are easily discernible
- Independent assessment of the quality of the test object
- Efficiency gain through reuse and test automation
- Permanently set up infrastructure facilitates a fast start
- Standard test process setup facilitates a fast start
- Increased motivation through career prospects of testers

Testing integrated in the line organisation

Within a development or system management department, the role of tester is often combined with other roles. The tester in this organisational form often has a lot of system and/or organisational knowledge.
- Excellent knowledge of the system and the organisation
- Close co-operation among users, developers and testers
- Short lines of communication
- Knowledge management concerning an application is easier to realise

Below, a few examples of organisational forms are set out.

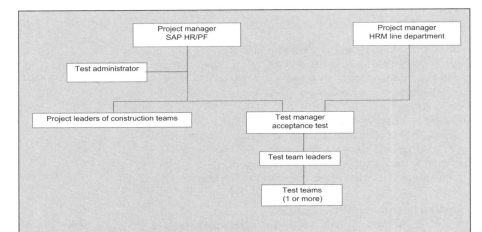

Figure 6.8: Example traditional organisation

The above is a rather traditional organisation where the acceptance test manager falls under the project manager and the system test under the project leader (Packaging Applications). Test support is supplied from within the line.

In the example below, the test manager comes under both the project manager of the SAP system and the project manager who has to implement it in the department. While answering to two clients may be an undesirable situation, in this practical example it has gone well. The test manager has stipulated at the beginning that if the two clients disagree, they should resolve their differences without involving the test manager. There has been no incidence of this.

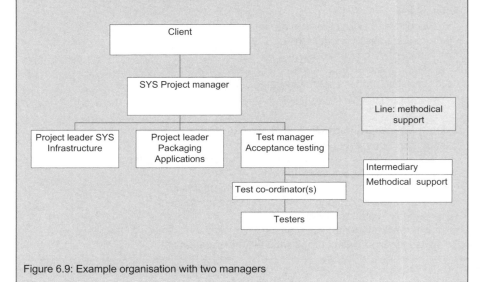

Figure 6.9: Example organisation with two managers

Tip

Iterative and agile system development

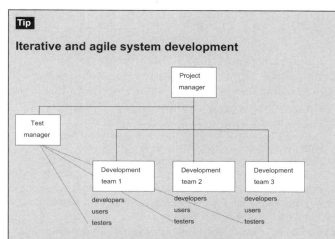

Figure 6.10: Example test management apart from teams

A disadvantage of integrated testing cited is that it can impair the independent quality assessment of the tester. A possible solution to this is to place the test manager apart from the development teams, with the testers in these teams answering to him. The advantage is that the gaps in the teams between developer, user and tester remain as small as possible, while the test manager can be alerted if the testing within a team runs into difficulties through planning pressure or other circumstances. This requires insight into the total product and project on the part of the test manager, combined with a good political feel for the balance between 'quality' and 'meeting deadlines'.

In more detail

RACI
If necessary, a RACI table could be set up, showing activities and stakeholders set out against each other. RACI stands for Responsible, Accountable, Consulted and Informed. At every crossroads, it can be indicated whether a party is directly responsible (R), is accountable (A), should be consulted (C), informed (I), or not at all.

It is impossible to determine one preferred organisation for testing. In general, the structure of the test organisation should resemble that of the associated process of system development or package implementation. In many cases, this means the project organisation. If there is to be frequent (re)testing in combination with scarce (test) knowledge, the permanent test organisation discussed in section 8.3 becomes a candidate.

4) Allocating personnel
When it has been established which test roles should be filled within the test process, the test manager delegates people to the roles. In this, of course, he makes allowance for their availability and skills in relation to the knowledge

and skills required in the relevant roles (see section 8.6 "Test professionals" and Chapter 16 "Test roles"). For the sake of clarity: the roles do not have to be filled by test professionals; end users or developers, for example, may be assigned the role of tester. The important thing is that the team as a whole has the right mix of knowledge and skills in the area of system, organisation and testing. Also, one individual can take several roles, while care should be taken that this does not result in conflicting responsibilities.

Tips

- To have more certainty that the testers have sufficient test knowledge, one can ask for certified testers. The ISTQB (International Software Testing Qualifications Board) is responsible for an international qualification scheme for testers (www.istqb. org). EXIN (Examination Institute for Information Science, www.exin-exams.com) organises a certification scheme specifically for TMap.
- When people are deployed from other departments, or even other organisations, the test manager should make allowance for agreements, procedures, selection processes, etc. This can take up a lot of time.
- There is often external pressure to accept certain people as testers into the team. If these people are not suitable, the test manager should be firm and spell out the consequences in terms of high training and coaching costs and low productivity.
- Employing or hiring in a tester cannot simply be left to a personnel or purchasing department. Good information on this can be found in [Rothman, 2006].

Besides the suitability of the individual for the role(s), there is a further dimension: that of the team. The natural inclination of the test manager is to select those persons whose personality most appeals to him. This can result in a team of similar characters. The theory of team formation teaches that, in fact, it is the team with a mix of personalities that achieves the best results. Possibly the best-known model in this area is the 9 team roles of Belbin (see also www.belbin.com). This differentiates between functional, organisational and personal roles. The ideal composition of each team depends on the aims. Belbin distinguishes the following roles, with a number of characteristics per role:

Plant	Creative, individualistic, imaginative, intellectual, knowledgeable
Chairperson	Calm, self-confident, sober, purposeful, brings out the best in every team member
Monitor/evaluator	Has strategic insight, is sober, unemotional, analytical and critical
Implementer	Conscientious, conservative, converts decisions into tasks, practical, self-disciplined
Finisher	Painstaking, concerned, works behind the scenes
Resource Investigator	Extrovert, seeks out new possibilities, enthusiastic, communicative
Shaper	Dynamic, energetic, extrovert, impatient
Team worker	Sociable, co-operative, listens well, encourages and integrates
Specialist	Professional, solo player, dedicated

For broader theory on this, refer to [Belbin, 2003]. A translation into the best test-team composition is provided [Roden, 2005].

5) Establishing training and coaching needs
The people involved in the test levels should have various types of knowledge, particularly in the areas of testing, domain knowledge and system.
- For testing, this may include: (the advantages of) the test approach, strategy determination, test techniques and tools to be applied
- For domain knowledge, bear in mind, for example, the organisation and its business processes
- System knowledge may consist of knowledge of the development or implementation process, design techniques, technical architecture, database or programming tools, etc.

In more detail

Knowledge input
The intention is not to include only very experienced testers with extensive knowledge in all 3 areas. Depending on the test level and the composition of the team, each individual will require to have a certain mix of these types of knowledge. If their knowledge is insufficient in one of the areas, it will have to be brought up to the required level. Training is the most obvious answer here, and a budget should be reserved for it. Timing is important: training is most effective if the knowledge gained can be quickly put into practice afterwards. A list of possible types of training can be found in section 8.6.6 "Training". Following any training given, people with insufficient knowledge should be coached in the beginning by someone with experience. This accelerates the learning process considerably. It often takes place "on-the-fly" during the test process, but if it is estimated to be a substantial activity, it should be planned for and hours made available for it.

6) Establishing communication structures and reporting lines
From within the test process, communication takes place with various parties. Examples of the parties with whom the test manager communicates are:
- Client
- Test manager of the overall test process
- Project management (including Change Control Board)
- Accepters (user organisation, system administration, functional management)
- Steering group
- Project leaders (design, construction and/or implementation)
- Developers
- Testing line organisation
- Quality management, QA
- Accountancy, EDP auditing.

It should be agreed with each party whether consultation and/or reporting is to take place, and what the aims and frequency of these should be.

Consultation forms
As regards consultation forms, it should be agreed who will be present and what, if any, the standard agenda will be.

Examples of consultation forms for use by the test manager are:
- Weekly consultation with all the other test managers, directed by the test manager of the overall test process
- Weekly project consultation
- Weekly Change Control Board consultation
- Defects consultation (1 x per week as standard; 3 x per week during test execution)
- Weekly test team meeting
- Daily stand-up meeting.

Below is an example of a fixed agenda for a test team meeting:

Agenda point	Subject	Time	Whom
1.	Opening - Establish the agenda - Notifications	xx.xx – xx.xx	<Test Manager >
2.	Notes of meeting dated <xx-xx-xxxx>	xx.xx – xx.xx	All
3.	Action list dated <xx-xx-xxxx>	xx.xx – xx.xx	All
4.	Status, progress and quality: - Test unit 1 - Test unit 2 - Test unit 3 - ...	xx.xx – xx.xx	<Tester 1> <Tester 2> <Tester 1> ...
5.	Quality of test process - <What is going well, and what could be improved?> - <TPI status> - <Defects management> - <Testware management> - <Reviews> - ...	xx.xx – xx.xx	All
6.	Question round	xx.xx – xx.xx	All

Reports

According to the BDTM view, reporting takes place on the four aspects of Result, Risks, Time and Costs.

- Result
  - The outcome of the tests executed at the level of characteristic/object part
  - The result in terms of obtained/not-obtained test goals (business processes, user requirements, etc.)
  - Any trend analyses
- Risk
  - Detection of parts that are being tested more superficially (or not at all) than the risk estimate indicates, thus presenting a higher risk
  - Detected (test) project risks
- Time + Costs
  - Progress of testing (in activities, products, hours spent and, optionally, money, dates)
  - Indication of when the testing will be completed.

Reporting on risks and results takes place at the level of test goals, as agreed with the client and other stakeholders. The risk tables of the product risk analysis are maintained with this aim. It is up to the test manager to translate test results on characteristics/object parts effectively, and on the basis of the tables, to this level.

Reporting can take place in various ways, to various target groups and at various times. The most important forms of reporting are:

- Progress and quality reports
  Information and advice on progress (and, optionally, quality) of the test process and on quality/risks of the test object, based on the four BDTM aspects.
  Frequency: periodically, preferably weekly
- Risk report
  With certain (project) risks, the test manager can, either upon request or at his own initiative, report on risk, the consequences for the test process and possible measures for dealing with the risk. In the Prince2 project management method these are known as 'exception reports'.
  Frequency: ad hoc
- Release advice
  Information and advice on quality/risks of the test object + formally established release advice.
  Frequency: towards the end of the test execution, before the decision has to be taken on release

■ Final report
Evaluation of the test process and test object, looking back from the original plan.
Frequency: once, at the end of the test process.

The test manager will determine, for each of these forms of report, to whom they should be sent, whether for approval or for information, with what content and degree of detail and with what frequency. In the activity, "Understanding the assignment" the test manager has already looked at which parties should, or wish to, receive reports. In consultation with the client, that is now determined in more detail. As an aid in overseeing who should receive which report, a matrix can be set up of report forms and target groups. The report forms and content are discussed in detail in section 6.3.3 "Reporting".

In more detail

As regards content, the progress and quality report is of the most importance, since it provides information and recommendations, on the basis of which timely management adjustments can be made. The data for this are supplied through management setup; see also section 6.2.12 "Organising the management". The report should contain details on the most recent reporting period and cumulative data on the entire test process.

Products
A description of the test organisation, established in the test plan.

Techniques
Not applicable.

Tools
Not applicable

6.2.11   Defining the infrastructure

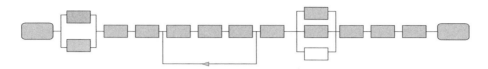

Aim
To establish the infrastructure required for the test process.

Method of operation
The method of operation covers the following subactivities:
1. Defining the test environment
2. Defining the test tools
3. Defining the office setup
4. Establishing infrastructure planning

Extensive descriptions of test environments and test tools can be found in sections 8.4 and 8.5 respectively.

1) Defining the test environment
Each test level requires a test environment in order to execute the tests. This environment is generally composed of the following components:
■ Hardware
■ Software
■ Interfaces
■ Environment data
■ System management tools
■ Processes.

The environment should be composed and set up in such a way as to facilitate, on the basis of the test results obtained, the best estimate of the degree to which the test object meets the set requirements. The environment has a considerable influence on the quality, duration and costs of the test process. In order to manage the test environment effectively, it is often separate from the development or production environment. Moreover, each test level sets its environment different requirements.
At www.tmap.net, a checklist "Test environments" is available that can be of assistance in defining the test environment. If the test environment already exists, for example in a maintenance process, it may be sufficient to refer to this and to mention any adjustments to be made.

2) Defining the test tools

It is established which test tools are required. Test tools can provide support with most test activities (see also section 8.5 "Test tools"). Besides the familiar test tools, such as test management, record&playback and defect management tools, you should also think of small, freeware or even self-built tools. Such tools can often be implemented for a small investment in time, but can be extremely valuable. The Internet is invaluable for seeking out freeware tools (search, for example, for "freeware test tool"). For self-built tools, it is advisable to consult the developers; they often already have such tools, otherwise they may be able to make them with very little effort.

> **In more detail**
>
> Since tools are to support the test process, the logical sequence would appear to be to define the process first and then select the tool: "structure before tool". However, this is not entirely true. Some very useful tools (test management and record&playback in particular) set requirements as regards process, e.g. the way in which test cases are established. If the test manager makes no allowance for this, the tool cannot be (efficiently) employed. It is therefore preferable to carry out process setup and tool selection more or less simultaneously.

3) Defining the office setup

The office infrastructure required for testing (workrooms, meeting rooms, telephones, PCs, network connections, office software, printers, etc.) is defined in outline. This concerns an office setup in the widest sense, since testers, too, need to carry out their work in the right circumstances. A checklist for the office setup can be found at www.tmap.net.

The appropriate and timely setting up of the office infrastructure will mean that all kinds of efficiency losses, such as relocations, waiting times and unproductive hours can be kept to a minimum. A bad example in this connection is if the testers have to be physically too far removed from each other and the rest of the project. An adequate setup of the workplaces also has a positive influence on the quality of the test process. This concerns, for example, the quality of both the internal and external communication and the motivation and productivity of the people involved.

> **Tips**
>
> - Find out at as early a stage as possible what the waiting times are in respect of the various requirements
> - Ensure that any relocations, etc., are separately budgeted
> - If testers are physically far removed from each other, extra hours for overheads may possibly be budgeted. This will make the disadvantages of the chosen office infrastructure clearer.

4) Establishing infrastructure planning
The test manager documents the agreements made and creates a general plan
containing the timings of the availability of the various facilities. The further
ordering and arranging of the infrastructure comes under the responsibility
of the test infrastructure coordinator.

Products
The description of the necessary infrastructure, including a planning,
established in the test plan.

Techniques
Checklist "Test environments" (www.tmap.net)
Checklist "Office setup" (www.tmap.net).

Tools
Not applicable.

6.2.12 Organising the management

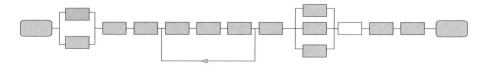

Aim
To establish the way in which the management of the test process, infrastructure, test products and defects is organised.

Method of operation
The method of operation covers the following subactivities:
1. Defining test process management
2. Defining infrastructure management
3. Defining test product management
4. Defining defects management.

At test plan level, norms and standards can be set up for this, supported by procedures, templates and tools (test management tools, plans and progress monitoring tools). Sometimes at the overall level facilities are arranged to be used.

1) Defining test process management
Test process management is aimed at administering the test process in terms of progress and quality, and providing insight into the quality of the test object. To this end, identification, registration, administration, storage and interpretation of the following details has to take place:
- Progress and the expenditure of budget and time
- Quality indicators
- Test statistics

This management is sometimes assigned to a dedicated role: test project administrator (see section 16.3 "Roles not described as a position").

This information forms the basis for managing and reporting by test management. Since control over the test process is increasing in importance, management is under pressure regarding the test process. Fast – preferably real-time – insight is required into the actual status quo. In this connection, the term **dashboard** is used: a simple overview from which all the superfluous information is removed and that provides the most important information at a glance: the quality of the test object (in terms of defects) and the progress of the test process. Planning and progress monitoring tools but also testware management tools can be an excellent support here.

Below is an example:

	Regression	Subsys 1	Subsys 2	Subsys 3
User Stories (test basis)				
Total	n.a.	103	23	n.a.
Status 1 (inferred)	n.a.	62	23	n.a.
Status >= 2 (part of testing)	n.a.	41	0	n.a.
Manual test scripts				
Total planned	291	145	35	111
Ready	291	62	0	93
To be amended	0	63	14	18
To be made	0	20	21	0
Results of last manual test round				
Date	n.a.	n.a.	n.a.	n.a.
Total run	n.a.	n.a.	n.a.	n.a.
OK	n.a.	n.a.	n.a.	n.a.
Not OK	n.a.	n.a.	n.a.	n.a.
Not run	n.a.	n.a.	n.a.	n.a.
Not completed	n.a.	n.a.	n.a.	n.a.
Automated test scripts				
Total planned	240	n.a.	n.a.	111
Ready	180	n.a.	n.a.	1
To be amended	180	n.a.	n.a.	0
To be made	60	n.a.	n.a.	110
Results of last automated test round				
Date	18-12-05	n.a.	n.a.	17-12-05
Total run	111	n.a.	n.a.	1
OK	43	n.a.	n.a.	1
Not OK	66	n.a.	n.a.	0
Not run	2	n.a.	n.a.	0
Not completed	0	n.a.	n.a.	0
Defects				
New	9	13	n.a.	0
Open	197	1	n.a.	22
Being solved	20	5	n.a.	0
To be retested	14	0	n.a.	1
Closed	274	5	n.a.	143

(n.a. = not applicable)

Progress and expenditure of budget and time
The progress information offers the client and the test management insight into the test process. On the basis of this, the test process can be redirected, if necessary. Where there are negative trends, timely measures can be adopted.

The parts to be managed are the activities and/or products, related to hours, resources, timeline and with mutual dependencies.

In more detail

Most activities result in one or more products, such as (master) test plan, reports, test scripts, test files, test logs, etc. Exceptions are supporting activities, which usually do not deliver any tangible products. A choice has to be made as to whether to register the progress at the level of activities or at the level of products, with the further possibility of the mix form. The advantage of managing at the level of products is that these are easier to measure than activities: it is easier to judge whether a product is 80% ready than an activity, and more and more development and project management methods manage on the basis of products. With the identification of activities or products, attention must be paid to the required degree of detail. Is it important to register an activity of several hours separately, or is it more efficient to register this as a part of a bigger activity? This is determined in consultation with the client.

Quality indicators

The aim of testing is to provide information and advice on the risks and quality of the object to be tested. To be able to provide this information, quality indicators are registered. The best-known and most obvious indicator is the defect. By establishing all kinds of details on a defect, such as e.g. status, severity, cause, quality characteristic and system part, all kinds of qualitative information can be gleaned from the defects at a later stage. Bear in mind the number of open defects relating to a particular part of the system, the number of defects found in a particular period, the number of defects relating to the requirements, etc. For more information on defects, refer to Chapter 12 "Defects management". Various other indicators are also possible. For example, the number of retests or the number of breakdowns within the test infrastructure (as an indicator of its reliability). The above-mentioned indicators tell us something about the quality of the test object. Another group of indicators tells us something about the quality of the test process itself. For example (see section 6.3.3 "Reporting"):

Effectiveness of testing	Are the (important) defects being found?
Efficiency of testing	Are the defects being found as quickly and cheaply as possible?
Checkability of testing	Is the test process progressing transparently and in the agreed way?

Test statistics

The test manager builds statistics based on the above information. Statistics can supply insight into the progress of the test process and quality of the test object, including any trends. And statistics can also apply to the quality of the test process itself.

2) Defining infrastructure management

The test infrastructure is subdivided into three groups of facilities:

- Test environment
- Test tools
- Office setup.

The test infrastructure is specified and ordered during the early stages of the test process. After installation, intake and acceptance of it, the infrastructure has to be managed. In practice, the management is usually transferred to a department, such as system management or operations, whether or not the test infrastructure coordinator forms the communication channel between the test process and the managing department.

In more detail

As regards the distribution of the management tasks, the various aspects of the test infrastructure can be divided into two groups:

Technical management
- test environment (hardware and software; management procedures)
- test files (physical)
- networks for test environment and office setup
- technical office setup
- test tools
  The most important tasks are:
  - Version management
  - Configuration management
  - Solving problem areas
  - Making logging available
  - Backup & restore
  - Recovery
  - (Technical) monitoring
  - Issuing authorisations
  - Providing availability
  - Implementing changes
  - Maintenance
  - Dealing with breakdowns.

The technical management tasks that have to be carried out belong to the role of test infrastructure coordinator. With the execution of these tasks, support is given as required by the supplier or a department, such as system management or infrastructure services.

Logistical management
- the non-technical part of the office setup, such as canteen provisions, transport, entry passes, etc.
The tasks in the context of logistical management are not test-specific and as such are not discussed further in this book.

3) Defining test product management
At test-plan level, norms and standards are set up for the management of the test products, supported by procedures, templates and tools. This promotes the reusability of the products and communication on it. It is advisable to adopt the norms and standards generally applied within the system development process to documentation and configuration management. Test product management is sometimes assigned to a dedicated role: testware administrator (see section 16.3 "Roles not described as a position").

The following are the various product groups to be managed:
- Products such as testware and test-project documents. Generally, higher requirements are set in respect of the management of reusable products like testware, e.g. that versions are retained. See also section 6.2.9 "Defining the test products".
- External products, such as the test basis and the test object. Responsibility for the management of this lies outside of the test process. However, the importance of good (version) management is extremely important to the test process. For that reason, requirements are often set from within the test plan in respect of the external management – e.g. that each product should be uniquely identifiable.

A choice has to be made as to which products are to be managed and to what degree. The management can be effectively supported by means of testware management tools.

In more detail
Below is a kick-start to a test-product management procedure. The procedure consists of four steps:

Delivery
The products to be managed are delivered by the testers to the manager. Preferably, the delivered files are placed in a separate directory. The products should be delivered

complete (among other things, supplied with a version date and version number). The manager checks for completeness. The following are some of the items that could be checked:

- Name of author
- Type of document (also in document name)
- The definitive version number and version date
- Accuracy of references to other documentation (the test products should refer clearly to the associated test object and test basis)
- Mutations overview: overview of the versions, version dates and reason for change, including the name of the person who made the change
- Products in electronic form should be delivered with a fixed nomenclature, in a form that includes the version number.

Registration
The manager registers the delivered products in his administration on the basis of supplier's name, name of product, date and version number. At the same time, it is registered how long the relevant products should be kept. In certain cases, it may also be necessary to include the information on products related to the product to be registered. We find this in organisations where traceability is an important issue, for example because of legal obligations. With the registration of changed products, the manager should ensure that the consistency between the various products is preserved.

Archiving
A distinction is made between new and changed products. Stated roughly, new products are added to the archive and changed products replace the previous version.

Consultation
The issue of products to project team members or third parties takes place by means of a copy of the requested products. The manager registers which version of the products has been issued to whom and when.

In more detail

Traceability
Partly because of legislation (IFRS, SOX, FDA (Food and Drug Administration) and FAA (Federal Aviation Administration)), it is becoming increasingly important to demonstrate both that testing is being carried out and also what exactly is being tested. Showing what is being tested is achieved through traceability (demonstrating which test cases bear a relation to which part of the test basis). The proof that testing is actually being performed has to be supplied through explicit reporting. A subsequent requirement is to provide proof that the defects have been dealt with. If these stringent requirements concerning traceability and submission of proof are to be met, then the test product management, defects management and quality assurance in respect of testing should be tailored to this end (and extra budget made available for it!). The test management should be set up in such a way that the traceability and evidence can be followed step by step. This means that:

- It is clearly indicated in the test specifications from which part of the test basis these are derived

---

- With the test execution, the evidence to be submitted relates to which test cases have actually been executed
- It is made apparent which test cases have led to which defects
- The evidence to be submitted is established during the retest; which defects have been solved and approved in a retest.

This apart, traceability has the following big advantages for testing:
- Much insight is gained into the quality and depth of the test, because from the requirements, the functional and the technical design and the software, it is known with which test cases these have been checked (or will be). The chances of omissions in the test are therefore much reduced
- With changes in the test basis or the test object, it can be quickly deduced which test cases need to be amended and/or carried out anew
- If, owing to pressures of time, it is not possible to carry out all the planned tests, test cases will have to be scrapped. Because the relationship with requirements, specifications and software is known, we can scrap those test cases of which the associated requirement or specification presents the least risk in production and it is clear with which requirements or specifications no, or no well-founded, decision is possible on the quality.

If we want to set up the test to provide traceability, then the deployment of tools for test product management is more or less indispensable.

---

4) Defining defect management
A defects procedure should be set up to facilitate the handling and managing of defects. Ideally, this procedure is supported by a tool. Since a defects procedure applies to the entire project and not to a separate test level, this procedure can best be defined at master test plan level. This also makes it possible to detect overall trends, over and above test levels. A description of the defects procedure is included in Chapter 12 "Defects management". This management is sometimes assigned to a dedicated role: defects administrator (see section 16.3 "Roles not described as a position").

Products
A description of the various management processes, established in the test plan.

Techniques
Not applicable.

Tools
Defect management tool
Testware management tool
Planning and progress monitoring tool
Workflow tool.

6.2.13 Determining test process risks (& countermeasures)

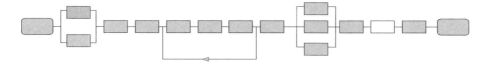

Aim
To cite explicitly the risks for the test level. This will provide the client and other stakeholders with a better understanding of the risks for the test, and they can allow for these in directing the total process.

Method of operation
In performing the preceding activities, the test manager has obtained a picture of the possibilities (and/or impossibilities) in connection with the test process, but also of threats and risks. In the test plan, an indication is provided per risk whether measures have been taken – and if so, which ones – to cover or reduce the risk found. Bear in mind here preventive measures for avoiding risks, but perhaps also measures to enable timely detection of problems. These risks are then monitored during the management of the test process.

It should be realised that this step is no more than paying mind to the risks as they are known *at the beginning* of the phase. Thereafter, the test manager includes these risks in the progress report under the separate section "Project risks". Subsequently, these risks are tracked, monitored, removed, new risks found, etc. If this activity takes place at project level, it can be combined with it.

In more detail

The risks can relate to, among other things:
- Planning realism
  The test plan depends on the plans of the various other parties. How realistic are these plans?
- Entry quality
  The two most important forms of input for the test process are the test basis and the test object. If this input is of insufficient quality, this will be very disruptive to the test process
- Resources
  Testing requires people and means, in a certain quantity and of a certain quality. In practice, it often appears at the execution stage that the resources agreed in the plan cannot be (entirely) delivered in time

- Stability
  To what extent will the test basis change during the test process? The more changes, the greater the consequences for the test process in terms of reworking
- Infrastructure
  Is it stable enough for the test; does the environment have to be shared with other parties, is the environment sufficiently representative; is enough support available? In many test projects, the infrastructure forms the most unmanageable risk.

Products
A description of the found (test) project risks and possible measures, established in the test plan.

Techniques
Checklist "Test process risks" (www.tmap.net).

Tools
Not applicable.

6.2.14 Feedback and consolidation of the plan

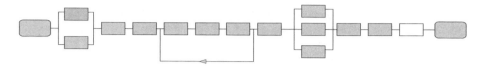

Aim

To document the results of all the activities performed to date and obtain the client's approval of the chosen approach.

Method of operation

The method of operation covers the following subactivities:
1. Creating the test plan
2. Feedback on the test plan
3. Consolidating the test plan

1) Creating the test plan

The results of all the activities carried out so far are documented in the test plan. The test plan contains the following sections, at a minimum:
- Formulation of the assignment
- Test strategy
- Approach (test units, with the test types and techniques to be used per test unit)
- Organisation
- Infrastructure
- Management
- Threats, (project) risks and measures
- Budget and planning
- Appendix: Product risk analysis

2) Feedback on the test plan

The various parts of the plan should be consistent. In practice, setting up a consistent plan takes place in several stages. The test plan with the results of preceding activities is fed back to the client and other stakeholders (such as the test manager of the overall test process) for approval or adjustment. This makes the test approach to be followed transparent and manageable, entirely in line with BDTM.

> **Tip**
>
> Some test managers have good experiences with going over the plan in a walkthrough session with the most important stakeholders. Any conflicts soon come to the fore, so that the number of feedback cycles can be kept to a minimum.

By adjusting the strategy (whereby the risk analysis is in principle unchanged), the test manager can enable the client to manage on the basis of the test effort weighed against the test depth. This results in a suitably adjusted strategy, with the scrapping or adding of test depth being shown by ○ or ● respectively, instead of ●, as earlier indicated in section 6.2.7 "Determining the planning". The test manager should make the consequences of this adjustment for the budget, planning *and* risks clear, and translate them into terms that the client will understand (referring back to the test goals). This is repeated until the client is satisfied with the balance between test depth and test effort.

> **Tip**
>
> A potential pitfall is that the communication on the adjusted strategy may be too "strong". If the client opts for a number of lighter tests than advised, a table is created that shows a lot of ○'s. If this table is shown repeatedly in progress reports or meetings, it gives two impressions: 1) the client is reckless, and 2) the test manager does not entirely approve and is distancing himself from the test approach. For that reason, it is advisable to use this table style only at the beginning and end of the test phase.

3) Consolidating the test plan
Following the feedback and possible adjustment of the plan, the test manager should submit the test plan to the client, at the least, for approval. Whoever else has to give their approval depends on the organisation. In many organisations, the test plan is also submitted to other stakeholders for approval, such as users and developers. Parties for whom requirements are set in the assumptions part of the plan should give their approval.

> **Tips**
>
> • To make creating a test plan easier and prevent approval delays, it may be decided to have the test plan approved in parts
> • The degree of formality of the approval depends on the organisation. In some organisations, it is advisable to enforce the approval formally by having the test plan signed by the client and/or other stakeholders. In other organisations, the sending of approval by e-mail or a verbal confirmation will suffice.

The plan is then placed under configuration management as a formal test product. Besides this, a presentation, for example to the various stakeholders, can contribute to obtaining approval and – at least as important – create support throughout the organisation.

Products
The test plan.

Techniques
Not applicable.

Tools
Not applicable.

6.3   Control Phase

Aim
Providing the client with sufficient insight into, and the opportunity to influence, the following:
- The progress of the test process
- The quality and risks of the test object
- The quality of the test process

To this end, the test manager manages the test process optimally and reports on it.

Context
The activity referred to relates to the system test or acceptance test. The testing may relate to new build, maintenance, migration, a package implementation or a mix, and the development approach may be waterfall, iterative, agile or – again – a mix.

Preconditions
This activity begins after the creation of the test plan.

Method of operation
The test manager and the administrator(s) perform the activities assigned to them in the test plan. They manage the test process, the infrastructure and the test products. Using the data thus obtained as a basis, the test manager analyses possible trends. He also keeps in close touch with developments outside of the testing, such as any delays on the part of the developers, upcoming major change proposals and project corrections. If necessary, the test manager proposes particular measures to the client. Information is the most important product of testing. Therefore, the test manager provides various types of reports to the different target groups, bearing in mind the BDTM elements of Result, Risks, Time and Costs.

Roles/responsibilities
The test manager, also known as test coordinator, has primary responsibility for the management of the test process.

Activities
The control of the test process covers the following activities:
1. Management
2. Monitoring

3. Reporting
4. Adjusting

The scheme below shows the sequence and the dependencies between the various activities:

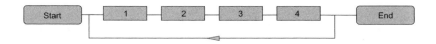

Figure 6.11: Control of the test process

6.3.1   Management

Aim
Managing the test process, the defects and the test products with the goal of providing continuous insight into the progress and quality of the test process and the quality of the test object.

Method of operation
The management activity can be divided into two sub-activities:
- The following forms of management are carried out in accordance with procedures established in the test plan: the management of the test process, test product management and defect management (see activity "Organising the management", section 6.2.12). Infrastructure management comes under the "Setting up and Maintaining Infrastructure", as described in section 6.4
- The test process is supported by – and checked for the application of – norms and standards.

These operations fall within the role of administrator or test manager, as defined in section 6.2.10 "Defining the organisation". Section 16.3 "Roles not described as a position" describes the following administrator roles for this: test project administrator, testware administrator and defects administrator.

In more detail

The real challenge in management is not so much following procedures, but ensuring that the other test team members do so. Matters such as submitting timesheets, placing the testware under configuration management and carefully administering defects are not equally high in the popularity stakes among all testers. Measures for ensuring that this remains in focus are:
- "Repeat, repeat, repeat" the message that good management is crucial to the success of the test process. Make the reasons and advantages clear
- Make "management and control" a fixed subject in the periodic team meeting
- Remind people (directly) when they do not, or do not sufficiently, keep to the agreements
- Check activities and results, particularly at the beginning of the process to prevent bad habits from starting, and at the start of the test execution when the testers are working under time pressure.

N.B.: The test manager can take on the role of supervisor, or delegate it to another individual. Obviously, in the latter case the person should have the full support of the test manager when he admonishes someone for not complying with the procedures.

In practice, the setting up of norms and standards takes place concurrently with the development of the first products, so they do not exist at the time of writing the test plan. The supervisor will have the task of supporting the development of the first products and subsequently of creating generally applied templates.

Products
A managed test process.

Techniques
Not applicable.

Tools
Defect management tool
Testware management tool
Workflow tool
Planning and progress monitoring tool.

6.3.2   Monitoring

Aim
Monitoring the test process, based on internally managed data and external information.

Method of operation
The principal and most difficult task of the test manager is the monitoring of the execution of the plan.

While this is described in the section below as mainly an instrumental activity, it is equally a *communication activity*. The biggest part of the test manager's task perhaps consists of "monitoring" the employees on the team. This includes everything, from recruiting new testers during the testing process, delegating the work, holding work consultations/team meetings, supporting, coaching and assessing employees, up to and including the conducting of exit interviews. Another very important task for the test manager in this same connection is the maintaining of contact with the world surrounding the test team, also known as *stakeholder management* or *expectation management*. Do the expectations of the test clients still correspond with what the test is going to deliver? Are there developments in the project that will influence the test process? It should be obvious that highly developed social and communication skills would not go amiss here.

In general, the activities described in the plan – such as preparing, specifying and executing the tests – should be carried out according to a particular timeline and in a particular sequence. To do this, the test manager has the necessary people at his disposal (including himself). He sets out a detailed planning for the coming period, outlining who will do what, in how many hours. This is necessary, as the planning within the test plan is not detailed to the extent that tester A knows that, in the coming week, she should specify test units X and Z, and tester B knows that he is to carry out test scripts Y1 and Y2 for test unit Y. Experience shows that such detailed planning only works for the initial short period, after which changes are always taking place, requiring the planning to be revised. Most obvious periods for which a detailed planning can be set up are the phases: Setting up and maintaining infrastructure, Preparation, Specification, Execution and Completion. With iterative system development, the test manager also makes a detailed planning per iteration. In setting up a detailed planning, the test manager makes allowance for all the aspects of planning, such as priorities, availability and skills (see also section 6.2.7 "Determining the planning").

Another of the test manager's tasks is to fill in "blank spaces" in the test plan during the course of the test process. This is the case when, at the time of setting up the plan, certain information is missing or there is no time to carry out a particular activity.

In more detail

For example, the allocation of test units and/or test techniques. Occasionally, information from the developers is lacking, so that it is not possible to arrive at a satisfactory distribution of test units. The test manager may also decide to delay the allocation of test techniques to test units until the testability review has been carried out (see section 6.5 "Preparation Phase").

Towards the end of the test execution, the monitoring becomes even more important, as the test manager must then be able to answer the question of whether stopping testing is justified. The exit criteria formulated in the plan are the deciding factors here, but if they are absent or no longer current, there are some rules of thumb available:

- Have all the planned tests been executed (in accordance with the latest test strategy)? This emphatically does not concern the original strategy, but the latest, amended version. This contains the most recent insights of the client and test manager into the balance between risk and test coverage
- Are the number and degree of severity of the outstanding defects at an acceptable level? And to this may be added: have the costs of the testing during this period risen higher than the returns ("damage prevention", see below)?
- Has the number of newly found defects as well as the number of solved and retested defects been reduced to a minimum during the latest period (e.g. week)? This last point says something about the stability of the system. Sometimes, in the last period, so much has been reworked and retested that the system has several releases per day. If only both of the above points were to be considered, it could be decided to stop testing. However, the system is still anything but stable, and a regression test is strongly to be advised.

Only when a positive answer can be given to these questions does it make sense to recommend ending the testing.

After the test team has completed all its tasks, including the Completion phase, the test manager asks the client to terminate the assignment and to discharge the test team. The team is then disbanded.

Tips

- Damage prevention: one of the benefits of testing is that in production costs do not arise because faults do not occur. This could possibly be conveyed by relating the severity and cause of a problem to any repair costs after going into production: what would the costs have been if the defect had not been found?
- It is possible to make a model with which the prevented damage of each defect can be estimated. In this, a certain factor is allocated to aspects of a defect (severity, cause and quality characteristic), e.g. a severe defect delivers on average 8 times the damage of a cosmetic defect. By estimating the prevented damage of a limited number of defects with the aid of experts, the factors are determined and the average sum per defect. The prevented damage of a new defect can then be quickly estimated by multiplying the average amount by the relevant factors (see [Aalst, 1999])
- A simple but useful graphic is the S-curve of the cumulative number of found defects per day. Where the S starts to flatten out, this could be an indication for stopping the testing. In any case, it is an indication that it is time to discuss whether or not to stop with the stakeholders.

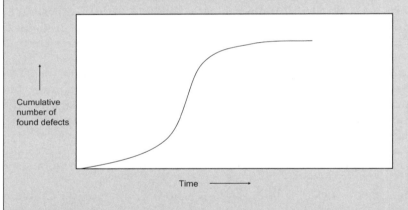

Figure 6.12: Example of S-curve

Practice also teaches that the original plan is bound to be amended. The amendments can have both internal and external causes, i.e. from both within and beyond the test process. It is up to the test manager to flag these events or trends as early as possible. Measures for redirecting a negative trend can then be adopted promptly. This is almost always better, cheaper and faster.

In more detail

While in practice there has probably never been a project where the plan was carried out unchanged, this does not mean that the plan is somehow unimportant. On the contrary, the plan provides a common framework that makes correcting the process easier and more effective than when working without a plan.

Information in respect of the events or trends comes from the internally managed data and information from outside of the test process, e.g. minutes or memos, but not least also from verbal interchange, such as the project consultation, stand-up meetings, bilateral discussions, etc. This is where a good social (project) network shows its worth to the test manager. Using this information, the test manager analyses possible trends and tries to apprehend threats (or indeed opportunities) in time: will the trend continue? What needs to happen to prevent it?

For this purpose, the test manager carries out the following steps:
1. Analysing the event, estimating risks and defining countermeasures
2. Coordinating with the client and other stakeholders (optional, depending on tolerance)

1. Analysing the event, estimating risks and defining countermeasures
The test manager analyses the cause of the event and determines the consequences for the test process. He also examines the significance of the event explicitly in respect of the risks that are covered at this stage of the testing. Events can influence the testing positively or negatively, and the test manager determines the possible countermeasures, depending on the timing of the event, the analysis and the consequences for the test process.

On the next page are some examples of common events and their causes, consequences and countermeasures:

In more detail

Event	The test object is delivered later than planned, while the deadline for the test process remains the original date
Possible causes	The causes of this will usually lie in the stage preceding the testing phase. Likely causes are higher degrees of complexity than expected, differences of opinion or expansion of the scope.
Consequences for the test process	• There is less time for the execution of the test cases • There is more time for specifying test cases • The required means for the test execution, such as a representative test environment, do not need to be available until later • Etc.
Possible measures	• Extra test capacity is requested for the test execution • The test cases are described more comprehensively during the specification phase, making their execution simpler for inexperienced testers • Tests are carried out in parallel with each other • Allowing for the risk category, it is decided to reduce or skip certain test activities • It is decided to push certain test levels or test types together, so that they can be carried out collectively • The rooftile method in respect of the specification of test cases and execution, i.e. delivering smaller batches more often from development to testing • An increase in budget is requested • Etc.

Event	The productivity of the employees is lower than expected
Possible causes	• The quality of the test basis is less than the advance estimate • The employees have on average less experience than was expected in estimating productivity • The test object is more complex than previously estimated, so that setting up the test cases is more difficult • Etc.
Consequences for the test process	The test activities take longer than planned
Possible measures	• Employees are replaced by others with more experience • Extra capacity is requested from the client • The test method of operation is adjusted, so that less risky parts are given still less attention, and more time is made available for the risk-bearing parts • A decision is made not to process all the test cases extensively and, for example, only to create logical descriptions (this generally places higher demands on the tester who executes the test) • Etc.

Event	The specifying of test cases takes more time than was planned
Possible causes	• The test basis is of less quality than was planned • The productivity of the employees is lower than was previously estimated • Etc.
Consequences for the test process	Overrun of test specification can mean that the test execution cannot start on time.
Possible measures	• Techniques are selected that will result in fewer test cases. This also means that there will be less test coverage and that the recognised risks will have less coverage • The logical test cases are not written out into physical test cases (this generally puts higher demands on the executor of the test) • Extra time or capacity is requested from the client • Extra support is provided by subject-matter experts or developers • Etc.

Event	The test basis keeps changing
Possible causes	• The test basis is of lower quality than was planned • The scope of the project keeps increasing • There are differences of opinion in the project concerning the functionality to be delivered • Etc.
Consequences for the test process	• (During specification and execution) The test specifications need to be continually reviewed and are never completed • (During execution) Extra retesting is required continually
Possible measures	• The logical test cases are not written out into physical test cases (this generally puts higher demands on the test executor) • Exploratory testing as a technique in order to be less dependent on the test basis and also to put off the need for this as far as possible • Extra time or capacity is requested from the client • Stricter configuration and change management at project level, (obviously with involvement of testing) • Etc.

In more detail

Retesting

A specific part of the strategy is how to deal with retesting. Normally, a test delivers defects that are then reworked. A choice must then be made as regards retesting. For example, limited retesting can be carried out, focusing only on the adjustment. Another possibility is to carry out retesting of the total function in which the adjustment was implemented, of the total function in conjunction with surrounding functions, or even of the total system. The change can also be retested with specific test cases and a regression test can be run on the (unchanged) rest of the system. The choice of the degree of retesting is made based on the risks. Sometimes guidelines are in place; sometimes the test manager determines the retesting level from case to case. In fact, the test manager takes a kind of mini test-strategy decision, with all the steps being gone through briefly.

2. Coordinating with the client and other stakeholders (optional, depending on tolerance)

Depending on the measures to be carried out, the test manager can carry them out independently, or prior agreement with the client and possibly other stakeholders may be necessary. The form that this coordination takes depends on the organisation. In practice, use is often made here of reports. The various forms of reports are described in section 6.3.3 "Reporting".

The margin that the test manager has for taking measures independently is determined by the following factors:

- The degree to which the difficulties of the test process can be solved within the set assignment, the product risk analysis, the test strategy, budget, planning and other preconditions. In other words: the degree to which the client is to be left out of it
- The degree to which the difficulties can be solved within the limits of tolerance, which were agreed in the planning phase (section 6.2.7 "Determining the planning").

In practice, the test manager should generally ask permission if the measures would influence the agreements that were made at the planning phase. In other words, if adjustments have to be made to the formulation of the assignment, product risk analysis, test strategy, budget and/or plan.

In more detail

The devil's quadrangle

A familiar trend is symbolised in the 'devil's quadrangle', with Time, Money, Functionality and Quality as the corner points. At the start of the project, there is a certain balance between the points. A predictable course of events is that all kinds of unforeseen events occur that introduce tension into the quadrangle (see diagram below). In particular, certain activities overrun (Time) and/or cost much more than was estimated (Money). The project manager corrects this by putting restrictions on the other corner points, i.e. Quality and Functionality.

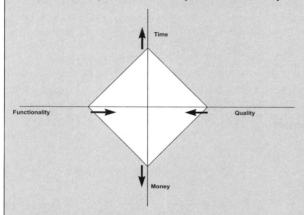

Figure 6.13: The devil's quadrangle

Although in itself this is not necessarily "wrong" behaviour on the part of the project manager, it is the test manager's job to monitor Functionality and Quality. Bearing the quadrangle in mind, the test manager indicates the consequences of the project manager's decisions and alerts the client, for example, if the choices repeatedly fall on restricting Quality and Functionality. Timely communication of this trend in particular is difficult, which emphases the importance of an independent test manager. Depending on their perceptions, the test manager is either the "conscience" or the "thorn in the side" of the project manager and/or client. This role requires a high degree of professionalism, for the test manager has to tread carefully regarding the politics of the various interests within and beyond the project.

Tips

- A tip that can be given in the above context is, when changes are requested or when the project manager proposes adjustments to the testing, never immediately to dig one's heels in and cry "No, not possible, because ..." It is better to respond in the manner of, "Hmm, interesting idea. Let's tease that out a bit further; what would it mean in relation to... The idea could work if we all accept these and those consequences."
- At the Preparation and Specification phases, the (project) management tends towards indifference in respect of the testing. Only at the test execution stage, at the point when the testing is on the critical path, is interest shown in the progress. The test manager should make allowance for this, by, for example, adjusting the form and frequency of reporting and consulting (more of it, and more frequently, during the test execution) and, in the process, might well transform his image (from "walk-on part" to "star").

Products
Proposed management measures.

Techniques
Not applicable.

Tools
Defect management tool
Testware management tool
Workflow tool
Planning and progress monitoring tool.

6.3.3   Reporting

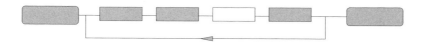

Aim

Creating reports that provide insight into both the quality of the test object and the progress and quality of the test process. These reports will ensure that the client and other stakeholders can steer the course of the testing effectively.

Method of operation

During the test process, the test manager compiles various reports. The form and frequency of reporting is established in the "Management" chapter of the test plan. Periodic reports are created on the quality of the test object and the progress and quality of the test process. Besides the periodic reports, the client or other stakeholders may request reports on demand. The most familiar example of this is the risk report, for outlining the possible consequences of a threat or risk to the testing. There may also be an unexpected request for an extra progress report, for example to provide the most up-to-date input for a steering group or project management meeting. At the end of the test process, a recommendation for release and final report are drawn up.

With all this information, the client, project manager and other stakeholders are supplied with insight into the extent to which:
- The intended result is achieved
- The risks of taking the system into production are known and are as small as possible within the set preconditions
- This has taken place within budget and term.

In other words, this refers to the BDTM aspects of Result, Risks, Time and Costs. Supplying insight implies that the report should have relevance to the recipient(s) of it.

The reports are based on the data as established in accordance with section 6.2.12 "Organising the management".

Tips

- Always report accurately and completely; it is in nobody's interest to present matters in an exaggerated light
- Report with precision and substantiate with reliable figures
- Report in the terminology of the client, not only in numbers of defects
- Report positive news, too, for example the number of test cases that have been

> processed without defects
> • Regarding the level of detail in the report, answer the needs of the target group
> • Be neutral in the wording; don't get personal
> • Respond to questions like "Can I go into production?" or "Can it be accepted?"
>   preferably not with "No!", but with "Yes, provided that ..." or "Not unless ..."

The content of the most important reports is described below:
a. Progress report
b. Risk report
c. Release advice
d. Final report

a) Progress report
Reporting takes place in accordance with the reporting structure described in the test plan. The progress report contains data on the most recent reporting period and cumulative data on the entire test process.

Besides figures, the report should also provide textual explanation and advice on the results, progress, risks and any problem areas. The latter is inclined to be forgotten in reports that are generated from test-management tools. It should be realised that explanation and advice are very important in the provision of quick and reliable insight into the figures. It is the most important product of testing. While the explanation can and should be given verbally, it most definitely should be contained in the written report. This forces the test manager to think carefully, as well as making the advice stronger, reaching a wider audience and helping with the process evaluation in retrospect.

In more detail

Progress report versus final report
Although the terms 'interim report' or 'progress report' may suggest that these are less important than the final report, in fact the opposite is true. The progress report supplies early information and advice, with which the recipients (such as client, project manager and others) can often make timely adjustments for keeping the total process on the right track. The final report is more a retrospective evaluation that mainly benefits subsequent test processes and projects.

In outline, a progress report has the following content (based on the BDTM method with the four aspects of Result, Risks, Time and Costs). In practice, the list of contents may follow a different sequence; subjects may be combined, or even omitted. It depends on the report's target group.

1. Status of the test object (BDTM: Result)
    1.1 Status per characteristic/object part
    1.2 Status of test goals
    1.3 Trends and recommendations
2. Product risk and strategy adjustment (BDTM: Risks)
3. Progress of the test process (BDTM: Time and Costs)
    3.1 Progress (in hours and data) of activities or products over the recent period
    3.2 Activities in the coming period
    3.3 Hours lost
    3.4 Trends and recommendations
4. Problem areas/points of discussion (all the BDTM aspects)
5. Agreements
6. Quality of the test process (optional, all the BDTM aspects)
    6.1 Effectiveness
    6.2 Efficiency
    6.3 Verifiability

These subjects are further explained below.

1. Status of the test object (Result)
1.1 Status per characteristic/object part
    It is shown per characteristic/object part:

- The status of the tests (not started, planned, specification, execution, retest X, completed), optionally with the progress percentage, e.g. the progress of the execution is estimated at 60%
- Overview of numbers of defects (sorted by status and severity, optionally also by other aspects, such as cause)
- If test products (such as test cases or test scripts) are seen emphatically as results, they can also be included in the overview, with an indication of whether a start has been made on the product and whether it is ready.

The closer the end of the test period approaches, the more attention is paid in the progress report to the consequences of open defects. In the beginning, it is less useful to include this in the report, since it is expected that the defects will be solved. But the consequences should always be included in the defect report itself.

- Defects that remain open and their impact
- Defects not solved (known errors), and their impact.

1.2 Status of test goals
Based on the above, the status per test goal (user requirement, business process, critical success factor, etc.) is reported. Sometimes a test goal can be directly linked to a number of characteristics/object parts and to the test

status related to them; sometimes the status per characteristic/object part is not sufficiently usable and the test manager still has to determine the test status per test goal. The risk tables from the Product Risk Analysis make the link possible.

1.3 Trends and recommendations
Relevant trends and related recommendations can be reported here.

In more detail

Below are some overviews that will reveal whether certain trends are taking place:
- The number of open defects per week will indicate whether the testing can tail off or if a backlog is building up
- The relationship between numbers of defects and test cases per subsystem provides an indication of whether extra testing on that part will deliver many more defects
- The number of found defects and number of solved (including retested) defects within a certain period says something about the stability of the system
- Status of the defect versus who should carry out the following step in the handling of it. This shows up where any bottleneck lies. For example, where all the complex faults are allocated to that one experienced developer, with the result that a backlog of unsolved defects is created
- Cause of defects (requirements, design, code, test environment, wrong installation/operation, wrong test case) versus subsystem. Provides insight into the concentrations of specific mistakes
- Number of defects versus tables (with data warehousing). This tells us what the error-sensitive system parts are.

In order to give the trend significance for the stakeholders, it is advisable to use graphics, making the trend visible. This is not as easy as it seems. It is difficult to produce a clear and legible graphic. A few tips (quoted freely from [Tufte, 2001]):
1. Make the data and the message the centrepiece
2. Maximise the data/ink ratio (i.e. leave out all the symbols, lines and colours that don't add anything)
3. Remove redundancies
4. Review and amend.

---

2. Product risk and strategy adjustment (Risks)
In this part of the report, the stakeholders are given insight into the degree to which the coverage of the various product risks has changed, as well as into any process risks.

In the test plan strategy, it is determined whether and to what degree product risks will be covered by testing. During the test process, aberrations may occur: the estimate of the risk appears different and/or the test coverage requires adjusting. The adjustments over the reporting period, with associated consequences, are reported in this part. In this, the translation is made into the test goals: what kind of impact will the changed risks have on the attainment of these goals?

3. Progress of the test process (Time and Costs)

Regarding the progress of the test process, the points below are significant.

3.1 Progress over the latest period

At the level of phases and/or main products, the following could be reported:
- Number of planned hours
- Number of hours spent so far
- Number of hours expected still to be spent
- Percentage completed
- Dates: planned/expected/actual start date; planned/expected/actual end date.

Products could be the test plan, test scripts, test-execution files and reports.

If the test manager is responsible for the budget, he will also include in the progress report information on completing the test process within budget.

3.2 Activities in the coming period

Here, the activities to be carried out in the coming period are reported.

3.3 Hours lost

This refers to non-productive hours of the testers. If the test process environment does not meet certain preconditions, this will result in inefficiency and loss of hours. Examples are a non-functioning test infrastructure, much or lengthy test-obstructing defects or lack of support. Hours lost, and the causes, are reported here.

3.4 Trends and recommendations

As with trends in the status of the test object, trends and recommendations in connection with the progress of the testing should also be reported. The central question here is whether the agreed milestones are (or appear to be) feasible.

In more detail

One of the trends that can be watched is the average time required for the reworking of a defect. If this increases, it is possibly a signal that the volume of the backlog of work is increasing sharply. The percentage of wrongly reworked defects can also be observed.

4. Problem areas/discussion points (all the BDTM aspects)

In this section of the report, the test manager points out any problem areas or points for discussion that jeopardise completion of the test assignment within the set limits of time and costs. For example:

- The test object being delivered later than planned
- The quality of the test basis being less than expected
- The test environment not being available on the agreed date
- Test-obstructing defects present in the test environment or test object.

Besides the various problem areas, their consequences and possible measures are shown. Here, too, the test manager makes the translation into the test goals.

5. Agreements

This part shows the agreements made in the current period between the test team and other parties that are relevant to the recipients of the report.

6. Quality of the test process (optional)

If required, this part of the report can include information on the quality of the test process. The following questions play a part here:

- Are the significant defects being found (as early as possible)? (Effectiveness)
- How economical is the test process with time and resources? (Efficiency)
- Is the test process working as agreed? (Verifiability)

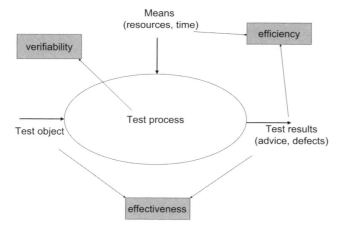

Figure 6.14: The three quality aspects of the test process

> **In more detail**
>
> A point of focus here is the general problem with metrics: how to draw the right conclusions from the figures; how to avoid comparing apples with oranges. See also Chapter 13 "Metrics".

6.1 Effectiveness

> **In more detail**
>
> The difficulty with the question of whether the testing is effective, is that this can usually only be established in retrospect. The effectiveness issue can be split into two parts:
> - Is there a good strategy in place?
> - Is the testing being carried out in accordance with this strategy?
>
> **There are various indicators that can be included in the report:**
> - The percentage of found defects in the test level / the number of defects present or an approximation thereof; the number of defects can be approximated by, for example, the number of defects still being found during the first 3 months of production
> - The percentage of found defects in a test level that should reasonably have been found in a preceding test (30% of the defects found in the acceptance test concern programming defects; these should actually already have been found in the development tests and system test)
> - Degree of testing coverage; the more thorough the test, the more defects will be found
> - The percentage of mistakes (= test faults).

6.2 Efficiency

> **In more detail**
>
> **The following are possible indicators of this:**
> - The number of defects found per test hour
> - Estimating prevented damage in relation to the test costs (through finding faults)
> - Number of specified or executed test cases per hour
> - Number of reviewed pages per hour.
>
> By comparing these figures with an established standard, a picture is created of the efficiency of the test process.

6.3 Verifiability

> **In more detail**
>
> This aspect is difficult to communicate through indicators. What the test manager can say in the report about this is whether and how in the latest period it was verified that the test team was working as agreed. The verification can focus on the test

products or the processes and can be based on the planned quality measures, or on monitoring, or on a random check at the overall level. The test manager should make a good risk estimate as regards what checking would be useful. In particular, the test levels that are placed with inexperienced test managers or that have been outsourced are eligible for verification.

Below is an example of a dashboard, enabling the most important information to be seen at a glance.

Part	Is	Was	Remarks
1. Quality of test object	☹	😐	...
2. Risks	😐	😐	...
3. Progress	☺	☺	...
4. Quality of test process	☺	😐	...

Later in the report, these points are worked out in detail in overviews with notes. Examples of overviews (without notes):

Quality of test object - defects

	Open	To be retested	Closed	TOTAL
Obstructing			4	4
Severe	1	1	12	14
Disruptive	3	12	49	64
Cosmetic	15	7	37	59
TOTAL	19	20	102	141

Quality of test object – subsystem x causes

	Requirements	Design	Software	Infrastructure	Test	TOTAL
Subsystem 1	3	5	18	6	2	34
Subsystem 2		1	16	2	4	23
Subsystem 3	6	14	30	14	1	65
Total system						
TOTAL	9	20	64	22	7	122

Progress

	Time			Hours			
Milestone/Activity	Plan	Expected	Realised	Estimate (A)	Spent (B)	To be spent (C)	Difference (A-B-C)
Planning							

	Time			Hours			
Milestone/Activity	Plan	Expected	Realised	Estimate (A)	Spent (B)	To be spent (C)	Difference (A-B-C)
- Test plan	Apr 1		Apr 1	60	54	0	6
Preparation							
- Testability review	Apr 8	Apr 12		40	46	4	-10
Specification							
- Test unit 1	May 2	May 2		120	60	60	0
...							

b) Risk report

The purpose of the risk report is to supply the various stakeholders with sufficient information to allow them to make informed decisions in respect of the test process. The information in the risk report should therefore also focus on the consequences of the event for the achievement of the agreed result within the agreed timeline and cost levels.

In more detail

The test manager creates a risk report if events take place for which measures are required to be taken that the test manager is not authorised to decide upon. Another reason for creating a risk report is if the client asks the test manager to set out consequences and possible measures for one or more scenarios upon which a decision is required to be taken. For example, a scenario in which the client sees that the development activity is overrunning and he considers making budget available from the test.

In a risk report, the following subjects are dealt with, at a minimum:
- A description of the event / the scenario
- The consequences of the event for the testing
- The significance of the event to the degree to which the various product risks are covered
- Possible countermeasures
  If possible, the test manager outlines several measures with the associated costs. An estimate is also made of the influence of the measures on the recognised consequences and degree of coverage of product risks
- Recommendation
  The test manager provides a recommendation in respect of the measure(s) to be selected.

c) Release advice

The release advice is created at the end of the test execution. The purpose of the release advice is to provide the client and other stakeholders with a level of insight into the quality of the test object that will allow them to make informed decisions on whether the test object can go on the following stage with its present status. The following phase in this connection refers to a subsequent test level, or production. For that reason, the release advice is usually created under severe pressure of time, since immediately after execution of the last tests and before the test object is released to the next phase, there is usually very little time available. The test manager would do well to have a draft release advice largely prepared towards the end of the last tests, so that only the last test results need to be processed.

The information in the release advice should not actually come as a surprise to the client. He has been kept abreast of developments relevant to him by means of reliable progress reports and, where necessary, risk reports. In order to supply the client with the information necessary at this stage, the release advice should cover at least the following subjects:

- A recommendation as to whether, from the point of view of the testing, it would be advisable to transfer the test object in its present state to the next phase
  The final decision on whether or not to go on to the next phase does not lie within the test process. Many more factors are at work here, other than those relating to the test process. For example, political or commercial interests that make it impossible to postpone transfer to a subsequent phase, despite a negative release advice

- Obtained and unobtained results
  Which test goals have been achieved and which not, or only to a certain degree? On the basis of test results on characteristics and object parts, the test manager gives his opinion and advice on the test goals set by the client. It is also indicated whether the exit criteria have been met. The number and severity of the open defects play an important role here. Per defect, it is indicated what the consequences are for the organisation. If possible, risk-reducing measures are also indicated, such as, for example, a workaround, allowing the test object to go on to the next phase without the defect being solved.

- Risk estimate
  During the planning phase at the beginning of the test process, an agreement is made with the client about the extent to which product risks will be covered, and with what degree of thoroughness. For various reasons, it may be decided to cover certain parts less thoroughly with testing than the risk estimate indicates. Moreover, during the test process, all kinds of changes are still usually being made to the original strategy; moreover, the original risk estimate has possibly been adjusted, perhaps resulting in additional or

different risks. In this part of the release advice, the test manager points out which characteristics or object parts have not been tested, or have been less thoroughly tested than the risks justify and so present a higher risk. The associated consequences are also shown.

d) Final report
The purpose of this report is to obtain insight into the way the test process has gone and to document empirical data for the purposes of future test processes.

The final report is created after issuing the release advice, usually when the test object has already been released to the next phase. More time is therefore available for it.

The contents list of a final report is more or less the same as that of a progress report:
1. Evaluation of the test object (BDTM: Result)
    1.1 Status per characteristic/object part
    1.2 Status of test goals
2. Product risk and strategy adjustment (BDTM: Risks)
3. Release advice (BDTM: Result, Risks)
4. Evaluation of the test process
    4.1 Progress (BDTM: Time and Costs)
    4.2 Quality of the test process (BDTM: all the aspects)
6. Recommendations for future tests
7. Empirical data (optional)
8. Costs/benefits analysis (optional)

However, whereas a progress report looks ahead, the final report looks back. In other words, it mainly concerns the difference between the original plan and the final realisation. What degree of deviation is there from the original plan? Was the plan a good one, or were issues wrongly estimated? Were adjustments always timely and effective? To what extent were the preconditions met, and met promptly enough? Could bottlenecks have been prevented? These differences are analysed in particular for purposes of the risk analysis, test strategy, estimate and planning. The quality of the test process is also considered: were the chosen procedures, tools and techniques used correctly and was the test environment satisfactory? Recommendations are provided, if possible, for future tests. The activity 'Evaluating the test process" (see section 6.8.1) supplies the input for this evaluation. Also, use can be made of the "Test process evaluation" checklist. In addition, empirical data may be collected and made available to the client, or, even better, to a Testing line organisation. A last, optional, part of the final report is a costs/benefits analysis.

The final report is made available to the client and other stakeholders, possibly by means of a presentation.

In more detail

Empirical data
Examples of empirical data are:
• Size of the test object
• Development effort
• Number of defects
• Duration and hours per main activity
• Duration and hours required for specifying tests
• Duration and hours required to execute the tests
• Number of test cases
• Analysis of lead time per defect
• Number of defects to be expected
• Number of retests.

A comprehensive summary of the empirical data that can be collected is included in the list "Metrics list" (see section 13.5). This chapter also discusses the Goal-Question-Metric method for implementing metrics.

Costs/benefits analysis
The costs of the test process are relatively simple to establish. Bear in mind, for example, the costs of the used resources, manpower and equipment. The benefits of the test process, however, are more difficult to establish. As indicated in section 2.2 "Why test", there are four types of benefits of testing. It is difficult, but not impossible, to provide a quantitative indication of these.

Products
Reports (progress report, risk report, release advice, final report)
Empirical data
Costs/benefits analysis.

Techniques
Checklist "Test process evaluation" (www.tmap.net)
Metrics list (section 13.5).

Tools
Defect management tool
Testware management tool
Workflow tool
Planning and progress monitoring tool.

6.3.4 Adjusting

Aim
Adjusting the test process (in consultation with the client as necessary)

Method of operation
When the proposed measures have been reported, the client has agreed and a selection has been made from one or more of the possible alternatives, the test manager can put them into effect. To this end, he carries out the following steps:
1. Implementing measures and evaluating effectiveness
2. Adjusting products from the planning phase (optional, dependent on tolerance)
3. Feedback to the client.

1. Implementing measures and evaluating effectiveness
In this step, the test manager implements the (approved) measures. After some time, he assesses whether the desired effect has been reached with the adopted measures.

2. Adjusting products from the planning phase (optional, dependent on tolerance)
The measures can have consequences for the agreements as set out in the test plan. In that case, the test manager adjusts the products concerned and submits them to the stakeholders for approval.

Examples of adjustments to the various products are:
- The scope of the assignment is adjusted. This is the case, for example, if it is decided to carry out one or more extra test types, or to omit them
- The product risk analysis is revised, because during the execution of the test process it appears that the probability of faults was wrongly estimated. This is the case if the development tests were limited because of pressures of time
- During the test execution, changes will be made in particular to the test strategy if the depth of testing or method of operation is amended. For example: under pressure of time, it is decided to create no more test cases for the testing of screens, but to use a checklist
- Many of the events mentioned in section 6.3.2 have consequences for the budget. A common example of such an event is delay in delivery of the test object while the deadline for the test remains unchanged. The planned

coverage is then only feasible if extra people are brought in, resulting in lost time (initiation) and management overhead.

Since the formulation of the assignment, product risk analysis, test strategy and estimate are required to be consistent with each other, a change in one of the products will usually lead to changes in the other products. Changes to the test plan are established in a new version or in a supplement, which is again submitted to the client for approval. It is the test manager's responsibility to communicate clearly to the client the consequences of the changes.

3. Feedback to the client
In this step, the test manager reports to the stakeholders, such as the client, on the measures taken and their consequences for the test process. If the client (and possibly other stakeholders) were involved earlier in giving permission to adopt the measure, this report will generally contain no new information. Even if the test manager is able to implement the measure independently, the event and associated measures are reported to the stakeholders to keep them abreast of the testing developments. The periodic progress report is a suitable means for this.

Products
Steering measures
Amended plan.

Techniques
Not applicable.

Tools
Workflow tool
Planning and progress monitoring tool.

6.4 Setting up and maintaining infrastructure phase

Aim

To provide the required test infrastructure, which is used in the various TMap phases and activities.

Context

The test infrastructure consists of the facilities and resources necessary to carry out the testing satisfactorily. A distinction is made between the facilities for test execution (test environments), for supporting the testing (test tools) and for the day-to-day work of the testers (workplaces).

Definition

The test infrastructure consists of the facilities and resources necessary to facilitate the satisfactory execution of the test. A distinction is made between test environments, test tools and workplaces.

The setup and maintenance of infrastructure involves specific expertise. It is something that testers in general have limited knowledge of, but upon which they nevertheless are very dependent (without infrastructure, there can be no test). All the responsibilities surrounding the setting up and maintaining of infrastructure are therefore often given to a separate maintenance department, necessitating close co-operation with these other (sometimes external) parties during the test. This means that test managers land in a situation where they have no authority over the setup and maintenance of the infrastructure (the maintaining party has the say-so), while they nevertheless depend on it. This can lead to conflict. For example, the situation could arise in which this maintaining party gives priority to solving production-disrupting problems above solving problems in a test environment. Furthermore, a maintenance department often also has particular security guidelines (e.g. authorisation checks, fixed backup times, installation procedures) that cannot easily be ignored. This is something that should be taken account of during the testing and, with that, the responsibility for the setup and maintenance of the infrastructure is an important area of focus for the test manager. A means of alleviating the concern for this support process is the permanent test organisation, which will take full responsibility for the setup and maintenance of the test infrastructure. This is described in chapter 8 "Supporting processes".

> **Example**
>
> An organisation's infrastructure is maintained by an external party, with the condition that a daily backup of the infrastructure is made. For this purpose, an automated process is created that makes a backup at night, somewhere between the hours of 22:00 and 06:00, depending on other processes.
>
> The building and testing of a new web application overruns and it is decided to extend the time spent on testing per day. This means that the testers plan to test (in shifts) from 06:00 to 01:00 hours. It is therefore necessary to change the times of the backup process. A request is submitted, but the external organisation is reluctant to grant it. Many other processes will have to be changed, and that could take up to two weeks. The option of not making a backup of the test environment is out of the question for all kinds of legal reasons. Meanwhile, pressure is being put on the test manager to find a solution for the problem of the overrun.

With a test project, it is important to pay special attention to the setup and maintenance of the infrastructure. In order to keep the focus on this during the test, there is a separate phase within the TMap life cycle model. It is a phase that runs parallel with the phases of Preparation, Specification, Execution and Completion. For some activities, there are dependencies between these and activities in the other TMap phases. This is explained later in this chapter in connection with the relevant activity itself.

Test environment

A suitable test environment is required for the dynamic testing of a test object (the running of software).

> **Definition**
>
> A test environment is a composition of parts, such as hardware and software, connections, environment data, maintenance tools and management processes in which a test is carried out.

Hardware refers to all the tangible parts of a computer (screen, hard disk, network card, et cetera). Test environment software refers to all the programs that should be present on the available hardware in order to run the software under test, such as operating programs, DBMS, network and other support programs. Connections are everything that is required to allow the test object to communicate with other systems. The environment data is the set of data that the test environment requires to be able to work with these (user profiles, network addresses, root tables, et cetera). Maintenance tools are tools that are required specifically to keep the test environment operational, and management processes are all the activities that are carried out around the setup and maintenance of a test environment.

In section 8.4 "Test environments", test environments are discussed in more depth.

Test tools

> **Definition**
>
> A test tool is an automated instrument that supports one or more test activities, such as planning, control, specification and execution.

Test tools can be used as instruments for achieving higher productivity and/ or effectivity on the part of the testers and the testing. With the use of test tools, the emphasis is on "support" (see the definition). This means that a test tool is only a tool if the use of it delivers something; using a tool should not be a goal in itself.

One of the conditions for the successful use of test tools is the presence of a structured test approach. In a well-managed process, tools can certainly deliver significant added value, but they are counterproductive in an inadequately managed test process. The reason for this is that automation (what test tools actually do) requires a certain repeatability and standardisation of the activities to be supported. An unstructured process cannot meet these conditions. However, the deployment of test tools can function as leverage for implementing a structured approach. Structuring and automation should therefore go hand in hand, in short: "Structure and Tool".

In section 8.5 "Test tools", test tools are discussed in more depth.

Workplaces

One of the aspects that is often forgotten in testing is the provision of a workplace, where testers can perform their tasks effectively and efficiently in satisfactory conditions. This involves an office setup in the most general sense, and so the workplace consists of more than just office space and a PC. Issues, too, such as e.g. entry passes, power supply and lunch-break facilities all have to be arranged.

If the testing is carried out in the framework of a project, extra office space should be organised. It is advisable to bring the test team together in one location (a room or a floor). This will form a basis for good mutual co-operation and coordination within the team. If that is not possible, the location of team members in various rooms should correspond with, for example, the allocation of the various system parts to the testers, the test types to be applied, et cetera. If developer and tester work together in multidisciplinary teams, they should be situated together in one location.

As with every project activity, a great deal of consultation takes place in testing. Because testing finds itself at the crossroads of the various activities in the project, testers have a lot of contact with the various groups (such as designers, programmers, administrators and users). It is advisable to place the test team in the vicinity of these groups. There are examples of improved test processes thanks to the relocation of the test team to the physical 'middle' of the project organisation. This resulted in, among other things, increased mutual respect between the testers and other project participants, which benefited the quality.

The workplace intended for a tester at first sight does not differ much from the standard workplace. But appearances are deceiving. What is being tested is often new to the organisation and the workplace. Testers may find themselves in a situation in which their workplace is unprepared for the new software. It is therefore often necessary to arrange separate authorisations for testers. For example, testers should have the possibility of installing the new software on their local PC, and this may also be necessary in order to use particular test tools.

> **Tip**
>
> Certain test types can deliver a great deal of data. An example of this is the performance test, in which a test tool is used. The output of this test tool may consist of thousands of lines of information. Stored in files, this may well grow to several gigabytes per test, often with printouts of over a hundred pages. It is therefore a good idea to adopt separate measures for dealing with this. For example, extra disk space could be reserved and an extra printer connected.

Preconditions

Before the setup and maintenance of infrastructure phase can be started, the description of the required infrastructure at an overall level, including the general plan, should be known and established in the test plan and/or master test plan. If test tools are being used, it should be known how the various activities within TMap are to be performed.

Method of operation

On the basis of the definition of the infrastructure set out in the test plan, it is considered whether closer specification and more detail are necessary. Besides the description of the required resources, it is also described what is expected of the suppliers during the maintenance of these resources. Since different expertise is required, the realisation of the infrastructure is often carried out by other parties. From within the test project, the progress of the realisation is monitored and if the progress is threatened, actions are devised. The realisation should be completed before the Execution phase begins, but preferably earlier. Simultaneously with the realisation of the infrastructure, a checklist is created that includes specific checks. This is used to determine, upon delivery, whether the infrastructure supplied meets the previously set requirements. After delivery, the infrastructure should be kept available for the testers at the quality level determined at the start of the phase. At the end of the test assignment, it is examined which parts of the infrastructure should be preserved. These can then be reused in future (re)tests.

Roles / responsibilities

It is advisable to delegate the organisation of this phase to someone other than the test manager. This individual then takes the role of test infrastructure coordinator, which is further explained in chapter 16 "Test roles".

Activities

The basis of the Setting up and maintaining infrastructure phase is defined in the Planning phase. Here, within the activity "Defining the infrastructure" the infrastructure required at overall level is described, including the planning. This description (from the master test plan or test plan), serves as input for the first activity in this phase.

The Setting up and maintaining infrastructure phase consists of the following six activities:
1. Specifying the infrastructure
2. Realising the infrastructure
3. Specifying the infrastructure intake
4. Intake of the infrastructure
5. Maintaining the infrastructure
6. Preserving the infrastructure

Figure 6.15 "Setting up and maintaining infrastructure" indicates the sequence and dependency between the various activities. Activities "Realising the infrastructure" and "Specifying the infrastructure intake" can be carried out in parallel. The dependency between the end of activity "Intake of the infrastructure" and the start of the Execution phase is significant. Before the test execution can start, there must be a correctly operating test infrastructure.

That is why it is essential to plan activity "Intake of the infrastructure" before the start of the test execution. It is even advisable to plan this well in advance (and the preceding activities as well) in order to prevent any start up problems with the test infrastructure from causing the test execution to overrun. Test execution often finds itself on the critical path of the entire project, and so problems with the test infrastructure indirectly cause the project to overrun. Also, an operational infrastructure is very handy in the Specification phase. Test scripts can be tried out, and test data (in files, for example) implemented.

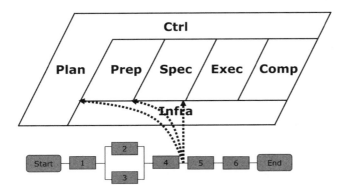

Figure 6.15: Setting up and maintaining infrastructure

In the definition of test infrastructure, it says that a distinction is made between test environment, test tool and workplace. For each of these three, the activities model, as previously described, should be followed. The activities of the three parts have a mutual relationship as regards timeliness. Activity "Intake of the infrastructure" plays an important role here. The intake of the infrastructure forms the link with the other phases in TMap and is also the common link between the three parts.

Tip

When test tools are used for automating the test execution the operational infrastructure must be in place before the Specification phase starts. This means activity "Intake of the infrastructure" is completed before the Specification phase starts. This is because in the Specification phase the automated test scripts are programmed and therefore you need an operational workplace, an operational test tool and an operational test environment.

It is advisable to organise the workplace as quickly as possible, and it should be ready before the testers arrive. This means it should be prepared during the Planning phase. Often it is even necessary to have the workplace operational before the intake of the test environment can begin. And, in turn, the test environment often needs to be operational before a start can be made on the intake of the test tool. This is made clear in figure 6.15 "Setting up and maintaining infrastructure". The setup and maintenance of the infrastructure is a very complex operation, with many internal and external dependencies. The organising demands close attention and it is therefore advisable to arrange this with the test infrastructure coordinator.

6.4.1   Specifying the infrastructure

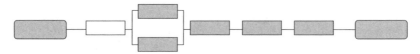

Aim
To specify the description of the required infrastructure (from the master test plan or test plan) in a more detailed level.

General method of operation
On the basis of the specification of the infrastructure contained in the (master) test plan, it is considered whether further specification and detail are necessary. The planning of the test environment, test tools and workplace is also worked out in more detail. Besides describing what resources are necessary, expectations are also set out in respect of the supplying party during the management of these resources. The timely involvement of the various parties is essential. Agreements should be made for the supply and build of the infrastructure, and these agreements should be checked at regular intervals. In consultation with the various suppliers (internal and external) it is determined how detailed the specification should be. The delivery times of the various parts are included in the detailed plan.

Workplace method of operation
The specification of the workplace covers tangible subjects, such as required locations, desks, chairs, telephones, PCs, et cetera. But it also covers less tangible things, such as required authorisations, disk space, software, e-mail accounts, et cetera. The realisation of these aspects may take a considerable amount of time. Occasionally it requires a special setup (e.g. project rooms) or special installation (e.g. the PCs). In other cases, items have to be ordered. It is advisable to emphasise at this stage specific requirements that are set in respect of management of the workplace. For example, obtaining separate status for the testers in the solving of problems in the workplace. This can be useful, since testers are no 'ordinary users' and sometimes require a different kind of support.

Test environment method of operation
In specifying the test environment, the various elements of the test environment should be considered. Definitions can vary among suppliers and organisations. For that reason, it should always be discussed clearly what is meant by particular terms. Another important point is the number of test

environments required and the various types there are. Each type of test environment has its own purpose, with specific requirements applying to it.

The specifying of the technical form of the test environment should be done in consultation with someone who has technical knowledge of the environments. This individual should translate the concrete requirements (based on the aim of the test served by the test environment) into the technical form. As a basis for this, an architectural overview can be created, for example. This can be a difficult process, since two worlds (testing and technology) speak two different languages. It is up to the test-team individual responsible (the test manager or test infrastructure coordinator) to check whether this is organised satisfactorily.

Besides requirements concerning the setup of the test environment, requirements should be set in respect of the maintenance of it. Examples of requirements are:
■ The backup activities that have to be carried out
■ The comprehensibility of the software versions present
■ The interfaces present
■ The ability to change the test environment
■ The ability to change the system date
■ The use and management of test data
■ Authorisations and their administration
■ The required timetable for the building of a test environment.

Agreements should also be made at this point on how the test environment will be tested (see also the activity intake of the infrastructure). Other agreements may concern the contact with suppliers (direct by the test team or via another party) and how to deal with licences.

Example

For the testing of a new customer administration, the following requirements were set during the specification in respect of the test environment and the maintenance of it:
• Backups are made upon request of the testers and take no longer than 15 minutes
• No changes are implemented in the environment without the explicit permission by mail from the test coordinator
• Created backups are returned upon the test coordinator's request within 15 minutes
• The resetting and securing of environments takes place between 20:00 and 06:00
• The operating system for the test environment is the same as that of the production environment
• Connection of system X and Y to the test environment should be available between 06:00 and 20:00
• Connection of system Z to the test environment should be available between 06:00 and 20:00 within 15 minutes of the request

- Connection with system W is simulated by a stub
- Testers have direct access to tables in the database (reading permissions)
- The system date should be open to change by the test team
- It should be possible to store 4 versions of test files
- Tool A should be available for the creating or copying of complete test cases.

Tip

In some organisations, a standard set of test environments is used and the test manager has to use these for his test. If that is the case, during this activity he investigates the specific characteristics of these test environments and how they fit within the test.

Test tool method of operation

If, in the creation of the (master) test plan, it is decided to employ test tools, this should be firmed up during this activity. The decision should be backed up by definite choices of one or more tools. As made clear in the definition of test tools, they are intended to support one or more test activities. During this specification of the test tools, it should be clear which test activities are to be supported and how this should be done.

The selection and deployment of a tool can be carried out according to the life cycle model, as described section 8.5.5 "Implementing test tools with a tool policy".

Products

Detailed specification of workplace
Detailed specification of test environment
Test tool(s) plan of approach.

Techniques

Not applicable.

Tools

Not applicable.

6.4.2 Realising the infrastructure

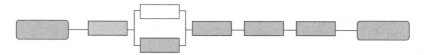

Aim
To realise the infrastructure according to the detailed specification from the previous activity.

Method of operation
The infrastructure is realised during this activity. The required hardware and software are purchased or ordered as necessary. The workplaces and test environment are organised and the test tools installed and configured. During this activity the framework of the test suite is built when tools are used for the automation of the test execution (see section 8.5.3 "Types of test tools" for more information on the framework of a test suite). Since all of these activities requires special expertise, it is usually carried out by parties other than the testers. From within the test project (the test infrastructure coordinator) the progress of the realisation should be monitored, in case it is threatened.

This activity should be carried out in parallel with the first phases of TMap and should be ready at the latest by the end of the Specification phase (preferably before, since time is required for the next activity, "Intake of the infrastructure"). When the activity is carried out depends on the part that is being realised and on the dependencies between the various parts. For example, the workplace should be realised first, preferably in the Planning phase. The realisation of the test environment often takes a lot of time and therefore should be started quickly. But the situation can arise in which a workplace is necessary for the realisation of the test environment. In that case, it is necessary to wait until the workplace is ready. If the test tool uses the test environment, the installation and configuration can only start when the test environment is ready. Otherwise, it is best to start this as quickly as possible. When tools are used for executing the test the realisation of the infrastructure must be finished before the Specification phase starts. In the Specification phase the tools are used for creating the automated test scripts.

Both internal and external parties (e.g. the supplier of the test tool) play a part here. This makes it a difficult activity to manage, demanding good coordination. The infrastructure coordinator should check the progress and quality of the work supplied. The following sub activities should be carried

out, for example:
- Check whether all the agreements are still valid
- Have bottlenecks and problems solved and adopted measures established in new agreements
- Check installations. The created checklists can be used for this (where possible) for purposes of the infrastructure intake (see the activity "Specifying the infrastructure intake", section 6.4.3).

Products
Operational workplace
Operational test environment
Installed test tools.

Techniques
Not applicable.

Tools
Not applicable.

6.4.3   Specifying the infrastructure intake

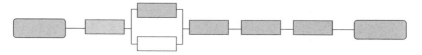

Aim
To specify the method whereby the intake of the infrastructure is carried out.

Method of operation
Because the infrastructure is often supplied by parties other than the test team and because it plays a very important role within the rest of the testing, it is important to designate a formal acceptance point. At this point, it will be determined whether the products will serve the intended purposes and whether they meet the previously set requirements. (It is a kind of acceptance test of the infrastructure.) This takes place by means of an intake: an activity in which, on the basis of a checklist, it is determined whether the workplace, the test environment and the test tool are functioning and whether they meet the previously set requirements.

The checklist is drawn up on the basis of the specifications of the various parts. It should be available before the end of the previous activity (realising the infrastructure), but preferably earlier, so that it can be used during the realisation for interim checks.

This activity bears a close relation to the activity of "Specification of the test object intake" in the Specification phase. There are situations in which certain aspects of the infrastructure can only be checked with the aid of the test object or an early or interim version thereof. For example, a release procedure for the test environment can only be checked with the test object. But the correct installation of a test tool for the automation of the execution, too, can only be checked with the test object.

Example

The following checks can be carried out for the workplace:
• Are the required PCs, printers, workplaces, telephone lines, routers, et cetera present and correctly installed?
• Is the required system software installed?
• Is the system software the right version?
The following can be carried out for the test environment:
• Has access to the test environment been provided?

• Has access to the application been provided?
• Has access to the database been provided?
• Has the database been filled with the correct data (e.g. a copy of production)?
• Have all the authorisations been provided?
The following checks can be carried out for the test tools:
• Are all the licences operational?
• Can the test tool be accessed from every workplace?
• Is the connection between test tool and test object operational?

Products
Checklist "Workplace intake"
Checklist "Test environment intake"
Checklist "Test tools intake"
Intake procedure.

Techniques
Not applicable.

Tools
Testware management tool.

6.4.4   Intake of the infrastructure

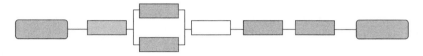

Aim
To carry out the intake as prepared in the preceding activity.

Method of operation
All the checks on the checklist, created during the preceding activity, are gone through. This determines whether the test environment, test tool and workplace function and whether they meet the previously set requirements. Any missing parts are reported to the stakeholders by means of a defects report. These parts should of course then be made available as quickly as possible. Missing parts in the test environment will have a delaying effect and have an impact on the entire project. The Execution phase is often on the critical path, and if it cannot start (because for example the test environment is not functioning), the entire project will be delayed. The intake should not be underestimated, and should be carried out as quickly as possible. The intake of the test environment is preferably carried out during the Specification phase. If this is not possible, then it should be done at the start of the Execution phase, at the latest. This may be the case if the test object is required and is only available at that time.

Products
Defects
Operational and usable workplace
Operational and usable test environment
Operational and usable test tool
Intake report.

Techniques
Not applicable.

Tools
Testware management tool
Defect management tool.

6.4.5   Maintaining the infrastructure

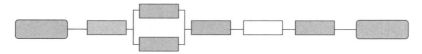

Aim
To keep the infrastructure (test environment, test tools and workplaces) available for the testers at a consistent level of quality.

Workplace method of operation
Maintaining the workplace, so that it is and remains available to the testers, is usually an activity that is organised as standard within other maintenance activities in an organisation. As regards the PC in the workplace, it is important that the usual maintenance organisations know that this is specially intended for the testers, since it can mean that other agreements apply concerning, for example, authorisations and prioritisation in problem solving.

Test tool method of operation
The test tool can be maintained within the test project by the testers who use it, but also by a separate maintenance department (e.g. a permanent test organisation). An important maintenance element is the regular checking for new versions of the test tool and then providing this to the users. Besides this, the management activities apply as described for the test environment and for the test tool.

Test environment method of operation
The supply of the test environment on an ongoing basis, so that the testers are able to carry out their test cases and analyse their findings, covers a range of activities. These take place during the Execution phase. Examples of these are:
- Solving bottlenecks
- Provision for logging
- Backup and restore
- Implementing changes
- Monitoring.

Further information on the maintenance of test environments and the associated management processes is contained in section 8.4 "Test environments".

Solving bottlenecks

The execution of test scripts may be delayed if problems occur in the test environment (e.g.: a batch program has not run). Since the execution of test scripts is often on the critical path of a project, it is important to give the highest priority to solving these bottlenecks.

> **Example**
>
> At a government institution, a project has a fixed deadline because the solution is related to a change in legislation that is to be implemented by a certain date. The Execution phase is on the critical path of this project and it is therefore in everyone's interest that this phase is not delayed. In consultation with the maintenance department, it is therefore agreed that the infrastructure that the testers use will be given a so-called "production" status. This means that the management department deals with bottlenecks experienced by the testers with the same priority as if it concerned the production environment. This is justified by the fact that, should the project not be completed on time, the legislation could not be implemented and so the primary process could no longer proceed. This separate status only applies during the test execution.

Provision for logging

Systems can provide information in the form of logging, which can be used in retrospect to check the actions that have been carried out. The logging is an important source of information for testers in the analysis of their findings. The provision of this information is therefore also an important activity. It may be decided to make it available on request, but another (less labour-intensive) variant is to give the testers themselves access to the logging.

Backup and restore

Particularly in respect of infrastructure used by testers, it is important to secure the data by means of regular backups. This may be for the purpose of securing starting situations and using them repeatedly for the test, but also of investigating particular defects. This concerns not only backups of the test environment, but also of test tools and the PCs in the workplace.

>
> Always test the backup and restore procedure before the test starts. The way to do this is to is to restore the backup immediately the first time it is created. This way the backup procedure and restore procedure are tested.

Implementing changes

During the project, the test environment is subject to changes owing to all kinds of internal and external causes, for example:

- Phased delivery and changes in the test environment
- Delivery or redelivery of (parts of) the test object
- New or changed procedures
- Changes in the simulation and system software
- Changes in the equipment, protocols, parameters, et cetera
- New or changed test tools
- Changes in the test files, tables, et cetera:
  - Conversion of test input files to a new format
  - Reorganisation of test files
  - Changes in nomenclature.

Changes in the test environment should only be implemented following permission from the test management. Depending on the nature and size of the change, this will be made known generally to the test team. A new intake will then take place in the test environment.

Tip
A pitfall in the planning is to assume that the installation of a new version of the test object takes no time. In a particular project, the first couple of versions took weeks because of the great complexity and instability of the entire test environment and test object. Later, this was optimised and subsequently never took more than a few days each time.

Monitoring
The situation can occasionally arise in which a defect requires further research and deeper technical knowledge than the tester has at his disposal. Assistance can be called upon and he can 'help to look' at a technical level (monitoring) at what happens in conjunction with certain actions.

Products
Operational and maintained test infrastructure
Defects test infrastructure.

Techniques
Not applicable.

Tools
Not applicable.

6.4.6 Preserving the infrastructure

Aim

The aim of this activity is the identification, updating and transferring of the infrastructure under maintenance, in such a way that it can be used again in future (re)tests. This activity is optional.

Method of operation

This activity starts simultaneously with the Completion phase and covers the following subactivities:
1. Selecting the infrastructure
2. Collecting and refining the infrastructure
3. Transferring the infrastructure.

1. Selecting the infrastructure
In consultation with the future maintenance department of the infrastructure, an inventory is drawn up of which parts are now actually used (the configuration) and what is 'worth' transferring. The decision should be made based on the consideration of what it costs to keep and maintain the infrastructure, and what it would cost to realise the infrastructure again at a later stage. Besides this, there is the possibility that certain software or hardware (such as parts of the test environment, but also certain test tools) are only of use during the initial phase of the testing and are no longer necessary. It is then a waste of effort taking this under maintenance. This identification can also clarify the difference between the specified infrastructure and the infrastructure actually used. There can be discrepancies here (certain software or hardware that was set up but never used) and this point of learning can be taken forward into the evaluation of the test process (see the activity "Evaluating the test process" in the Completion phase, section 6.8.1).

2. Collecting and refining the infrastructure
The description of the infrastructure in the "Detailed specification of the infrastructure" should be adapted to the configuration that is to be transferred. This is of essential importance, as otherwise everything will have to be created anew for future tests. It is important with this description to look carefully at the configuration of the workplaces. In this "Detailed specification of the infrastructure" a list is included containing the components that are transferred. Components may be licences, environment data, scripts, software, tools, registry files, hardware, accounts, databases, files, et cetera.

3. Transferring the infrastructure
Finally, the actual transfer of the infrastructure takes place. The configuration is transferred according to the adapted list in the document "Detailed specification of the infrastructure".

Products
Preserved test infrastructure.

Techniques
Not applicable.

Tools
Not applicable.

6.5   Preparation phase

Aim

To obtain, with the client's agreement, a test basis that is of sufficient quality for designing the test cases. In order to determine this, a testability review of the test basis is carried out during this phase, which will provide insight into the testability of the system.

> **Definition**
>
> Testability is the ease and speed with which characteristics of the system can be tested (following each adjustment).

Early defect detection

There is another reason for assessing or evaluating the test basis, apart from establishing its testability. Evaluation activities can reveal potentially expensive defects at an early stage of the development and test processes. The test basis forms the blueprint for the new system to be built. Anything that is not mentioned in the test basis is left to the development team to solve. The development team goes to work on developing the new information system on the basis of the system documentation, which may contain mistakes. If these are not found in time, it can lead to a lot of (often expensive) corrective work. The sooner a mistake is found in a development process, the simpler (and cheaper) it can be reworked [Boehm, 1981]. If, for example, a defect in a specification or requirement is not discovered until the execution of the acceptance test, the reworking costs are high. Not only must the software be amended, but also, for example, the technical and functional designs. In general, it appears that early defect detection makes savings of 50%-80% possible.

By assessing the test basis and detecting defects early, the quality of the test basis will increase.

> **Practical example**
> In the real-world examples below the testability review was carried out as an activity of evaluation:
> • A supplier of packages has achieved a return-on-investment of 10:1 through early testing of the designs. Because of this, €21.4 million is saved annually on project costs, and the average time-to-market has been reduced by 1.8 months.
> • A company in the telecommunications sector avoids 33 hours of reworking per defect by evaluating the code.

- A large computer manufacturer saves 20 hours of test effort and 82 hours of reworking for every hour spent on inspections.
- A multinational in the chemical sector spends 10 times less maintenance money on 400 inspected software products than on 400 non-inspected software products.

Context

While both the (definition of the) test basis and the agreed test strategy are specified in the test plan, the test basis is often not yet available at the time of creating the test plan. In the Preparation phase, it has to be investigated whether the test basis delivered corresponds with, and is usable for, the previously established agreements in the plan. If this does not appear to be the case, it may be necessary to adjust the plan, which can have both a negative and a positive influence on one or all of the money, time and quality aspects.

Negative influences are, for example:

- the lack of a definitive test basis
- a qualitatively inadequate test basis
- a test basis with more complex algorithms than expected.

Positive influences are, for example:

- a test basis with less complex algorithms than expected
- a test basis that anticipates the making of logical test cases (see tip).

Amending the plan is an activity from the "Control phase" (section 6.3) and is further explained there.

> **Tip**
>
> A government organisation decided to have the designers supplement the functional design with decision tables. The idea behind this was that the designers themselves knew the intention of the design better than the testers, who had to create the (logical) test cases based on the design. Since the testers were thus given a 'head start' and needed to investigate less, the organisation reduced the amount of time by 25% in the Specification phase.

Preconditions

The Preparation phase starts as early as possible following the consolidation of the test plan *and* after the consolidated test basis is made available (see "In more detail").

> **In more detail**
>
> The test basis is consolidated when the client indicates that enough activities have been carried out that guarantee the quality of the specifications and other information. Consolidation of the specifications is of great importance, since they form the basis for both the testers and the developers and may subsequently only be changed by means of formal change procedures. While, in principle, only the client may consolidate the test basis, situations are conceivable in which the test manager considers proceeding as though a test basis has been consolidated. For example, because the test manager doesn't want to hinder the progress of the test, or if testers are in danger of 'being freed up'. In making such a decision, it is important to make clear agreements on this with the client. There is a good chance that the test basis will change, with the possible consequence that previously created test designs have to be amended. This can lead to extra costs and extension of the timeline. It should be established in the agreements with the client how this is to be dealt with, so that there is no need for discussion in retrospect.

Method of operation

Once the test basis has been put at the disposal of the test team, a start is made on its testability review. It is first examined whether the summarised information, of which the test basis consists, is still correct. If necessary, it is brought up to date in consultation with the client. During this examination, it may appear that all of the information is not yet available for the tester, or perhaps will not be arriving at all. In such a situation, a way must be found of obtaining the missing information.

When the test basis is clear, this is assessed from the testing perspective for e.g. consistency, understandability and completeness. Subsequently, on the basis of checklists, an assessment is made as to the extent to which the established test strategy and associated test (design) techniques are applicable. The conclusions are documented in a testability review report and discussed with the client. The results of this report may give rise to adjustments to the test basis, the test strategy and the test techniques to be employed.

> **Tip**
>
> **Synergy between evaluation and development / testing process**
> In some organisations, design specifications are structurally evaluated before a subsequent development phase is started. By making the various points of focus from the Preparation phase part of such an evaluation, a satisfactory degree of synergy is created between the structural evaluation and the test activities from the Preparation phase. In this situation, one or more members of the test team participate in the evaluation process. They take responsibility for the aspect of testability in relation to the design specifications. The testers can also take the initiative of introducing a

structural evaluation process (requirements being, for example, set out in a SMART[1] framework), using evaluation techniques as described in Chapter 15 "Evaluation techniques". Evaluation then becomes an integral part of the test approach. In the execution of the evaluation activities, use can of course be made of the various checklists as described in the activity "Creating checklists" (section 6.5.2).

Roles / responsibilities

The testability review report is created by the test manager or test coordinator. All the other activities can be carried out by any of the test team members. The report is intended for the commissioner of the test (the client).

Activities

The Preparation phase consists of the following activities:

1. Collection of the test basis
2. Creating checklists
3. Assessing the test basis
4. Creating the testability review report.

The diagram below depicts the sequence and dependencies between the various activities (figure 6.16):

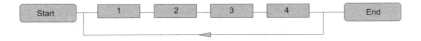

Figure 6.16: Preparation phase

---

[1] SMART: S=Specific, M=Measurable, A=Attainable, R=Realistic T=Time-based

6.5.1 Collection of the test basis

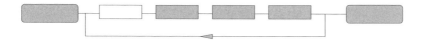

Aim
The collection of, the definitive, if necessary overhauled, test basis is established in consultation with the client.

Method of operation
The definition of the relevant information for the execution of the test is in principle already established in the test plan (e.g. functional and technical designs, requirements, use cases, user manuals, interview reports, prototype, and reference system). However, it is possible that, in respect of the exit information, changes have taken place. The test plan should then be amended and the identification of the information reviewed. Finally, the various parts of the test basis are actually collected. Eventually, of course, the test team should have the correct (version of the) test basis at its disposal.

A point to bear in mind here is that the test basis does not always have to be present, complete, up to date, or established in documentation. A test basis often appears to be incomplete because, for example, non-functional requirements have not been specified, while they are nevertheless considered to be risk-related. By alerting the project to this, a (timely) trigger is created for bringing it to attention.

Alternative test basis
If test basis problems do indeed arise, some solutions obtained from practice for obtaining an alternative test basis are listed below:

- Present system in production as reference system
  Supposing the system documentation is missing, obsolete or incomplete in a conversion or migration project, for example. The creating, supplementing or updating of this documentation normally does not belong within the scope of the project. In such a situation, the present production version of the system is used as test basis. This is a particularly good alternative in situations that involve few or no changes to the functional operation of the system, or if the changes are well documented.

- Prototype as test basis
  In a situation that does not accord high priority to the production of system documents, which are possibly only to be delivered at the end of the project, a prototype is sometimes made. This occurs, for example, with Rapid Application Development or variant of this (including SP, DSDM

and RUP). Since the prototype is often made in co-operation with the user, this can also be used as the test basis.

■ Information session
  During, for example, maintenance operations, it often appears that neither the system in production nor the changes to it have been well documented. The organisation of information sessions for everyone involved (developers, designers, users, administrators, etc.) is a good way of clarifying both the operation of particular system parts and the changes to be implemented. The information obtained during such a session can be used as a test basis.

■ System documentation from the last-but-one iteration as a test basis
  With iterative and incremental system development approaches, there is a possibility that the system documentation will only become available to the tester at a later stage. In a situation where it is not permissible to change the system documentation during the last iteration, the test basis is made available to the tester at the end of the last-but-one iteration. In the situation where it is permissible to change the system documentation during the last iteration, it may be considered whether to use the system documentation from the last-but-one iteration as the test basis (often more than 80% ready). At the end of the last iteration, the – often small – changes to the system documentation have to be processed in the test cases by the tester.

An important point in connection with the above means of obtaining an alternative test basis is that this is seen by the client (and any other stakeholders) as *the* test basis. However, a test basis obtained in this manner will seldom be approved or consolidated. It is therefore important for the client and the tester to be aware of the risks that this involves. It is advisable not only to inventory these risks, but also to establish the associated countermeasures. For example, who has the 'deciding vote' if it appears that the realised functionality of a (sub)system differs from expectations based on the alternative test basis?

Occasionally, so little information is present that even establishing an alternative test basis is impossible. In such a situation, other sources of information may be resorted to, and while they cannot be used as an alternative test basis, they are perfectly usable for, for example, deriving logical test cases (see tips on "Absence of test basis").

Tips

Absence of test basis
If no test basis is present, the tester should go in search of other sources of information that can serve as a basis for creating test cases. Bach, Whittaker and Kaner have devised an approach for this:

- HICCUPP [Bach, 2003]

  Information for creating test cases may be obtained, for example, from norms and standards, memos, user manuals, interviews, advertisements or rival products. Bach has set this out in his HICCUPP approach:

  History. Is the present operation of the software consistent with the previous operation

  Image. Is the operation of the software consistent with the image of the organisation?

  Comparable. Is the operation of the software consistent with that of other comparable products?

  Claims. Is the operation of the software consistent with how people say it should operate

  User expectations. Is the operation of the software consistent with what we (the testers) think the user wants?

  Product. Is the operation of specific software components consistent with comparable software components within the product?

  Purpose. Is the operation of the software consistent with the apparent aim of the software?

- 18 Attacks, by Whittaker and Jorgenson [Whittaker, 2000]

  Some software defects are so trivial that good standard tests (attacks) can be defined for them. The 18 attacks of Whittaker and Jorgenson listed below can form an excellent basis for creating tests or be used to supplement existing tests:

  User interface (input)

  1. Generate input that will provoke all the error messages.
  2. Generate input that will require all the default values to be entered
  3. Try to enter all the permitted symbols and data types
  4. Enter too many symbols
  5. Find correlations between input fields and test combinations of their values
  6. Enter the same data repeatedly.

  User interface (output)

  7. Try every possible output for every input
  8. Try to cause incorrect output.
  9. Try to change characteristics/values of the output.
  10. Refresh the screen

  Stored data

  11. Enter data from every possible starting point.
  12. Try to save too many or too few characters in the database.
  13. Try to find alternative ways of changing internal data restrictions.

  Calculations

  14. Try out incorrect operand and operator combinations.
  15. Try to get a calculation module to call itself.
  16. Try to make the resulting values too high or too low.
  17. Try to find functions that make use of the same data.

  System interface (media)

  18a. Make all the storage space unavailable.
  18b. Make the system busy or unavailable.

18c. Damage the system.
System interface (files)
18d. Allocate an incorrect file name.
18e. Change the permissions (including reading and writing permissions) of a file.
18f. Change the content of a file, or corrupt it.

- Kaner's 480 bugs [Kaner, 1999]
Kaner has created a list of common software defects. This list can be used to find the same or similar defects in the software under test. Alternatively, the list can be used in a more general sense for:
Gathering test ideas
Investigate whether a defect on the list could arise in the software under test. If this is theoretically possible, consider how you might find it. Then create test cases (or not) depending on the damage the defect could cause in production.
Test design review
Select a few test situations from the test design and find a possible defect from the list for each test situation. Then examine, for each possible defect, whether it could occur in the software under test and whether it would then be found by the test cases created
Wider perspective
Check the list for types of defects that are often overlooked (out-of-the-box thinking).
Training
Show new testers what can go wrong and have them create test cases with which these defects can be found.

When using one or more of the approaches mentioned with a view to arriving at an alternative test basis, or a basis for deriving test cases, the tester would do well to bear in mind that it is not the tester's job to create the test basis. The tester assesses and uses the test basis exclusively for testing purposes. The creation of system documents was, is and remains the responsibility of e.g. the project or the development department. The tester should avoid sitting in the place of the designer. This means that the test basis that is obtained from one of the above-mentioned approaches should always be agreed with all the stakeholders, on the one hand to confirm the way the system should function and/or be built, and on the other hand to confirm agreement that this is indeed the alternative test basis against which testing is to be carried out, or the basis from which test cases should be derived.

Products
Consolidated test basis.

Techniques
HICCUPP [Bach, 2003]
18 Attacks by Whittaker and Jorgenson [Whittaker, 2000]
Kaner's 480 Bugs [Kaner, 1999].

Tools
Not applicable.

6.5.2   Creating checklists

Aim
The checklists are created, on the basis of the test strategy laid down in the test plan, for the various part objects/characteristics under test. These checklists form a guide in assessing the test basis.

Method of operation
With the aid of checklists, the test basis is checked for testability. During this activity, the checklists needed for the testing are created. Depending on the selected test design techniques, test types, information sources that determine the test basis and the part objects/characteristics under test, one or more checklists should be created (see also the tip "Test design techniques in the absence of a test basis" below). Each checklist should indicate which specific verification aspects play a role in the testability review. If you wish to avoid duplicating work on identical parts of the test basis during the evaluation, the separate checklists could be consolidated into one checklist. In creating the checklist, use could be made of the general checklist of "test design techniques", to be found at www.tmap.net.

Partly owing to the diversity of test design techniques and information sources that determine the test basis, it is not possible to create one general checklist per part object/characteristic. Therefore, checklists should be created specific to the situation per organisation and per project. It is advisable always to create a checklist, as in practice it often appears that too much attention is paid to the use of standards and correct spelling, or even to these aspects alone. This can be a cause of friction among the various people involved.

> **Tip**
>
> **Test design techniques in the absence of a test basis**
> The test plan contains, among other things, a summary of the information of which the test basis consists, as well as the test strategy. However, if it appears that the agreed (documented) test basis is partly or entirely lacking, it may be that the testing has to be carried out on the basis of different (non-documented) information. In that case, not all the test design techniques are suitable. Some test design techniques that are often suitable in such a situation are:
> - The data combination test (DCoT), also known as the "classification tree method" (CTM)
> - Error guessing
> - Exploratory testing
> - Boundary value analysis
> - Checklist.
>
> For notes on these test design techniques and the use of them, refer to Chapter 14 "Test design techniques".

Products
Various checklists or one consolidated checklist for assessing the test basis.

Techniques
Checklist "Test design techniques" (www.tmap.net).

Tools
Not applicable.

6.5.3   Assessing the test basis

Aim
To establish the testability of the test basis. Testability here means completeness, consistency, accessibility and translatability into test cases.

Method of operation
The test basis is assessed using evaluation techniques and the previously created checklist(s) to obtain insight into the applicability of the established test strategy and related test design techniques. If it appears that the test basis falls short, it is of course important to report this to the supplier of the test basis via the client as quickly as possible. This party can then take responsibility for clarifying and/or filling in the gaps. The registration and flagging of these defects in the test basis take place by means of the procedures established in section 6.2.12 "Organising the management".

Products
Test basis defects.

Techniques
Checklist for assessing the test basis (product from section 6.5.2).
Evaluation techniques (Chapter 15).

Tools
Defect management tool.

6.5.4 Creating the testability review report

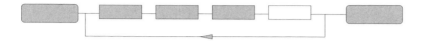

Aim
The testability review report:
- provides feedback on the quality of the test basis and its impact on the planned test programme
- discusses the weak spots in the system design timely
- obtains information on project risks.

Method of operation
A testability review report is created based on the individual test basis defects. This report supplies a general summary in respect of the quality, or testability, of the test basis. Any consequences of inadequate quality should also be described. Discrepancies in respect of the summarised information in the test plan of which the test basis consists and the agreed test strategy are also described. This can give rise to adjustment to the plan in connection with, for example, the strategy to be followed and the test techniques to be employed. For further explanation of this, refer to the "Control phase" (section 6.3).

The testability review report could consist of, for example, the following sections:
- Formulation of the assignment
  An identification of the original (or, if necessary, amended) test basis and a description of the client and the contractor.
- Conclusion
  The final conclusion in respect of the testability of the examined test basis and any related consequences or risks: is the test basis of sufficient quality to justify starting on specifying tests as established in the (amended) test strategy?
- Recommendations
  Recommendations in respect of the assessed test basis and any structural recommendations with an eye to producing a better test basis in the future.
- Defects
  The defects found are described in detail or reference is made to the associated defects forms.
- Appendices
  The checklists used.

Products
Testability review report.

Techniques
Not applicable.

Tools
Not applicable.

6.6   Specification Phase

Aim

During the Specification phase, the required tests and starting points are specified. The aim is to have as much as possible prepared, in order to be able to run the test as quickly as possible when the developers deliver the test object.

Context

This phase begins when the testability review has been carried out on the test basis and the defects in it have been processed as far as possible. The test specification runs in parallel with the completion of the software (or parameterisation, in the case of packages). The software is the primary product of the development process and is usually also on the critical path of the process. The focus of the (project) management is therefore upon this. The test specification is only of indirect interest, but this changes at the point when the software is transferred for the test execution and the attention of the (project) management is then drawn to it. The test team has to be ready then to start the test execution. The test specification is aimed at preparing as much as possible so that the test execution can be performed as fast as possible and be on the critical path for as short a period as possible. The test manager has to be aware of this. He should translate, as far as possible, the signals given by the test specification problems into consequences (in terms of time, finance and quality) for future test execution and the total productive process.

Preconditions

The following preconditions should be met before the Specification phase can be started:

- The test basis is available and placed under configuration management
- Defects from the testability review have been processed.

Method of operation

During the Specification phase, the testers specify the required tests per test unit. This is done by creating checklists or specifying test cases on the basis of the allocated test design techniques. In the latter case, the testers also create test scripts, in which the test cases are put into an efficiently executable sequence. On this basis, and partly in parallel with it, the testers define one or more central starting points for the testing that the test cases can use. This may be a copy of production or a central base table listing. A special form of a test to be specified is the test object intake. This test should check in the Execution phase whether the test object is sufficiently testable for a meaningful and efficient test execution.

Roles/responsibilities

The activities in the Specification phase are carried out by the testers.

Activities

Within the Specification phase, the following activities are distinguished:
1. Creating test specifications
2. Defining central starting point(s)
3. Specifying the test object intake.

The diagram below shows the sequence and the dependencies between the various activities. Activities 1 and 2 run in parallel, but mutually influence each other.

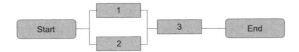

Figure 6.17: Specification Phase

6.6.1   Creating test specifications

Aim
The creation of the test specifications per test unit.

Method of operation
The testers specify the necessary tests for the test units in the test plan. After completion, the test specifications are placed under configuration management.

Definition

A test unit is a collection of processes, transactions and/or functions that are tested collectively.

Depending on the test type and test technique selected for the test unit, this activity may consist of anything from the creation of a checklist to the design and specification of test cases according to a test design technique or to the design of a test with other techniques. The possibilities are further explained below. Explanations are also given of a scalable regression test and of the relationship between this phase and exploratory testing.

In the course of this activity, problems may arise with the test basis. Roughly, these can be categorised as follows:

- Defects
  As with the testability review, the testers may find shortcomings and/or ambiguities in the test basis. The testers create a defect report on this. Via the defects procedure, it is passed to the test basis supplier, who can then solve it

- Absence of test basis
  If the testability review has been insufficiently executed, it may only appear at this stage that certain parts of the test basis are missing or not detailed enough, so that they are not, or not sufficiently, testable. The same types of measures as adopted with the testability review may be considered; see section 6.5 "Preparation Phase".

Tip

With iterative or agile system development, the test basis is often not 100% complete at the start of the iteration, but is completed during the iteration. Besides the above-mentioned measures, it is advisable to carry out a minimal testability review with each addition to the test basis before specifying tests based on the addition.

■ Unstable test basis
  If the supplier of the test basis makes regular changes to it, for example because of defects or change proposals, this makes for an unstable test basis. With every change, the testers have to examine the relevant test specifications to see whether adjustments are necessary. These reworking operations are always difficult to estimate in advance. The test manager is well advised to arrange a certain level of reserve budget and time for this when creating the test plan. If these are exceeded, the project management should be notified that more time and finances are required (see also section 6.3 "Control Phase"). Other possible measures are to defer the specifying of the tests for the unstable parts in the plan or to create the logical test cases, but to delay the physical makeup of them until the test basis is (more) stable.

Test design techniques

Test design techniques are employed in the creation of the test cases (see Chapter 14). They enable the testers to derive test cases that achieve a particular coverage from a test basis in a clear, transferable and reproducible manner. A test case consists of a description of the initial situation, the test action and the predicted result. The specifying of test cases according to a test design technique follows the following general steps:
1. Identifying test situations
2. Creating logical test cases
3. Creating physical test cases
4. Establishing the starting point
5. Creating the test script.

The concepts in these steps are explained in more detail in section 14.2.1 "Test situation, test case and test script", including examples. Further explanation of the steps themselves is given below.

A choice has to be made in the establishment of the result of these steps, which collectively form the test specification. Generally, two options are possible. The first is to put everything together in one file, usually a Word document or spreadsheet. The second is to make a split in the design steps (identifying test situations and creating logical test cases) and the steps required for test execution (the rest, resulting in the script). The advantage of the first is that maintenance on the test cases is made easier, since everything is together. The second option does not have this advantage, but does have two others. The testing operative (e.g. a user who has to carry out the test but who has not designed it) is not distracted by the design steps and only sees the information that is necessary to carry out the test. The second advantage is that the information required for the execution can be documented in a form other than word processing or spreadsheet, such as a testware management tool or a database or directly in a tool for automated test execution.

1. Identifying test situations

Each test design technique is aimed at achieving a certain coverage in order to find particular types of defects. In this, the first step is to distinguish the situations in the test basis that are to be tested. The test basis consists of, for example, the system requirements, the functional design, the user manual and/or the administrative procedures. This test basis is gone through and each situation to be tested is identified in it. The test design technique prescribes, as regards situations to be tested, for example that the true and false situation is tested in respect of every condition, or that each input field is tested with a valid and invalid input value. Since the distinguishing of test situations is different for every test design technique, this step contains the biggest differences between the various test design techniques.

In more detail

Converting the test basis

In some cases, the test basis is not directly suitable for the selected test design technique, and an extra conversion operation has to be carried out. For example, a data cycle test requires a CRUD matrix and the decision tables technique requires decision tables. If these are not available, they can sometimes be derived from the available type of test basis. Apart from the question of whether the chosen test design technique is the right one (for sometimes there is little choice), there is also the question of who should perform this conversion. Ideally, it should be the designers. However, if the testers are the only ones requesting this addition, there is little chance of the designers taking it upon themselves. The other possibility is that the testers do it themselves. In this, they should take care that they only convert and do not add any information. In the latter case, they would be adding to the design themselves, and that is not the testers' job.

2. Creating logical test cases

In principle, a test case goes through the relevant part of the test object (e.g. a function) from beginning to end, covering one or more test situations in doing so.

The logical test cases clearly demonstrate:

- What the test situations are
- That all the defined test situations have been covered by test cases.

The creation of logical test cases may be skipped if the test situations can be directly executed and assessed one by one.

3. Creating physical test cases

In practical terms, the physical test case describes what needs to be done, in which the three basic elements of a test case are recognisable: initial situation, action and predicted result. In the physical makeup, each situation to be tested, or logical test case, is completed with as much detail as possible, so that later, during the test execution, the work can be performed as efficiently as possible. Obviously, the choice of physical makeup is based on the preceding steps, but it is also influenced by agreements on, for example, the use of a certain (central) starting point, e.g. a (blind) copy of the production database. It should also be agreed that the various tests should not be able to disrupt each other during the execution, for example because different test cases use the same data (competition). If one test case is "Remove order lines" while the other is "Change order lines", there is a strong chance that the predicted and justifiable results will not be realised. A solution is, for example, to agree particular series of numbers for the order rules for the sake of the testing of various functions (see also section 6.6.2.). In this connection, it is also advisable to create no dependencies between test cases. If the execution of one test case is conditional for the execution of another, the failure of the first test case will also mean that the second test case cannot be executed. Only when the defect that is blocking the first test case is solved can the second test case be executed. If this again results in a defect found, it can lead to extra and unnecessary reworking operations.

Section 14.2.1 "Test situation, test case and test script" contains a number of considerations as to how far the tester should go in the physical makeup of test cases.

4. Establishing the starting point

To be able to execute a test case, an initial situation is necessary. Initial situations often contain the same data for several test cases. Such data are therefore included in a so-called starting point for the entire test and not separated for each test case. This starting point is made ready prior to the test execution. A step further is where the starting points for various tests may also show a (big) overlap. For that reason, it is often a case of one or more central starting points applying to several tests. This is described extensively in section 6.6.2.

5. Creating the test script

As a last step, one or more test scripts are produced. In this, the test actions and checks of the physical test cases are described in a sequence that best suits test execution. In this, the test cases should not be able to disrupt each other. The test script as such is the stepped plan for the test execution and also offers the possibility of progress monitoring. The physical test cases and the starting points naturally form the basis for the creation of the test script.

Considerations for combining test cases in a single script are described in section 14.2.1.

The generic content list of a script is as follows:

- Unique identity, consisting of:
  - Version
  - Creator
  - Test basis, including version.
- Preparing the starting point
  For example, by setting the system date, restoring a particular backup and adding particular test data
- Test actions and verification
  The physical test cases in a sequence suitable for execution, with the necessary initial situation for each test case, action and result verification. When an appropriate starting point is established, nothing more is usually required to be done in respect of the initial situation
- Cleaning up the environment
  Ensure that the results of the executed test are cleaned up if necessary so that they do not get in the way of other testers (remember, for example, to restore the system date).

The above says nothing about how the script is stored, for example in a Word document, spreadsheet, automated test or a database. Section 14.2.1 supplies a number of possibilities and considerations.

In some cases, the support of tools is possible, for example, tools for generating test data for deriving test cases, or even model-based test tools (see section 8.5.3 "Types of test tools").

Checklists

Besides the specifying of test cases, many tests take place with the aid of checklists. These are used with simple functional tests, but also for the static testing of e.g. maintainability, manageability, user-friendliness or security. While a checklist is usually specific to the situation, testers often use a general checklist as a basis and make specific adjustments to this. The general checklists may be supplied from within the organisation (by the test department) or from the literature or via the Internet. Various examples of checklists for testing certain quality characteristics can be found at www.tmap. net. The creation (and execution) of a checklist requires a competent tester with the necessary knowledge of the object part or characteristic under test. It is therefore advisable to have the checklist reviewed.

Other techniques

Apart from the specifying of test cases according to test design techniques and the creation of checklists, other techniques are possible that do not fall into either of the above categories. These techniques mainly apply to the testing of quality characteristics, such as portability, usability, performance and security. Examples of these are provided in section 10.3 "Test types".

Constructing and managing scalable regression tests

In more detail

In practice, regression tests are often inadequately set up. In this section, an approach is described for the constructing, using and managing of regression tests based on the Test Cube principle [Test Cube, 2006]. In this, connected principles are described, which make it possible to:
• Specify test cases and execute them based on priorities
• Report quickly and adequately on the progress of test specification and/or test execution
• Plan and estimate tests accurately
• Create fast and variable regression tests
• Process changes in the test object easily into the test.

The principle behind the Test Cube is that, per test case, a collection of supplementary data is established: the test cases within the test are 'classified'. With the aid of these classifications, selections can be made through all kinds of cross-sectioned subsets of test cases from the entire test.
Examples of classifications are:
• Application
• Object part
• Function
• Risk category
• Process (part)
• Release
• Requirement
• Transaction
• Depth of testing.

The right selection of classifications and the correct classification of the test cases will determine the usability of this concept. Essential in this is the classification according to depth of testing. This classification indicates the 'weight' of the test case in the test and makes it possible to create a risk-based regression test of variable depth.
The application of these depth-of-testing categories in the creation of regression tests is as follows (using three categories):
• By only selecting the test cases of an object part from category 1, a small regression test is created. This subset is used for an object part to which no amendments have been made (or for a pretest on a new or radically changed object part)
• The test cases from category 2 (includes category 1) deliver a normal regression test, for example for an object part in which amendments have been made

• The test cases from category 3 (includes categories 1 and 2) cover the entire object part and are applied to the new or radically changed object parts.

No requirements are set as regards the degree of detail in which the test cases are specified. If test cases are expected to be executed by testers who have no domain knowledge, the test cases should be written in more detail.

The concept only sets one specific requirement of its own in respect of the test cases, and that is that they should be independent of each other, as described for the creation of the physical test cases. This is the so-called independence principle of the concept. It should also be possible to execute the test cases in parallel with each other. Test cases that require exclusive use of the test environment for a specific period hamper the execution of other test cases. This in turn hampers the plans for the timeframe of the testing process.

Application of this concept facilitates measurement of the size of the (regression) test and associated activities in the test process.

As with the testware in general, careful consideration should be given here to when, how and by whom this test can be kept current.

For further explanation, refer to the relevant white paper [TestCube, 2006].

Session-based exploratory testing

In more detail

While exploratory testing (ET) is discussed in more detail in Chapter 14, it is actually not purely a test design technique. With ET, the tester makes decisions during the test execution as to which test he is going to execute. He designs a test on the spot, using his knowledge of test design techniques, without documenting them. As such, ET has no place in the Specification phase, since everything takes place during test execution. The reason we are paying attention to it here is that, in order to make ET more manageable, it is often organised in the form of sessions with clear test goals that can be completed in a few hours. These test goals are known as test charters. While the list of test charters is dynamic, the testers are well advised to compile an initial list of test charters prior to the Execution phase.
For further information on ET and test charters, refer to section 14.4.6.

Products
Test basis defects
Test specifications (checklists, test cases, test scripts)

Techniques

Test design techniques (Chapter 14)
Checklists for various quality characteristics, www.tmap.net.

Tools

Defect management tool
Test design tool
Model-based testing tool
Testware management tool
Automated test execution tool
Performance, load and stress test tool.

6.6.2　Defining central starting point(s)

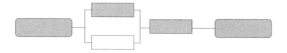

Aim

The defining of one or more central starting points from which the testers can obtain data for their test specifications.

Method of operation

A good starting point is of essential importance for the sake of being able to (re)test. This will contain everything necessary to prepare the test object and the test environment before starting with the test cases in the test script. This involves not only the test data required for the processing, but also the condition in which the system and its environment should be. It relates to, for example, the setting of a certain system date or the running of certain weekly and monthly batches that put the system into a particular condition.

In practice, incorrect starting points appear to be a significant source of problems for the testing. To avoid testing using the wrong starting points during the test execution, it should be considered at an early stage how these are to be constructed and which process is to be employed in using them. If this is not done, the following problems may arise:

- Non-reproducible test results
  If a test script is executed twice on the same version of the test object and the results vary, this may be the result of divergent test data in the starting point. Extra data may have been added to or removed from the starting point for other tests.
- Deteriorating starting point
  During the test execution, test data are used and amended. New data come into the system; existing data are amended or perhaps even removed. If no process exists to manage the starting point, nothing is known regarding its quality.
- Testing gets increasingly expensive
  If the starting point is of poor quality and is not documented anywhere, the testers are obliged to make increasing efforts (in seeking or creating test data) for the execution of the test cases. Moreover, the risk of mistakes on the part of the tester increases. This will increase further in time, as the starting point becomes increasingly less well known and therefore poorer.
- Insufficient information on defects causes delay
  The starting point takes an important place in the reporting of a defect. It clarifies a defect. If this starting point is not known during the analysis of

the defect, delay will result. Developers themselves have to go in search of the original starting point or have to ask the tester for clarification.

In the test specifications, the necessary starting point is specified per test script. To avoid redundancy and to restrict the number of physical files needed, one or more central starting points are defined that the testers can use in the creation of their test cases.

The creation of central starting points can take place in parallel with the setting up of the test specifications and is often an iterative process. Often, a tester will start with a central starting point by, for example, proposing the contents of master files. Master files are data that drive the system, but are not part of the primary data processing. Examples are discount tables, tax percentages, postcode tables, product types and customer types. A subsequent step may be to propose an initial content of primary data, e.g. a number of customers, products, orders and invoices. It may be decided to define several central starting points, if this appears to be useful in specifying the tests. The difference may be the type of data, e.g. the one central starting point with all kinds of variations in customers, and the other with all kinds of variations in orders. Another possibility is a difference in time. For example, a central starting point could be defined just before the year's end and just before disbursement of holiday pay, since these are significant testing points.

In addition, all kinds of starting points emerge in the creation of the test specifications, usually one per test script. The tester who manages the central starting point will consult on this with the tester of the starting point of the script as regards which data are suitable for adding to the central starting point. In this, the following criteria, for example, could be used:
- Can other testers reuse (part of) the starting point of the test script?
- Does the starting point of the script conflict with the (consistency of) the central starting point?
- Can including the starting point of the script in the central starting point disrupt other tests?
- Will including the starting point of the script in the central starting point lead to efficiency benefits in the execution of the script?

There are various possibilities for loading the central starting point with test data. These are described later in the book.

The description of the central starting points is created in accordance with the established norms and standards for testware and taken under configuration management after completion.

Naming test data

A point of focus when creating your own physical test data is the business of naming. It may be decided to name the data similar to those in production. In that case, realistic (although fictional) names are given to e.g. test customers, test addresses, test codes, test products, etc.

It may also be decided to give the data a name that is relevant to the test, for example by including the test-case number, test unit, object part or test goal in the name. This will also help with the solving of defects and transfer to other testers.

The third option is to generate meaningless names. For the foregoing example of test customers, then, these would be:
Person1
Person2
Person3
Person4
Etc.

This last option saves time in searching for and creating realistic or test-related names, but also involves a risk. It may cause a certain functionality or other characteristic of the system to respond differently. Examples are the operation of the sorting algorithm (which is now fairly simple and therefore cannot be extensively tested), long names of individuals or letters with accents. Another example is performance. On a table with 1,000 fictitious names that are numbered consecutively, the database management system might treat them differently from a table with 1,000 fictional names. The so-called index on a table may be differently constituted, which may be detrimental to performance.

Entering test data

There is a choice of three possibilities for the entering of test data:
1. Entering through regular system functions
2. Entering through separate front-end software
3. Use of production data.

1. Entering through regular system functions
Entering test data through regular system functions has the disadvantage that those functions themselves have often not been exhaustively tested and that the data entered therefore need to be thoroughly checked. The advantage is that during the accumulation of the files, the regular functions are implicitly tested simultaneously and the consistency between the data is guaranteed. A condition, however, is that the input functions need to be delivered first. This should be agreed in advance with the supplier of the software.

2. Entering through separate front-end software
Entering test data through separate front-end software and test files has the risk that the test environment will contain inconsistent or non-permitted situations, since there was no check on the input. This means that technical support is required with the accumulation and, of course, tested front-end software must be available. The advantage is that the files can be accumulated relatively quickly.

In more detail

Working with 0 data, 0 scripts and 0 files

0 Data are test data that are initially required for the execution of the test. 0 Data can take many forms. It can consist of, for example, persons with a name, address and other features that are used in various test cases. It can also be the users who are permitted to use the system (the testers). Another form again is the data in so-called master tables. It is important to identify and describe the required 0 data in the specification of the test cases.

0 Scripts are test scripts with which the 0 data is placed in the system. This takes place via the regular system functions, with the advantage that the functions of the system concerned are already being tested. An added advantage is the clarity of the starting point/data (0 scripts are executed on an empty database). 0 Scripts are executed first, and therefore, with the execution, the tester can gain an initial impression of the quality of the test object.

A condition for working with 0 scripts is of course that the functions required for inputting 0 data are built first. If that is not the case, it may be decided to work with so-called **0 files**. These files contain the 0 data and can be read into the database direct via separate front-end software (e.g. based on SQL).

---

3. Use of production data
The use of production data as test data has the advantage that testing can be done with a lot of data, that the files can be built up quickly and that any conversion software is tested implicitly. A disadvantage is that these data show little variation and it can mean a lot of searching for the right variation in starting point data in a test case. Another disadvantage is that it is not always permitted to work with production data (because of privacy legislation or openness to fraud). This makes it necessary to make identifying data unrecognisable. In some cases, a production copy is not frozen for the test, but a new copy is periodically placed in the test environment. The disadvantage of this is that the tests are not directly repeatable, because the production data of each copy are different each time, so that the test result predictions are no longer correct.

Tip

A variant on obtaining test data from production is to have test data supplied by users. No one knows the system and associated data better than they do, including the 'difficult' cases. Ask each user for a number of difficult cases in the form of test data. This can be done by having the user himself take his place behind the test object and input these cases. Another possibility is to copy the specific cases from production and put them into the test environment.

Aside from planning and budget difficulties, the first alternative, entering test data through regular system functions, is preferable. If the test team has permission to obtain test files from production, it is also possible to combine the three alternatives. Choose a collection of production data that, for example, contain a particular type of information (customer, order, invoice, etc.). This subset is loaded into the test environment (retaining consistency among the various data). Subsequently, with the aid of regular system functions, changes are made to these data to create the desired starting point.

In more detail

Test data in data-warehouse testing
A data warehouse can be generally split into two groups of programs:
• The extraction and conversion programs for filling the data warehouse
• The reporting programs for obtaining information from the data warehouse.

While it is preferable to use separate test data for testing individual extraction and conversion programs, production data are inclined to be used with integral testing of the reporting programs. The reason for this is that the creation of a consistent set of fictional test data is demanding and with a set of production data, this consistency is almost automatically guaranteed. Besides, a big advantage is that a user can assess the outcome of a report more easily when using real production data.

Disadvantages of using production data in testing a data warehouse, however, are:
• The difficulty of making exact output predictions, since it is difficult to find out what the input was
• The confidentiality associated with some data. In practice, this means that the use of production data is not possible, or only after application of scrambling techniques (depersonalisation, making data unrecognisable)
• The continually changing situation: the production data of today are different from those of a week ago, which hampers retesting.

This last disadvantage can be helped by suspending the daily/weekly reloading of data, so that the same starting point can always be used. An applied simplification is not taking the entire production files, but a selection of them. However, this requires focus (and time) for the mutual consistency of the data.

Delta test1

As an addition to this, the following procedure may be gone through:

- Take a subset of production data and call this X
- Run subset X in its entirety through the data warehouse and record the results
- Now add to subset X a number of self-created test cases and call this set X+1.
- Run subset X+1, too, in its entirety through the data warehouse
- The results of X+1 can be predicted by adding to the results of X the same self-created test cases
- Then add test cases to subset X+1 and call this X+2
- Run subset X+2 in its entirety through the data warehouse
- The results of X+2 can be predicted by adding the self-created test cases to the results of X+1 (this second run is useful for checking changes in time).

Delta test2

The following is a somewhat simpler variant of the above:

- Empty the database(s) of the delivering systems
- Put a number of self-specified test cases into these systems
- Run the extraction and check the result in the data warehouse
- Now put the same test cases as a kind of regression test into the full database(s) of the delivering systems
- Run the extraction and check the result (of the test cases) in the data warehouse.

Example

For a test process in a big data warehouse, the following test files are used as test data:

- The small test set: this is as small a test file as possible, with which the, possibly obvious, functional problems in the use of the prototype are searched for effectively. This test set is used as the first test after the development or reworking of the prototype and with all the other tests to quickly obtain an impression
- The 1,000-records test file is used for the functional acceptance test and consists of around 1,000 records from a daily file. The daily file that is used for this should concern a day in which as many (problem-generating) different cases occur. The choice of this is determined together with the client
- The 5% (or X%) test set is a representative sample compiled by the client from the source files for the third increment
- The 'daily files' test set consists of a complete daily file. The daily file that is used for this should concern a day in which as many (problem-generating) different cases as possible occur. The choice of this is determined together with the client. The execution of a weekly process in order to check whether starting status + mutations = final status is an important point of focus here. Preliminary dates of Wednesday 1 March, Thursday 2 March and Friday 3 March are used, after which a weekly process is run to check this.

Use of starting points during the test

The use of the central starting point during the test should be considered in advance. This chiefly concerns the choice between:

1. The cumulative construction of the central starting point (unstructured or structured)
2. Periodic restore with the central starting point (master copy)
3. The parallel use of several versions.

1. The cumulative construction of the central starting point (unstructured or structured)

With cumulative construction, the central starting point grows along with the tests. If this is done in an unstructured way, the testers input new test data as required. This gives the testers much freedom and flexibility, but also has a disadvantage. A variety of testers input their own test data, which can influence the test results of other tests. This can cause a lot of wasted searching time in the analysis of test results. Besides, data will quickly become inconsistent. With the structured variant, the testers make agreements in order to prevent such influences. For example, they may agree that only certain types of test data may be entered or changed, or that test data should be identified so that it can be seen to which tester they belong.

Example

For the testing of a mobile telephone subscription billing system, a test team of 5 persons was involved. Each of these individuals was responsible for the testing of a specific subsystem. In order to avoid the testers getting in each other's way when using the central starting point, it was proposed to link a range of telephone numbers to each subsystem. The starting point of the test cases for a specific subsystem then had to fall within that range. A range was also agreed for the integral test that ran across the various subsystems. This resulted in the following division:

Subsystem 1: range of telephone numbers +31610000000 to +31619999999
Subsystem 2: range of telephone numbers +31620000000 to +31629999999
Subsystem 3: range of telephone numbers +31630000000 to +31639999999
Subsystem 4: range of telephone numbers +31640000000 to +31649999999
Subsystem 5: range of telephone numbers +31650000000 to +31659999999
Integral: range of telephone numbers +31690000000 to +31699999999

---

2. The periodic restore with the central starting point (master copy)

A second approach is the regular restoring of the central starting point (also called the 'master copy'). This is done via a backup-and-restore procedure. A backup is first made of the master. At certain times, the administrator of the master restores it. That may be periodically, for example every day of the week, but also on request, for example after the execution of a test. A special management procedure can provide for the structurally adding of test data to the master. A big advantage is the manageability of the data, but disadvantages are the dependency of the restore point and the extra work to go from the master to the starting point necessary for the test.

3. The parallel use of several versions

A third possibility is the use of several environments with parallel versions of the data. Each tester has his own test environment and starting point(s). Having a central starting point at your disposal may remain useful, but each tester is able to amend it as he wishes in his own environment. A big advantage of this approach is the independence of the tests: disruption by other tests is barely possible, since the tester knows exactly what is in his own starting point. That delivers great savings in time. A disadvantage is that, because of the isolation of the tests, faults in starting points can remain undetected for long periods and integral test aspects are only dealt with at a late stage. Another disadvantage is the extra cost for the required test environments, both in terms of hardware and of administration.

An important condition for this method of operation is good configuration management. This should ensure that the software deliveries and follow-up deliveries in connection with solved defects are rolled out to every test environment simultaneously. This could be a risk factor.

In more detail

Test environments and test data within SAP®

The terminology of SAP speaks of a system landscape, containing the various environments. A system landscape often consists of separate development, test, acceptance and production environments (also known as DTAP). These environments are called clients. There can be several clients per environment (instance) present. Several clients ensure that the testers do not get in each other's way as regards test data. It is advisable to set up a separate master client to secure the test data. Through copying, these data can be placed in another client. SAP also has the Test Data Migration Server tool, with which data from a productive environment can be reduced and if necessary anonimised and transferred to non-productive environments.

The transferring of changes (customising, new software) in SAP from one environment to another is done by means of so-called transports (SAP Transport Management System). Transporting can be client-dependent or client-independent. With transporting, it is necessary to maintain a certain sequence and it is sometimes necessary to create certain settings manually per environment. All of this requires very good configuration management containing release or transport administration. Figure 6.2 contains an illustrated example of the environments and associated transports.

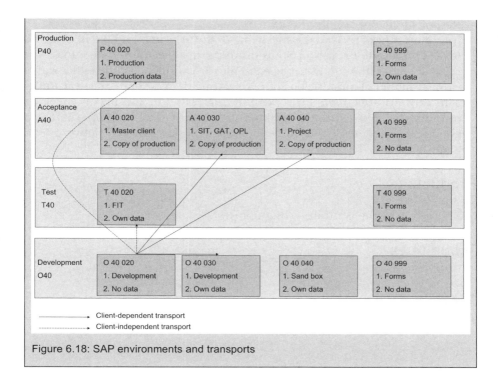

Figure 6.18: SAP environments and transports

Test data with outsourcing

A development that is attracting the attention of various legislators is the handling of electronic data during outsourcing. Two subjects warrant special attention here:

■ Confidentiality of the data used

Increasingly, it is being established in laws or formal guidelines how electronic personal details should be dealt with and how to guarantee that such information remains confidential. When test data are created from production databases, it is necessary in cases of outsourcing that the data is made anonymous, since the data departs the organisation and sometimes the country. Cases are known of employees of the supplier abusing software and data belonging to the outsourcing organisation

> **Tip**
>
> With anonimisation, take care that all the data are anonimised in the same way, so that they remain consistent with each other in a variety of files.

- Responsibility for supply of data
  Another point of focus is the specifying of the test cases and the necessary 0 data. The supplier sometimes has insufficient subject knowledge to create realistic values himself. Extreme examples are: using postcode tables with a wrong number of numeric positions or setting the VAT percentage at 100%. This can seriously disrupt the execution of tests and also makes checking of the test results extremely difficult. If certain 0 data are important to a good test, agreements should be made concerning who will deliver them, and when.

Products
Test basis defects
A description of the central starting point(s).

Techniques
Not applicable.

Tools
Testware management tool.

6.6.3   Specifying the test object intake

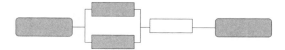

Aim
The preparation of the intake of the test object so that testing can start as soon as possible after delivery of the test object.

Method of operation
This activity contains the following subactivities:
1. Creating a checklist for the test object intake
2. Creating a pre-test test script.

1. Creating a checklist for the test object intake
At a certain point, the test team takes delivery of the test object. This first activity has the aim of establishing whether the delivery of the test object is complete, i.e. that it contains what was agreed with the supplier of the test object – no more and no less.
The test object usually consists of all kinds of software components (each with a particular version), but a user manual and installation guide, too, for example, may be part of it. The tester documents in the checklist which parts are expected with the delivery. Besides information on the test object itself, the checklist also contains questions on the delivery information. It should be apparent which changes the delivery contains and which parts are related to which change. This prevents the test team from receiving changed software parts, while they have no change proposal and therefore no test planned for it.

> **In more detail**
>
> This occurs with specialist packages, in particular, because the supplier implements the change proposals of a number of customers simultaneously, but only provides feedback to each customer individually concerning the changes requested by them.

2. Creating a pre-test test script
After installation of the test object, a pre-test takes place in order to determine whether the test object is good enough to start testing. In this activity, the testers prepare this pre-test by creating a test script. This can involve several degrees of thoroughness. Below are a few examples:
■ Checklist with all the functions, which should all be accessible

- For a number of representative functions, a simple test case with valid input ("good case") is specified
- Specification of test cases solely aimed at integration to check that the various parts can communicate with each other. The data-cycle test is a good choice for this (section 14.4.7).

The test cases may be obtained from the regular tests, but the results check is much more flexible. For example, it is not important for the pre-test that the test case delivers a correct result, as long as it delivers a result and does not crash, for example.

Examples
- For a banking application, the pre-test consists of a script of 25 end-to-end test cases.
- With another financial organisation, the pre-test takes a day in which a tester executes the test cases which contain the most important functionality.
- A telecommunications organisation requests the supplier of the software to execute a number of end-to-end test cases as a pre-test.

Products
Checklist of test object intake test
Pre-test test script.

Techniques
Not applicable.

Tools
Testware management tool
Test data tool
Test design tool
Automated test execution tool.

6.7 Execution Phase

Aim

To obtain insight into the quality of the test object through the execution of the agreed tests.

Context

The actual testing takes place during this phase. The test object is delivered and as much as possible has been prepared in the preceding phases in order to keep the test execution as brief as possible.

Preconditions

The following conditions should be met before the Execution phase can commence:

- The test object, or a separately testable part of the test object, should have been delivered.
- The test scripts for the test object, or the separately testable part of the test object, should be ready.
- The intake of the associated test infrastructure should have been completed successfully.

Method of operation

The actual execution of the test begins at the point when the test object, or a separately testable part of the test object, is delivered. The test object is first checked for completeness. Subsequently, it is installed in the test environment to assess whether it functions as it should. This is done by carrying out a preliminary test, the so-called pre-test. This is a general test, with the aim of examining whether the information system under test, in conjunction with the test infrastructure, is of sufficient quality to undergo extensive testing. If, on the whole, it is of sufficient quality, the central starting point is prepared. The test may be executed on the basis of the (manual or automated) test scripts that were created in the Specification phase. In that case, the starting points for the test scripts should first be prepared. Execution of the test can also be carried out in an exploratory manner, or on the basis of checklists. During the execution, the test results are logged. Investigation of the causes of any differences between expectations and obtained test results takes place after the test execution. Causes of differences may lie in software faults, but other causes are possible. For example, there could be mistakes in the test basis, in the test environment or in the test cases. When a fault has to be solved, this is formally reported as a defect. When the defect has been solved, a new test can be executed. Thus, this phase often involves an iterative process of test-rework-retest. The substance of this iterative process depends on the cause of the fault. For example, a fault in the test basis can result in a renewed (re)planning of the test, after which the phases of Preparation, Specification and Execution are gone through again. With a fault in the software, the iterative process of test-rework-retest may be restricted to a repeat of the Execution phase.

Roles / responsibilities
All the activities can be carried out by all the test-team members. However, the check on completeness of the test object is done by the test manager, aided by the (if applicable) test infrastructure coordinator.

Activities
Within the Execution phase, the following activities are distinguished:
1.   Intake of the test object
2.   Preparing the starting points
3.   Executing the (re)tests
4.   Checking and assessing the test results.

The following scheme shows the sequence and dependencies between the various activities.

Figure 6.19: Execution phase

6.7.1 Intake of the test object

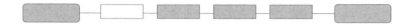

Aim
To establish whether the delivered parts of the test object function in such a way that adequate testing can be carried out.

Method of operation
The method of operation includes the following subactivities:
1. Checking completeness of the delivered test object
2. Executing the pre-test.

1. Checking completeness of the delivered test object
With the aid of the checklist created in the Specification phase, the delivered test object is checked for completeness. This is done by the test manager, assisted by (where this role is taken) the test infrastructure coordinator. Missing parts are reported, by means of a defect, to the parties involved. If the defect is test-obstructive (i.e. the subsequent subactivity, the pre-test, cannot start), then this should be solved immediately. It is advisable to carry out this subactivity together with the department that maintains the test environment, since this department depends on a complete delivery of the test object, otherwise the installation will be wrong. Moreover, they have the technical knowledge to be able to check the test object on the aspect of completeness. Following approval, the test infrastructure coordinator can install the test object (or have the administrators do so).

2. Executing the pre-test
As soon as a (version of the) test object is installed, it is important to carry out a pre-test. This takes place before the actual testing begins. The purpose of the pre-test is to evaluate whether the test object is of sufficient quality for testing. The pre-test is carried out by executing the test script that was created for this during the Specification phase (see section 6.6.3 "Specifying the test object intake"). It regularly happens in practice that systems are wrongly delivered or wrongly installed in the first days of testing, thus delaying the start of the test execution. This is not only a waste of time, it also demotivates the test team. It is important to consider this when creating the test plan (see also section 6.2.7. "Determining the planning").

Tip

The pre-test as negotiation reinforcement
With a pre-test, the test manager's position is strengthened considerably when he wants to argue that the clock has not yet started for the main test. That is to say, if from Monday, 10 days of test execution were planned and the pre-test only succeeds on Wednesday, the 10 days only begin from Wednesday. There is room for discussion here, but the test manager will have a much stronger negotiating position.

A condition of the execution of these subactivities is that the required test infrastructure is available. This means effectively that the intake of the infrastructure should have gone successfully (see section 6.4.4 "Intake of the infrastructure"). A successful pre-test is a condition for the starting of the subsequent activities in the Execution phase. The defects from the pre-test are registered and, if a defect is test-obstructive, it is immediately submitted to the parties involved. Every effort should be made, with the highest priority, to solve the test-obstructive defects and allow the pre-test to complete successfully.

Example 1

With the building and testing of a new registration system, time is running out. It is decided to ask the testers to sacrifice their free Saturday and Sunday and to test over the weekend. Experience shows that the delivery and installation of the test object in the test environment does not always progress smoothly. In many cases, parts of the test object are missing or do not work at all.

In order to avoid the testers turning up on Saturday for nothing because the installation of the test object has failed, it is decided on Friday evening to carry out a pre-test. This is done by the test manager and the test infrastructure coordinator. Together, they check at 18:00 hours, on the basis of a selection of test scripts, the quality of the delivered test object. If this is sufficient for testing, they contact the test team members before 20:00 hours to tell them that the test is going ahead.

Example 2

A new version of an administrative system has been developed by an external supplier on the other side of the world. It is agreed with the supplier that, before it is delivered and the FAT is carried out, a pre-test will take place. This test is carried out, via the Internet, on the supplier's infrastructure. It provides an initial impression of the quality of the system and confirms that the FAT can actually begin. This also avoids the installation of the test object in the company's own infrastructure causing problems through distrust of the supplier. They have witnessed it working there, after all!

Products

Defects
Installed and testable test object.

Techniques

Not applicable.

Tools

Testware management tool
Defect management tool
Automated test execution tool
Monitoring tool
Comparator
Database manipulation tool
Simulator
Stubs and drivers.

6.7.2   Preparing the starting points

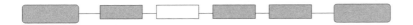

Aim
To prepare the starting point required for the execution of the tests.

Method of operation
Before the execution of the test cases in the test script can begin, the test object should be placed in the appropriate condition or situation. This not only involves the preparation of the test data necessary for the processing, but also the setting of the system and test environment in a particular condition. It may concern, for example, the formatting of a disk, or even the configuring of an input device.

Two types of situations of the test object are distinguished within TMap:
1. A *central starting point* for a number of tests
2. A *starting point* per test script.

At the start of a test, the central starting point is created. The test object and test environment are then ready to receive the input in accordance with the test scripts (at any rate those that are executed first). The test data are gathered as described during the activity "Defining central starting point(s)" in the Specification phase (see section 6.6.2). The gathering of these test data can take place in various ways. Defects found during the gathering of the test data are registered in accordance with the procedures laid down in the test plan.

 Tip

Backing up the central starting point and checking this
As soon as the test object has been placed at the central starting point and checked, it is advisable to create a backup. This can be restored at any given point. It is important to carefully check this principle of backup and restore before commencement of the tests.

Products
Defects
Central starting point
Starting points.

Techniques

Not applicable.

Tools

Testware management tool
Test data tool
Model-based testing tool
Automated test execution tool
Performance, load and stress test tool
Database manipulation tool.

6.7.3   Executing the (re)tests

Aim
To obtain test results, on the basis of which evaluation of the test object can take place.

Method of operation
The method of operation includes the following subactivities:
1. Executing dynamic explicit tests
2. Executing dynamic implicit tests
3. Executing static tests.

1. Executing dynamic explicit tests
In dynamic explicit testing, explicit test cases are executed to obtain information on the property (quality characteristic) or system part under test. Results are obtained by running software and executing operations on the test object. These results are compared in the subsequent activity against the expected results, thus delivering any defects. Dynamic explicit testing is the most usual way of testing. There are two possible types of dynamic explicit testing:

■   Testing on the basis of specified tests created in the Specification phase.
     The specified tests that are created in the Specification phase form the starting point for the tests to be executed here. These may be test scripts containing the test actions and checks or the physical test cases. The test scripts are described in an optimal sequence and form the stepped plan for the test execution. If it has been decided to use tools for automated test execution, then the specified tests are executed with the aid of a test tool (see also section 8.5 "Test tools"). In addition, tests can also take place on the basis of checklists or in another form, as described in section 10.3 "Test types". An important condition for a worthwhile dynamic explicit test is that the testers do not deviate from the test cases and execute at least the described test cases. Otherwise, there is no way of guaranteeing that the strategy laid down in the test plan is actually being carried out.

■   Testing on the basis of an exploratory technique.
     With this type, the tester carries out exploratory work during the dynamic explicit test. This means that the tester is examining the application under test piece by piece, thinking about what should be or could be tested (test

design) and then does it (test execution). In doing so, the tester is gaining knowledge of the application, considering what should be tested next, testing it, et cetera. The design and subsequent execution of the tests take place in close succession. Possible techniques are "Exploratory Testing" and "Error Guessing". These are explained in section 14.4 "A basic set of test design techniques".

Tip

A quick way of helping inexperienced testers on their way is to carry out this activity in pairs. Team up an inexperienced tester with an experienced one [Kaner, 2001]. In this, one tester is responsible for the test. He involves another tester, with one of them operating the keys and the other thinking about the things to be tested, observing, taking notes and researching. By thinking aloud, the testers together generate many more ideas than they would separately. They also help each other not to lose sight of the test goal because of unimportant details. Coaching in pairs is certainly to be recommended, particularly in the beginning. Testing in pairs is less successful if the individuals are very introverted or very assertive.

These two types of dynamic explicit testing do not exclude each other. In fact, when applied in combination, they can reinforce each other. Reasons for combining the two types may be:

- During the execution of the specified tests, it is felt that insufficient insight into the quality has been obtained. By now testing exploratory in a number of areas within the test object, this impression can be either substantiated or dispelled.
- The strategy for a retest may be that only those parts of the test object are tested that have been amended by the programmers. In order to be sure that the unchanged parts still work, they can be subjected to some extra, exploratory, testing.
- The addition of exploratory testing over and above the specified testing can be useful as a stimulus for creative testing. This could be scheduled, for example, for a Friday afternoon. Many testers are more creative during this part of the week. Just before the weekend, the mood is good and everyone is open to experimentation. These experiments may cover very exceptional situations, but perhaps also those that are so ordinary that they are overlooked. It is then that crucial faults may be found in the test object.
- During the execution of a test script, a fault may occur. This has to be investigated further, before it is reported as a defect. It can be observed whether the defect always occurs or only in the specific situation. Alternatively, perhaps the defect occurs in other (similar) areas in the test object. There is also the possibility that several defects are located together. This investigation can take place on the basis of exploratory testing (see also chapter 12 "Defects management").

Tip

Faults located together
Faults have a tendency to clustered together within a test object. If a fault occurs in a particular function, screen, operation or other part, the chances are that other faults are there as well. There are various causes for this. For example, the particular part may contain more complex code, so the likelihood of the programmer making a mistake is greater. Alternatively, a particular part may have been created by an inexperienced programmer, or by one who was having an off day. It is therefore advisable, when a fault is found, always to search the area for other faults.

---

2. Executing dynamic implicit tests
During dynamic explicit testing, information can also be gathered on other properties (quality characteristics). No explicit test cases are designed for these. This is referred to as dynamic implicit testing, and the tests can be executed planned or unplanned. If planned, it is agreed in advance that this is to form an actual part of the test strategy. Testers can then be asked in advance of the test execution to observe a number of characteristics (such as performance or usability) of the test object. This is therefore not based on any targeted test cases. Another way is to question the testers after the execution of the dynamic explicit test. However, there is the risk that, since no specific attention has been paid to these things, wrong information will be given.

Unplanned implicit testing arises because, during execution of the test, certain things start to catch the attention. It is agreed to observe them more closely. If, for example, regular system breakdown takes place, a decision can be taken as regards reliability. Alternatively, if certain screens do not have an appealing look and feel, something can be said about the usability.

3. Executing static tests
It is laid down in the test strategy whether static tests should be carried out. In static testing, end products are assessed without any software being run. This test usually consists of the inspection of documentation, such as security procedures, training, manuals, et cetera and is often aided by checklists (see section 14.3.10 "Checklist"). On the basis of these, it is attempted to obtain insight into the relevant quality aspect. Here too, any defects are registered and processed by means of the defects procedure (see chapter 12 "Defects management").

Products
Test results.

Techniques

Exploratory Testing
Error Guessing.

Tools

Testware management tool
Defect management tool
Model-based testing tool
Automated test execution tool
Performance, load and stress test tool
Monitoring tool
Code coverage tool
Comparator
Database manipulation tool
Simulator
Stubs and drivers.

6.7.4   Checking and assessing the test results

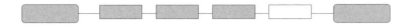

Aim
To analyse the differences between the obtained test results and the predicted results in the test scripts or checklists.

Method of operation
The method of operation includes the following subactivities:
1. Comparing test results
2. Analysing differences
3. Determining retests.

1. Comparing test results
The test results are compared against the predicted results in the test scripts and checklists. If testing is being done based on an exploratory technique, the tester will compare the outcome against the documented test basis, such as the functional design or a requirements document. If there is no documented test basis, the tester needs to find other ways of comparing the outcome. This information can be obtained, for example, from norms and standards, memos, user manuals, interviews, advertisements or rival products (see also the tip "Absence of test basis" in section 6.5.1. "Collection of the test basis").

In more detail

The dangers of testing without a documented test basis
If no documented test basis is available to the tester, there is a real risk that he or she will begin to rely on information sources other than the test basis, such as his or her intuition. An unwanted end result may be that system and documentation are running out of sync. If the system is correct and the documentation wrong, this can lead to maintenance or administration problems. Conversely, it is possible that (deep) functionality is described in the documentation that has been incorrectly implemented in the system and that has not emerged with testing based on sources other than the system documentation. Another unwanted end result may be that, in the absence of clarity concerning the scope, the testers generate an endless stream of change requests in the form of defects.

If there are no deviations, this is logged. If deviations are found, they are analysed. The comparing of the test results often takes place simultaneously with the execution of the test. For example, by checking off the steps in the test script it can be indicated whether a test result corresponds with the expected result. In certain cases, it is not possible to do this during the test (e.g. with batch systems, where the output of several test cases is presented).

2. Analysing differences

The differences found are further analysed during this subactivity. The tester should perform the following steps:

- Gather evidence
- Reproduce the defect
- Check for own mistakes
- Determine suspected external cause
- Isolate the cause (optional)
- Generalise the defect
- Compare with other defects
- Write defect report
- Have it reviewed.

These steps are explained in section 12.2 "Finding a defect". The steps are listed in the general sequence of execution, but it is entirely possible to carry out particular steps in another order or in parallel. If, for example, the tester immediately sees that the defect was already found in the same test, the interim steps need not be performed. In the test scripts, the numbers of the defects are registered with those test cases where the defect was found. In that way, it quickly becomes clear in any retest at least which test actions need to be carried out again. Various test tools are available both for comparing the test results and for analysing the differences (see section 8.5 "Test tools").

3. Determining retests

Reasons for carrying out retests may be found defects. If the cause of the defect concerns a fault in the test execution, the relevant test is carried out again. Defects that have their origin in a wrong test script or checklist are solved. Thereafter, the changed part of the test script is executed again or the entire checklist is gone through again. Faults in the test environment should also be solved, after which the relevant test scripts are executed again in their entirety.

Faults in the test object or the test basis will usually mean a new version of the test object. With a fault in the test basis, the associated test scripts will usually also need to be amended. This often involves a lot of work. When retests take place, it is important to establish the way in which they are to be carried out. The test manager will determine in the Control phase whether all the test scripts should be carried out again in whole or in part, and this partly depends on:

- The exit criteria set out in the test plan

- The severity of the defects
- The number of defects
- The degree to which the earlier execution of the test script was disrupted by the defects
- The time available
- The risks.

In more detail

When to test solved defects
Defects that have been solved must be tested again. The timing of these tests can be quite different.
1. Test as soon as a defect is solved. The advantage of this is that the programmer, who has solved the defect, still has it fresh in his memory. He can therefore act quickly in the event that the defect appears not to be solved. The disadvantage is that the code is often changed, delivered and tested. Mistakes can be easily made here, and that is less efficient for the tester.

2. Gather solved defects and test these. The advantage of this is that defects can be solved and tested collectively (e.g. per module or per screen), which is a more efficient way of working. The code is also more stable, so that the chances of a defect returning are minimal. The disadvantage, however, is that this method takes longer.

The choice of option 1 or 2 depends on the project and the way of working. If it is possible to deliver a release of an application every day[1] and there are a large number of defects to be retested, the strategy may be to choose a mix of the above. It is then determined each day which solved defects will be included in the release and these can then be tested by the test team the following day. It is important in that case to set up a separate test environment and only to use it for testing the solved defects in the releases. In addition, a test of the entire test object will have to take place at the end, in order to establish that nothing else has changed (regression).

Products
Defects
Logging of the test results.

Techniques
Not applicable.

---

1 Also known as the 'daily build'.

Tools

Testware management tool
Defect management tool
Test data tool
Automated test execution tool
Performance, load and stress test tool
Monitoring tool
Code coverage tool
Comparator
Database manipulation tool.

6.8   Completion Phase

Aim
To learn from experience gained during this test and to preserve testware for reuse in a future test.

Context
With the structured test approach of TMap, much benefit is to be gained from the possibility of repeating the process. This allows products, provided that they meet certain requirements, to be reused in a subsequent test. In turn, this can ensure that certain activities will proceed faster. Products may be tangible things, such as test cases or test environments, but also intangible things, such as valuable experience.

Preconditions
The following condition should be met before the Completion phase can commence:
- The test execution is almost finished.

Method of operation
The test process is evaluated. The aim here is to learn from the experience gained and to apply the points of learning to any new test. This also serves as input for the final report, which the test manager creates in the Control phase. Also a selection is made from the often large quantity of testware, such as the test cases and the description of the test infrastructure. The point here is that with changes and associated maintenance tests, the testware only requires adjustment, so that it is not necessary to design a completely new test. During the test process, efforts are made to keep the test cases corresponding with the test basis and the developed system. If necessary, the selected test cases should be updated.

Roles / responsibilities
All the activities can be carried out by all the team members.

Activities
The Completion phase consists of the following activities:
1. Evaluating the test process
2. Preserving the testware.

The scheme below shows the sequence and dependencies between the various activities:

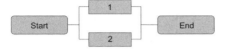

Figure 6.20: Completion phase

6.8.1   Evaluating the test process

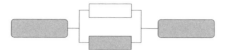

Aim
To learn from experience gained during the completed test and to document the learning points for future tests.

Method of operation
Continuous learning, followed by using the new knowledge, is an important topic in TMap. A way of doing this is to organise evaluation sessions. These sessions are mostly aimed at generating lessons and learning experiences for the future. The subject of evaluation may vary, according to requirements. It may concern the evaluation of the test process, the results of the test, the involvement of the various parties in it, the use of the test infrastructure et cetera. It is important here to clarify how the people involved in the test experience the subject. An evaluation should take place upon completion of the test, but it is advisable also to do this regularly during the test itself. In this way, it is possible to learn continuously and to apply what has been learned. An aid for asking the appropriate questions during an evaluation is the "Evaluation of the test process" checklist (www.tmap.net).

The test manager creates a final report in the Control phase. This report describes how the test process has performed. It also supplies figures for purposes of future test processes, and the result of the evaluation serves as input here.

Tip

Evaluations as leverage for change
The carrying out of evaluations may have a purpose that extends beyond simply reusing the acquired knowledge. It may also have the purpose of setting up the knowledge as leverage for change. A condition for this is that the test manager's role is one in which he can propose changes. These proposals can then be included in the final report. If this process is already taking place during the execution of the project, there is the great advantage that the changes can be implemented immediately. A condition for success is that the sharing of knowledge be encouraged at every level, this is possible by, for example, organising (informal) meetings. During these meetings, there should be a relaxed and egalitarian atmosphere. Involve all the parties in the meeting, talk about the problems and try to find immediate solutions.

> **Example**
>
> **Testers as sounding board**
> During a test, more and more English-speaking developers came to the Dutch-speaking testers to ask questions concerning particular functional specifications. It appeared from various informal meetings on Friday afternoons that they had difficulty with the combination of the broken English of the Dutch designers and the long screeds of text. From within their expertise, the testers had built up in-depth knowledge of the system. In consultation with the various parties, it was then decided that the testers could serve the developers as a sounding board. In addition, a selection was made from existing test scripts that had to be executed by the developers before they delivered their piece of software. This benefited the general quality and pace of the test process, defects were now found during development and there was a greater involvement of the developers in the testing and vice versa.

Products
Evaluation of the test process.

Techniques
Checklist "Evaluation of the test process" (www.tmap.net).

Tools
Testware management tool
Defect management tool.

6.8.2   Preserving the testware

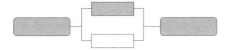

Aim
To select and update the produced testware in such a way that optimal use can be made of it in future tests.

Method of operation
The method of operation includes the following subactivities:
1.   Selecting testware
2.   Collecting and refining testware, making it accessible
3.   Transferring testware.

This activity has a close connection with the activity "Preserving the infrastructure" in the Setting up and maintaining infrastructure phase (see section 6.4.6).

Tip

Starting the activity of preserving testware earlier
Although Preserving Testware is the last activity in the TMap life cycle model, it is advisable to start this early on. By allowing for the possibilities of preserving testware as early as the Specification phase, certain standards can be developed or certain tools can be employed, so that the eventual preservation will proceed faster. By, for example, working from the start with consistent version-numbering and a central store for all the products, there is no need to search for the latest version of all the products during this activity. The use of a testware management tool can help with this. How the preserving takes place is defined in the activity "Organising the management" in the Planning phase (see section 6.2.12).

---

1. Selecting testware
In consultation with the future administrator of the system, an inventory is drawn up of which testware is to be made available to him. The purpose is to render the testware reusable for changes and associated maintenance tests, so that it will not be necessary to design a completely new test. The final choice of testware to be made available is made on the basis of a costs/benefits analysis. Subjects in this would be 'What will it cost to maintain the testware (storage and updating)' and 'What will it cost to make it anew'.

The test products to be delivered are set out in an inventory. This is an overview of the test products to be preserved. It is important to indicate the way in which the test products were created, in order to facilitate appropriate future maintenance. Bear in mind here in particular the test design techniques, tools, et cetera that were used.

2. Collecting and refining testware, making it accessible
The testware to be transferred should be completed and adjusted where necessary. During the last phase of the execution, in particular, maintenance of the testware is often postponed. Before transfer to the future users can take place, any changes should be processed. The testware should also be made accessible. This means that it should be stored in such a way that it is readily available to the future users. That may mean, for example, that the directory structure has to be set up differently or a particular tool must be used.

In more detail

Adjust regression test set
The updating of a regression test set is often overlooked. For that reason, it is advisable to include this activity as standard within the activity of "Preserving the testware". During the test execution, it may have been that the system reacted differently from what was assumed in the test script. If this is the case, the test script should be amended in accordance with the new situation. It should also be determined whether, and if so which, new test scripts need to be added to the existing regression test set.

---

3. Transferring testware
Finally, the actual transfer of the testware takes place. In accordance with the testware inventory, all the selected parts are electronically, and sometimes also physically (on paper), transferred to the maintenance department.

Products
Testware inventory
Reusable testware.

Techniques
Not applicable.

Tools
Testware management tool
Test data tool.

7 Development tests

Guest author: Rob Kuijt

7.1 Introduction

To allow them to perform at their best in the market, users of information systems demand ever-faster delivery of the systems as well as more flexibility. Development methods are increasingly geared to follow changing requirements closely, even in the midst of a project. The architectures and development environments that make all this possible are becoming more complex and bigger in scale. This changes the development requirements.

The growing demand on the developer: to deliver the right quality, on time and right first time!

In addition to increased knowledge of development languages, methods, environments and architectures, this also calls for deeper knowledge of quality delivery. Difficult questions in this connection are: what is the quality level required for the client, and how can this be realised and demonstrated through testing? Individual interpretation of the required quality and random testing provide no guarantee of eventual success. Predictable and proven quality of the delivered software gives the project or the department the opportunity to organise the subsequent test levels, such as the system test and the acceptance test, more efficiently. A reduction in the number of redeliveries and retests in those test levels, in particular, delivers significant timesavings. In order to realise the higher quality of software, increasingly high demands are placed on the development tests, and development testing is fast becoming a mature part of the entire testing process.

Soon the time will be over that barely any requirements are being set as regards the development tests, and the (increasingly mature) system and acceptance tests are being relied upon to rectify the lack of quality for going into production. The resulting lengthy and costly reworking and retesting cycles have become unacceptable to most organisations.

Section 7.2 discusses the development tests, makes a comparison with the other test levels and describes specific test tools for development testing. Various quality measures are also discussed that can be used in, or can influence, the development tests. An important measure here is the concept of selected quality. Subsequently, section 7.3 describes the activities of development testing according to the TMap life cycle model.

While developers and development testers are a logical target group for this chapter, they should not expect, after reading this one chapter, to know all about how to organise and execute development tests. The target groups of this chapter are:
- The developer/development tester, for ideas on a better development test
- The test consultant who is asked to support (the organisation of) the development testing
- The test manager for the overall test process who has to coordinate the development tests with the other test levels
- The line manager or project manager of the developers who is interested in improved control over the quality of the software produced, and who wants to know how this can be achieved.

7.2   Development testing explained

This section consists of a number of subsections. These are, in sequence:
- What is development testing?
- Characteristic
  With a focus on how they differ from system tests and acceptance tests
- Advantages and disadvantages of improved development tests
- Context of development testing
  The influence of the development method and technical implementation
- Unit test
- Unit integration test
- Quality measures
  Various measures, including the concept of selected quality of development tests
- Test tools for development tests.

7.2.1   What is development testing?

Development testing is understood to mean testing using knowledge of the technical implementation of the system. This starts with the testing of the first/smallest parts of the system: *routines, units, programs, modules, components, objects, etc.* Within TMap, the term 'unit' and therefore *unit test* is used exclusively in this context.

> **Definition**
>
> **Unit Test (UT)**
> The *unit test* is a test carried out in the development environment by the developer, with the aim of demonstrating that a unit meets the requirements defined in the technical specifications.
>
> **Unit Integration Test (UIT)**
> The *unit integration test* is a test carried out by the developer in the development environment, with the aim of demonstrating that a logical group of units meets the requirements defined in the technical specifications.

When it has been established that the most elementary parts of the system are of sufficient quality, larger parts of the system are tested integrally during the unit integration tests. The emphasis here lies on the data throughput and the interfacing between the units up to subsystem level.

7.2.2 Characteristics

A pitfall in organising development tests is the temptation to set up the test process from the viewpoint of a system test or acceptance test. For when development tests are compared with the system test and the acceptance test, a number of significant differences come to the fore:

- In contrast to the system test and acceptance test, the development tests cannot be organised as an independent process with a more or less independent team. The development tests form an integral part of software development, and the phasing of the test activities is integrated with the activities of the developers.
- Because development testing uses knowledge of the technical implementation of the system, other types of defects are found than those found by system and acceptance tests. It may be expected of development tests, for example, that each statement in the code has been touched on. A similar degree of coverage is, in practice, very difficult for system and acceptance tests to achieve, since these test levels focus on different aspects. It is therefore difficult to replace development tests with system and acceptance tests.
- With the unit tests, in particular, the discoverer of the defects (i.e. the tester) is often the same individual who solves them (i.e. the developer). This means that communication on the defects may be minimal.
- The approach of development testing is that all the found defects are solved before the software is transferred. The reporting of development testing may therefore be more restricted than that of system and acceptance testing.

- It is the first test process, which means that all the defects are still in the product, requiring cheap and fast defect adjustment. In order to realise this, a flexible test environment with few procedural barriers is of great importance.
- Development tests are often carried out by developers themselves. The developer's basic intention is to demonstrate that the product works, while a tester is looking to demonstrate the difference between the required quality and the actual quality of the product (and actively goes in search of defects). This difference in mindset means that sizeable and/or in-depth development tests run counter to the developer's intention and, with that, meet with resistance and/or result in carelessly executed tests.

In more detail

The table below [Pettichord, 2000] sums up a number of salient characteristics of testers and developers:

Testers	Developers
Get up to speed quickly	Thorough understanding
Domain knowledge	Knowledge of product internals
Ignorance is important	Expertise is important
Model user behaviour	Model system design
Focus on what can go wrong	Focus on how it can work
Focus on severity of problem	Focus on interest in problem
Empirical	Theoretical
What's observed	How it's designed
Sceptics	Believers
Tolerate tedium	Automate tedium
Comfortable with conflict	Avoid conflict
Report problems	Understand problems

Table 7.1: Characteristics of testers and developers

7.2.3   Advantages and disadvantages of improved development tests

In practice, development testing is often unstructured: tests are not planned or prepared; no test design techniques are used and there is no insight into what has or has not been tested or to what depth. With that, insight is also lacking into the quality of the (tested) product. Often during the system and acceptance tests, there are lengthy and inefficient cycles of test/repair/ retest in order to get the quality up to an acceptable level. It therefore stands to reason that development testing should be better organised. A number of arguments are presented below as to why this does not take place in practice (arguments against) and why it is important that it should take place (arguments for).

Arguments against

The most important arguments as to why the need for more structure and thoroughness in development testing is not self-evident are:

- *Pressure of time / not cost-effective*
  Developers are often under severe pressure of time. The priorities of the development team are defined by the criteria by which it is judged. Assessment is usually made based on hard criteria, such as lead-time and delivered functionality. Assessment by a much softer criterion, such as quality, is more difficult and is therefore rare in practice. A developer who is committed to a completion date will either communicate openly and honestly when things are not going smoothly, or give less time to his own testing if the coding is in trouble. From the point of view of personal performance (and assessment), the latter is not unthinkable. After all, benefits to a development team of thorough testing are relatively small, even though they are many times greater for the project as a whole
- *Sufficient faith in the quality*
  A developer is usually proud of his product and considers it to be of good quality. It is therefore not logical as a developer to expend a lot of effort in finding fault with his own product
- *There will be another thorough test to follow*
  In the subsequent phase, e.g. the system test, a much more intensive test will be carried out than development testing can ever do. Why should the development tester then pay much attention to more and better testing, when it is to take place later more extensively?

Arguments for

The most important argument for more structure and thoroughness in development testing is that it enables the developer to establish for himself that the software is of sufficient quality to be delivered to the next phase, probably the system test. The meaning of "sufficient quality" is of course open to discussion. Below is indicated that "sufficient quality" has many advantages *for the development team*:

- Less reworking will be necessary after delivery, since the products that are delivered to the subsequent phase are of higher quality.
- The planning is better, since the often uncertain volume of rework declines.

- The lead-time of the total development phase is, for the same reason, shorter.
- Reworking as early as possible is much cheaper than at a later stage, since all the knowledge of the developed products is still fresh in the memory, whereas by the later stage people have often already left the development team.
- Analysing defects you find yourself is much faster and easier than analysing defects found by others. The more distance (both organisational and physical) the finder has, the more difficult and time-consuming the analysing often is. Even more so, since in later phases the system is tested as a whole and the found defect may be located in many separate components.
- The developers get faster feedback on the mistakes they make, so that they are better able to prevent similar mistakes in other units.
- Certain defects, particularly on the boundaries of system functionality and underlying operating system, database and network, can best be detected with development tests. If the development testing finds too small a proportion of these defects, this will have consequences for the system and acceptance tests, which then have to produce a disproportionate effort (in the detection of such defects), using inefficient techniques, in order to achieve the same quality of the test object had the development tests been adequately executed.

These advantages apply for the total project, and even for the total life cycle of the system *to a greater degree*, because the later test levels also benefit from these advantages (often even more so!), for example because much fewer retests are necessary. Accordingly, the advantages of a more structured development test approach far outweigh the disadvantages. However, a necessary condition for successful structuring of the development testing is that the various parties involved, such as the client, the line and project manager and the developers, are aware of the importance of a better test process. For example, the project manager should assess the development team much more on delivered quality than simply on time and money. The development department may also set requirements on all the executed development tests. Each development test in an individual project should at least meet these requirements. This is explained in section 7.2.7 "Quality measures".

7.2.4 Context of development testing

Development testing bears a very close relationship with the development process and cannot really be considered separately from it. Much more knowledge of the technical implementation of the system or package is required as far as development testing is concerned than for a system or acceptance test. In order to organise the development test well, allowance must certainly be made for the development process used and the technical implementation.

Tip

Ensure that, as adviser or test manager in the organisation of the development testing, you have sufficient knowledge of the development process used and the technical implementation. This will also make you a useful partner in the dialogue with the developers, without having to be an expert.

Influence of the development method

Roughly three streams of development methods can be distinguished: waterfall, iterative and agile.

- Waterfall, which includes the following characteristics: the development of a system in one go, phased with clear transfer points, often a long cyclical process (including SDM)
- Iterative, characterised by: incremental development of the system, phased with clear transfer points; short cyclical process (iterations) (including DSDM and RUP). Iterative methods take up an intermediate position between waterfall and agile.
- Agile, characterised by four principles: individuals and interaction above processes and tools, working software above extensive system documentation, user input above contract negotiation, responding to changes above following a plan (including eXtreme Programming and SCRUM)

To discover what influence the development method has on (the organisation of) the development testing, it should be considered to what degree the following aspects play a role:
- Instructions for development test activities
  Many methods go no further than indicating that development tests need to be carried out. Structured guidelines are seldom supplied. Extreme Programming (XP), as one of the agile methods, is a positive exception in this area. Three of the most important practices in development testing are Pair Programming, Test Driven Development and Continuous Integration. These practices are briefly explained later in section 7.2.7 "Quality measures".
- Quality of the test basis
  The waterfall method is usually established in a formally described form. With iterative and agile development methods, the form of the test basis is much less formal and often agreed verbally (through consultation with users). This means that it is more difficult with iterative and agile methods

to discover all that requires to be tested. For example, the fault handling and exceptional situations (together estimated to be as much as 80% of the code) are often under-exposed in such forms of test basis. Greater reliance is placed on the expertise and creativity of the development testers as regards devising and executing tests for these

- Long- or short-cyclical development
  With short-cyclical development, proportionately more time is spent on testing, particularly due to the need to execute a much more frequent regression test (every cycle at minimum) on the system so far developed.

Influence of the technical implementation

Over the years, the IT world has grown into a patchwork quilt of technological solutions. To represent this simply, you could say that the first systems were set up as monoliths, meaning that the presentation, application logic and information storage were one giant whole. Some of these systems have been in operation for more than 30 years now. The monolithic systems were followed by systems based on client/server architectures. Then came the 3-layer systems with separate presentation, application logic and database layers. In parallel with this, obviously, there was the rise of the big software packages, such as SAP, and of Internet and browser-based applications. These days, many systems are set up in distributed fashion, which means that they consist of different, often physically dispersed, components or services, while the system is still seen by the outside world as a cohesive whole, owing to close collaboration.

The systems were developed with the aid of a large arsenal of programming languages, whether or not object-oriented, in development environments that support (automated) testing to a greater or lesser degree.

In more detail

In system development, increasing use is being made of so-called services. A service in this connection can be seen as an 'independent' repeatable business task, such as "Check credit rating" and "Open new account". Services are set up as modular and usually small applications that can be found, accessed and used by other applications, without knowledge of these being required as regards the underlying technical implementation of the service.

A Service Oriented Architecture (SOA) is a framework for integrating business processes and supporting IT infrastructure as secure, standardised components – services - that can be reused and combined to address changing business priorities [Bieberstein, 2005].

As indicated in Chapter 3, "The essentials of TMap", testing is a risk-based activity, in which risk = chance of failure x damage, with chance of failure = frequency of use x chance of a fault. The relevance of the above summary of 50 years of system development in one paragraph is that the technical implementation determines to a great degree the type of faults that can be made and in which parts the chances of faults are the greatest. The test strategy of development testing is thus strongly dependent on the technical implementation, more so than the system and acceptance tests, where more attention is paid to the specifications of the system and the potential damage.

> **In more detail**
>
> The increasing use of distributed systems with large numbers of components and services places high demands on the quality of the individual components or services. The complex collaboration between all these components and services makes the finding of the source of a defect very difficult and time-consuming. The result of integrating qualitatively inadequate components or services into the system and hoping that the defects will be found by the system or acceptance tests will be that the required system quality (on time and within budget) cannot be delivered. The technical nature of many components and services means that the development tests bear a heavier responsibility for establishing that the separate components or services are of sufficient quality *before* they are integrated.

7.2.5   Unit test

In unit testing, it is important to realise what the place of testing is within development, as described in section 7.2.2. The unit testers are usually the developers, who test their own unit. The development project leader, a separate test coordinator or the application integrator described in section 7.2.7 coordinate the tests.

A point to note is the specifying of test cases. Developers do not always see the usefulness of this. By opting where possible for 'light' test design techniques and elementary forms of test documentation in particular, the degree of acceptance is considerably increased. Particularly with manual unit tests, considerable powers of persuasion are necessary to convince the developers that the writing out of test cases in those specific instances offers advantages over the unprepared execution of the tests.

> **In more detail**
>
> A good example that shows the advantage of test design techniques and the specifying of test cases is the testing of a multiple condition (IF A=1 and B=2 and C=3 THEN ...).

> With the aid of the test design technique of Elementary Comparison, it is relatively simple to derive a limited set of test cases (4 in this example) that provide a high degree of test coverage. Devising test cases without a technique here quickly leads to either too meagre test coverage or a multiple of test cases ($2^3 = 8$ in this example).

More and more development environments are now making it possible to include the (automated) test code in the (source) code. The unit test then consists of starting the test code, which subsequently executes (a part of) the source code. Such unit tests are grouped into a 'test harness'.

> **Definition**
>
> A *test harness* is a collection of software and test data configured for a development environment with the purpose of dynamically testing one unit or a series of units, whereby the behaviour and output are checked.

The writing of unit tests in a test harness is an extra effort that should not be ignored. Experience teaches that the developing of test code costs 10%-30% extra effort [Vaaraniemi, 2003].

Development methods have firmly embraced the possibility of including test code directly with the (source) code. Initiatives like Test Driven Development (see section 7.2.7) make testing an increasingly important part of system development.

7.2.6   Unit integration test

When a unit has been tested and approved, it can be integrated with other units into a working (part of the) system. Rarely are all the units combined and tested at one time – the so-called "big bang" scenario. The disadvantage of this late integration is that, in general, many defects are found, and tracing the causes takes up a lot of time. A more effective method is integrating numbers of units together in steps and testing after each integration step. In this way, defects are found at an early stage, when the cause is still relatively easy to detect. Unit integration testing thus plays a role particularly in repeatedly demonstrating that the new or amended unit(s) continue to work well in conjunction with earlier integrated units.

The best sequence of integration and the number of integration steps required depends on the location of the most risk-related parts of the system. Ideally, the integration starts with those units in which the most problems are expected. This prevents serious problems arising at the end of the unit integration test.

Executing unit integration tests requires extensive knowledge of the content, structure and especially the information exchange of underlying units. This in-depth knowledge means that often a separate role is allocated to the integration of units: the application integrator (see section 7.2.7).

The developments in the area of development environments also facilitate automated compilation, integration and testing. This takes place with the aid of 'build & deploy' scripts. 'Build' in this context is the combining of the various software components into a software package that can be exported to a particular environment. 'Deploy' is the rolling out of the software in the target environment, in other words the conversion of the software package into the operational (installed) form. Scripts make it possible to execute build & deploy by automation. Within the build & deploy scripts, the test harness is called up. In this, besides the automated unit tests, tests are also built and executed that exceed the boundaries of the units and the integration tests. Integration test cases often form a functional path from beginning to end through the application. By making use of stubs and drivers (see section 8.5.3 "Types of test tools") tests can be included at an early stage that run through the application from beginning to end. As with automated execution of unit tests, this possibility of automatic integrating and testing has found its way into the development methods. Rather than seeing the integration (test) as mainly a concluding activity, the Continuous Integration method (see section 7.2.7) has been introduced, which brings to the fore as much as possible any problems in connection with the combining of units.

7.2.7 Quality measures

In this section, a number of measures are described that can be used in, or be of influence on, the development tests. Most of these measures have consequences for the way in which the unit test and/or the unit integration test is carried out, apart from the code review which is an addition to the development tests and has no direct influence on these. It depends on the situation whether any of these measures, and if so which ones, will be chosen. For that reason, they are not included in the development test activities discussed in section 7.3, but are briefly described below. The fact that they are optional emphatically does not mean that they only have limited advantages. On the contrary, appropriate application of the measures in the right context can deliver huge advantages.

The following measures are discussed in succession:
- Test Driven Development (TDD)
  TDD is a development method that strongly influences the UT, because it

presupposes automated tests and ensures that test code is present for all the (source) code.

- Pair Programming
A development method in which two developers work on the same software and also specify and execute the unit test in mutual co-operation.
- Code review
This evaluation of the code supplements the development tests.
- Continuous Integration
An integrative approach that requires automated unit and unit integration tests, minimising the chance of regression faults.
- Selected quality of development tests
This approach is closely connected with, and forms part of, the test strategy. The choices made exert a strong influence on the method of specifying and executing the UT and UIT.
- Application integrator approach
An organisational solution for achieving a higher quality of the UT and UIT.

Test Driven Development (TDD)

Test Driven Development, or TDD, is one of the best practices of eXtreme Programming (XP). TDD has a lot of impact on the way in which development testing (also outside of XP, particularly with iterative and agile development) is organised these days. It is an iterative and incremental method of software development, in which no code is written before automated tests have been written for that code. The aim of TDD is to achieve fast feedback on the quality of the unit.

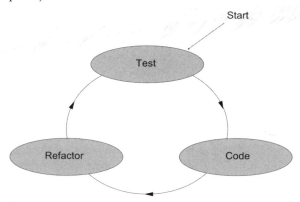

Figure 7.1: Test Driven Development

Development is carried out in short cycles, in accordance with the above scheme:

Creating a test
- Write a test
  TDD always begins with the writing of test code that checks a particular property of the unit.
- Run the test (with fault)
  Execute the test and check that the result of the test is negative (no code has yet been written for that piece of functionality).

Encode and test
- Write the code
  Write the minimum code required to ensure that the test succeeds. The new code, written at this stage, will not be perfect. This is acceptable, since the subsequent steps will improve on it. It is important that the written code is only designed to allow the test to succeed; no code should be added for which no test has been designed.
- Execute the test and all the previously created tests
  If all the test cases now succeed, the developer knows that the code meets the requirements included in the test.

Refactoring
- Clean up and structure the code
  The code is cleaned up and structured without changing the semantics. The developer regularly executes all the test cases. As long as these are successful, the developer knows that his amendments are not damaging any existing functionality. If the result of a test case is negative, he has made a wrong change.

The application of TDD has a number of big advantages. It leads to:
- More testable software
  The code can usually be directly related to a test. In addition, the automated tests can be repeated as often as necessary.
- A collection of tests that grows in step with the software
  The testware is always up to date because it is linked one-to-one with the software.
- High level of test coverage
  Each piece of code is covered by a test case.
- More adjustable software
  Executing the tests frequently and automatically provides the developer with very fast feedback as to whether an adjustment has been implemented successfully or not.
- Higher quality of the code
  The higher test coverage and frequent repeats of the test ensure that the software contains fewer defects on transfer.
- Up-to-date documentation in the form of tests
  The tests make it clear what the result of the code should be, so that later maintenance is made considerably easier.

> **Tip**
>
> The theory of TDD sounds simple, but working in accordance with the TDD principles demands great discipline, as it is easy to backslide: writing functional code without having written a new test in advance. One way of preventing this is the combining of TDD and Pair Programming (discussed later); the developers then keep each other alert.

TDD has the following conditions:

- A different way of thinking: many developers assume that the extra effort in writing automated tests is disproportionate to the advantages it brings. It has been seen in practice that the extra time involved in test driven development is more than made up for by the gains in respect of debugging, changing the software and regression testing.
- A tool or test harness for creating automated tests. Test harnesses are available for most programming languages (such as JUnit for Java and NUnit for C#).
- A development environment that supports short-cycle test-code-refactoring.
- Management commitment to giving the developers enough time and opportunity to gain experience with TDD.

For more information on TDD, refer to [Beck, 2002]

> **In more detail**
>
> **TDD strategy for testing GUI**
> TDD also has its limitations. One area where automated unit tests are difficult to implement is the Graphical User Interfaces (GUI). However, in order to make use of the advantages of TDD, the following strategy may be adopted:
> - Divide the code as far as possible into components that can be built, tested and implemented separately.
> - Keep the major part of the functionality (business logic) out of the GUI context. Let the GUI code be a thin layer on top of the stringently tested TDD code.

Pair Programming

Pair Programming is another best practice of eXtreme Programming (XP) that is also popular outside of XP. With Pair Programming, two developers work together on the same algorithm, design or piece of code, side by side in the same workplace.

There is a clear division of roles. The first developer is the one who operates the keyboard and actually writes the code. The second developer checks (evaluates!) and thinks ahead. While the code is being written, he is thinking about subsequent steps. Defects are quickly observed and removed. The two developers regularly swap roles.

The significant advantages of Pair Programming are:
- Many faults are caught during the typing, rather than during the tests or in use
- The number of defects in the end product is lower
- The (technical) designs are better and the number of code lines is lower
- The team solves problems faster
- The team members learn considerably more about the system and about software development
- The project ends with more team members understanding all parts of the system
- The team members learn to collaborate and speak to each other more often, resulting in improved information flows and team dynamic
- The team members enjoy their work more.

In recent decades, this method has been cited at various times as a better way of developing software. Research has demonstrated that by deploying a second developer in Pair Programming, the costs do not rise by 100%, as may be expected, but only by around 15% [Cockburn, 2000]. The investment is recouped in the later phases as a result of the shorter and cheaper testing, QA and management.

Code review

A subsequent measure for increasing the quality of the developed products is an evaluation activity: the *code review*.

Definition

The code review is a method of improving the quality of written code by evaluating the work against the specifications and/or guidelines and subjecting it to peer review.

The code review can be carried out as a static test activity within development testing. Its aim is to ensure that the quality of the code meets the set functional and non-functional requirements.

In the code review, the following points can be checked, independently of the set requirements; see also figure 7.2:

1. Has the product been realised in accordance with the assignment? For example, are the requirements laid down in the technical design realised correctly, completely and demonstrably?
2. Does the product meet the following criteria: internally consistent, meeting

ptandards and norms and representing the best possible solution? 'Best possible solution' means the 'best solution' that could be found within the given preconditions, such as time and finance.

3. Does the product contribute to the project and architecture aims? Is the product consistent with other, related products (consistency across the board)?

4. Is the product suitable for use in the next phase of the development (integration)?

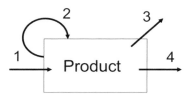

Figure 7.2: The 4 types of review goals and questions

For the review, various techniques can be employed; see also Chapter 15 "Evaluation techniques".

Tip

The code review is also applicable to development environments and development tools that are mainly used for configuration (rather than coding, e.g. with package implementations). In that case, the parameter settings are the subject of the review.

When carrying out the code review, allowance should be made for any overlap with the use of code-analysis tools; see section 7.2.8. These tools are increasingly being included in the automated integration process, in which they perform all kinds of static analyses and checks automatically. The code review therefore does not have to focus on these. It is advisable to include the output of the tools in the code review report.

Continuous Integration

Continuous Integration has a particular influence on the organisation of the unit integration tests. It is a way of working in which the developers regularly integrate their work, at least on a daily basis and increasing to several integrations per day. The integration itself, consisting of combining the units and compiling and linking into software, is automated. Each integration is verified by executing the automated tests in order to find integration defects as quickly as possible. The method minimises the chances of regression faults. Continuous Integration ideally lends itself to combining with Test Driven Development, requiring a development environment that supports automated integration and testing.

Selected quality of development tests

An important reason for development testing is the meeting of the obvious expectation of the recipient party (client, project, system test, etc.) i.e. that the developed software 'simply' works. If many defects occur in the delivered software, this will cost (a lot of) time and money to solve. The developers get the blame for this and are accused of operating unprofessionally.

But what is obvious quality to the client(s)? It is wise to make these seldom-expressed expectations explicit. They can be roughly divided into obvious expectations in respect of skill, and obvious expectations in respect of product quality.

In more detail

In order to simplify the inventory, a summary of possible expectations is shown below.

Obvious quality of the product:
- Good is good enough
  The delivered product is not required to be perfect, but should be good enough to be transferred to the next phase (of testing). What often happens is that developers test the first units (too) thoroughly. They then come under pressure of time with later units and then do not test thoroughly enough.
- Once good, always good
  Changes to the product should not lead to lower quality of the total product, therefore regression faults are not tolerated.
- Processing of the most normal cases works flawlessly.
- Basic user-friendliness (e.g. standard validations, technical consistency, uniformity).

Obvious skill:
- Basic knowledge of working in projects
- Knowledge of the delivered quality
- Obligation to obtain confirmation of the assumptions (interpretations of the specifications)
- Obligation to signal "known errors" and/or "delay reports"
- Awareness of own inexperience and/or incapacity
- Optimum deployment of the available tools/facilities
- Enlisting support when in doubt.

Obvious product quality is important, but particularly difficult to establish. The product quality to be delivered is usually determined by the project, for which the developers work. This project, after all, has the purpose of delivering a product that works satisfactorily within a certain time and budget.

However, there is a footnote to this. What does the developer do if a project sets *no* specific requirements on the quality of the delivered software, neither in the master test plan nor as suggested by the need for haste? Or even requests a "panic" delivery of the barely tested software? Are no development tests then carried out? At first sight, it seems acceptable to then leave out the development tests. If the project issues the order, delivery may take place without testing … however, experience teaches that it is extremely unwise to carry out no, or inadequate, development tests. Although the project will make the milestone at that point, a time will come during the system test or acceptance test, or even worse - in production, when the defects will stream in nevertheless. In the end, this reflects badly on the developers.

For that reason, the development department, for which the developers work, also bears a responsibility here. It can instruct that, irrespective of the project pressures, the developers should always deliver a consciously selected basic quality at minimum.
If the basic quality is clearly established, attention need only be paid in the formulation of the development testing task within a project to those parts of the system in which a higher level of certainly is required.

To this end, the developer (development department) should have the depth, clarity, provision of proof and compliance monitoring of the development tests established. An important decision to be made is the required degree of proof of the testing. How much certainty is required that the tests have actually been executed entirely in accordance with the agreed strategy? And how much time and money can be spared for providing this proof? Increasingly, external partners, too (e.g. supervisory bodies) are setting requirements on the proof to be supplied.

> **Example**
> Within an organisation, basic quality is defined as follows:
>
> **Depth of test coverage:**
>   The basic depth of test coverage is when all the statements in the realised software have been touched on in a development test at least once (statement coverage).
>
> **Clarity:**
>   Enumeration of the situations under test with reference to the development basis (requirements, specifications, technical design), with indication of whether the test of the situation takes place in the code review, unit test or unit integration test.

Provision of proof:
In the list of situations under test, initialling to indicate what has been tested and by whom, without explaining how the testing was done.

Compliance monitoring:
Code reviews (random checks).

In addition to the basic quality, the development department may also opt for a model with several quality levels. This makes it easier for projects to make variations on the quality to be delivered.

Example
Over and above basic quality, an organisation defines three other quality levels. The basic quality is given the label of *bronze* and the levels above it the labels s*ilver*, *gold* and *platinum*.

	Bronze	Silver	Gold	Platinum
Depth	Statement coverage	Condition/decision coverage	Modified condition/decision coverage	Multiple condition coverage
Clarity	Enumeration of the situations to be tested with reference to the test/development basis (requirements, specifications, technical design), indicating whether the test of the situation takes place in the code review, unit test or unit integration test	Test cases (logical), indicating whether the test takes place in the code review, unit test or unit integration test	Test cases (logical and physical), with indication of whether the test takes place in the code review, unit test or unit integration test	Test cases (logical and physical), with indication of whether the test takes place in the code review, unit test or unit integration test
Proof	Initialled checklists	Test reports	Test reports + proof	Test reports + proof
Compliance monitoring	Code reviews and internal monitoring of test results (random checks)	Code reviews and internal monitoring of test results	Code reviews, internal monitoring of test results and random external audit checks	Code reviews, internal monitoring of test results and external audit

With the creation of several quality levels, a situation arises in which the client chooses the required quality for the various parts of the system, and the development department hangs a price tag on each quality level. In short, a first step towards negotiable *selected quality*. The selected quality is an agreement in respect of the formulation of the development tests in connection with the clarity, depth and proof of the executed tests.

Proof

There are several possibilities for demonstrating that the required quality has actually been delivered (on time). Firstly, there is the provision of proof option as established in the development testing strategy, with the exit and entry criteria. These should be met before the next test level starts. The project manager may also require additional proof in order to monitor specific project risks. The decision regarding (additional) proof involves weighing up experience, risks and associated costs. Possible forms of proof, which can often be combined, are:

- Marked/initialled test basis
  Initialling whatever has been tested in the development basis (requirements, functional design, use case descriptions and/or technical design), without indicating how the testing was done.
- Initialled checklist
  Deriving a checklist from the test basis (e.g. requirements, use case descriptions and/or technical design) and initialling what has been tested, without indicating how the testing was done.
- Test cases
  Test cases created using particular test design techniques with selected depth of coverage.
- Test cases + test reports
  As above, plus a report of which test cases have been executed, with what result.
- Test cases + test reports + proof
  As above, plus proof of the test execution in the form of screen and database dumps, overviews, etc.
- Test coverage tools (tools for measuring the degree of coverage obtained)
  The output of such tools shows what has been tested, e.g. what percentage of the code or of the interfaces between modules has been touched on. This can be a part of the build report.
- Automated tests
  The automated execution of tests in the new environment (e.g. system or acceptance test environment) very quickly demonstrates whether the delivered software is the same as the software that has been tested in the development tests and whether the installation has proceeded correctly.
- Demonstration
  Demonstrating that the (sub)functionality and/or the chosen architecture works according to the set requirements.
- Test Driven Development compliance report
  By means of review reports, it can be demonstrated that the guidelines concerning the application of TDD have been met.

It should also be agreed how the reporting should be done. Perhaps a separate test report is to be delivered, or it may form a part of regular development reports.

Application integrator approach

If both the unit test and the unit integration test are employing a structured development test method, they should obviously be aligned, so that there are neither unnecessary overlaps nor gaps in the overall coverage of the development tests. A practical method is described below for simplifying this coordination, clearly stating the test responsibilities and offering an easy aid to the structuring of the development testing.

In this approach, an application integrator (AI) is given responsibility for the progress of the integration process and for the quality of the outgoing product. The AI consults with his client (the project manager or development team leader) concerning the quality to be delivered: under what circumstances may the system or subsystem be released to a subsequent phase (exit criteria). The AI also requests insight into the quality of the incoming units (entry criteria), in order to establish whether the quality of these products is sufficient to undergo his own integration process efficiently. A unit is only taken into the integration process if it meets the entry criteria. A (sub)system is issued if it (demonstrably) meets the exit criteria (see figure 7.3).

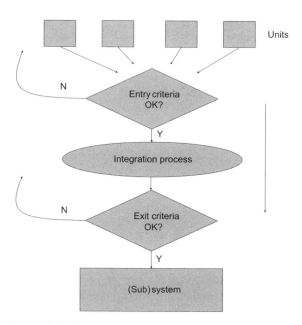

Figure 7.3: Entry and exit criteria

It should be clear that the proper maintenance of exit and entry criteria has a great impact on (obtaining insight into) the quality of the individual units and the final system. Testing is very important for establishing these criteria, since parts of a criterion consist of, for example, the quality characteristic under test, the required degree of coverage, the use of particular test design techniques and the proof to be delivered. The entry and exit criteria are therefore used in determining the strategy of the unit test and the unit integration test. This method of operation also applies when the integration process consists of several steps, or in the case of maintenance.

To avoid conflicts of interest, ideally the AI does not simultaneously fill the role of designer or development project leader. This deliberately creates a tension between the AI, who is responsible for the quality, and the development project leader, who is judged in particular on aspects such as the delivered functionality, lead-time and budget spend. The role of the AI is described in Chapter 16 "Test roles".

Salient measures in the approach are:
- A conscious selection is made of the quality to be delivered and the tests to be executed before delivery to the following phase (so that insight is also obtained into the quality).
- The tests carried out by the developers become more transparent.
- Besides final responsibility on the part of the project or development team leader, the responsibility for the testing also lies with an individual inside the development team.

Implementations of this approach have shown that the later tests will deliver a lower number of serious defects. Another advantage of the approach is that earlier involvement of the system test and acceptance test is possible. Since there is improved insight into the quality of the individual parts of the system, a more informed consideration of risk can take place as regards earlier execution of certain tests. An example of this is that the acceptance test already evaluates the screens for user-friendliness and usability, while the unit integration test is still underway. Such tests are only useful when there is a reasonable degree of faith in the quality of these screens and the handling of them.

7.2.8   Test tools for development tests

In the development tests, different tools are used from those used in the system and acceptance tests. A number of these types of tools are discussed below. They are often a part of the development environment. Many of these types of tools can be found on the Internet. In addition, there are tools that are used for the system and acceptance tests and also for the development tests, such as code-coverage tools, monitoring tools, stubs and drivers. These tools are described in the general part on test tools in section 8.5.3 "Types of test tools". It is worth noting that code-coverage tools are usually integrated with development environments that support automated unit tests.

The following types of test tools are explained here:
- Debugger
- Code-analysis tool
- Unit test tool.

Debugger
Using a debugger, it is possible, for example, to trace the cause of a specific fault and then to solve it. Debuggers make it possible, depending on the tool, to view software logic and software data and/or manipulate them at source and/or object level.

Code-analysis tool
There are tools that use the (source) code as input and, based on that, carry out all kinds of statistical analyses and checks. The aim is not so much to detect "hard faults", but to detect "unsafe" programming and fault-sensitive code. This provides the tester, for example, with information on the maintainability of the system. This information is also used to recognise more complex, and so more risk-related, system parts. A relatively higher level of test effort may be spent on these parts. With these kinds of tools, it is often possible to employ them independently of the environment (hardware, software, etc.) in which development is being carried out. This relates to a static test, in contrast to a dynamic test in which the software actually operates. This means that no input or output data is necessary and that the software does not generate any output. The tools often have certain code-analysis possibilities in the development environment. For example, compilers often have all kinds of built-in monitoring possibilities. Also, such tools are commercially available or self-built. For example, a tool that checks the code for (a part of the) norms and standards. The functionalities on which static analysis tools focus are roughly divided into three groups:

1. *Analysis of the code structure*
   Is the structure of a unit or module set up in a particular way? The tool will try, for example, to generate a Nassi-Shneiderman diagram. If this fails, a structure fault will be detected. By means of structure analyses, an assessment of the software architecture is provided.
2. *Code lines*
   Has the development been done according to the norms and standards?

Does the code comply with the style guide (e.g. are there sufficient comment lines or has appropriate indentation taken place)? Is every field in a unit given a value before it is used? Are any endless loops being created? Are the various types of variables perhaps being wrongly interspersed and used? Compilers often offer functionalities to answer these questions. For example, besides syntax monitoring, compilers can build in certain runtime checks as standard and detect non-initialled variables, unused code and infinite loops. Most compilers also produce an overview of variables and the use of these – the cross-reference overviews. HTML monitoring tools are available for web applications.

3. *Code metrics*

With the aid of this functionality, metrics can be generated in respect of the code, including in terms of size, complexity or frequency of comments. An example of a complexity metric is the McCabe formula [McCabe, 1976], with which a statement is made on the degree of complexity of the units. By complexity is meant the number of paths that can be taken within a unit. The basis of McCabe's theory is that with the increase in the number of decision points in a unit, the complexity of the unit also increases, and equally the chances of defects.

Unit test tool

Tools for the unit test are specific to the programming language. It is used by the developer to create test scripts that automatically test a unit or a piece of code in a test harness. The test cases are then included as code within the (source) code. There is often a simple management function around a unit test tool to manage several scripts for the various unit tests. With the rise of test driven development, unit test tools are attracting increasing attention.

7.3   Test activities

The development tests, i.e. the test levels of unit test and unit integration test, form an inextricable part of the developer's activities. They are not organised as an independent process with an independent team. Still, a number of different activities can be identified for the process of the unit test and unit integration test. In this section, the activities of the development tests are described in terms of the TMap life cycle model. With this, the sequence and dependencies become clearer and the process becomes more recognisable to the test adviser or test manager. In the TMap life cycle model, the test activities are divided across seven phases. These phases are Planning, Control, Setting up and maintaining infrastructure, Preparation, Specification, Execution and Completion. In practice, development-testing activities are very much less visible and recognisable than in the system or acceptance test. The results of activities are also not well documented. For that reason, the reading of the activities below may create an impression of unwanted formality. This is not the intention. The descriptions are intended to provide a rounded picture of the activities to be carried out, unmindful of the degree of formality.

> **Tip**
>
> Enumeration of all activities makes it difficult for a developer, project leader, test adviser or test manager to determine where to start if the development testing requires to be better organised. Suggestions for first steps are:
> - Investigate which test activities are already taking place. Make allowance for the fact that the test concepts are often not (all) known to the developers.
> - Instigate discussion with developers/IT manager/project manager concerning the quality of the delivered software.
> - Make agreements on the basic quality to be delivered (what to test, how to test, required degree of proof).
> - Support this by using (elementary) test techniques (in which the developers should be trained).
> - Anchor the method of operation by making the testing guidelines for basic quality a part of the programming guidelines (e.g. in the development reference chart).
>
> The above steps will lead to an increased level of quality of the development (or development tests) that can be characterised as basic skill. If higher quality is required, the following steps can be performed in a subsequent process:
> - Investigate the level of satisfaction on the part of the recipient party concerning the quality of development testing now reached.
> - If necessary, take measures for preventing defects (e.g. the quality measures from section 7.2.7).
> - Investigate whether automated testing is possible (if the development environment offers the necessary facilities) and whether it would be a useful investment. Implement this method, in the event of a positive outcome.
> - Is a level of quality higher than basic quality required for certain parts? In that case, product risk analysis and test strategy will play a role and the above discussion of basic quality will be carried out in respect of higher quality levels.

7.3.1   Planning phase

The aim of the Planning phase is the formulation of a cohesive and sound approach with which the development tests can be carried out satisfactorily. Since the development tests form an inextricable part of the development activities, no separate test plan is created for these. The reasons for this are that a parallel plan would only lead to confusion in organisational terms and that it would wrongly create the impression that the development testing is a separate, independent, activity. However, in order to inform the parties involved concerning the approach, this can be described within the development plan and is often supplemented by the distribution of separate testing instructions.

Tip

With the description of the approach to development testing, it is advisable to give emphatic attention to the *Why* of testing, so that the test levels of unit test and unit integration test will be given a more obvious place within the process of software development.

The Planning phase consists of the following activities:
1. Establishing the assignment
2. Determining the test basis
3. Analysing the product risks
4. Determining the test strategy
5. Estimating the effort
6. Determining the planning
7. Allocating the test techniques
8. Defining the test products
9. Defining the organisation
10. Defining the infrastructure
11. Organising the management
12. Feedback and consolidation of the plan.

Establishing the assignment

The development testing assignment is given implicitly in most situations. With the issue of a development assignment, it is obvious that the development tests are expected to be carried out, but it is often unclear how this should be done. In order to coordinate expectations, there should be clarity as regards which result the project requires of the development tests. That is described in an assignment description, which should correspond with the assignment description as formulated in the master test plan.

The assignment description contains the following subjects:
- Client
  The client issues the instruction for the execution of the development test. This is often the (overall) project leader or someone else with final responsibility.
- Contractor
  The contractor coordinates the development tests. This may be the development project leader or a developer in the role of test coordinator or application integrator.
- Scope
  The scope describes the limits of the development tests. If work is carried out

in accordance with the principle of basic quality and selected quality (see section 7.2.7), then the parts of the system are mentioned here, for which demonstration of the basic quality does not offer adequate certainty.

- Preconditions and assumptions
Preconditions describe the conditions laid down by third parties in respect of the development tests. Examples of preconditions are:
  - Requirements set from within the subsequent test levels (often formulated in entry criteria)
  - Minimum delivery of basic quality as a requirement of the development department
  - Compatibility with the development approach used, e.g. test driven development or pair programming.
  The assumptions describe the requirements set by the development testing on the others.
- Assignment
Finally, all the agreements between the developer and client are documented in an assignment, e.g. in the development plan. If there are no explicit requirements in the master test plan of a project in respect of development testing, this assignment formulation should also serve to obtain confirmation of the absence of these requirements.

Determining the test basis

The aim of this activity is to establish the test basis for the development tests. At first sight, this seems problem-free. After all, the test basis is the same as the development basis. Nevertheless, it makes sense to give careful consideration to this activity, as things may be overlooked, especially in the area of standards and guidelines. With waterfall methods, it can be established whether all the documents have been included in configuration management and approved. With methods where user participation is required, a list of involved users with their decision-making powers is drawn up during this activity.

Analysing the product risks

Since, in testing, there is never any question of unlimited time and resources, it is important to make well-founded choices as to which units (or combinations of units) of the system require more, or even less, test effort. The basis for making well-founded choices in this forms the risks of the system units and the system as a whole.

An aid in determining the risks is the execution of an elementary product risk analysis (PRA). Chapter 9 "Product risk analysis" describes the PRA. In a few cases, the PRA of the master test plan is sufficient, and in other cases, an elementary PRA is initiated from within the development testing. The way to simplify the PRA is to invite fewer participants, for example, just a few developers, a user and the test manager of the overall test process. Before the

PRA can be carried out, the following points should be known:

- What is the influence of the development method and architecture employed? These influence the way in which object parts can be classified. They also bring their own risks
- To what degree is automation used in unit and integration tests. This influences the risks (see section 7.2.7)
- If the work is being carried out in accordance with the principle of basic quality and selected quality, it should be known what the agreements are in respect of this basic quality (see section 7.2.7).

The risks that emerge from the PRA may influence the way in which the process of the development tests is organised. They can also influence the order in which the system will be developed. For example, in view of the risks, it may be advisable to include a Proof of Concept within the development process, in which a number of targeted development tests are explicitly executed.

Determining the test strategy

Based on the results of the PRA, the depth of testing is determined for each unit (or combinations of units) of the system. This is established per test level (unit test and unit integration test). The depth of testing is determined per characteristic/object part combination. If the method uses basic quality and higher quality levels, the testing depth is related to these. As further detailing, or as an alternative, a choice may be made from the following possibilities:

●●●   Thorough testing
●●   Average testing
●   Light testing
S   Static testing; checking and inspecting products without running software

If a cell is empty, this means that the relevant evaluation or test level can ignore the characteristic. The result of the activity "Determining the test strategy" is established in a strategy matrix and might look as follows:

Unit test example

Characteristic	RC MTP	UNIT MTP	Screen-validation routines	Database routines	Payment module units
Functionality	B	●●●	A/●●●	B/●●	A/●●●
Performance online	B	●	-	A/●●●	C/●
…					

RC MTP	=	Risk class assigned to the characteristic from within the master test plan
UNIT MTP	=	Depth of testing allocated from within the master test plan to the test (in this case, the unit test)
A, B, C	=	Risk class allocated from within the PRA; A=High, B=Average, C=Low

In addition, it should be considered whether code reviews are necessary, whether on all the code, on the code of the more risk-related units, or on the components and/or tools configured using parameters.

Estimating the effort

Based on the chosen test approach and depth, it should be considered whether the estimate of the development needs to be adjusted. Often, the estimate is included as standard in the development budget. Only when the requirements are more stringent than the basic quality will an increase to cover the extra test activities require to be estimated. Another point of focus is whether, with automation of the unit tests, the extra effort for this has been estimated. The estimate of the unit integration test will be determined much more by the scope and the chosen strategy. The various estimating techniques and the steps for arriving at an estimate are described in Chapter 11 "Estimation techniques".

Determining the planning

The developers work with one plan: the development plan. This development plan should be checked as to whether there is room for the development tests to be carried out. Unit test and integration (test) activities are usually already implicitly included, but the question is whether sufficient time has been reserved for this. Activities for the test preparation, code reviews, reworking and retesting are easily forgotten.

If it appears that the plan does not offer room for the development tests, this is the time to consult with the client. If the test strategy and resulting estimated effort and planning are not acceptable, then these steps are repeated. It can be considered here whether to test certain units in less depth (but to a minimum of basic quality). This can save time and/or money, but involves more risk.

If the strategy is amended, a new version of the strategy matrix is created. An amended strategy matrix looks as follows, in which less testing depth is shown by ○ instead of ● and more testing depth by ●.

Unit test example

Characteristic	RC MTP	UNIT MTP	Screen-validation routines	Database routines	Payment module units
Functionality	B	●●●	A/●●○	B/●●●	A/●●●
Performance online	B	●	-	A/●●○	C/●
...					

Allocating the test techniques

When the definitive test strategy has been established in keeping with the development process estimated effort and planning, the development tests should be fleshed out further. This takes place through the allocation of test techniques to the various (groups of) units. The choice of test technique to be used depends on the selected depth of testing. Suitable test design techniques for development testing are, for example, the elementary comparison test and the decision table test. Techniques such as error guessing or checklists are equally applicable (see section 14.4 "A basic set of test design techniques").

The integration of a system normally takes place in a number of steps, in which one or more units are integrated with each other and tested each time.

For the unit integration test, there are various possibilities as regards the sequence of unit integration:

- Top down
  Testing takes place from the top downwards (e.g. working from within the menu screen). Units are replaced by stubs (see section 8.5.3 "Types of test tools")
- Bottom up
  Testing is done from the bottom upwards (e.g. first data manipulation and only later the relevant screen). Units are replaced by drivers (see section 8.5.3 "Types of test tools")
- Available parts first
  Integration purely based on the sequence of delivery of the units
- Function by function
  Integration based on the functions, as established in the functional design.

What the best integration sequence is and how many integration steps are necessary depends on the position of the most risk-related parts of the system. Techniques based on paths or equivalence classes are particularly to be recommended with integration testing, depending on the size of the parts to be integrated.

Defining the test products

The aim of this activity is the unambiguous defining of the test products to be delivered and of the way of reporting. Test techniques are selected based on the test strategy. Depending on the selected quality, certain proof of the test may be required. Using this results in the following testware:

- Test cases, checklists, etc
- Test results in the form of completed checklists, logging reports, screen dumps, checked off reports, etc.

Defining the organisation

Development testing, too, requires organisation. The primary test tasks lie with the developers, but responsibility for the test process should be placed with one individual. This may be someone with the role of test coordinator, or it may be the person with final responsibility for the development. It should also be known where support in this area of testing knowledge can be obtained.

In cases of manual execution of unit tests, the choice should be made as to whether the unit test is to be done by the creator of the unit, by a fellow developer or, in the case of pair programming, by a pair. The advantage of carrying out his own test is that the developer has a lot of knowledge of the internal operation of the unit. This is the most efficient way, since no knowledge transfer is required and there are almost no communication overheads. The advantage of testing by a fellow developer is that possible blind spots on the part of the developer are discovered earlier and that the colleague will carry out a more objective test than the developer himself. A variant of this is where the developer executes his own unit's test, but a fellow developer prepares the test. The above-mentioned choices to be made are also strongly linked to the test strategy.

For the unit integration test, responsibility for the test process may be placed with the application integrator; see section 7.2.7. This application integrator is responsible for the progress of the integration process, as well as for the quality of the outgoing product. Since the application integrator does not have the volume of tasks and responsibilities that the project manager has, the testing, and with that the quality of the test object, gets more attention. The role of application integrator is further discussed in Chapter 16 "Test roles".

In development testing, thorough system knowledge and adequate knowledge of testing is required. In practice, it appears that the system knowledge is usually present, but knowledge of testing is often lacking. Ways of bringing this knowledge up to standard are:

- Training courses, in the areas of test techniques and test management and also of testing awareness
- Support and coaching by a test specialist.

Defining the infrastructure

While development testing is usually a part of the total development process, there may be specific requirements from within the testing in respect of the infrastructure. Defining this has the aim of clarifying the requirements at as early a stage as possible, so that appropriate measures may be adopted. Specific requirements may include, for example, links to adjacent systems, authorisations to be able to monitor, the necessary number of test databases or the ability to manipulate the system parameters. Any necessary test tools are also identified here. For more information on test tools that can be used in the development tests, see section 7.2.8 and section 8.5.3 "Types of test tools".

Organising the management

Management here involves the management of the development test process, the infrastructure and the test products. This is a normal part of development activities, but now there is also the issue of defects administration.

In the system test and acceptance test, the administration of each found defect is sacrosanct, for the content of this administration is used to obtain insight into progress and activities still to be carried out (retests), to create reports, to gather metrics and to analyse trends. While this is also possible for the development tests, it is much less necessary. When a unit tester finds a defect, but it is immediately solved and retested, then the defect need not be recorded (unless the unit is being used elsewhere). On the one hand this relieves the developer from 'washing the dirty laundry in public' and on the other hand it saves time. In cases of doubt as regards the cause or lack of clarity concerning the development basis, the defects are recorded in some detail, since in such cases they should be submitted to the designer within the development team. From the point when the test object is formally taken into configuration management and is to be used elsewhere, the known errors and defects found thereafter should be administered.

Feedback and consolidation of the plan

The last activity of the Planning phase concerns the documentation of the results of all the activities carried out so far and obtaining the client's approval of the selected approach. The results of all the activities carried out so far are documented in the development plan. These results should be consistent with each other. In practice, the creation of a consistent plan involves a number of cycles.

The results are fed back to the client and other interested parties (such as the test manager of the overall test process) for approval or amendment. This clarifies the test approach to be followed and makes it manageable, entirely in line with BDTM. In the event of amendment, this may lead to adjusting the strategy, in which the decreasing or increasing of testing depth is shown respectively by ○ or ● instead of ●, as previously indicated with the activity "Determining the planning".

7.3.2   Control phase

The aim of the Control phase is to provide the client of the development tests sufficient insight into, and the possibility of managing:

- The progress of the development tests
- The quality and risks of the units (or combinations of units)
- The quality of the development testing.

To this end, the responsible individual should manage the development tests optimally and report on them. The Control phase consists of the following activities:

1. Management
2. Monitoring
3. Reporting
4. Adjusting.

Management

The aim of management is to offer continuous insight into the progress and quality of the development tests and the quality and risks of the units (or combinations of units). Besides carrying out the prescribed procedures, the development testing is also supported by, and monitored for, the application of norms and standards of management. The challenge for the test coordinator or application integrator in management is not so much in following the procedures themselves, but in ensuring that the developers do so as well.

Monitoring

Monitoring progress of the plan execution is the most difficult task. It is more of a communicative activity than an instrumental one. It covers, on the one hand, the monitoring of the activities and on the other the monitoring of the world surrounding the development testing: are there any developments that influence this? Alternatively, perhaps certain information was missing when the plan was being set up. A possible situation, for example, would be one in which, based on the complexity of units measured by the code analysis tools (see section 7.2.8), it is decided to adjust details in the strategy and depth of testing.

Reporting

Periodically, and upon request, reports are issued on the progress of the (testing) process and the quality of the test object, in accordance with the agreements established in the formulation of the assignment. The progress and risk reports are usually combined into one report and included in the progress reports to be drawn up within the system development process. The content of reports depends on the defined basic quality and the selected quality. In the report, for example, the following aspects are documented:

- Status of the test object (per unit, group of units or integration step)
  - Total number of test cases
  - Number of test cases still to be executed
  - Number of test cases correctly executed
- Bottlenecks and points of discussion.

In addition, at the end of a test:

- Evaluation of the test object, what has been tested, including known errors, i.e. defects that have not (yet) been solved
- Evaluation of the test strategy, with any deviations from the original agreed test strategy being communicated to the client.

Adjusting

When a proposed measure from the reporting has to be implemented, it takes place within this activity. Measures may be:

- Adjusting the test strategy (see 'Monitoring' activity)
- Adjusting the scope. This may be the case, for example, if the scope of development is adjusted
- Adjusting the organisation. This may be the case, for example, if it appears that the chosen structure is not working in practice, or if it appears that training is required.

7.3.3   Setting up and maintaining infrastructure phase

From within the testing, there may be specific requirements as regards the infrastructure. If this is the case, it is dealt with within the phase of "Setting up and maintaining infrastructure". If there are no specific requirements, then this phase is passed over.

The specific requirements may concern the following parts of the infrastructure:

- The environment in which the testing is taking place
- The tools being used for the test
- The developer's workplace.

Requirements may be set for the organisation, use and management of these resources. Requirements may also be set in connection with the later preservation of (parts of) the infrastructure for reuse.

Environment data as a specific requirement
Something that is often forgotten is the data in respect of the environment in which the testing takes place. The environment data is the set of data that the environment needs to be able to operate (user profiles, network addresses, master tables, etc.). In order to simulate a sufficiently representative situation during the development tests, it is advisable to pay some attention to this. This is not to say that production data should be used, but data that meet as near as possible the requirements and guidelines set from within production. For example, a code for a user should have the same structure as in production. The required flexibility of the development (test) environment should be weighed against the required representativity.

7.3.4 Preparation phase

While in the Planning phase, the (definition of the) test basis is established, the test basis is often not yet available at the point of execution of this phase. In the Preparation phase, it should be examined whether the delivered test basis corresponds with and is usable in context with the agreements previously documented in the plan. If this does not appear to be the case, it may be necessary to adjust the plan. Inspection of the test basis is done by means of executing a testability review.

The form of the review is strongly dependent on the development method used. With iterative and agile methods, in which user participation plays an important part, there is generally nothing more to do beyond the review of the guidelines to be adhered to and to obtain clarity on the decision-making powers of the users involved. With waterfall methods, in which documentation is important, the delivered specifications often form a development contract. The development testability review then becomes a part of the development intake. The purpose of the development intake is to examine whether the delivered specifications are sufficiently buildable and testable for controlled progress. The development intake covers the evaluation activities that provide clarity on the completeness, clarity and consistency of the functional specifications, whereby a decision can be made concerning the potential for development, the testability and/or the conditions under which a commitment to produce results may be embarked upon.

7.3.5   Specification phase

In the Specification phase, the testers specify the required tests per unit, or integration step on the basis of the allocated test techniques from within the test basis (development basis) and make any support software for the testing, with the aim of having as much prepared as possible in order to allow the test execution to proceed as quickly as possible.

Within the Specification phase, the following activities are distinguished:
1.   Investigating test patterns (optional)
2.   Creation of test specifications
3.   Creation of support software.

Investigating test patterns (optional)

As with designing functional code, many issues in the designing and coding of the tests will have been solved earlier by other people in other projects. It is therefore important to avoid reinventing the wheel every time! Since the introduction of object orientation, developers have been using design patterns to solve design issues within their projects. Patterns provide a formal approach to the describing of a development problem, with the proposed solution and the associated factors that may have an impact on the problem or the solution. With the rise of automated development tests, *test patterns* have made their entrance, particularly in respect of iterative and agile methods.

Definition

A *test pattern* is a general solution for a specific recurring test problem.

The test world now has a number of usable test patterns. During this optional activity, the development testers examine which test patterns may be applicable to the tests to be built in. While they were created with automated testing, test patterns are also very applicable to the design of test cases for manual tests.

In more detail

Test patterns are described in the literature by the following information: name, purpose, context, fault model (environment factors; conditions for detection), proposed solution, entry criteria, exit criteria, consequences, known usage and related patterns.

Examples of available test patterns are:
- pass/fail pattern,
- collection management pattern,
- data-driven pattern,
- performance pattern,
- process pattern,
- simulation pattern,
- multi-threading pattern,
- stress test pattern.

For more information, refer to [Clifton, 2004]

Creation of test specifications

The creation of test cases takes place per unit or integration step based on the allocated test techniques, in which it is also possible that no technique is prescribed for a particular unit. If no technique is prescribed, the developer has the responsibility during the development simultaneously to design *and* execute the test cases, documenting in accordance with the agreements in the strategy and with the selected quality.

In more detail

For the situation in which a test harness (automated unit and unit integration tests) is employed, the requirements from within the test strategy are largely specified in the technical design, insofar as they are higher than the basic quality, so that the developer cannot forget this during the coding of the tests.

Not prescribing a technique does not mean that the testing may be skipped; the basic quality (100% statement coverage in the example of section 7.2.7) should always be achieved. It is possible that during this activity shortcomings and/or anomalies will be found in the development basis. It is of course important to establish these as soon as possible, in order that they may be rectified or clarified as quickly as possible. The registration and reporting of these defects should take place by means of the procedures generally set out in the development process. In respect of the execution phase, this activity takes up fewer hours than with system and acceptance tests, because the test cases are only written out if the development basis is not directly suitable as a basis for testing, unless explicit requirements are established in the strategy.

Creation of support software

In order to execute the testing of a unit or an integration step satisfactorily, it is necessary in a number of cases to create stubs (also known as mock objects) or drivers. The stubs replace units that are called by the units to be tested.

The drivers create units that call the units to be tested. The communication between the units to be tested and the stubs and drivers takes place by means of an interface. The stubs and drivers should be such that these interfaces contain realistic values and correspond with the eventual, actual interfaces between the various units. Of course, the stubs and drivers themselves are also subjected to testing.

7.3.6   Execution phase

The execution phase of the development tests takes place in parallel with the development and integration itself. In the case of Test Driven Development, the actual development starts with the coding of the unit tests (see section 7.2.7). Even when not working with such an approach, it is advisable to carry out the coding in cycles. Typing all the code in at once generally leads, in retrospect, to long searches for the causes of defects. With such reworking operations, the overview of whether all the statements have been touched on at least once is soon lost.

The activities that can be distinguished in the framework of development testing are:
1. Development of unit tests (TDD)
2. Executing (re)tests
3. Checking and assessing test results
4. Executing a code review (optional)

Development of unit tests (TDD)
In the case of Test Driven Development:
- Implement the unit test before the coding of the functionality is started
- All the code paths should be tested
- Add any extra test coverage on the basis of the technical design (where selected quality applies)
- Make the unit test independent of other tests, so that failure of one test case will have no consequences for other test cases
- In the event of a defect, prior to solving it, write a unit test that shows the presence of the defect (and the absence of it after solving it).

Executing (re)tests
Discipline is of extreme importance during the execution of the tests. The tests (unit tests and integration tests) should be executed as determined in the test strategy. If this is deviated from, it should always be reported to the development project leader, test coordinator or application integrator, so that measures can be taken. When all the tests have been successfully gone

through, the unit or the integration is ready. There is no point in carrying out extra tests under your own initiative. This makes the development (unnecessarily) more expensive. Execute the test coverage according to the agreements – no more, no less!

Checking and assessing the test results

The test results are compared against the expected results. The causes of differences may lie in a development fault. If the unit test is carried out by the developer himself, development faults are immediately reworked, until all the test cases succeed. However, there are also other possible causes: ambiguities in the development basis, faults in the development environment, but also defects in the test cases. All the problems outside the immediate responsibility of the developer, and in certain situations also the development faults, are formally reported according to established procedures. After the repairing of a defect, the relevant tests are executed again until all the tests have been executed and there are no more outstanding defects. The defects that are not, or cannot be, solved, are put together in a known-errors test report.

Executing a code review (optional)

During, or immediately after, the execution of the unit test, a code review may be carried out. By citing the (demonstrable) execution of a code review as exit criterion of the unit test, it is established at the start of the integration that operations have been carried out in accordance with the development guidelines and standards.

7.3.7 Completion phase

The aim of the Completion phase is to end the development test in such a way that a subsequent test level or development test can proceed more efficiently and more effectively.

The Completion phase includes the following activities:
1. Delivery to the next test level
2. Preserving the testware
3. Evaluating the test process (optional).

Delivery to the next test level

Delivery to a subsequent test level (usually the system test) can be done in many ways. The simplest variant, the delivery of installable software, has the big disadvantage that, particularly at the start of the subsequent test level, many apparent obstructive defects are reported, which in the end are mainly owing to unfamiliarity with the operation and to incorrect authorisation or parameter settings. The ideal form of delivery is a demonstration, in which the developer (often the application integrator) demonstrates that the system will function in the (subsequent) test environment. This can be done, for example, based on an agreed small set of functional test cases.

Preserving the testware

With this activity, it is determined which testware should be preserved for future (re)tests, so that these can be executed with a minimum of adjustment. It is very important to preserve the automated tests in particular, since the investment really starts to show returns in the subsequent tests. If possible, in consultation with the future administrator of the system (otherwise the client) an inventory is made of which documentation, tools or code is/are made available. The test products, including the proof of selected quality, are documented. Finally, the actual transfer of the testware takes place.

Evaluating the test process (optional)

At the end of the test it is established how the test process performed. Evaluation of the test strategy is particularly important here, together with the methods and techniques used and the feedback of the results from the subsequent test levels (especially the defects that should have been found during the development tests).

8 Supporting processes

8.1 Introduction

In previous chapters, we discussed the TMap test process and how it is organised. Often this is organised in projects but in addition to this project-based approach, testing (or parts thereof) can also be organised on the basis of a line organisation. More and more organisations opt for this alternative. This can be explained based on the four developments which can be summarised as *'more for less, faster and better'* (see section 1.2 "TMap evolves in step").

These developments have an impact on all disciplines within the playing field of IT. For instance, new (highly advanced) development environments are created for programmers, allowing for the relatively simple and fast design and build of complex software. Also, new (iterative) development methods emerge that assume far-reaching interaction with the users, resulting in, among other things, a significant reduction of project lead times. Moreover, management aims more and more for reuse of (internal and external) components that must be integrated into the existing IT architectures.

In short, more is built and maintained in IT these days in the same time as used to be the case. The result is a lot more test work. In addition, creating the right test approach for the IT has become far more difficult because the IT has become more extensive and complex. Combined with the increasing attention for quality in organisations, this means that the relative share of testing in IT is on the increase.

As a result, management often feels that testing, with all of the related resources, is a costly matter. Other complaints are that it takes too long and that the quality of the process is disappointing. The TMap process has a number of process elements that recur in each test. For instance the concrete activities relating to setting up a test organisation, test environment, or the deployment of test automation. But other activities, like gaining test experience, learning the test object, or defining the standards used, also recur in every testing programme. In a project-based test approach, these elements are set up for the duration of the project. Moreover, the organisation works with project standards that are often created at the beginning of the project. This results in start-up costs. Furthermore the learning effect will be limited when working with temporary personnel. The knowledge and experience gained is largely lost at the end of the project. And the test environment, which was created with such effort, is dismantled. A project must also be completed within budget and the predefined planning. This means that there is little concern for executing activities that do not yield a return on investment (ROI) within the framework of the project. Setting up testware for reuse is an activity that has little or no interest, while a structured test approach like TMap requires it.

As such, this is clearly not an optimal situation focusing on controlling costs, time and quality. A solution to this problem is assigning the execution of these set process elements in TMap to a line organisation. Such a line organisation is then called a permanent test organisation. It ensures that the knowledge concerning these process elements and the associated products is retained, and activities with a longer ROI time can be developed. When projects want to use one of the process elements (such as a test environment, using test tools or standard templates), they can be acquired as a service from the permanent test organisation.

8.2   Test policy

The test policy defined within the organisation determines which elements of the test process are allocated to the permanent test organisation and the structure of the permanent test organisation.

> **Definition**
> The test policy describes how an organisation deals with the people, resources and methods involved with the test process in the various situations.

The test policy must apply to all types of systems, infrastructures and development methods. Since testing is one of the tools to ensure quality, the test policy will have to be in line with the other policy measures and initiatives in relation to quality management. We recommend making sure that the test policy is in line with the strategic, tactical and operational policy of the organisation. At the strategic level, the impact of the organisation policy in relation to testing for the entire organisation must be determined. This results in the strategic test policy, which must be imposed and actively supported from this level. At the tactical level, the test policy must be translated to the setup per organisation component, department, product group, programme or project (depending on the setup of the organisation in question). This also involves the resources and budgets to guarantee unequivocal implementation of the test policy. Consistent implementation of the test policy results in a uniform test approach at the operational level.

Strategic

The strategic policy of an (IT) organisation has an impact on all of the underlying organisation components and its activities, including testing. The strategic policy can have many forms. For instance, it may define conditions for the internal (IT) organisation, but also for the quality objectives and the possibilities to realise these. The strategic policy can be shaped by wishes and requirements from within the organisation. But factors outside the organisation may also play a role. Examples are requirements set by external monitors and regulators, (local) legal requirements that must be complied with, or industry agreements.[1]

Tactical

At the tactical level, the strategic policy is translated to its operational implementation. This is achieved by creating regulations that specify the preconditions and standards to which the deployment of people, resources and methods must comply to realise the strategically defined objectives. They describe how the content of a structured test approach must be set up within an organisation, department, product group, programme or project (depending on the setup of the organisation in question).

Operational

At the operational level, a distinction can be made between support of the test process and the actual execution of the test process. Examples of support are issues relating to method, technical and functional advice to the testers. Examples of the execution are testing itself and test management, which each can be organised their own way. For instance, they can be executed in a matrix organisation, but also on a project basis, or partly in the line.

Example 1

A ministry has several organisational components that each offer and execute their own services autonomously. Each organisational component has its own local IT department to support these services (each with their own test approach). At the strategic level, the policy was formulated to enable fast changes (such as legal changes) in supporting IT. At the tactical level, this was translated into the consolidation of all local IT departments and their centralisation into one large IT department. In the new IT department, testing was assigned to a permanent organisation that works according to fixed methods and techniques.

Example 2

A package supplier states, in its strategic quality policy, that the quality of all (software) products delivered to clients is verified by an independent external organisation. This policy has an impact on the organisation of testing at the tactical level. For instance,

---

[1] The collective term 'compliance' is often used for factors that play a role from outside the organisation.

an overall test coordinator was appointed that acts as the liaison to the external organisation.

Example 3

As an external monitor, the central bank inspects the solidity and integrity of financial institutions. An important part of its activities involves defining requirements for the quality of the IT of financial institutions and its verification. A financial institution expresses the enforcement of these requirements in its policy. At the tactical level, this is translated to requirements specified for the use of production data. For instance, these data have to be depersonalised before using them as test data.

Reading guide

The test policy has the greatest impact on a tester at the operational level. This chapter therefore describes at the operational level how a permanent test organisation can be set up. This can be found in section 8.3 "Permanent test organisation". Test environments and test tools are two other elements that can be set up and managed outside a project. These are described in sections 8.4 "Test environments" and 8.5 "Test tools". Finally, section 8.6 "Test professionals" describes HRM for test professionals. It discusses jobs and training courses that can be identified in a test organisation.

8.3 Permanent test organisation

8.3.1 Introduction

A permanent test organisation is another way to organise the test process than discussed so far. The differences are discussed in the next sections. Section 8.3.2 "Permanent test organisation explained" describes the phenomenon of the permanent test organisation and defines what it is. Section 8.3.3 "Benefits, conditions and points of concern" discusses its specific advantages and the areas of concern involved in organising the process. The services that a test organisation can offer and the way in which agreements on these services are reached are discussed in section 8.3.4 "Supplying test services". Section 8.3.5 "General process model" then describes a general process model, after which this is elaborated on for two common types of permanent test organisations (section 8.3.6 "Two common types of test organisation"). These two types are described in section 8.3.7 "Test Expertise Centre and section 8.3.8 "Test Factory". Section 8.3.9 "Role of a permanent test organisation in outsourcing" explains the role of the permanent test organisation in the phenomenon of outsourcing (of the entire IT organisation or just the testing team). The final section (8.3.10 "Setting up a test organisation") discusses the phases and steps that must be executed when an organisation decides to set up a permanent test organisation.

8.3.2 Permanent test organisation explained

Organisations can decide to set up a permanent test organisation that offers various test services. A permanent test organisation, contrary to project-based testing, does not implement a specific element of the test process on a per project basis, but across all projects. This does not mean that no test activities are executed within the projects.

Definition

The permanent test organisation is a line organisation that offers test services.

There is no set list of activities that can be executed by the permanent test organisation, but this varies per organisation. For instance, the entire preparation and execution of tests can be moved to a permanent test organisation, but also setting up and maintaining the test environment, or setting up and maintaining test tools. As a result, every process in relation to that specific part of testing (test execution, test environment, test tools, etc) is executed according to a fixed method and with reusable resources. The process will have the same quality regardless of the project. The permanent test organisation provides these elements to projects via so-called test services.

It depends on the client how the elements of the test process are elaborated on by the permanent test organisation (and therefore which test services it delivers). Test services are acquired by clients of the permanent test organisation. The wish of the client determines which services are offered. The client can have many forms, which also determines the service delivered. For instance, when a test environment is delivered, the client may be the specific tester in a project, but also the developer of the application who wishes to try out something. Another example is a test automation service. This, too, may have different clients. It may be the tester who wants an environment in which to automate his manual test scripts. But it may also be the owner of the application who wants to have an automated test set for regression. In other words, just as there are different services, there are different clients.

Besides the client, the objective of a permanent test organisation may also determine the test services. The objective (often translated to a mission) reflects the ambition level and depends on many factors. For instance, the organisation may have been given an assignment from outside ("ensure that all test environments are set up and maintained efficiently" or "offer a solution to all issues surrounding test automation"). But an organisation may also create its own objective ("we execute all regression tests"). The objective of an organisation may change over time, as may the test service offering.

The permanent test organisation must be set up in such a way that it can offer optimal service (one or more services). The organisation is set by up by defining the tasks, authorisations and responsibilities in jobs for the employees. In addition processes will be defined, set up and selected for an organisation in which everything functions optimally. There are no hard and fast rules for this, nor is there such thing as *the* ideal setup.

8.3.3   Benefits, conditions and points of concern

Benefits

Usually the reasons to opt for a permanent test organisation are a reduction of lead time, cost reduction, and improvement of the quality of the test process. The idea is to organise specific elements of the test process across all projects, contrary to a project-based approach. But what exactly are the benefits of a permanent test organisation?

Optimal leveraging of (scarce) expertise
Often, test expertise is scarce within an organisation. Not only expertise in relation to setting up and executing test scripts, but also, for instance, to the deployment of test tools or setup of test environments. By combining all available expertise and consolidating all requests for this expertise into one place, you can optimise several issues. For instance, it is easier to find the required expertise because there is insight into all the available expertise. Furthermore, the available expertise can be divided across the various issues more effectively. Other requests can then be considered at less busy times. For instance, employees with knowledge of test tools can work for several projects at the same time.

Predictable quality of products
The services offered by the test organisation are standardised. There are products and processes with applicable standards. As such, there is no such thing as a new service - it has been done before and each employee knows how to execute it. Naturally every assignment is different, but the variation in services is limited to a minimum. This means that the quality of a service can be predicted. E.g., the service "setting up a test environment" can become a routine-based task because the process with the associated templates, tools, techniques and checklists can be used off the shelf. And because it is executed by experienced and qualified employees.

Short start-up time
Since the services are standardised, the start-up time is limited to a minimum. There is no need for courses to be attended, aspects to be tried out first, or the best approach to be determined. The start-up time of a service like setting up a test management tool can be limited to the minimum. Everything is readily available. It is just a matter of determining the client's specific wishes and requirements, configuring them and starting up.

Continuous improvement of the process embedded in the organisation
The test organisation is responsible for the services provided and executes them. It can be decided to have each execution end with an assessment of the delivered service. The lesson learned from the assessment is fed back into the organisation and incorporated into the (new version of the) service. Such formal assessment and processing of results must be embedded into the processes of the test organisation.

Consolidation and development of experiences
Combining all of the available expertise with the above, where experiences are assessed and processed, results in a continuous learning effect. This is further strengthened by cross-fertilisation between employees.

Costs and lead time easier to plan

As earlier stated, the services are standardised, the employees have the expertise and experience to execute the services. "Reinventing the wheel" is unnecessary and there is clear insight into costs and results, and how long it takes.

Cost reduction due to centralisation and scale

Testing in different places in the organisation often means that negotiations with external suppliers occur in different places. By centralising all testers and test-related activities, the test organisation can make one central price agreement with the various suppliers, e.g. suppliers of tools and testers. Furthermore, the associated advantage of scale strengthens the negotiation position, and the possibility of getting a discount.

Example

A logistics service provider uses test tools for automated testing in various locations in the organisation. Every department purchased its own licences of the test tool, handled its own negotiations about the price with the various suppliers, and organised its own training for the tools used. When it was decided to centralise the setup and maintenance of the automated tests in the organisation, one party that used the test tools was created. This benefited not only the logistic service provider, but also the various suppliers. Because instead of many different (unclear) points of contact, they also had one single point of contact. This translated to improved efficiency, reducing the number of tools in use (from 23 to 6). The licence and training costs were also reduced by 35%.

Conditions

Not every (IT) organisation can have a permanent test organisation. The organisation must comply with a series of conditions, which are:

- To achieve the benefits described above, there must be a minimum quantity of work for the permanent test organisation. This is often the case in somewhat bigger organisations.
- There must be a culture in which formal work agreements are possible. This is necessary to ensure that the permanent test organisation can reach concrete agreements with its clients.
- The organisation must deal with repeatable processes and projects. Only then can a test organisation offer standard services.
- The organisation must be able to handle and accept central organisations, such as a permanent test organisation. Central organisations can be perceived as a threat (e.g. due to their size). This must not be the case.

> **In more detail**
>
> **The permanent test organisation as a catalyst for professionalisation**
> Many IT organisations want to professionalise, but do not have the time or money. One option is to find a lever. A lever due to which professionalisation in one specific location in the IT process chain has a direct impact on multiple parts of that process chain. A permanent test organisation has the potential of acting as a lever. This is because it is at the point where the results of all earlier processes in the development chain come together in an assessable end result. The test organisation is like the spider in the web. As such, it is in an excellent position to facilitate the mutual alignment of the parties and at the same time define requirements for the quality of the process and output. Several parties can benefit by setting up a permanent test organisation. For instance, the test organisation can identify unclear or missing requirements at an early stage and detect potential problems in the development or maintenance process. Furthermore the test organisation keeps the parties involved on their toes as to the required quality and output, meaning that the end product as described at an early stage is actually realised. The test organisation is 'the conscience' of the IT process chain. In practice, this means that the test organisation is closely involved in every step in the chain and has an advisory role.

Points of concern

After setting up a permanent test organisation and making it operational, continuous attention must be devoted to a number of points. These points of concern are the precondition for the organisation's continued success.

Test services
It must be determined on a continuous basis whether the services offered by the permanent test organisation still match the client's demand. The client, not the permanent test organisation, determines the required quality level.

Test professionalism
The professionalism of the test organisation is based on the knowledge and competency of the testers on the one hand, and the stability of the tester population in the organisation on the other. If there is a continuous inflow and outflow of people in the test organisation, there is no stability and no solid basis for knowledge building. It is therefore important to keep the testers motivated. There are resources like career and compensation standards to achieve this, which are discussed in more detail in section 8.6 "Test professionals".

Reuse
Often, an important objective defined for the permanent test organisation is cost savings. One way to achieve this is by reusing e.g. testware, test data, and test infrastructure. Continuous attention will have to be devoted to the actual reuse and how it can be organised as efficiently and optimally as possible.

Autonomy

As a permanent test organisation, it is important to render an objective assessment of the delivered software or hardware, independently of the rest of the IT organisation. On the other hand, the test organisation is (still) part of a bigger unit with a bigger interest. This is an important challenge that may pose contradictions.

Preventing the 'over the wall' effect

Centralising testers and their objective role may result in a division within the IT organisation. An 'us against them' feeling may emerge, causing the common goal to be lost. One result may be that collaboration ceases and that products are thrown 'over the wall' towards the test organisation and vice versa.

Example

The following awareness grew within a government institution.

- Testing occurs in many different places in the organisation (in the IT department for different projects on the client side within various organisations).
- Everyone has their own test approach (structured or unstructured).
- The work pressure for testers varies enormously (high time pressure before a release, low time pressure after a release), which means that testers sometimes have nothing to do (the so-called 'waiting for work' situation).
- The turnover among testers is huge, a lot of acquired knowledge is lost.
- The government institution's reputation often is damaged because public software does not function properly.

An order is issued to set up a permanent test organisation with the following two objectives:
- The use of a method and techniques that conform to market standards.
- Being an attractive employer.

The objective of the permanent test organisation was to increase productivity. Less 'waiting for work' and lower turnover of testers. A 10% cost saving is realised one year after the permanent test organisation is established. This is realised in part by deploying testers more effectively, and in part because less knowledge is being lost and therefore less training required.

Points of concern for the coming year are:
- Further professionalisation of HRM.
- Further development of test services.

8.3.4 Supplying test services

A test service is a certain element of the test process for which the organisation is responsible and that is offered to the client. The services of a permanent test organisation can be highly varied. Moreover, the service offering can be expanded or reduced when new services are introduced and existing services are eliminated. All this in close relation to the policy pursued within an organisation.

Example

A financial institution opted to set up a permanent test organisation in mid 2000. The services provided by the permanent test organisation changed over the years:

2000 permanent test organisation is established
employees: 7
Services: executing tests
Development: development of new test method

2001
employees: 15
Services: executing tests & advice on use of test methodology
Development: implementing test method in projects

2003
employees: 30
Services: executing tests, test management, advice on use of test method and test tooling
Development: Testing integrated component of project process, use of metrics

2005
employees: 5
Services: instruction, advice and support
Development: Testing allocated to various product teams. Permanent test organisation is staff department.

Establishing possible test services

A service is identified by combining three aspects:
- The element (part) of testing
- The activity that is executed
- The responsibility of the organisation.

The test process consists of many process elements, which each in turn consist of elements (sub-process elements). These elements can be identified in

different ways. For instance by looking at the phases and sub-activities within
TMap. Another option is to look at the products that are delivered. There is
no set list of elements. Examples are:

- Master test plan
- Test scripts
- Tests
- Defect management tool
- The test execution phase
- Test script automation
- Defect management
- Setting up test environment.

5 activities can be executed for each element, i.e.

- Support (presentation, training, coaching, advice)
- Checking (quality checking, executing audit, reviewing)
- Preservation (administration, maintenance)
- Execution (execution, coordination)
- Research & development (development, implementation).

The organisation may bear responsibility for each combination of sub-element
and activity. Three types of responsibility can be distinguished. In ascending
order, these are: *None, Obligation of effort, Obligation to deliver results.*

No obligation
The permanent test organisation delivers the required expertise on the basis of
the request (if present and available). There is no obligation or responsibility
as to how the request is to be answered.

Obligation of effort
The permanent test organisation must deliver the required effort on the basis
of the request. The delivery must occur within a pre-defined timeframe. The
permanent test organisation is responsible for guaranteeing continuity in
delivering the effort.

Obligation to deliver results
The permanent test organisation must deliver a result on the basis of the
request. The delivery must occur within the pre-defined timeframe, at
pre-defined costs, and at a pre-defined quality level. The permanent test
organisation is responsible for guaranteeing continuity in delivering the
result.

These three aspects of element, activity and responsibility identify a service.
The service matrix is created by entering them in a table. The matrix
describes the various testing elements in the left-hand column. The topmost

row shows the activities. The junctions contain the responsibility of the test organisation.

ELEMENTS / ACTIVITIES	Supporting	Presentation	Training	Coaching	Advising	Checking	Quality checking	Execution of audit	Reviewing	Preserving	Administration	Maintaining	Executing	Executing	Coordinating	R&d	Developing	Implementing
Test tools																		
Defect management tool		X	X	X	X						X	X		XE	XE			
Test data tool																	X	X
Test environment																		
ST environment														XR	XR			
AT environment														XR	XR			
Structured testing																		
Test plan		X	X	X	X						XR	XR		XE	XE			
Logical test design		X	X	X	X						XR	XR		XE	XE			
Physical test design		X	X	X	X						XR	XR		XE	XE			
Test script		X	X	X	X						XR	XR		XE	XE			
Test execution		X	X	X	X						XR	XR		XE	XE			

X = Service without obligation
XE = Service with obligation of effort
XR = Service with obligation to deliver results

Table 8.1: an example of the service matrix.

Offering service levels

For services where obligations play a part (*Obligation of effort* and *Obligation to deliver results*), we recommend agreeing on the standard for the obligation in advance. Compliance with the standard may serve to indicate the performance level of the permanent test organisation. The standard for the obligation is laid down in so-called service levels[2] in consultation with the

---

[2] Another commonly used term is 'performance requirement'

client. A service level applies to a specific service (e.g. the service "execution of the test execution phase"). This does not mean that service levels have to be defined for all services. How service levels are established depends on the policy of the permanent test organisation. For instance, it can be decided to customise them. In this case, the service levels are established in close consultation between the test organisation and its client for each request. The consultation looks at what the client thinks important in terms of money, time or quality. It is then determined how it will be measured and which principles and preconditions will apply. An important starting point is clearly the test strategy selected.

Another way to identify service levels for test organisations is to define a number of possible options per standard service. E.g. for the service "setting up system test environment", the three possible sets of service levels are X, Y and Z. Each of these sets comes with its own price tag and requirements for the client.

Below you will find a number of examples of service levels as identified in practice for different projects and services. It is specified per service level:
- To which *aspect* it relates (e.g. the quality of the product of the service or the reliability of the service planning, or the costs for execution of the service)
- A description of the *service level* (the obligation incurred expressed in measurable units)
- The *standard of the service level* (the minimum performance to comply with the service level).

Aspect	Service level	Standard of the service level
Quality	Quantity and severity of the defects the organisation incorrectly failed to detect during the test	For each severity class, the number of defects that is detected unjustly in the first three months after the test less than 3% of the total number of defects in the severity class.
Reliability	Degree to which activities are executed conform the agreed plan and deadlines	The maximum delay on the agreed milestones is 5% of the lead time of the milestones.
Response speed	Speed at which new requests are tackled	1. Sub-process "registering assignment" completed within 1 work day. 2. Sub-process "intake" completed within 2 work days after registration. In case of requests to change the assignment, the client is notified of the consequences at the latest within 2 work days.
Knowledge retention	Effort the supplier must invest in training the core team	This is no more than 5% of the total number of test hours.
Cost reduction	Average costs of test projects	Test costs as a percentage of overall project costs is, on average for all projects <= 35%
Lead time reduction	Average lead time of test projects	Lead time of tests (on critical path) as a percentage of overall lead time of projects <= 20%

The following challenges and problems are associated with agreeing on service levels:

- The definition of the aspects and service level. Which must be chosen and how to prevent overly unilateral service levels from being defined. (e.g. focusing exclusively on cost aspect and not other aspects)
- The ability to recognise the chosen service level for the client and his organisation (the test techniques to be used, for example, don't mean anything to most clients)
- The inability to accurately measure the chosen service level
- The fact that other parties usually have an impact on the degree to which the agreed service level is realised (e.g. speed of testing depends heavily on the quality of the delivered software)
- Inadequate analysis of causes of the realisation of or failure to realise the service level
- Lack of historical data, making it difficult to define hard standards for the service level
- The standard for the service level is not realistic
- Measuring the service level has become a goal in itself and not a means to measure the quality of the service.

Publicising the test services

A success factor for the permanent test organisation is the uniformity and transparency with which the organisation offers its test services. This is important to the client, but also to the test organisation. It is vital to the clients that they know what to expect from a test organisation. Which services are offered and what do they represent exactly? For instance, what does the service "providing training" mean? Which courses are provided, how long do they take, and so on. This information is described in a so-called service catalogue, which is made available to the clients (in a document or e.g. via a page on the intranet).

The service catalogue specifies the following properties for each service:

Service description	Summary description of the service
Relationship with other services	Any relationships of the service with one or more other services. For instance, the service "supplying test tool programming" has a relationship with the service "installing test tools".
Input	The input expected from the client. For instance, a risk list is required for the service "creating MTP".
Condition	The condition that a client must meet if the service is to be successful. For instance, the requirements must be frozen for the service "creating logical test cases".
Output	The expected output of the service. E.g. a coaching plan for the service "employee coaching".
Service level	The service level of the service. E.g. for the service "making defect management tool available", this might be that it is available within 12 hours following the request.
Costs	The costs relating to a service. The costs can be specified in prices/rates, but also in hours. For instance 20 hours (4 hours preparation, 2 days course) for the service "acceptance test introduction course".

Example

"Setup and maintenance of system test environment" is a service of permanent test organisation X in a production company. It is described as follows in the service catalogue:

Service name
Setup and maintenance of system test environment.

Service description
Test organisation X ensures that the client has access to a system test environment during the test phase. In the event of problems with the environment, test organisation X repairs them. There are a number of standard components, i.e. key systems like CICS, WebSphere and Windows XP.

Relationship with other services
The condition for this service is acquisition of the service:
- Test infrastructure.
Acquisition of this service is a condition for the services:
- Support
- Maintenance.

Input
Problems with the availability of the system test environment must be reported via the Test Organisation X Service Desk.

Output
The system test environment is available and registration, solution and feedback of disturbances in relation to the system test environment are provided in the agreed test period.

Service level
70% availability. Test organisation X provides feedback on the status and progress of the incident to the reporting party within one hour following the first report in 100% of the incidents reported to the Service Desk.

Costs
Cf. production agreements.

8.3.5   General process model

A number of processes have to be set up in the permanent test organisation to offer the services. These processes are split up into two groups. The processes for the *services* act on behalf of the execution of the services provided by the organisation. The processes of the permanent test organisation serve to support the execution of the services. This is shown in figure 8.1 "Process model of the permanent test organisation".

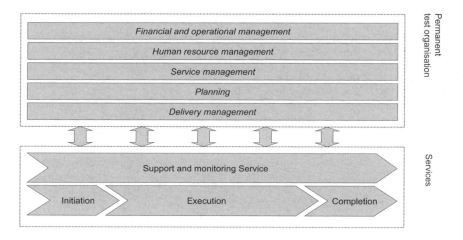

Figure 8.1 Process model of the permanent test organisation

The service process consists of two parallel primary processes: The process for the actual execution of the service in an assignment, and the process that supports and monitors the execution from the organisation. The processes serve to support and focus on the services that are provided, the employees providing the services, and the combination thereof. The processes are described in greater detail below.

Initiation

This is the first phase for execution of the assignment. The assignment always comprises one or more services of the organisation tailored to the client's specific situation. The initiation phase serves to describe the scope of the assignment accurately. This can be done by creating a so-called *assignment description* and asking the client to approve it. An assignment description concretely describes:
■ The assignment and the client's expectations in relation thereto
■ The preconditions and basic assumptions

- The agreements concerning the delivery of support for workplace, methods, training and coaching by the organisation
- The agreements on monitoring by the organisation in relation to communication lines, progress reporting and consultation
- The deliverables.

Furthermore the initiation phase is used to identify what is available in the permanent test organisation for (re)use on behalf of the assignment. This may include templates and standards, but also existing test scripts from previous releases, test environments or tools.

Execution

In this phase, the assignment is executed conform the agreements with the client. Furthermore, the parties communicate via the agreed communication lines on the results, progress, risks and bottlenecks in the execution of the assignment.

Completion

Reuse of resources is one of the success factors of the permanent test organisation. In this phase, the assignment is assessed and a satisfaction measurement made with the client. The lessons learned from the assessment are fed back into the organisation and incorporated into the (new version of the) service. This results in formal process improvement embedded into the processes of the test organisation.

In addition to the assessment, attention is devoted to the handover of products to the test organisation. The products were identified during "initiation". It is determined to what extent these products must be retained for reuse. If necessary, the products are adapted. Examples are templates, test environments, test scripts and tools.

Support and monitoring

The organisation continuously supports and monitors the assignment process as described above. The progress, risks and bottlenecks involved in the execution of the assignment are monitored. Where necessary, new agreements are made on the assignment. It may also be decided that the organisation will provide support for the execution of the assignment, in the form of coaching or training.

Delivery management

This process covers activities that aim to win assignments for the organisation and manage (long-term) assignments. Examples of long-term assignments are maintaining the test environment or repeated testing of releases. In this case, a contract is created concerning how both parties will handle the assignment. It specifies agreements on the service level provided by the organisation. Other subjects are the manner in which the specific assignments (test this release) are executed within the context of the general assignment (release testing). As such, this contract does NOT replace the assignment description from the initiation phase, although it may serve as a basis for it.

Planning

The planning process ensures that the right employee is deployed for the right assignment. 'Right' in this context means that the knowledge and competencies of the employee match the knowledge and competencies required for the assignment. Other aspects relating to 'right' are:

- Availability (short term, is the employee available in the short and long term, does the employee have impending leave, courses, etc?)
- Career perspective (how does the employee want to evolve and what new knowledge and competencies must he gain to this end?)
- Location (this is true only for organisations with multiple geographic locations).

These aspects make clear that the planning process is interwoven with all of the other processes and has many stakeholders. It serves the interests of the employee, assignment management and the entire permanent test organisation.

Service management

The range of services provided by the organisation is not set in stone – it may grow or be reduced. To this end, it must be determined periodically whether the current service offering is in line with demand and with what the employee can do. In addition services must be known (to the client, assignment management and employee) and the products for the services must be up-to-date and in line with the latest developments. Various activities can be set up to this end:

- Research (monitoring the market to map which new services must be developed and which existing services can be eliminated)
- Development of new services (the development of new services with related products and resources)
- Knowledge management (managing the services with related products and resources)
- Service marketing (ensuring that current and prospect clients are aware of the services).

Human resource management

The process of human resource management (HRM) aims, among other things, to continuously develop the career of the test organisation's employees. In combination with planning, this creates the instrumentation for the employee's career development. It allows him to continue to develop and grow in the compensation and career areas. This requires matters like defined job positions with associated competency and compensation levels. Attention must also be devoted to individual training plans and assessment and reviews. Section 8.6 "Test professionals" discusses these matters in greater detail.

Financial and operational management

Management has two key aspects – the financial and the operational. Financial management is a continuous process based on budgeting (what are the expected costs and benefits) and monitoring (what are the actual costs and benefits). Operational management can be executed on the basis of many factors, an example is KPI (key performance indicator).

A KPI is an indicator to establish the performance of an organisation or part of it. There is no fixed set of indicators for test organisations. These depend mainly on the objective and policy of a test organisation and how they are defined. A few options:
- The percentage of employees executing assignments for clients
- The percentage of assignments completed within budget
- The number of defects (in relation to defects detected earlier) occurring in production
- The percentage of test services purchased as compared to test services provided by others.

8.3.6   Two common types of test organisation

As described above, there are many types of test organisation. For instance, a distinction can be made in the services offered. The choice of services depends on the objective of the organisation, which in turn depends on many internal and external factors. As such, there is no right or wrong structure for a test organisation. Two types of test organisation are common in actual practice. These are:
- The permanent test organisation as a test expertise centre (TEC)
- The permanent test organisation as a test factory (TF).

The two differ, among other things, in the services they offer and their responsibilities in this respect. The TEC is mainly a supplying and advisory organisation that takes on an "obligation of effort" at most when providing services. For instance, it may outsource testers or test managers to a project. Or offer advice on a test approach or test tool to be used. The activities are always executed under the responsibility of the project.

However, the TF accepts an "obligation to deliver results" for many of its services. The process can be compared with a factory with permanent personnel (testers), machinery (infrastructure), standardised work procedures, etc. Different clients (departments, projects, systems) can outsource their complete test assignments to this type of test organisation. The client takes his assignment to the test organisation, the assignment is scheduled in the form of work assignments for the employees, the infrastructure is configured the right way, the assignment is executed, and the client can pick up the product (reports, advice and possible defects in the tested objects) at the agreed time.

Both test organisations make a distinction based on demand frequency in the test services. The test service is approached from a different perspective for incidental requests ("set up a test environment") than for structural requests ("test releases"). Service levels are agreed on when structural questions are involved. The following two sections discuss both types of test organisation in greater detail.

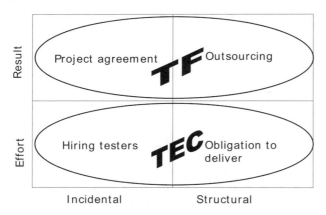

Figure 8.2: Two common types of test organisation

8.3.7 Test Expertise Centre (TEC)

The TEC is a permanent test organisation in the line that usually provides services to projects that require testing. It constitutes the interface between the test activities in the projects and e.g. organisation-wide test regulations as described in the test policy. With the TEC, the execution of and responsibility for the activities lies with the projects, the TEC only provides people and expertise. An important reason to set up a TEC is efficiency. A properly functioning TEC prevents that new methods, techniques and standards are developed time and again in projects. The wheel does not have to be reinvented over and over again.

In addition to delivery and support for projects, the test policy is anchored in a structural manner. The TEC manages the universal resources and monitors their correct use in the various projects. Another advantage of a TEC is that it bundles usually scarce test expertise. The manner in which a TEC is set up and organised depends on matters like the test policy, the type of organisation within which the TEC operates, and its maturity.

Organisation
The organisation of a TEC can vary considerably per organisation. For instance, a TEC may only employ a group of test consultants, with the testers themselves based in other parts of the organisation. In this case, the testers may be employed by the departments created per system. They are hired directly by the projects, and the test consultants monitor the correct use and implementation of the test methods, techniques and tools. Figure 8.3 "Possible organisational position of a TEC" shows the TEC as a sub-department within the IT department.

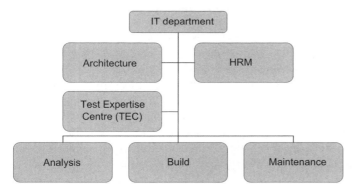

Figure 8.3: Possible organisational position of a TEC

In another variation, the TEC may outsource testers to projects. The TEC then bears line responsibility for testers, but it can also hire and outsource external testers. In this case, the TEC is also responsibility for entering into business relationships with suppliers of such test capacity. In this way, it ensures that testing proceeds efficiently without compromising continuity and required knowledge.

Processes

The service process of a TEC aims to deliver employees with a certain expertise. As such, it will focus on finding the right employee for an assignment in the initiation phase. The expectations of the client in relation to the expertise required from an employee are specified in the assignment description. The assessment serves to feed the newly acquired expertise (e.g. in the form of testware) back into the organisation for reuse at a later time. Support and monitoring during the execution of the assignment focuses primarily on the correct use of methods and techniques. The TEC is managed mainly on the basis of the number of 'outsourced' employees and client satisfaction. It must also keep up with new developments in the organisation, for instance the future use of new hardware or software. The TEC must anticipate such developments by ensuring that its employees receive new or additional training at an early stage.

Services

The services provided by the TEC therefore focus on supplying capacity and expertise. These services never involve an "obligation to deliver results". The only responsibility it may have is an "obligation of effort" when providing capacity. Examples of services that the TEC may provide:

- Supplying testers, test managers and test automation experts
- Giving courses on the subject of test techniques and test management
- Reviewing various aspects of testware
- Providing advice on the use of tools, setting up test data and environments
- Coaching users in an acceptance process
- Managing corporate test methodology, techniques and regulations
- Answering questions in relation to testing.

Figure 8.4 "The TEC as manager of test processes" shows how the TEC can act as the manager of test processes in an organisation. In this example, the TEC advises the project manager on the test process to be followed and the organisation of the test in the project. The TEC supplies (outsource) the test managers and testers for the system test. It also provides services to train the testers for the UAT (e.g. future users of the system) in the project in the relevant test techniques and coaches this group during test execution. Lastly, it monitors all test activities, ensuring that methods and techniques are applied correctly.

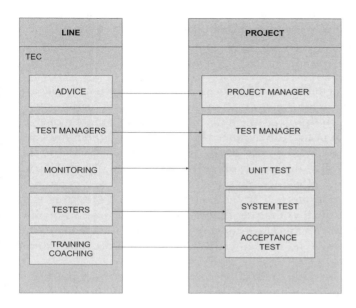

Figure 8.4: The TEC as manager of test processes

Service: Test process monitoring

In the example above, the service Test process monitoring has a special place. A number of specific elements that can serve as a source of information can be distinguished in its setup. For instance, the test process itself generates a number of testware products (such as a test plan and e.g. test cases) that give an indication of the way of the testing. The test process can also yield data (such as executed tests and numbers and types of defects) that provide more information on the progress of testing and the quality of the system to be tested. Two monitoring techniques have been set up on the basis of these sources of information:

Checklists and audits
The checklists contain a number of questionnaires on the testware the test process is expected to deliver. The main testware products are the master test plan and test strategy, the detailed test plans, the progress report, test cases, test scripts, and final report. The checklists focus on the content of these products, as well as the standard according to which the products are created.

The checklists can be used in two ways. The TEC can make them available to the projects. The projects can use them to gain insight into how well they are executing the test process. However, there is a risk that projects handle them subjectively and a conflict of interests emerges (checking one's own work). An objective way is to use these checklists to have a TEC test consultant perform a periodical audit.

Metrics
Another way to gain insight into the test process is by using metrics. Metrics are data compiled into useful information, often in a diagram or a mathematical formula. To this end, the project will have to maintain a number of data – such as the number of hours, the number of test scripts, and the number of defects per severity class. Based on this data, insight can be obtained into the progress of testing as well as the quality of testing and the test object. Metrics like test effectiveness and efficiency can serve this end. The coverage ratio of testing can also be used as metrics. In the end, the main aim of testing is to provide insight into the quality of the test object – or rather the missing quality. The most important metrics therefore concern the data on the quality of the system to be tested. Please refer to chapter 13 "Metrics" for more information on this subject.

The degree to which the techniques are used is closely related to the type of project and application. With the information generated by these techniques, the TEC obtains good insight into the risks of the test process and the performance of the project. Based on the information obtained this way, the TEC can report, advise and manage the organisation and project on the basis of standardisation, test process quality and therefore product quality.

Tip

Monitoring when outsourcing
The monitoring service has a very useful place in organisations that outsource all or part of their testing. Please refer to section 8.3.9 "Role of a permanent test organisation in outsourcing".

Success factors

Whether the TEC is successful, depends on a variety of factors (see section 8.3.3 "Benefits, conditions and points of concern"). A few examples:

- The continuity of delivery of capacity and required expertise may represent a risk. This may be the case in particular when the TEC does not employ the testers as permanent employees, but acts as an intermediary between projects and test personnel suppliers. This problem can be remedied by building good relationships with the suppliers and making strict agreements concerning the deployment of testers.

- An adequate work reserve in the form of test assignments needs to be available to safeguard the TEC's manpower. One way to guarantee this is the principle of the 'forced sourcing'. It means that within the IT organisation, projects are forced to acquire services exclusively from the TEC and from no other (external) party.

■ Adequate system and domain expertise must be available for every assignment. If this is insufficient (e.g. in the case of very obsolete or rather innovative systems), knowledge can be extracted from the project or other departments.

■ Conflicts may emerge between the TEC and project management as to the degree to which test processes must be implemented. The TEC processes must therefore have organisation-wide support, and good communication and escalation lines must be arranged for possible differences of opinion. The cooperative stance that the TEC takes in differences of opinion partly determines the success. So-called 'ivory tower' behaviour, where the TEC takes the position of a bureaucratic department that strictly monitors a variety of rules and regulations, is punished immediately.

Example

A TEC for a medium-sized service provider reports so-called realised results every month. This is achieved by maintaining a results file. This clarifies, in concrete cases, the added value of the TEC. Part of this results file is shown below:

Date	Project/Service	Situation	Result
2006-05-12	XYZ	Received request for 5 testers	After review of test strategy, managed to reduce request to 3 testers initially
2006-05-27	Test tools	Supplier price agreements	After consultation with supplier, managed to eliminate 3 licences and agreed master price for remaining 8 licences
2006-06-04	Test execution	Temporary drop in requests	Structuring own process. Testers deployed ad hoc for ABC release testing.
2006-06-10	ABC	Test manager for project gets stuck	Situation remedied through test consultant coaching
...	...	...	...

8.3.8 Test Factory (TF)

As described earlier, a project-based test approach means that a test is set up for the duration of the project. A test process will have to be created specifically for the project in this case. The project has to be manned and the infrastructure ordered and installed. Because the tester is usually assigned to the project only temporarily, the learning effect is limited and the acquired knowledge and experience are often largely lost at the end of the project. And the test environment, which was created with such effort, is dismantled at the end. This is clearly not an optimal situation focusing on controlling costs, time and quality.

One permanent test organisation type that mitigates the aforementioned disadvantages of a project-based approach is the Test Factory (TF). It allows clients to allocate their test assignments on a structural basis. The TF has a fixed team of testers, workplaces, test infrastructure and test tools. The TF can execute complete tests (from test plan to final report) but also parts of such tests (e.g. test specification). The test process in a TF can be compared with a factory with permanent personnel (testers), machinery (infrastructure), standardised work procedures, etc. Different clients (departments, projects, systems) can outsource their test assignments to this type of test organisation.

A TF is organised in so-called *test lines*. A test line is set up for clients that outsource test activities to the TF on a structural basis. Every test line has a permanent key team of employees that ensure continuity and knowledge retention. There is also a flex team. When the work available in their test line is insufficient, they are assigned to other test lines (temporarily). They thus represent a flexible pool of employees that are deployed to a test line depending on the work pressure. Figure 8.5 "Possible organisational structure of a TF" shows a possible organisation structure of a TF.

Definition

A test line is the operational organisation to provide test services to one or more clients. A test line has a fixed team of testers, infrastructure, test tools and standardised work procedures.

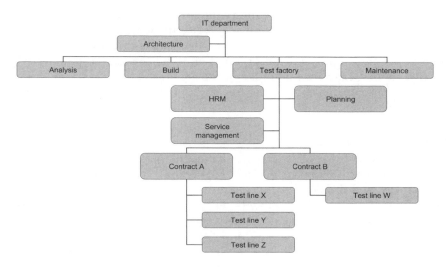

Figure 8.5: Possible organisational structure of a TF

Processes

The client takes his assignment to the test organisation, where it is scheduled in the form of work assignments for the employees. The infrastructure is configured the right way, the assignment is executed and the client can pick up the product (reports, advice and possible defects in the tested objects) at the agreed time. The quality standards of the test organisation guarantee consistent high quality of testing for the client. Another advantage is that the usually scarce expertise in the field of structured testing, test environment and tools is leveraged optimally this way. A TF emphasises the long-term aspects of the test process (efficiency, quality) far more than a one-off project aspect like providing quality advice in time and budget. A lot of attention is devoted to e.g. the reusability of testware, flexibility of the infrastructure, test automation and review, and optimisation of the standardised method. Personnel must be trained in testing to realise a core team of professional testers. To ensure that the employees become and remain motivated, the personnel department sets up test positions and the TF offers the employees a career path in testing.

The service process of a TF aims to execute services under its own management with its own employees. As such, the initiation phase of the primary process will be more comprehensive in a TF. More attention is devoted to preparatory work, such as creating the estimate and performing an intake of the required resources of the client. Examples are the object to be tested, requirements, test environment, or available test scripts.

The completion is also somewhat more extensive because it involves an internal and external delivery. The internal delivery is within the TF, the test line makes the delivery. A first quality check occurs here. The result is then delivered externally to the client, once again involving a series of assessments. There is also a later assessment (after 2 to 3 months) to review the delivered work in the longer term. Support and monitoring during the execution of the assignment focuses primarily on costs and lead time in addition to the correct use of methods and techniques.

Testware management

An important task of the TF is testware management. Good organisation in this respect can yield many advantages. This benefit translates to the quick start-up of tests and the efficient execution of the test of a new release. It is necessary that the testware is kept up-to-date. A number of preconditions must be met to set up this management correctly. The main thing is that there must be an administrator. Someone must fulfil the role of administrator to manage the testware between the various tests. A second precondition is that this role must have the right tasks, authorisations and responsibilities. A last precondition is that the service level must be specified for the management, for instance how fast and when the testware must be supplied. This is balanced, naturally, by the condition that must be met for testware management. This covers issues such as working with certain templates and according to certain techniques.

The administrator in consultation with (assignment) management of the TF ensures this. Managing testware is a vital part of the various services that are provided. Service management is responsible for executing the management. The following activities must be organised in relation to testware management in a TF:

Phase Initiation
Activity 1: Establishing the required testware
The trigger to start a new test assignment is the notification, from assignment management, that a new release of a system is delivered, for instance. The (functional and technical) changes compared to the previous version are indicated. This makes it possible to determine which testware is necessary and when it must be delivered.

Activity 2: Delivery of testware
The administrator collects the available testware and delivers it physically from service management to the test assignment. This can be registered in a delivery document or materials list.

Phase Execution
Activity 3: Adapting testware and executing test
After the administrator has delivered the testware, the testers involved in

the project update its accuracy and completeness. Changes in the testware may be necessary due to the changes implemented in the system. The testware changes are made in the version delivered to the testers, not the central version. They may involve both adding and modifying test cases, for instance. But test cases can also be eliminated. This is important to ensure that the number of test cases does not become unnecessarily large, reducing manageability and overview.

Phase Completion

Activity 4: Returning testware

After the test assignment is completed, the testware is frozen and physically handed over to the administrator in the service management process. This can be registered in a return document or materials list.

Activity 5: Archiving testware

This step involves archiving the testware in such a way that exactly the same testware can be retrieved for a new request. An important condition is that the testware cannot be changed between assignments without prior agreement from the administrator.

Service contracts

A service contract is used for structural assignments that recur regularly. It contains all contractual arrangements in relation to the structural assignments. Subjects are:

- Client/supplier
- Objective of the client
- Scope (which systems, which test levels, which test services)
- Execution site
- Method
- Quality assurance
- Organisation
- Facilities
- Service levels
- Preconditions and principles
- Financial arrangements
- Term and termination
- General terms and conditions
- Signature.

8.3.9   Role of a permanent test organisation in outsourcing

More and more often, competencies like testing or development are outsourced in part or completely. Sometimes even the entire IT department is eliminated, and all IT operations are outsourced because the organisation wishes to focus on its core activities. When the entire outsourced operations chain is seen as one single unit, we do not recommend implementing the products of these activities in the organisation without due consideration. The risk that certain functional and non-functional properties are not realised or realised only in part, is great. Another risk is that what has been built does not comply with the required quality level. Outsourcing works only when a close collaboration exists between the outsourcing organisation (demand organisation) and the supplier (supply organisation).

The permanent test organisation plays an important part in this collaboration. Because however good the processes or intermediary products may be, the end products (such as the system, but also e.g. the procedures) must always be tested by the outsourcing organisation. Only then can the delivered system be taken into production on the basis of a thorough advice on the quality and risks. If the supplier does not provide adequate testing, an excessive number of defects will be detected at a late stage (acceptance test or production) resulting in project delays or other damage.

To be certain that no duplicate testing occurs and no parts are forgotten, it is vital to align and monitor the various test levels of the demand and supply organisations. This can be done by a test professional with the role "overall test coordinator" (OTC, described in section 5.2.8 "Defining the organisation"). The task of the OTC involves coordinating the various tests, specifying and monitoring the test method, and informing and advising the project management on test progress and the quality of the tested system. The permanent test organisation is in the perfect position to host this role. The level of verification and management depends heavily on the type of outsourcing. This can be organised in a service, such as monitoring, as is described in section 8.3.7 "Test Expertise Centre".

One tool for the OTC is creating a master test plan covering all test levels. By default, the master test plan applies to one project. However, outsourcing generally goes beyond one single project. The initial investment does not usually begin to yield a return until subsequent releases of the system, i.e. during maintenance. To prevent new agreements on the what and how of testing having to be made for every release, so-called Generic Test Agreements (GTA's, described in section 5.4 "Generic Test Agreements") are created. GTA's resemble a master test plan and sometimes even replace it. The

GTA's contain the general agreements on e.g. the test process, estimating method, procedures, communication, documentation, etc. In fact, GTA's are a kind of contract specifying service levels between the demand and supply organisations. This in turn is a part of the contract, also containing e.g. agreements on timely delivery of capacity, response times, training new people, pricing, etc.

If only the test process is outsourced, the collaboration involves highly specific challenges. One of these is the manner in which the test effort will be financially settled. How will this be established? Aspects like the availability of domain expertise, the responsibility for the test environments, the available tools for testing (and licences), and sometimes legally required function separations require attention as well.

> **Tip**
>
> Overall test coordination is useful in organisations in which all or a part of the testing is outsourced. It can also be used in situations where many projects are involved, where testing occurs in multiple locations, or where the supplier handles the testing.

8.3.10 Setting up a test organisation

When an organisation decides to use a permanent test organisation, a process is started to create that organisation. Setting up a permanent test organisation involves six activities that are described below. Setting up a permanent test organisation represents an organisation change. A new organisational unit is created, and in some cases this means that people have to switch departments, with consequences for their tasks, authorisations and responsibilities. As such, the execution of the general activities relating to organisation changes (e.g. tuning with the Works Council) will have to be taken into account in addition to the six activities. All this makes setting up a permanent test organisation a long-term process that may take months or even years.

Activities
The migration process to switch from the existing situation to a permanent organisation involves six activities:
1. Inventory
2. Definition
3. Organisation
4. Awareness
5. Trial
6. Implementation

The diagram in figure 8.6 "Setting up a test organisation" shows the overall order of and dependencies between the various activities.

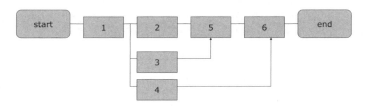

Figure 8.6: Setting up a test organisation

Method of operation

A preliminary study is done when there is an interest in setting up a permanent test organisation. A preliminary study proposal is created that indicates how to clarify the issue, the direction in which a solution can be found, and the content. Subjects are a feasibility study, organising a session, and use of the service matrix. The proposal contains an overview of the stakeholders in this activity, plus an overall time estimate and planning. The preliminary study ends with a plan of approach for setting up the test organisation, on the basis of which the project board can make a go/no go decision for the follow-up process. The plan of approach for setting up the organisation is complete at the end of the preliminary study. It contains an overall overview of the 5 other activities and an estimate of the lead times. It describes the activities definition (with as important product the process description), organisation, trial, awareness and implementation. The plan of approach also contains a proposal for the trial project. This project ends with a report, on the basis of which the project board can make a go/no go decision for the implementation activity. During the implementation, the organisation set up for a trial project is adjusted if necessary and implemented in the organisation in an increasingly broadly-based manner.

Activity 1: Inventory

This activity involves an inventory of the current testing method in the organisation. The test policy of the organisation that describes how the organisation deals with the people, resources and methods involved with the test process in the various situations plays an important part in this activity. The inventory results also contain a conclusion and approach for the subsequent activities: definition, organisation, awareness and testing. The result is described in a plan of approach. The (final) activity, implementation, follows at a later stage after the trial project is completed.

Activity 2: Definition

Based on the results of activity 1 "Inventory" the preconditions for a permanent test organisation are elaborated step by step. A process description of the test organisation is created. The result is a concrete process description of the permanent test organisation for the trial project, including the deliverables of the trial project. The services to be delivered by the organisation are specified unambiguously. The agreements considered necessary in the preliminary study are made and confirmed.

Activity 3: Organisation

Based on the results of activity 1 "Inventory" and in parallel with activity 2 "Definition" the organisation is set up. While the activities to be executed here depend on the results of activity 1 "Inventory" a possible description follows to clarify this step. Setting up an organisation is done in terms of services. Examples are test expertise, test lines, and testware management. For test expertise, this means elaborating the various test functions. The aspects that can be considered generic to a test are set up in the test lines. This means procedures, methods, techniques, test strategies, test environments, testware and test tools. The process from the existing situation to the permanent test organisation is a migration process, which is described in a migration (activities) plan. The result is a concrete description of the organisation and its position in its environment (internal and external organisation). A step-by-step plan according to which the organisation can be established.

Activity 4: Awareness

In parallel to a number of other activities, the organisation works on the awareness of the test organisation. Activities are presentations, workshops, articles in internal magazines, etc. It is important in this activity to obtain and retain continuous commitment on the part of the management, clients, and personnel executing the activity. The stakeholders in the migration process to the test organisation at the various levels in the organisation must be aware of the significance of the test organisation. If this is not the case, the proposed changes will never be assimilated into the organisation and the organisation will tend to return to the old methods. In fact, awareness must not be considered a separate activity but rather a vital precondition. If there is inadequate commitment, it is better to cancel the migration process. As a result there is support from the stakeholders, such as line managers, project managers and (test) personnel.

Tip

Support from line management
It is important in this activity that the people see that the line management supports the migration process. Tools to achieve the required awareness are presentations and workshops. For this reason, the awareness-building process must start with the line management and only later move to the project management, test leaders and testers.

The long-term objectives and costs/benefits are discussed with the line management. The operational issues and short-term migration activities are discussed with the testers. If the line management is skipped, the test organisation runs a great risk of failing, in particular when the regular operations and the migration process have clashing priorities at one point.

Activity 5: Trial

The (new) approach in the test organisation is tested via one or more trial projects to demonstrate the feasibility both internally and externally. The results of the trials are recorded. Any improvements in both the organisation and the approach are implemented. The result is an adjusted test organisation for the trial test process with a justified go/no go decision for wider implementation.

Activity 6: Implementation

To work as efficiently as possible with a test organisation, it must be used as widely in the organisation as possible. Based on the results of activity 5 "Trial" and with the support realised via activity 4 "Awareness" the organisation is implemented and anchored, if necessary with some adjustment. The end result is a permanent test organisation supported by the client organisation, which can be used by multiple projects for their test activities.

In more detail

Pitfalls in setting up the test organisation
The success of a permanent test organisation involves conditions and factors as described in sections 8.3.3 "Benefits, conditions and points of concern" and section 8.3.7 "Test Expertise Centre". There are a number of pitfalls that must be taken into account when setting up a test organisation:
• Everyone is enthusiastic while the plans are created. When people (projects, managers, programmers, testers, etc) actually experience what it means and what impact it has on their day-to-day work, their enthusiasm might falter. This must be kept in mind.
• There is no such thing as too much communication. It is often said that organisational changes are 20% change and 80% communication. The same holds for setting up a permanent test organisation. It is important to continue communicating and repeating about the test organisation. This involves communicating about the objectives, activities, name, services, role, location, etc. It helps to have a name and logo for the new organisation at an early stage. Use every available option to communicate, for instance the intranet, corporate magazine, posters on walls, and the notice board near the entrance. Use the e-mail medium with restraint.
• The current testers are unavailable. A situation that might occur is that the testers who are all over the organisation before the change are recruited by other organisation units (by means of new promises or jobs). This makes them unavailable for the new

permanent test organisation, meaning that there is a risk that the first obligations cannot be complied with. This recruiting is based on the fear to lose knowledge and competency.

- Unrealistic expectations can inhibit the success of a test organisation. Expectation management is therefore a vital part of setting up a new test organisation.
- The 'What are all these testers doing here' syndrome. Once all testers and the test activities are centralised in an organisation, it becomes really clear how much an organisation spends on them. As a result, the management may be shocked and impose the first cost reduction measures. This might result in problems when done before the test organisation is properly set up.
- The forced sourcing system is a condition. To ensure that the test organisation starts up quickly, it is important for an adequate work reserve in the form of test assignments to be available. One way to guarantee this is the principle of 'forced sourcing'. It means that within the IT organisation, projects are forced to acquire services exclusively from the new test organisation and from no other (external) party. It is an option to link this to a maximum period in order to force the permanent test organisation to operate competitively.

8.4   Test environments

8.4.1   Introduction

A fitting test environment is required for dynamic testing of a test object (running software). Setting up and maintaining the test environment represents an expertise of which testers generally have no knowledge. This is why a separate department – outside the project – is generally responsible for setting up and maintaining the test environment. Testers are, however, heavily dependent on the test environment – no test can be executed without a test environment.

This section discusses in greater detail what a test environment is and what its setup and maintenance look like. Section 8.4.2 "Test environments explained" defines what a test environment is, after which section 8.4.3 "Setting up test environments" describes the setup requirements for test environments. It also discusses the factors that determine the setup. The next section (8.4.4 "Problems in test environments") describes typical problems relating to test environments, followed by two solutions to prevent these problems: the DTAP model in section 8.4.5 "DTAP model" and three management processes (Configuration Management, Change Management and Release Management) in section 8.4.6 "Processes in test environments". Section 8.4.7 "Two special test environments" then describes two special types of test environment. The points of concern when the test environment is outsourced are described in section 8.4.8 "Test environments when outsourcing". To conclude this section, the last section 8.4.9 "Setting up and maintaining test environments as a service" explains how a permanent test organisation can set up a service for setting up and maintaining a test environment.

8.4.2   Test environments explained

> **Definition**
>
> A test environment is a composition of parts, such as hardware and software, connections, environment data, maintenance tools and management processes in which a test is carried out.

Hardware refers to all the tangible parts of a computer (screen, hard disk, network card, etc.). Test environment software refers to all the programs that should be present on the available hardware in order to run the software under test, such as operating programs, DBMS, network and other support programs. Connections are everything that is required to allow the test object to communicate with other systems. The environment data is the set of data that the test environment requires to be able to work with these (user profiles, network addresses, root tables, etc.). Maintenance tools are tools that are required specifically to keep the test environment operational, and management processes are all the activities that are carried out around the setup and maintenance of a test environment.

The setup and composition of a test environment depend on the aim of the test. The success of a test environment depends on the degree to which it can be determined to what extent the test object meets the requirements. Every test may have a different aim, which is why every test can use a different test environment. A unit test, for instance, requires a completely different configuration of the test environment than a production acceptance test.

Sometimes a test environment has a limited size (e.g. one single PC when testing a small accounting package), while sometimes it involves a huge collection of hardware and software, interfaces and procedures, set up in many different sites (e.g. for testing the reservation system of an airline company). In addition to the test level and test type, other aspects - like the maintenance standards, the type of application, the organisation structure and, not least, the available budgets - play an important part.

Test environments represent a critical success factor for virtually every automation project. There are various reasons for this. For instance, in a production environment the maintenance processes have been established for a long time and are still being improved. This does not apply to a test environment. Processes are not yet or partly established, and this may often vary per department and platform. The complexity increases further if the test environment also uses new technologies that have not yet been taken into production and with which the organisation therefore has less experience.

Another development in recent years is that applications use an increasing number of different types of hardware and software. When setting up a test environment for this type of applications, this is translated to a chain of different hardware and software configurations with mutual interfaces. The metaphor 'the chain is as strong as its weakest link' then holds true. If one configuration or interface in the chain fails, the entire chain is useless and complete testing is impossible.

Furthermore, a problem or bottleneck in a test environment is not always quickly solved by an administrator. After all, production always has the priority. This is neglecting the fact that delays in the test process result in delays in commencement of production. Such delays can have the same (or worse) consequences as defects that occur in production.

8.4.3   Setting up test environments

Setup requirements

The degree to which it can be established in how far the test object complies with the requirements determines whether a test environment is successful. The setup and composition of a test environment therefore depend on the aim of the test. However, a series of generic requirements with which a test environment must comply to guarantee reliable test execution can be formulated.

Representative

The test environment must have the properties (as much as possible) that are required for the planned test. This does not mean that the entire test environment must always equal the production environment. For instance, for a functional test of an interface between two applications you do not need a complete environment that matches the future production environment.

Example

For the development of an application intended for eventual use on a UNIX platform, a Windows-based platform was used as the test environment for the system test. The assumption was that the functionality would not be affected by the platform difference. A UNIX-based test environment *was* used for the UAT and PAT.

Manageable

A manageable environment is required to test the test object under the same conditions every time. It must be clear at all times which version is installed in a test environment. This applies not only to the test object, but also to all of the software (i.e. the operating system, database management system, network protocols, etc). Changes in the components of the test environment (hardware and software, test object, procedures, etc) cannot be implemented unless with permission from the environment's owner (in projects, often the test management).

Flexible

A test environment must be easy to adapt. This may conflict with the previous requirement. Which of the two requirements (manageable or flexible) takes precedence, depends on the aim of the test and the phase of the test process.

For instance, adjustments may be necessary when analysing defects or implementing a new version of the software. It may also be necessary to create or eliminate specific connections with other systems. If this is done in a test environment of one project, which has no impact on anybody else, flexibility wins. In case of a shared environment (e.g. an end-to-end test environment), manageability is preferred. Other examples of possible changes are the system date and time, currency, calculation units and regional settings. Adjusting the system date and time may be necessary to make time jumps during testing. This is also called time travelling, making it possible for the system to be moved to the past or the future. It can be used, for instance, to run a system cycle of one year in just half a day. Changing regional settings is important when testing software that will be used in several countries.

Continuous
If there are disturbing situations in the test environment, one must try to continue testing as much as possible. The consequences of a failure must therefore be limited to a minimum. An important mitigating measure is making regular backups so that they can be restored if necessary. Furthermore, these secured initial situations can be used time and again for the test or to investigate a specific defect. Another mitigating measure is to create a fallback option for the test environment. The fallback option may consist of a second logical environment in addition to the existing test environment. The risk is that, if problems occur in the hardware, they affect both environments. Another option is therefore to set up a second physical environment. To limit the costs to some extent, the organisation may decide to combine the second environment with the fallback facility for the production environment.

Example

When adapting an application that was used for annual contract renewals, it was necessary to perform tests on several dates and times (time travel). As such, easy modification of the system date was a requirement for the test environment. Furthermore it was necessary, due to the time travel, to create regular backups and restore them later. Not a complex combination of operations, but it did put a lot of work pressure on the administrators of the test environment. It was therefore decided to develop a menu screen containing the various operations and make it available to the testers. This relieved the administrators and allowed the testers to have better grip of their environment.

Factors determining the setup

Translating these requirements to the actual setup of a test environment varies for each test. For instance, the test environment for testing the screens in the system test may be different from that for testing security during the acceptance test. A large number of factors play a part in setting up the test environment. You will find a list of determining factors, with a summary explanation, below.

- The test level for which the environment is intended - unit, system or acceptance test or possibly a combined test.
- The test type for which the environment is intended - performance, usability, security or regression test?
- Requirements made by the external organisations for the environment, e.g. supervisors or (local or central) authorities.
- Requirements made for the test data to be used. Are they small or big volumes? What is the refresh rate?
- Existing test environments in the organisation, if any. Can they be used? How can individual requirements be implemented?
- Is there a budget for setting up test environments and which options are available?
- Does the organisation have standards for setting up test environments?
- The hardware and software architecture. Which development or production platform is being used? What are the options and which limitations exist, if any?
- The manner in which system development is organised. The methods, techniques and phasing used for system development have an impact on the test environments in terms of procedures.
- The type of system. Clearly the test environment has a strong relationship with the nature of the test object, e.g. batch, online, mainframe, PC application, custom or package.
- The level of distributed processing. What extent of data communication exists? And in what form? Is the network or network programming part of the test object? Are decentralised test sites used? Are there any interfaces with external organisations?
- Scope of the test. Should manual processes in e.g. input and output processing be tested as well?
- The test environments of the programmer and tester must not be too distant in terms of geography. While communication resources like telephone and e-mail may respond to part of the communication requirement, frequent consultation between the various stakeholders will be necessary. An optimal location choice can save a lot of time and money.
- Sometimes the use of test tools makes demands on the test environment in relation to e.g. security, data storage and communication resources.

> ### Tip
>
> **The cube notation for test environments**
> A lot of characteristics must be recorded for test environments. Characteristics that are determinants for the identification of an environment, but also those about which an agreement has to be reached with other parties. The registration method for these characteristics partly determines the success of the various arrangements. When multiple test environments are involved, the clear and structured recording of the characteristics may be problematic. One way to do this is to work with the so-called cube notation. A number of characteristics are placed in each visible plane of the drawn cube. An example is shown in figure 8.7 "Cube notation of the various characteristics of a test environment".

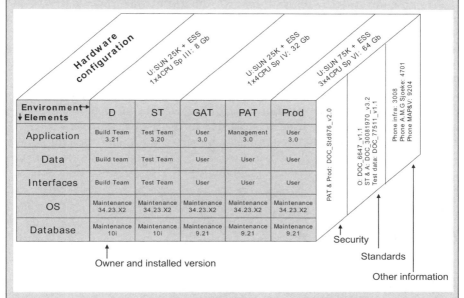

Figure 8.7: Cube notation of the various characteristics of a test environment

This makes everything clear at a glance. We recommend hanging this plate in the common test or project space so that everyone can see the applicable arrangements at any time.

8.4.4 Problems in test environments

In automation projects, it often happens that many different environments are being used. An organisation may have one or more development environments, one or more test environments, a production environment with a fallback environment and sometimes also several maintenance environments. In this situation, the following problems might emerge:

- Returning defects. A defect detected in version X is solved in version X+1 but suddenly reoccurs in version X+2.
- No guarantee that it still works. The development team cannot guarantee that everything still works despite the fact that the release covers only a limited number of defects.
- Unannounced new features. When testing a new version, it is found that specific features (new functionality, specific technical aspects) have already been realised while the testers are not aware of them.
- No connection between defect and environments. A defect detected in environment X does not occur in environment Y while they seem to be the same environments. E.g. a defect does present itself in the acceptance test environment, but not in the system test environment.
- Defects cannot be investigated. A defect can not be investigated anymore because a user other than the tester has modified the test environment.

There are two solutions to prevent these problems. In the first place, the environments must be separated according to the DTAP model. That model and how it can be used is explained in the next section (8.4.5 "DTAP model"). In the second place, formal processes must manage the setting up and maintenance of the environments. Section 8.4.6 "Processes in test environments" discusses these management processes and how they must be organised.

8.4.5   DTAP model

DTAP

DTAP stands for **D**evelopment, **T**est, **A**cceptance and **P**roduction. The basic principle of the model is that every user of the infrastructure wants to do his or her job undisturbed, without being hindered by anyone else. For instance, the end user does not want to be bothered by the tester, who in turn wants to be left alone by the programmer. This is why a separate type of environment is defined for each of these parties. The 4 environment types are analogous to the 4 stages software goes through: the software is developed (development), tested (test), accepted (acceptance) and used (production).

While the DTAP model may initially look like a technical solution, it is not. The model does not prescribe that there are 4 environments, but simply that there are 4 environment *types*. Each of these 4 types has its own characteristics. As such, the DTAP model makes allowance for the use of 7 environments, for instance, in a project (see figure 8.8 "Different environments in a development project according to the DTAP model"). There might be two development environments (local and centralised), one test environment, two acceptance environments (user acceptance test and production acceptance test environment), and two production environments (production and shadow).

Environment type acc. to DTAP	Development		Test	Acceptance			Production	
Environment in development project	Local develop ment environ ment	Central develop ment environ ment	ST environ ment	UAT environ ment	PAT environ ment		Produc tion environ ment	Shadow environ ment

Figure 8.8: Different environments in a development project according to the DTAP model

Owners and administrators of the environment types

Test activities can be executed in every environment type of the DTAP model. Since every environment has an owner, administrator (manager) and its own group of users, the various activities have their own characteristics. For instance, the test environment type is managed differently than the production environment type. In the DTAP model, it is important to distinguish which parties are the owners or administrator of each type of environment. The owner is the party who determines which users are allowed and what the administrators need to do. In the DTAP model, the aim for which the environment is used determines the owner. Sometimes the owner is also the economic owner, but not necessarily.

In the development environment type, it is generally clear who the owner and administrator are. Both roles are fulfilled by the programmers. They acquire and maintain the environment. It is equally clear for the production environment type. The user organisation is the owner, and often the maintenance is handled by a special maintenance organisation (on behalf of the user organisation).

For the test and acceptance environment types it is often a bit more complicated because multiple parties are involved. The user organisation is the owner of the acceptance environment and the testers are the owners of the test environment. But the environments can be maintained by several parties. It may have been acquired by either the project or the maintenance department. In the latter case, the maintenance may be handled by the maintenance department or the testers themselves. The maintenance can even be in the hands of the developers.

Environment type	Owner	Administrator
Development	Developers	Developers
Test	Testers	Developers/Testers/Maintenance organisation*
Acceptance	User organisation	Developers/Testers/Maintenance organisation*
Production	User organisation	Maintenance organisation

* = different possible options

Table 8.2: The possible owners and administrators of the 4 environment types.

Test types and the 4 environment types

The DTAP model does not impose a consistent link of a test type to one environment type. This is to prevent negative consequences. Because of the consecutiveness of the test process in the test environments defects may be discovered too late. This can be prevented by executing a test type in more than one environment type. Clearly, the delivery of the testable parts of the test object must be related to the test type (and the associated environment). In this construction, the user may execute some tests in the development environment.

The realisation of this model is a challenge for the test management and stakeholders. The owner of the environment must accept that his environment may be used for any test type. Different user groups can use the environment. The time gain that can be achieved thanks to parallelism of the tests and reduction of the repair costs due to earlier detection of defects are more than worth the effort. It is therefore especially important that the test environment fit the test type, in the DTAP model this is a perfect fit.

Tests in the development environment type
The unit test is executed in the same environment type in which the software and other system components are developed: the development environment. Setting up this environment and the related test activities are executed as part of the development process. When a part of the environment must be used for a test, the developer himself is usually the party arranging this. Often the development platform contains standard facilities for testing, such as files, test tools and procedures for e.g. version management, transfer, defect administration and defect repair. These facilities offer the developers adequate options to manage their test process correctly. If there are no specific requirements for the unit tests and the above standard facilities are available, the tests can be executed correctly. An important aspect that programmers must deal with is the manageability of their environment. In

practice, a programmer often has five or more versions of his software under management. Maintaining the relationship between the test cases, test results and the test object requires a lot of attention in this case.

Tests in the test environment type
The test environment type is created to test (parts of) the entire system for both technical and functional aspects. This test must be executed in a manageable environment. Manageable means that resources are available to transfer and manage, among other things, the software, documentation, test files and testware. The tester must be able to control the transfer of new or changed software. The tests must be reproducible. It must be possible to execute the individual tests of one (sub-)system separately from the tests of other (sub-)systems. The simultaneous use of the same test data in particular may cause a lot of trouble. In this environment type, tools can be used that provide the tester with insight at a technical level into various events. Examples are the use of SQL to look directly in the database, having direct access to the system's log files, and being able to start up and stop batches (see section 8.5.3 "Types of test tools").

Tests in the acceptance environment type
The acceptance environment type offers future users and managers the possibility to test the test object in an environment resembling the production environment as closely as possible. Usually the test in this environment type is split up into a user acceptance test and a production acceptance test. The UAT checks whether the test object provides the required functionality in relation to production facilities and procedures. The PAT checks whether the system complies with the management and production standards, in terms of both procedures and aspects like volume processing and performance. It is preferable to create a separate environment for the test types UAT and PAT, although it is naturally possible to execute them in the same environment.

In more detail

The PAT environment as a production environment
Organisations often feel that a test environment for the PAT is costly. Not surprising, because it is especially important for the PAT that the test environment is not only functional, but even more so technically equivalent to the production environment. Logically, this means that a PAT environment requires the same hardware as the production environment (types and quantities). As such, a PAT environment is a second production environment.

A solution is, in new development processes, to promote the PAT environment to production environment when the system is delivered. This means only one production environment is necessary. In maintenance projects, an option is to execute the PAT in a fallback environment, which is often a copy of the production environment. If there is no fallback environment, it can be decided to execute the PAT in the production environment at a moment when there are no users (e.g. at night or during the weekend). Clearly this last option involves some risk in terms of availability of the production systems – it is therefore recommended exclusively for relatively simple systems.

Tests in the production environment type
Testing in an environment that is used for production is not desirable, and sometimes even prohibited by regulatory bodies and other supervisors. In very exceptional situations, it is sometimes unavoidable to test in the production environment type. In these cases, the required test environment is so complex that it cannot be simulated or built. Example is a complex system chain (often across several organisations or even countries). In this type of cases, in-production testing is an option. But a lot of things have to be arranged for that purpose. For instance, the new version of the software must be accessible exclusively to the test team. Furthermore the execution of the test must not disturb the regular production process. Furthermore an (external) supervisor often checks the test execution because operations are executed (orders, payments, etc) that are not formal.

8.4.6   Processes in test environments

To prevent the problems described in section 8.4.4 "Problems in test environments", processes need to be in place for managing the setup and maintenance of the environments. These management processes are:
- Configuration management
- Change management
- Release management.

Configuration management
The aim of configuration management is to be clear of the configuration of the various environments at all times. In addition to the test object itself, configuration is understood to mean the set of components as summed up in the definition of test environment (hardware and software, interfaces, environment data, and management tools). This involves not only the components themselves, but their version as well and in particular. The CMDB (Configuration Management Data Base) contains the data for these components. This process ensured that only authorised changes are implemented in the environments. Using the CMDB, the differences between the environments can be established quite easily.

It is important for the tester to be involved in this process, for the following reasons:

- To know in which configuration the defects occur. This configuration must be reported with the defect
- To know how the versions of the testware must be built. There is a close relationship between the testware and the version of the configurations. It is important to copy the configuration structure and naming and numbering methods for testware management.

Change management

The aim of change management is to implement all individual changes about which stakeholders are in agreement in the various environments in a controlled manner. The implementation should not result in new defects. Changes may be delivered as a result of defects, hardware modifications, the implementation of newly developed software, or data file changes. The change management process looks at the total impact of a change. An up-to-date CMDB (see configuration management) is necessary to determine the impact in a specific environment. It is important for the tester to be involved in this process, for the following reasons:

- Changes in requirements result in changes in the test basis. It is therefore important for the tester to know which parts of the test object change and what the changes involve, so that the test cases and test scripts can be adapted if necessary.
- Changes often must be tested. For each change it is necessary to determine whether it has to be tested and whether it can be tested. The testability of a change depends, among other things, on the quality of the change description. This can be taken into account when a tester is involved in the change description at an early stage.
- Changes often result in test work and must therefore be scheduled.

Release management

The aim of release management is the implementation of one or more combined and approved (via change management) changes from one environment to the other. Release management covers all of the components that are part of a change.

Version management (the right version in the right environment) is an important part of release management. It is important for the tester to be involved in the release management process, for the following reasons:

- To know which versions of the test scripts are necessary. As a tester, it is important to know which versions of the various components are installed. In practice, this is most important for the version of the software (which usually is the test object). Depending on the version, specific requirements are built or not, and therefore specific test scripts are necessary or not.
- To know which release is sent to the client. The test occurs on a specific release and the release advice is therefore linked to it.

8.4.7   Two special test environments

Two variations of the test environment require some extra attention: the end-to-end test environment and the production fix test environment. This because they involve some specific aspects that are less important in the other environments.

End-to-end test environment

The end-to-end test environment is an environment in which one or more process chains can be tested. Process chains are business processes that run across multiple applications (and often different hardware and software configurations). The output of one application constitutes the input of the other. The tester is not interested in the separate applications (and hardware and software configurations), but views the entire chain as one composite unit. End-to-end tests are usually executed in the acceptance test.

The end-to-end test environment therefore has an additional dimension in the organisational challenge, which testers must face in any case. Since the chain runs across multiple applications, several departments are involved. Moreover, all components of the test environment must be complete at the same time and arrangements have to be made for the test data in the various components.

To organise this well, the various stakeholders have to agree on these matters in advance in the (master) test plan. It is recommended to create the role of chain coordinator in the test organisation. He is responsible for setting up and maintaining the end-to-end test environment. While the end-to-end test is being executed, the chain coordinator ensures that all parts of chains are available and acts as the primary point of contact for the various parties. The required tasks, skills and knowledge for the role of chain coordinator is the same as for the role test infrastructure coordinator (see chapter 16 "Test roles").

When several projects use an end-to-end test environment, arrangements have to be made about the use of test data. E.g. when project A executes tests using account data from the 'account source system', and project B is required to modify the 'account source system'. The situation might occur that project A retrieves account data from another version of the 'account source system' in the afternoon than in the morning, which would of course affect the reliability of project A's tests.

Production fix test environment

The production fix test environment is the environment in which solutions for production-disturbing defects (often also called 'fixes') are tested. The characteristic of fixes is that they must be solved and tested with the highest priority (production-disturbance equals loss). Therefore is no time to test them as well through the line of system and acceptance tests. Moreover, these environments (if they are even available immediately) are often used to test another, future version of the system. A solution may be to transfer the fixes directly from the development environment (where they are made) to production - but this involves great risks. Moreover, it is not allowed in some market sectors, where supervisors and other regulatory bodies prohibit it.

A solution is the production fix test environment. This environment is always available or can be made available very quickly. The production fix environment is an acceptance environment type and closely resembles the production environment. It contains the same versions of the operating system, databases, network protocols, etc. The authorisations are also set up the same way and the test data are a mirror of production.

One point of concern here is the availability of the parties involved in the test environment. As we mentioned before, production-disturbing defects need to be solved quickly, so administrators and programmers may be called on often. The same holds for the administrator of the test environment and the testers who are expected to execute tests in it.

Example

Figure 8.9 (next page) "Use of the PFT environment" illustrates the use of the production fix test (PFT) environment. The situation is as follows: Version 1.0 of a system is running in production. The organisation is simultaneously developing version 1.1 and testing it in the system test environment. The production-disturbing defect, which needs to be solved, occurs. This is done in the development environment where version 1.01 is created. This version is installed in the production fix test environment, where it is tested. This fix for 1.0 must also be implemented in version 1.1 (or the defect might reoccur when 1.1 is in use). As such, a new version of 1.1 needs to be created after the system test. That is version 1.11, which can be taken to the system test environment and on.

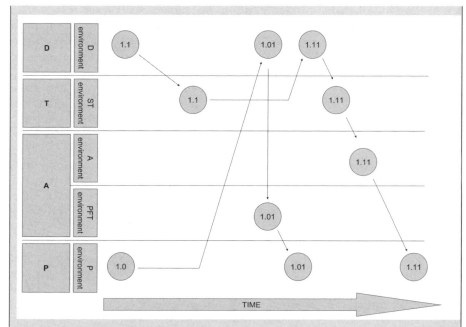

Figure 8.9: Use of the PFT environment

This example also demonstrates how production-disturbing defects can impact the rest of the organisation. When systems cause a lot of production disturbances, the work for new versions is interrupted every time. This might even result in new versions not being completed at all because they need to be adapted to the new fixes all the time.

8.4.8   Test environments when outsourcing

When an organisation outsource testing activities (exclusively or as part of a bigger service), the subject of test environments requires extra attention. For instance, the organisation might have the supplier (supply organisation) execute all activities relating to the test environment. In the case of complex environments with many interfaces to external systems, the outsourcing (demand) organisation might prefer to retain the management. In this case, the test environment must be accessible to the supplier's testers, which results in several points of concern. Another important aspect is which party bears the costs of the infrastructure. Often this is the supplier, the costs are charged directly to the client.

As a rule, there are various aspects that require a well-considered decision.

For instance:

- Access to the environment: arrangements about how the test environment can be accessed and by whom, e.g. via a remote connection.
- The way who the test environment is set up, in particular for structural outsourcing services.
- Updating the test environment: agreements on informing on and tracking required upgrades, required configurations, DBMSs, the specific operating system and middleware versions, licence costs.
- Arrangements about handling limitations of the test environments as perceived by one of the stakeholders.

8.4.9 Setting up and maintaining test environments as a service

A development in recent years is that applications use an increasing number of different types of hardware and software. In many (big) organisations, different hardware and software components are also maintained by different parties. This makes setting up a test environment an organisational challenge. Many contacts and arrangements have to be made. It might happen that problems remain 'hanging' between parties: hardware configuration 1 is active, hardware configuration 2 is active and the interface between them is active, but messages don't arrive and none of the three (or more!) parties feels it is the owner of the problem.

In summary, the availability of (chains of) test environments is a regular source of problems, both in terms of availability and consistency. As a result, automation projects must make a choice: take the system into production without adequate testing, or delaying the commissioning date. The bad availability of test environments is caused by both organisational and technical complexity. Tasks and mandates are broken up between the user (tester, test manager) and suppliers of (parts of) the test chain. Moreover, organisations often assign low priority to solving a non-functioning test environment.

Organisations may decide to solve the bottleneck of bad availability by allocating responsibility for it to the permanent test organisation described in section 8.3 "Permanent test organisation". The permanent test organisation can provide services in setting up and maintaining (chains of) test environments.

The following sections discuss setting up and maintaining test environments as a service in greater detail. In the first place, the possible role of the permanent test organisation in setting up and maintaining test environments is established. We then look at the processes that need to be set up in the test organisation. The next step is identifying what type of environments can be provided and what makes them unique.

The control centre's role of the test organisation

A permanent test organisation can fulfil the role of control centre in setting up and maintaining test environments. This should reduce costs and improve the quality for setting up and maintaining test environments. As a control centre, the test organisation acts as the single point of contact for the clients of test environments. It is a fixed point of contact for the client. The latter does not need to solve test environment-related problems himself. The test organisation handles all internal and external contacts with the various suppliers of the (components of) test environments. Service levels relating to the services procured from these suppliers can be agreed upon, as well as in relation to the services offered by the test organisation (see figure 8.10 "Control centre's role of the permanent test organisation", next page).

When an incident (problem)[3] occurs in the test environment, the test organisation will have to solve it or have it solved. By definition, the test organisation is the initial owner of the incident, until it becomes clear that the cause is to be found elsewhere. By controlling the various processes (up to the production environment), incidents due to other parties changing environments can be prevented. The test organisation needs to have a total picture of the available components distributed across the various hardware and software configurations and any interfaces between them. This will make it easier to determine and solve causes of incidents.

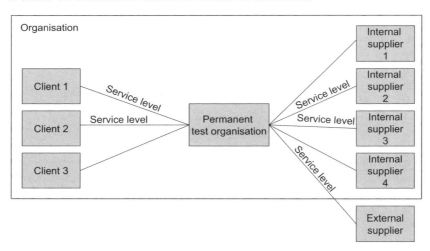

Figure 8.10: Control centre's role of the permanent test organisation

---

[3] ITIL is often used for the terminology of management. It stands for Information Technology Infrastructure Library and was developed as a reference framework for setting up a management organisation in IT. ITIL talks of incidents, not of problems. For more information, please refer to www.itil.com

The services offered by the test organisation need to be standardised. Only then will the benefits of central maintenance and availability of test environments come to fruition. The availability of standard services translates to offering a fixed set of possible test environments. This means that the demand of the client must always be translated to one of these possible test environments. Here, the personnel of the test organisation act as an advisor.

One condition is that the employees providing the service need to have technical content-related knowledge of the test environments. The organisation around this service is much more of a maintenance organisation than a test organisation. Which also means that the employees' profile must emphasise maintenance over testing.

Example

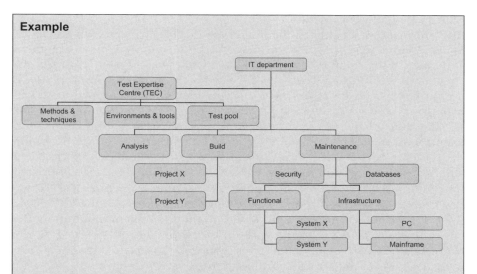

Figure 8.11: Sample organisation chart in which a Test Expertise Centre (TEC) acts as the control centre for setting up and maintaining test environments.

This figure shows an example of an organisation chart containing a Test Expertise Centre (TEC) as described in section 8.3.7 "Test Expertise Centre". The TEC has a department called "environments and tools". That department fulfils the control centre function for setting up and maintaining test environments. The test environment suppliers consist of many parties. In 'maintenance', for instance, there is an infrastructure department. It is organised according to the two types of hardware configuration they are maintaining (PC and mainframe). For the test environments, they are responsible for supplying the hardware, network components, operating systems, etc. There are also two maintenance services departments within maintenance: security and databases. The first handles requests for the various authorisations at the logical level for the systems in use. The other, databases, is responsible for maintaining the various databases. Finally, there is the functional maintenance which maintains the

> software. When project X or Y wants a test environment, it must contact a number of parties (all of them in the worst case scenario). They are therefore the TEC's clients.

Required processes

As described in section 8.3.5 "General process model", a number of processes have to be set up to offer the services in the permanent test organisation. This also applies to the situation in which the test organisation fulfils the role of control centre for test environments. Two important service processes can be distinguished:

- Setting up a new test environment
- Maintaining a test environment.

Setting up a new test environment
After the first contact with the client, a review will be held in the initiation phase of the assignment. The basis is the definition of the required test environment as defined in the client's (master) test plan. It contains a first inventory of the client's wishes and requirements. The next step, in the initiation phase, is the further specification of the test environment. One or more environment experts of the test organisation provide support. The client must supply the specifications of the test environment (e.g. as an architectural chart). The expert must describe what can and cannot be realised and how it fits within the standard services of the test organisation. From the moment the client and the test organisation reach an agreement about the plan, with associated timelines and costs (formal starting point), an assignment description is created describing the required setup. The assignment is then executed: realising the test environment in question. Based on the assignment description, the environment experts set up the entire test environment. Depending on the lead time, the experts will submit status reports to the test organisation, which in turn reports to the client according to the agreed timelines.

Maintaining a test environment
A number of management processes need to be set up in the test organisation for managing the maintenance of test environments. These are:

Process	Description
Configuration management	See section 8.4.6 "Processes in test environments"
Change management	See section 8.4.6 "Processes in test environments"
Release management	See section 8.4.6 "Processes in test environments"

Process	Description
Incident management	The process that is responsible for solving defects in the test environment during the test as quickly as possible. It also covers defect management: handling defects during testing. These do not only have to be defects in the test environment, but also defects that result in a change in the software or hardware. An important part of this process is setting up a service desk, which is used to handle queries and complaints of clients relating to the use of the test environment.
Problem management	Where incident management is responsible for solving defects as quickly as possible, problem management focuses on searching for a structural cause of defects and disturbances. This often requires more detailed research. This is done in consultation with developers and technical and functional administrators.
Data management	Every test and environment sets demands in relation to the availability, scope and content (correctness and completeness) of the data. For instance test data, but also necessary user profiles or network addresses. When the various types of tests are executed, the right data need to be available. This process is responsible, including the execution of backups and restores.
Operational Management	This process is responsible for keeping the various components in the test environment operational and monitoring them. This is done in accordance with the requirements agreed with the client.

Very likely, the various departments supplying the environments to the permanent test organisation already work conformable to ITIL. In this case, we recommend using existing procedures, processes and products already available in those departments for the subjects described above. For instance, the permanent test organisation could use the service desk tool already implemented by an IT helpdesk, if it exists.

In more detail

Different interests

A potential bottleneck when a permanent test organisation maintains test environments is the difference in interests. A test project has other interests than the test organisation. The test project is accountable for a project result, often the deadline is sacred. The manager of the test environments is accountable for other aspects, often things like the quality of the environment, robustness, availability, consistency of (test) data, or the speed with which an incident is handled. These are translated to so-called KPIs (see section 8.3.5 "General process model"). Being able to work according to an accountability model based on KPIs requires formal processes. In situations in which the test project asks for speedy action (e.g. when the deadline draws near), this formal working method of the test organisation may seem 'bureaucratic'. It is important that both parties are aware of, and understand, the difference in interests and, in the case of (potential) problems, try to find a solution.

Identifying test environments with service levels

What makes a system test environment a system test environment? At first sight it might seem an irrelevant question, but it is extremely important in the light of the test organisation's control centre role. Because what does it mean to the client when the organisation offers a service called 'setting up a system test environment'? Or what does the client want when asking for an end-to-end test environment?

As described in section 8.3.4 "Supplying test services", a test organisation may be responsible for delivering a service. Its highest responsibility is when services involve an 'obligation to deliver results'. The permanent test organisation must deliver a result based on the request. The delivery must occur within the pre-defined timeframe, at pre-defined costs, and at a pre-defined quality level. The permanent test organisation is responsible for guaranteeing continuity in delivering the result. The standard for this obligation is laid down in so-called service levels.

When a test organisation offers a service to set up a system test environment, the service can be rendered more specific by using service levels. Service levels for test environments are defined by completing specific characteristics of the environment. For instance:
- Goal of the environment and test levels for which it can be used
- The test environment's target group
- Interface with other systems or use of stubs and drivers
- The test data in the environment and the refresh rate
- The security requirements applying to the environment
- The environment's availability
- Tooling available in the environment
- Any entry and exit criteria.

Example

A permanent test organisation offers a service to set up and maintain a system test environment. This service involves the following service levels:

Aim: controlled environment in which the client validates whether the application was built according to specifications
Test levels: system test and functional acceptance test
Target group: the client's testers
Interfaces: standard stubs & drivers, but real interfaces possible on demand

Test data: no test data available, client is responsible for this
Security: standard set provided, further management responsibility of the client
Entry criteria: none
Exit criteria: test data eliminated, no remaining data
Tooling: Tools for database manipulation and time travel
Availability: 80% availability during office hours (09:00 – 17:00) with a maximum downtime of 2 hours.

In more detail

Availability of test environments
When the availability of the test environment is specified in a service level, it is important to agree on how availability will be measured. In other words, how do both parties define the availability of the test environment? This might differ. For instance, one party might feel that having the most important components available is adequate, while the other feels everything should be available. These two different interpretations yield a different result in the figure 8.12 "Schematic overview of the availability of various components in a test environment". In this figure, a test environment consists of five components (A, B, C, D and E). A, B, and C are identified as the main components. These are e.g. components on which the correct operation of the test object depends directly. Examples are a database server, web service, or mailboxes. Components D and E are considered less important, e.g. interfaces with other systems.

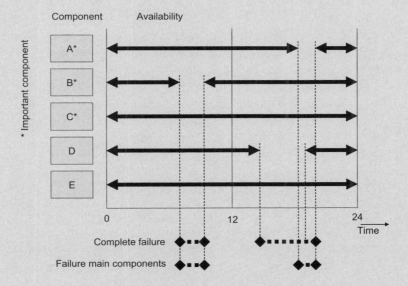

Figure 8.12: Schematic overview of the availability of various components in a test environment.

The availability is measured for each of these components. For instance, C and E are available continuously, but some problems (interruption of the line) occur in the other three. When looking at all components taken together, the total of failures are bigger than when looking solely at the main components.

The difference in availability is important mainly for different test levels. For a system test, for instance, it is less important that the interfaces are available continuously than for an end-to-end test.

8.5 Test tools

8.5.1 Introduction

The development in recent years that can be summarised as *'more for less, faster and better'* has an impact on all IT disciplines (see section 8.1 "Introduction"). With highly advanced development environments, developers can design and build complex programs relatively easily and quickly. The iterative development methods that are based on far-reaching interaction with the users ensure, among other things, that projects make interim deliveries faster. Such interim deliveries are then evaluated against the users' wishes and requirements and the defects are reworked in the software. This means that the software changes continuously and regression risks are always there. Moreover, development is based more and more often on reusing internal and external components that must be integrated into the existing IT architectures. This has reduced the time required to develop new systems, putting testing even more emphatically on the critical path in terms of development and maintenance. It even threatens to become an obstructing factor.

All these factors, taken together with the fact that testing is already perceived to be a time-consuming and costly activity, make higher productivity of the tester and higher quality of the test a requirement. Test tools can be used as an instrument to achieve this.

Making test tools available to testers is often the responsibility of a separate department. One reason is the fact that setting up and maintaining test tools is a specific expertise. It is something of which testers generally have little knowledge. Another reason for making test tools the responsibility of a separate department is that big investments are often required to introduce tools in an organisation. In addition to the high acquisition costs, investment is required in training the people and developing new procedures. In other words, it takes time to realise a return on investment, often longer than one single project.

This section discusses test tools and their use in greater detail. Section 8.5.2 "Test tools explained" explains what a test tool is. Section 8.5.3 "Types of test tools" then describes the various types of test tools. Section 8.5.4 "Advantages of using test tools" discusses the advantages of using test tools. The subsequent sections describe how test tools can be implemented in test organisations on the basis of a tool policy. To this end, section 8.5.5. "Implementing test tools with a tool policy" explains the concept of tool policy and describes the life cycle model. The three phases are then listed, i.e. the Initiation (8.5.6

"Initiation phase"), Realisation (8.5.7 "Realisation phase") and Operation phases (8.5.8 "Operation phase").

8.5.2   Test tools explained

Definition

A test tool is an automated instrument that supports one or more test activities, such as planning, control, specification and execution.

One of the conditions for the successful use of test tools is the existence of a structured test approach. In a properly controlled process, tools can certainly add a lot of value, but they are counter-productive in an inadequately controlled test process. In fact, test tools automate the test process, which requires a certain repeatability and standardisation in the activities to be automated. An unstructured process cannot comply with these conditions. The deployment of test tools, however, can serve to leverage the implementation of a structured approach. However, the least that is required is structuring and automation combined.

In more detail

Terminology: tools, test tools and CAST tools
Tools used in a test process are referred to in different ways. For instance, some simply talk of *tools*, others of *test tools*, *CAST tools* (CAST stands for Computer Aided Software Testing), or *test automation*. It is not possible to make an unequivocal choice for the right terminology. There are parties that state that a tool is a test tool when it can be used exclusively to support a specific test activity. The counter-argument is that some test tools that serve to support test execution are sometimes used for other work. One example is a test tool that can be used to automate test execution. This tool works on the basis of automating operations and can also be used for data conversion. And that makes it a tool in a wider sense again. TMap uses the terms tools and test tools interchangeably.

Being able to use test tools is now assumed to be one of the tester's basic skills. However, being able to set up and manage test tools and the far-reaching automation of routine work (e.g. test execution) still requires specialist and in-depth knowledge of programming and tools. Not every tester has that knowledge. As a result, new types of specialism have emerged: test tool programmer, test tool expert, and test tool consultant. These functions are described in more detail in section 8.6 "Test professionals".

In more detail

Price structure of test tools
There are all kinds of test tools, all with their own price structure. Commercial tools often have a licensing system where a one-off price is agreed based on the number of users of the tool. In addition to this one-off price an annual contract is signed, ensuring the organisation that the tool's supplier will provide support and new updates and releases. Often, this is called a maintenance or service contract.

In addition there are test tools with price structure on the basis of the variants *shareware, freeware* and *open-source software*. The price structure for shareware is such that it can be distributed without or with few restrictions, but a fixed price having to be paid when used repeatedly. Freeware is software for which the author has issued a licence for use and further distribution in unchanged form without requiring compensation. Open-source software goes one step further than freeware. In addition to the free distribution of the software, the author gives permission for modifying the software. The modified software can also be distributed freely. Contrary to open-source software, freeware is protected fully by copyright. And contrary to open-source software, the source code of freeware is not usually made available. More and more (self-made) test tools are made available by the creators through the Internet on the basis of these variants.

8.5.3   Types of test tools

Test tools provide support in the execution of certain activities in the various TMap phases. There are different types of test tools, which can be classified in four groups:
1. Tools for planning and controlling the test
2. Tools for designing the test
3. Tools for executing the test
4. Tools for debugging and analysing the code.

The test tools in groups 1, 2 and 3 are used mainly by the testers in the independent test team. A description and overview of various available types of test tools are given per group in this section. The test tools in group 4 are used mainly by the developer. These are described in chapter 7 "Development tests". www.tmap.net contains the "Tools per TMap activity" matrix with an overview of the type of test tool associated with each of the TMap activities.

Tools for planning and controlling the test
Like a business process can be supported by automated resources, a test process can be supported by automated instruments. These are test tools that support activities in relation to planning and controlling the test, like creating the planning, monitoring progress, and registering defects. Because the tools

focus on the process, in a technical sense they operate independently of the test object. The following tool types are in this group:

- Testware management tool
- Defect management tool
- Planning and progress monitoring tool
- Workflow tool.

In more detail

Test management tool not a separate tool type

Test management tools are not defined as a separate tool type in TMap. The reason is that it offers an integrated set of functionalities in the field of various tool types. For instance, a test management tool often supports testware management, defect management, and planning and progress monitoring. While the functionality for each field is not usually as comprehensive as in a specific tool type, the power of a test management tool lies in the integration of the various tools. Often the test management tools are also integrated with tools for automated test execution. The test management tool may also contain an automated workflow. This means that the tool supports the entire test process – from making the test plan to reporting on the results.

Testware management tool

All kinds of products are created in the course of the test process and together they form the testware. It is very important that the products are adequately managed during a test process. Testware management tools support the registration of the various versions of testware that are created in the test process and the possible relationships between the testware. For instance, it can be derived which test result belongs to which version of the test scripts, or which version of the test specification belongs to which version of the test basis. Furthermore, testware management enforces a certain level of structure and uniformity.

Defect management tool

These tools support the registration and handling of defects found during a test process. The process of defect management is complex and voluminous. Sometimes the number of defects, depending among other things on the size and quality of the test object, may amount to hundreds or thousands. Defects can also contain one or more annexes with screen prints or parts of the test basis to clarify the problem. Several parties, often in different locations, are involved in handling defects. Sometimes the procedure to handle defects depends on the urgency of the defect. Tools are available to support these activities. In addition to the registration the lifecycle of a defect can be monitored and tracked. Some tools also enable the creation of management reports and metrics.

Planning and progress monitoring tool
A tool to support the process of planning and progress monitoring is indispensable in large-scale test processes. A planning must be calculated through and through in terms of activity time, start and end dates (if any), and allocated resources. Often, planning packages provide 'what if' analyses and are able to generate both planning and network planning units. These tools help with estimating the effect for the test. See www.tmap.net for an example. Progress monitoring must provide insight into the progress made, and reports on this must be generated. Furthermore it must provide insight into the required time and resources to complete the test process. An important aspect in the selection of tools for planning and progress monitoring is the possibility of creating management information, e.g. overviews of resources and costs.

Workflow tool
The TMap test process has various phases with activities and sub activities. Some of these are interdependent: the output of an activity is the input for another activity, resulting in multiple chains of activities (workflow). The activities in a chain are executed by one or more persons in the test team. In the case of large test teams, managing the entire process with the various activity chains is a complex task. A workflow tool can provide support. The workflow tool knows the activities to be executed and ensures that the work is routed to the relevant persons. With the tool, the test manager has continuous insight into the status of the activities to be executed, and is aware of the total work stock. The tool generates an alert when plans are exceeded or work stocks become unusually high so that the test manager can intervene.

Tools for designing the test

Tools that support the specification of test cases or generate them fully automatically belong in this group. This group also contains the test tools to create, set up and maintain the test data. Tools that support the creation of test cases usually do this on the basis of a basic technique (see section 14.2.3 "Test design technique and basic technique"). When the test basis is described in a formal notation, the test tools can generate test cases automatically. In many cases, these test cases require further processing. The tool provides support in this. The following tool types are in this group:
- Test data tool
- Test design tool
- Model-based testing tool.

Test data tool
This tool helps build physical sets of test data. Using generators, random content can be created on the basis of a file and/or database specification. This makes it possible to create a sizeable set of test data relatively quickly, for

instance for a real-life test. The 'rules' to generate test data must be pre-defined in the tool. Think, for instance, of defining collections with boundaries from which a selection can be made and relationships between various data types (consistency rules).

Test design tool
These tools provide support when test design techniques are used during the specification of test cases. In particular when various possible combinations of input are used during testing, these tools quickly add value. For more information on this subject please refer to section 14.3 "Coverage types and basic techniques".

Model based testing tool
These tools offer support in the approach of Model Based Testing. This is an approach in which test cases are designed on the basis of a model of the test object (figure 8.13 "Model based testing"). These test cases are then used for automated execution on the test object. One of the challenges in this approach is the creation of a formal model in which the operation of (part of) the application is shown. Creating this model is work for humans. When the model is complete, it can be read by a tool that handles the creation and execution of test cases. This method is particularly valuable for (a combination of) complex systems that have an unlimited number of possibilities. For more information on Model Based Testing, go to *www.model-based-testing.org*.

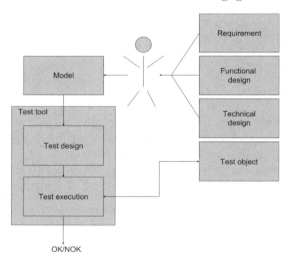

Figure 8.13: Model based testing.

In more detail

Word-processing and spreadsheet programs viewed as test tools

It is sometimes said that the test tools most often used by a tester are word processing and spreadsheet programs. At first sight this might seem a funny statement. But when looking beyond the standard functionality of these tools, there might be some truth to it. These tools can support a tester's work and in some cases even automate it. By simply copying and pasting pieces of text, reuse in the creation of test scripts is simplified. The use of a spreadsheet for the notation of the logical and physical test cases (in the different cells) imposes a standard work method, which benefits interpretation by the various testers. Furthermore most word-processing and spreadsheet programs contain so-called 'macro' functionalities to automate operations. In some cases, links can even be made to external programs. This makes it possible to automate an activity like test execution (in a very light form) with a word-processing or spreadsheet program.

Example

A batch system uses text files as input. The text files contain lines with various data. Each line consists of 10 or more data elements separated by a comma. The text files are used to test the batch system. Thus, testers must deliver their test cases in the format of the text files. Reading and understanding the content of a text file is difficult. The meaning of a data element depends on its position and value. Creating text files for testing is therefore very complex. It was decided to create the text files in a spreadsheet program. By linking each column to a position (and the meaning) in the text file, the testers can build the text file quite easily. A text file is then created for the batch system with a click of the button based on the various cells. See figure 8.14 "Use of a spreadsheet to create a text file" for a schematic representation.

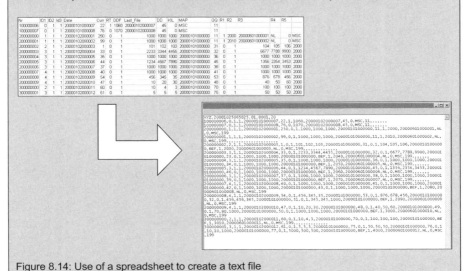

Figure 8.14: Use of a spreadsheet to create a text file

Tools for executing the test

These test tools are deployed on the critical path of testing: executing test scripts. Because the tools focus on the product, they must, technically speaking, cooperate with the test object and the associated hardware and software combination. The deployment of this type of test tools is beneficial when the test work requires great accuracy and is relatively routine. Examples are the frequently repeated execution of the same test and comparing sizeable overviews with the aim of determining whether they are both the same. Also activities requiring a lot of technical knowledge (e.g. security testing) or many testers (e.g. testing with load profiles) can be executed by these test tools.

The following tool types are in this group:
- Automated test execution tool
- Performance, load and stress test tool
- Monitoring tool
- Code coverage tool
- Comparator
- Database manipulation tool
- Simulator
- Stubs and drivers.

Automated test execution tool
As the repeated testing of unchanged functionality (regression testing) is the most sizeable and time-consuming part of the test, tools for automated test execution are attractive to many organisations. Regression testing starts as early as when a system is being built and takes up an increasing part of test work during the life cycle of the system (see figure 8.15 "Increasing share of regression testing during the lifecycle"). The automated execution of such regression tests can save time. This is attractive not only to the tester, who is relieved of repetitive and therefore boring daily activities, but also to the calculating test manager who can save tens of percents.

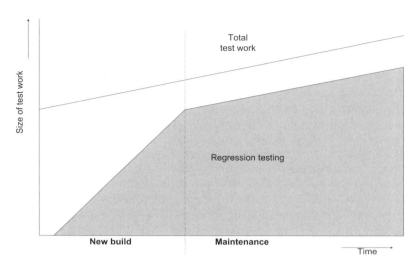

Figure 8.15: Increasing share of regression testing during the lifecycle

There are two variants of this test tool type:

■ Tools that automate test execution via the user interface (GUI) of the application to be tested. These are also called record & playback tools. A record & playback tool records the test input (data and actions) and the expected result in a script. The tool can play back the script at a later time, so that the test can be repeated easily (please note that the term 'script' in this context should not be confused with the manual test scripts that are part of the test specifications).

■ Tools that automate test execution via a program interface. Examples of a program interface are Application Programming Interface (API) or messages in XML format. Often this tool type offers the possibility of mutating stored input data and provides support when generating test input. Generally speaking, these tools are combined with comparison tools to enable analysis of the test results.

The great advantage of automated test execution tools is that a test can be repeated by automation at a later stage. This advantage is nullified if the test object is changed in such a way that the automated script blocks during playback. Maintenance to the automated scripts is necessary to use the tool efficiently. Such maintenance should not cost more than the benefit yielded by automated test execution. Changes in the test object must result in a limited number of changes in the automated scripts. This is often the case in regression testing, so that this tool type is extremely suitable for this test type.

The combination of tool, framework, test cases, automated test scripts, and recorded results is called a test suite. The framework in a test suite is a library of reusable automated scripts. Each script is in fact a small program. Use of the basic principles of modular programming increases the maintainability of the scripts: each group of successive actions that must be carried out repeatedly (for example moving to a certain screen in the application) is best stored as a separate module. If something changes in the group of activities (for example because of a different menu setup), then only one module will need to be adapted. Modules exist at different levels of abstraction, varying from activating or checking a specific object of the system to be tested, to carrying out a business process. Having such an architecture makes it possible for new test suites (for new systems) to be created in a short period of time, because many of the necessary building blocks (modules) are already present in the library. To construct a test suite in such a modular fashion, expertise in the fields of testing and software development is required. The required effort to adapt a test suite (and therefore also the framework) for a new release must not outweigh the benefits of the use of the test suite. The main quality requirements for a test suite are: maintainable, flexible, robust and reusable (see also [Fewster, 1991]).

Performance, load and stress test tool
Performance, load and stress test tools can load an information system by simulating (large numbers of) users. The purpose of this type of testing is to determine whether the system continues to function correctly and at the required speeds under the expected production load. For more information on this subject please refer to section 14.3.8. "Statistical usage: Operational profiles and Load profiles", and section 10.3.3. "Performance". To determine the possible causes of problems in the measured results, these tools are often used in combination with monitoring tools.

Monitoring tool
Monitoring tools are used in the test process to gain insight into aspects like memory use, CPU use, network load and performance. All kinds of data relating to resource use are measured and saved and presented by means of a report. Configuring such tools is often complex. However, often a maintenance department already has monitoring tools to monitor the operational production environment, perhaps these can be used in the test environment as well. In performance, load and stress test tools, monitoring functionality is often an integrated component.

Code coverage tool
Code coverage tools yield information on which parts of the program code were used during a test. As such they provide practical support to measure the effect of the test design techniques used. The measurements are made

at the program or subsystem level. In this way, it is established whether each program statement is executed at least once during testing. The conclusions drawn must be investigated because:

- 100% coverage of the program statements does not guarantee by any means that no defects remain! Compare section 14.2.2 "Coverage, coverage type and coverage ratio".
- A test designed to achieve 100% coverage of the functional specifications does not generally automatically achieve 100% statement coverage.

Comparator

A comparator compares data and reports the differences. The latter must then be analysed manually to determine whether the differences coincide with expectations. These tools are used to e.g.

- Compare test output against the test output of the previous test
- Compare a data collection before and after one or more test actions
- Compare the results of shadow production against the results of production.

Such tools are often an integrated part of record & playback tools. As an alternative, the simple file compare functionality[4] or the revision functionality of a word processor can be used.

Data base manipulation tool

Directly viewing and manipulating data in a database represent a powerful instrument for testers. It enables them to execute checks to make sure whether a test was truly successful. This tool type is a vital part of the standard equipment of a tester. In addition to retrieving data, the data can also be changed. This can be used to create start situations. The manipulation language on which such tools are based is often SQL.[5]

Simulator

A simulator simulates the operation of the environment of the (part of the) test object to be tested. A simulator is used to test software for which it is too costly, dangerous or even impossible to test the actual environment, e.g. testing the operating software for an aircraft or nuclear reactor. The simulator communicates with the test object as if it were the actual environment. It supplies input to the test object and receives its output. Simulators are generally not standard and must be developed in parallel with the development of the test object. The simulator in turn must also be tested.

Stubs and drivers

A system is generally tested in parts. A part may be a module or component. To test a module that has relationships with modules not yet realised at an early stage, you need stubs and drivers that replace the missing modules. A

---

[4] Often included by default in the operating system.
[5] Structured Query Language.

stub is accessed from the module to be tested, a driver accesses the module to be tested (see figure 8.16 "Stubs and drivers in relation to module A and module B").

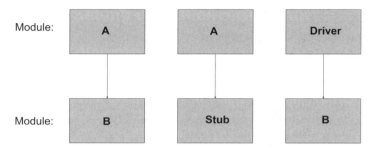

Figure 8.16: stubs and drivers in relation to module A and module B

Example

A reporting function that prints the payroll per employee is tested. In this function, the payroll calculating program (tested earlier) is accessed. The test aims to select all employees and print the payroll for every employee. However, preparing a test database with all of the required data for the various payroll calculations can be a huge task. A stub that returns a specific salary amount (e.g. based on the entered employee number) can significantly reduce the test effort. Naturally, the relationship between the real programs must always be tested once.

8.5.4   Advantages of using test tools

A test tool introduces an automated instrument that provides support to one or more test activities. The introduction of test tools can have various advantages, which are described below. These advantages do not apply to all of the tool types discussed above. This is specified for each advantage.

Increased productivity
By using a test tool for routine test work, the tester has much more time for other tasks. In particular with tools for automated test execution, a sizeable quantity of tests can be executed 'unmonitored', e.g. at night. This means that much more thorough testing can be done in different fields, but also that the test environment can be used more efficiently. The test environment is then used 24 hours per day, with test execution at night and the results being verified during the day. All this means much more testing in the same time.

> **Tip**
>
> **Overnight backups**
> Backups are usually made during the night. This is when the systems are not being used and most resources, such as CPU and memory, are available. When an automated test must be executed at night, it is important to determine in advance whether backups are made during that period. These might block the automated test execution, which will only be detected until the following morning. This also applies to interfaces and other systems that are shut down at night.

Tool types that manage data (e.g. testware management tools and defect management tools) take over the routine management tasks from the tester. The labour-intensive task of creating reports is also reduced to one click of a button when using these tools. This leaves more time for other activities.

Higher testing quality

The use of test tools to support a structured test approach is an emphatic next step towards higher testing quality and quality software. The reason is the consistent execution of an activity that is supported by the tool. A tool imposes a standard work method, eliminating the human factor. The human factor makes that not every operation is precisely the same as the other, increasing the risk of errors. This effect becomes stronger with drawn-out repetitive activities, such as writing similar physical test cases or the execution of the test scripts. This standard work method also means that all information (input and output) for an activity is presented in a consistent manner. This minimises interpretation errors by different testers in a team.

> **In more detail**
>
> Very regularly, deviation from prescribed steps or operations results in finding defects. Therefore the human (unpredictable) factor is important. As such, deploying tools for automated testing is never the only and ultimate solution to realise a high-quality test.

More work enjoyment

The execution of routine tasks is experienced as boring. When such tasks are automated, it increases the work enjoyment of the test team in addition to increasing reliability. Naturally this also results in improved productivity of the test team. Moreover, test teams generally perceive working with tools as pleasant. The reasons are the professional image towards the rest of the organisation and the new tasks (realisation and maintenance of the tools) that are created due to the use of the test tools.

Extension of test options

Some tests cannot be simulated fully when done manually. One example is the execution of stress tests. The deployment of test tools is virtually indispensable here. The deployment of a large number of 'real' users to achieve representative manning is usually feasible once, with a lot of effort, but not twice. Moreover these tools can trace defects that are very difficult to detect manually. For instance, measuring memory use of a website when more than 1000 visitors are online. Another example is testing a system without a user interface (e.g. middleware). Such a system can be accessed by using a test tool.

8.5.5   Implementing test tools with a tool policy

Tool policy

The activities in the test process supported by a test tool and how this will be set up depends on the tool policy pursued in the organisation.

Definition

The tool policy describes how an organisation handles the acquisition, implementation and use of test tools in the various situations.

The tool policy is part of the test policy (see section 8.2 "Test policy"). The tool policy describes in a uniform manner what the purpose of the implementation of test tools must be. The use of test tools is never an objective in and of itself. The test tool is just a means to realise a specific objective in terms of time, money and/or quality. This is called the test tool objective. The tool policy also describes the requirements, wishes and conditions (if any) defined for test tools. These can be based on requirements, wishes and conditions defined in the test policy.

Furthermore, the tool policy describes the approach to be followed for the acquisition, implementation and use of tools. As such, this part of the tool policy resembles a general plan of approach, with the difference that it represents the basis for a long-term investment. It has been written before: the deployment of tools usually only yields a return on investment in the long term, which is why it must be governed by a policy. A tool policy constitutes the basis on which the organisation can base the use and implementation of tools (in the future). It is not a one-off document that is archived. It must be updated and adapted to new developments and insights continuously.

Example 1

A package supplier pursues a policy of acquiring building and test tools as much as possible from one single supplier. This is incorporated into the tool policy, which contains a list of preferred tool suppliers.

Example 2

The objective of an organisation is to migrate all systems to a new hardware and software configuration within 3 years. The tool policy therefore specifies that new test tools can be purchased only if they will also operate in the new hardware and software configuration. The tool policy also states that the deployment of automated test execution must have a ROI within 2 years. The reason is that systems will change during the migration to the new hardware and software migration, meaning that the automated test execution will also change.

Example 3

An organisation listed on the stock exchange must comply with legal requirements. These specify conditions with which the organisation's systems must comply. These conditions can only be tested with specific test tools, which in turn must comply with these conditions. The list of test tools that comply is incorporated into the tool policy.

Example 4

A medium-sized organisation has included a requirement in its tool policy that the organisation does not need to have knowledge concerning the deployment of load, performance and stress test tools. This results in the fact that all performance tests are executed by an external supplier.

Example 5

The tool policy of a power supplier states that every project must use the standard available test management tool. Other tools must be open-source tools by preference. Commercial tools can be bought only with permission from the IT manager.

Life cycle model for tool implementation

The implementation of test tools in a structured test process is a program with several process steps. These process steps are incorporated in a life cycle model (see figure 8.17 "Life cycle model for test tool implementation"). This defines the activities from the early start of the use of test tools through to the structural embedding in the test process. The life cycle model distinguishes three phases: *Initiation, Realisation* and *Operation*. Each phase has its own objectives, activities and products which are verified against the tool policy. The phases are explained in the following sections.

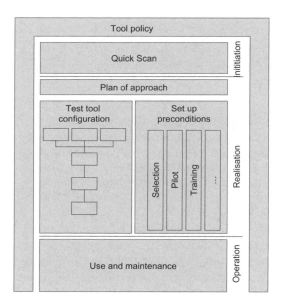

Figure 8.17: Life cycle model for test tool implementation

8.5.6   Initiation phase

The first phase in the life cycle model is the Initiation phase. This phase contains activities that serve to obtain a univocal picture of the applicability of a test tool in a specific situation. An important condition for applicability is the information in the tool policy. Based on this, a well-considered decision concerning the deployment of and investment in test tools is made. The main activity in the Initiation phase is the execution of the *quick scan*. This provides information on the technical environment, the maturity of the test process, and the management's expectations concerning the deployment of test tools. Characteristics of the quick scan are its limited lead time and relatively low investment. Various other activities are possible in addition to the quick scan. Think of product presentations, a demo session, and visiting operational test tools in other organisations.

The quick scan

The quick scan is the instrument used to obtain specific information concerning the implementation of test tools. It has not yet been established whether tools will be used and which tools they should be. The aim of the quick scan is to collect and report information with a relatively low effort (from 2 to 15 days duration) about the possible applicability of a test tool in a specific situation. This results in a first (rough) version of the so-called business case for the implementation of tools.

An important source of information during the quick scan is the interviews. These are conducted with the main stakeholders in the test process. Examples are:

- Line manager (responsible for finance)
- Project manager
- Test manager
- Test consultant
- Application expert
- Developer
- Technical system administrator.

In addition to taking interviews, the quick scan also assesses various test products for their usability in a test tool. It is investigated in how far existing products, such as test cases or defect procedures, match the work method of test tools. Three aspects to determine the applicability of a test tool are taken into consideration. These are:

- Test tool objective:
  The quick scan inventories to what extent the test tool objectives have been defined and are in line with the objectives as described in the tool policy. Often those involved only have expectations at that point, which may not prove realistic or translatable to concrete objectives. A precondition for the successful introduction of test tools (see section 8.5.7 "Realisation phase") is a client who is aware of the opportunities in the existing test process. These opportunities are the basis for concrete improvement goals. Based on these improvement goals, the objectives of the introduction of a test tool are compiled and rendered as concrete as possible. This makes it possible to render the achieved results measurable later.
- Infrastructure and test object:
  The infrastructure (test environments, workplaces and possibly other tools) and the test object play a vital part in determining the added value of a test tool. It must be investigated whether a tool matches the test object and the technical environment. This is a requirement in particular when the organisation opts for automated test execution. Another important aspect is to investigate whether there are special test tools for the test object and, if so, what their possibilities are. This occurs often, especially when the test object is a standard package.
- Test approach:
  The implementation of tools as an efficiency measure adds value in particular when the processes are repeatable and predictable. In addition the process method must be supported by the tool – a test tool that serves to support defect management, for instance, must fit into the process of defect management. Location is a key aspect. When a test organisation works in several physical locations, the tool will have to support this as well. In the

example of the tool for defect management, it must be accessible from the various locations and all testers must work with the same database.

The results of the interviews and the assessments of the various test products are used to compile a first (rough) version of the business case. The most important aspects here are the expected investments and the expected benefits. This is a mix of tangibles and intangibles, which is why it is always very difficult to create a business case. Moreover, many things are still unknown after the quick scan. For instance, no specific test tool has yet been selected. A first version of the business case will therefore consist of the benefits expected by the stakeholders and an estimate of the costs that must be incurred to use the test products in a test tool. A business case can also consist of several scenarios elaborating the deployment of different tool types.

In more detail

Tangible and intangible benefits of tool deployment
Defining the business case for the deployment of test tools is always difficult. Partly because fixed and variable costs are involved, and partly because tangible and intangible benefits are involved. A reduction of the lead time is an example of a tangible benefit. But often there are also indirect benefits that do not have a direct bearing on money. For instance, the test organisation's image will improve. It will radiate professionalism. Users and maintenance organisations like to see demonstrations of automated testing. The test organisation is more often asked to help with a variety of events. Employees will become more motivated. New career opportunities: technical specialisation and working with modern tools.

A report is created on the basis of the results of the interviews, the assessment of the various test products, and the business case. In addition to the business case, the report contains a conclusion focusing on the possible deployment of test tools. In addition to this conclusion, it makes concrete recommendations for the follow-up process and which steps must be taken by which people.

8.5.7   Realisation phase

The second phase in the model is the Realisation phase. Based on a *plan of approach* that has to be created, all of the activities are executed and products are realised that are necessary to use a test tool in an organisation. The aim of the Realisation phase is the implementation of a test tool, including the required *configuration*. Another part of this phase is elaborating the *preconditions* to enable use of the tool. Three sub-phases, associated with these three parts, can thus be distinguished:
1. Plan of approach
2. Setup preconditions
3. Test tool configuration.

The sub-phases are executed in parallel, making it possible to take account of findings (e.g. due to advancing insights) from one sub-phase in the execution of another sub-phase. Also this is time saving.

Sub-phase: Plan of approach

The quick scan provides information to create a first draft of the plan of approach. It describes the first setup of the preconditions. We recommend beginning with a test tool selection and the execution of the pilot. These are explicitly included as activities in the plan. At the end of the pilot, the plan of approach can be updated and concretised. The main aim of a plan of approach is the univocal definition of aspects like the objective, activities, planning and deliverables. Examples of subjects listed in the plan of approach are:

- Test tool objective
- Preconditions
- Pilot approach
- Configuration approach
- Activities
- Planning
- Products
- Organisation.

Sub-phase: Setup preconditions

A number of preconditions must be met to enable the use of test tools. The main precondition is clearly the presence of a structured test process in which the use of tools may result in improvements. In addition to preconditions enabling deployment of the test tool, there are preconditions that must be met to enable use of the tool by the testers. The testers must be able to use the tool not just for current test work, but also for future test work. The way in which the preconditions are elaborated may depend on what is specified in the tool policy. Which preconditions must be met and how they must be set up depends on the specific situation. However, a number of generally applicable conditions can be identified:

- Test tool selection
- Pilot
- Business case
- Management commitment
- Maintenance in the line
- Trained testers
- Structured test process
- Communication.

These are explained in further detail below.

Test tool selection

There is a large variety of test tools that can be deployed in a test process. The specific environment and objectives determine which test tool(s) are most suitable in any situation. The strategy (for the future) of the test tool supplier is also gaining importance in the selection of a tool. Because an increasing number of test tools are integrated, selecting a product often also means selecting a supplier. If no test tool is available in the test, a test tool selection is done. Several approaches are available to this end that strongly resemble a regular package selection. Various tools are assessed on the basis of a pre-defined list of criteria. The criteria depend on the tool type for which the test tool selection is done. A list of example criteria can be found on www.tmap. net under "test tool selection criteria".

Pilot

The introduction of a test tool is not a standard process that can be done the same way in every situation. Every test has its own pitfalls. Often, many people have very high expectations from test tools. People are usually not aware that the deployment of tools requires an investment, the benefits of which do not usually become visible in the short term. Therefore one must proceed very carefully when implementing tools to avoid losing out to the difference between expectations and reality. By starting with a pilot project, insight into the added value of a test tool is provided in a relatively limited environment and in the relatively short term. The tool can be used on a small scale in a pilot, for example by part of the team or by testing a specific function. This makes it possible to evaluate the feasibility of the test tool aims. With a limited effort, insight thus is provided into whether the test tool is technically feasible, whether it matches the current test method, and the expected costs and benefits.

In more detail

The dip in the performance curve or why a pilot is necessary

What are the consequences for the employees of introducing test tools? This can be explained with figure 8.18 "Performance dip in the introduction of a new work method". The figure describes the situation in which an organisation wants to improve its performance in a certain field. Current performance is at level M1. The organisation wishes to perform at level M4. A new work method is introduced to achieve this.

The figure shows how the introduction of a new work method initially causes a dip in the performance curve. The path to move from performing at level M1 to performing at level M4 is not a straight upward line. A new work method must first be learned and, in most cases, adapted to the specific situation. If the stakeholders are not aware that the performance level will drop initially, there is a danger of measuring too early. The (lower) benefits of level 2 are then measured. It is concluded that this is not the right work method and another solution must be found. Often, the use of test tools is interrupted and the tool is shelved (also known as "shelf ware").

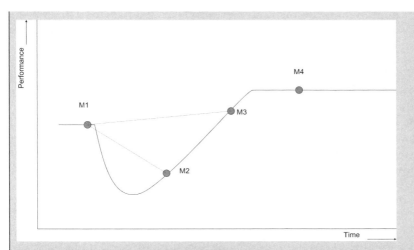

Figure 8.18: Performance dip in the introduction of a new work method

We recommend measuring the benefits of the new work method when the rising line compared to level M1 is started. In this example, this is point M3. It is an assessment that is difficult to make. When, in the introduction of a new work method, the organisation also opts for a long chance process, the danger of overly early measurement and drawing the wrong conclusions is even greater. This is one of the reasons for using a short-term pilot. The dip will certainly show up during the pilot, but the dip in a "real production situation" will be smaller (and at least more easily predictable) based on the learning points and findings of the pilot.

Business case

The first version of the business case created in the Initiation phase is elaborated further. The figures in the business case can now be concrete. When specifying the costs, the fixed and variable costs must be taken into account. Fixed costs may be: hardware, licences, installation, maintenance and training. Variable costs may be: test script creation, execution of test scripts, analysis of results, test script maintenance and training.

Management commitment

Even when the testing is sufficiently mature to use tools, it is not always certain that the desired benefits are realised. One of the main success factors for the deployment of test tools is the management's commitment. The management must be made aware that the use of the tool is an investment that usually yields an ROI in the longer term in terms of faster and/or better testing. If this awareness is inadequate, there is a great risk that the tool is taken out of production after the very first disappointment. This is even more true when the tool is deployed for the first time in a project with a fixed end date. If the project experiences time pressure, there is a great risk that the tool is taken out of production.

Maintenance in the line
An operational test tool may consist of a large number of items: modules in the test tool, framework, test data files, documents for use and maintenance, etc. All of these items must be maintained to enable reuse in the future. Test tool deployment only pays back over longer periods and therefore often across projects. By assigning the maintenance of tools to the line, knowledge retention is guaranteed.

Trained testers
The testers must be trained when the test team has not yet worked with a tool. Both the tool and working with it are new for the test team. The testers must acquire knowledge to ensure good use and maintenance. Training staff thus focuses on two aspects: gaining knowledge of the tool and of the use of the tool in the test process.

Structured test process
The deployment of test tools focuses on improving the test process in terms of money, time and quality. As such, it contributes to improving the efficiency of the test process. Before a test process can be made more efficient, it must be executed in a controlled manner. It may be necessary to define additional activities in the context of controlling the test process. For instance the use of test design techniques (see chapter 14 "Test design techniques"), which also increases the traceability of the test process. The measures to be implemented are highly situation-specific. We recommend using an improvement model (e.g. TPI [Koomen, 1999]) when implementing the improvement.

Communication
When the test team and the rest of the organisation are not familiar with working with test tools, the aspect of communication requires extra attention. The stakeholders are informed of the plans in the field of test tooling as early on as possible. What are the plans, why are they executed, who is executing them, what are the planned results, and when will they be realised. We strongly recommend using the available communication resources for such communication. For instance a regular work meeting, a newsletter and the intranet. When these options are not available, information sessions should be organised.

Sub-phase: Test tool configuration
In many cases, the test tools support a specific work method. Often this work method deviates from the situation in the organisation that will use the tool.

The tool must therefore be configured (see figure 8.19 "Configuration of the test tool"). Test tool configuration to ensure that it is in line with the organisation is customisation work. It involves activities like setting standard tables, defining a workflow, or programming a framework for automated test execution. The basis for the configuration is formed by the three aspects discussed in the Initiation phase. These are test tool objectives, infrastructure, and test object and test approach. A configuration plan is created on this basis. It describes concretely what and how the tool will be configured. This is vital to maintain the tool and its specific configuration in the future. The tool is then configured on the basis of the plan. We recommend doing this in collaboration with the future administrator of the tool, or asking him to do this. This ensures the first knowledge transfer. During the tool configuration, the configuration must also be tested. Any defects showing up in this test can be solved or incorporated in the configuration plan as known problems during completion. When a new version of the tool is developed, it can be examined whether these problems can be solved then.

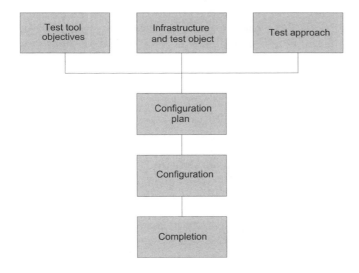

Figure 8.19: Configuration of the test tool

8.5.8 Operation phase

The third phase in the model is the Operation phase. This phase starts when the test tool is taken into production by the test team. To ensure that the test tool can continue to be used, maintenance must be executed. The use of the test tool will be part of the regular test process. This means that new activities must be executed by both the testers and the test manager. This also means that these people must be able to use and maintain the test tool the right way. The tool must have a place in the regular test process. When using the test tool, data must be collected on its functioning. Does its functionality fit in with the overall work method? If this is not the case, it must be examined whether this can be changed. The same applies to the evaluation of the test tool aims defined in the Initiation phase. It must be checked periodically whether the aims are still realised with the implementation of the tool.

One of the main principles in the use of test tools is the aspect of maintainability. The actual maintenance occurs in the Operation phase. When automated execution is used, issues like new releases, changes and incidents in the test object will have an impact on the test suite. But new releases of the test tool itself may also result in changes. These can be implemented, if necessary, after which the test tool is ready for use again.

Three types of maintenance can be distinguished:
- Technical maintenance
  The installation of the test tool (on the server or workplaces), implementation of new versions or patches, solving technical incidents, etc. Often the maintenance department that also handles the technical maintenance of other applications in an organisation is responsible for this.
- Operational maintenance
  Enabling users to work with the test tool. This may involve issuing authorisations or configuring project-specific components (e.g. database). Often the maintenance department that also handles the technical maintenance of the tool may be responsible for this. Another option is to allocate the maintenance within the test project itself or to a permanent test organisation.
- Functional maintenance
  Enabling users to work 'well' with the test tool. This means creating work instructions, manuals for the organisation's own work method, procedures, templates, etc. It is important that functional maintenance does not maintain the functionality of the tool itself – this is the supplier's responsibility. The test project itself or a permanent test organisation may be responsible for this aspect.

The three maintenance types have separate responsibilities, but clearly they must collaborate as well. For instance, when a new version of the test tool becomes available, functional maintenance assesses its added value and impact. Functional maintenance then determines whether the new version must be introduced and when. Functional maintenance then directs technical maintenance to handle the implementation.

8.6   Test professionals

8.6.1   Introduction

A great variety of expertise is required for a tester to be able to function well in the discipline of testing. A tester needs to have knowledge of:

- The domain (e.g. logistical processes or financial reports)
- The infrastructure (test environment, development platform, test tools)
- Testing itself.

The management is responsible for ensuring that the right person with the right expertise has the right job, preferably in collaboration with personnel and training experts. A carefully controlled inflow and internal mobility policy supported by related training for test personnel are required. However, the negative image of testing makes suitable and experienced test personnel scarce.

The challenge for HRM lies in this combination of the negative image on the one hand and the importance of testing on the other, who can we find to execute this task and, more particularly, how can we keep them happy? An important tool to achieve such satisfaction is to offer the tester a career path.

These sections discusses how to handle this issue. Section 8.6.2 "Points of concern" devotes attention to a number of points that require attention when setting up HRM for test professionals. Section 8.6.3 "Characteristics" describes what makes a tester a tester. What, for instance, are the personal characteristics of a tester? The next section (8.6.4 "Career path") gives insight into a possible career structure for testers, followed by a section (8.6.4 "Positions") describing the possible positions. Finally, the last section 8.6.5 "Training" discusses the aspect of training.

8.6.2   Points of concern

Despite the fact that everyone is aware of the use and added value of testing these days, its image is not exemplary in every organisation. Sometimes a test position is considered boring, mind-numbing and not very challenging. Or, it is perceived as the final stop in one's career or a necessary side-road when there is really nothing else to do. We describe a number of points of concern to set up HRM for test professionals below.

Tasks, authorisations and responsibilities

Many organisations have a comprehensive competency profile, the growth opportunities (in roles and salaries) and the available courses for roles and jobs. Such a profile is sometimes missing for test professionals, with the excuse that testing is a one-off activity for instance. It may be clear that this is not the case. This is why a written career structure is necessary for testers as well.

> **In more detail**
>
> **Growth opportunities for testers**
> The job description of a tester must make clear the growth opportunities both within and outside the discipline of testing. Since testing acts at the crossroads of many professions, there is a range of (external) directions for growth. For instance, a tester who is regularly involved in testing a specific business application may evolve into a process analyst for that specific domain. Something that often happens as well is that an experienced test manager is asked to become a project manager.

Training options

Since testing is a risk-mitigating measure, a tester is a risk in and of himself. If the test professional does not test correctly or adequately, certain risks cannot be resolved. As such, it is important for a tester to know not only what well structured testing is, but also what he is testing. Taking the definition of a product risk in account (see also chapter 9 "Product Risk Analysis"), the tester must have a feeling for the domain (damage part) and the technology (chance of failure part) on which the system is based. He must master them and know where the risks are generally (e.g. that one calculation or that one specific combination of architecture and hardware). Concretely, this means that testers, too, can (must) attend courses relating to e.g. the tool that is used for programming or the domain for which the solution is being built.

Workplace location

Because testing is at the crossroads of many professions, testers have a lot of contacts with the professionals in these disciplines. Putting the testers in the middle is killing two birds with one stone. Their image is that they are truly at the crossroads, and there they have a lot of contacts. There are examples of an improved test process after the test team physically moved to the 'centre' of the organisation. Among other things, it improved the mutual respect between programmers and testers, which in turn had a positive impact on quality.

Reviews

Reviews are generally performed by a superior with experience in the tasks executed by the person reviewed. This is the only way to achieve an objective picture of the past period and reach agreements. It is done this way in many

IT disciplines. A programmer, for instance, is assessed by a project leader who used to work in programming himself. An information analyst is assessed by a business analyst with a similar past. Testers are often reviewed by the project leader. In his current role he has a lot to do with it, but he was never a tester himself. To avoid any suspicion of conflicting interests, a tester should be assessed by a superior or immediate stakeholder with actual testing experience. For instance the test coordinator or test manager.

Compensation

One current trend is to offer a variable salary in addition to a fixed salary. The size of the variable component (bonus) depends on the realisation of certain objectives (Key Performance Indicators or KPIs). A tester in an organisation has different interests than e.g. an information analyst, programmer or project leader. A test professional must be held accountable for other results. The situation in which everyone (including the tester) is held accountable for achieving the project planning is not ideal. The tester is at the end of the workflow and is often – incorrectly – perceived as the one causing the delays. It is better to assess a tester on the basis of his work's results. Examples are achieving his planning for one test cycle or the number of incidents during production. Clearly, a number of principles apply in this context. Never award a bonus to a tester for the number of defects detected, because this depends on the quality of the software (and is therefore someone else's point of concern).

8.6.3   Characteristics

What are a tester's characteristics, in other words, what properties must a person have to be an ideal tester? In the first place, the ideal tester does not exist. It varies per situation. We can, however, list a number of generic properties:

Communication, spoken and written
The tester maintains contacts with many different parties. For instance, he talks to e.g. the programmer, the information analyst, the project leader and other testers. It is important for a tester to be able to understand the interests of his discussion partners and communicate effectively. Written communication is important to record defects and write reports.

Accurate and analytical
A tester must focus on detail. It is important to establish for every requirement or wish what is actually being asked. In case of doubt, questions must be asked. It is important for the tester to go about his job analytically and refrain

from making assumptions. A test basis is at the basis of his test, if this is not complete or contains defects, it is registered as a defect. A tester must never ever make assumptions in this respect, even though they may be self-evident.

Example

A test of a financial application required sums to be shown in euros and dollars. The requirement contained a list of screens in which this occurred. Careful analysis by the tester showed that there were more screens in which this could occur. When the client was questioned, it was found that the requirement was indeed incomplete and the list of screens was modified. If the tester had not performed a full analysis, incomplete screens would have been taken into production.

Convincing and persevering
A tester communicates the detected defects to the party that caused them. This is where the extent to which the tester is convincing plays a part because the receiving party must consider the reported defects as actual defects. The tester must have power of conviction and persevere in affirming the importance of the quality of the product.

Objective and positively critical
When a defect is communicated or questions are asked about a requirement, it is important to do so objectively. Comments like "bad software", "again an incorrect requirement" or "irritating colours" should not be used. In discussions about defects, it is important that the tester makes the problem clear to the other parties in a constructive, positive way. This means a certain level of diplomacy and refraining from pointing fingers at various parties.

Creative
The tester must simulate reality to make a statement about the quality of the software. Test cases are created, test data compiled, and a test environment defined for this purpose. This requires creativity.

Sensitive
The tester is at a crossroads between professions. The point of gravity of the tester's activities lies at the end of a process, when the pressure is highest. The tester must be aware of the tensions and interests and handle them correctly, so that the required objectives can be realised.

8.6.4   Career path

One condition to professionalise testing in an organisation is to offer test professionals a career path. This section provides a method to define such career paths. Training, creating work experience and a coaching programme are vital components. These are shown per job type and per level in the so-called career cube (see figure 8.20 "The career cube"). The cube is a tool for career coaching by HRM to align demand from the organisation, the available knowledge and competencies, *and* the ambitions of test professionals. The three dimensions of the career cube are defined as follows:

- Height: functional growth
- Width: functional differentiation
- Depth: training and coaching.

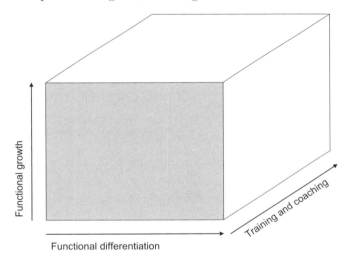

Figure 8.20: The career cube

First dimension: functional growth

Functional growth is about the vertical career path that an employee can follow. This roughly covers three main job categories: junior, intermediate and senior. Classification in these three categories occurs on the basis of the three-role model. It specifies in which 3 types of roles the test professional can act in a test, and therefore where he has experience or is even an expert.

The three possible role types are:

- Executing role
- Advisory role
- Leadership role.

The distinction between junior, intermediate and senior is then made as follows (see figure 8.21 "Functional growth in the career cube"):

- *Junior:* experience with the executing role of testing
- *Intermediate:* expert in the executing role of testing and experience with advisory or leadership role
- *Senior:* expert in the executing role of testing and expert in advisory or leadership role.

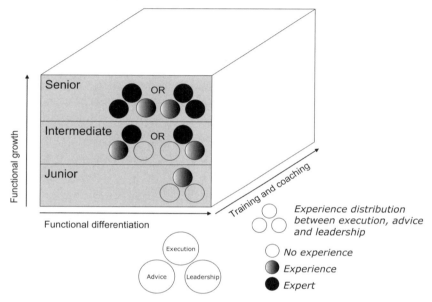

Figure 8.21: Functional growth in the career cube

Second dimension: functional differentiation

TMap and the associated career paths make three differentiations in the discipline of testing. The test professional can specialise in one or more of these differentiations, which are:

- The execution of the test process
- The use of tools for the test process
- Management of the test process.

Together with the 3 role types (executing, advisory and leadership), these three differentiations constitute the various positions a test professional can have. Combined with the 3-bullet model described earlier, this results in figure 8.22 "Functional differentiation in the career cube".

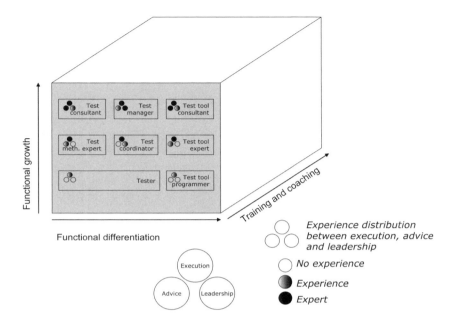

Figure 8.22: Functional differentiation in the career cube

Third dimension: knowledge and competencies

To support the tester in his functional growth and differentiation and to keep in line with demand from the organisation, it is important to offer the right training and coaching. The structure of training and coaching forms the third dimension of the career cube.

The training must focus on the profession, related professions (e.g. quality management, requirements), IT knowledge (development environment, languages), competencies (communication), and domain expertise. The coaching concentrates on the attitude and the application of the acquired knowledge and experience. Good coaching is a condition for a well-considered career path. Every employee receives support in several ways. It can be provided by a colleague test professional and/or other experienced employees. Beginning testers can be coached by their manager or a suitable coach. As their job level increases, the importance of continuous new practical experience and social competency training grows exponentially in relation to (test) training and coaching and support. The right things must be offered by the organisation.

8.6.5   Positions

The possible positions of a test professional are described below. They are based on the model of the career cube as described above. The positions are classified as follows:

Junior positions:

- Tester
- Test tool programmer

Intermediate positions:

- Test method expert
- Test coordinator
- Test tool expert

Senior positions:

- Test consultant
- Test manager
- Test tool consultant

The possible tasks and required knowledge and skills are explained per position.

In more detail

Position of a test professional versus role of a test professional

The significant difference between a position and a role is that the professional holds a position and fulfils a role. A role is aimed at the performance of tasks for the test project or the permanent test organisation in a specific situation. Roles are fulfilled by a test professional. A position of a test professional formally describes which tasks the individual should be able to perform and what knowledge and skills he should possess. A position says something about the suitability for a role. The exact content of the role depends on the situation and varies per project or organisation. In some cases the role is equivalent to the position (e.g. the role of tester). Possible roles of a test professional are described in chapter 16 "Test roles".

Example 1

A test project wishes to fill the role of tester. To this end, an individual is sought who holds the function of tester.

Example 2

A test project seeks to fill the role of test-team leader with an individual who will also be required to carry out testing (a co-working supervisor). To this end, an individual is sought who holds the function of tester, has practical experience as a tester, possesses the capacity to manage and has the desire to become a test-team leader.

Tester

The tester executes the primary test tasks, i.e. the core of the test process. The test tasks are the most creative, but also the most labour-intensive test activities. In the TMap life cycle model, the function of tester is active from the testability review of the test basis in the Preparation phase through to the preservation of the testware in the Completion phase.

Possible tasks
- Testability review of the test basis (the specifications)
- Specification of logical and physical test cases, starting situations and test scripts
- Creating starting situations
- Executing test cases (dynamic testing)
- Checking and assessing test results
- Executing checks and investigations (static testing)
- Recording defects
- Preserving testware.

Required knowledge and competencies
Test-specific
- Overall knowledge of TMap life cycle
- Skills in testability review and test design techniques
- Skills in applying checklists.

Automation
- General automation knowledge and experience
- Overall knowledge of system development methods
- Skills in interpreting the test basis (requirements, functional and technical design)

General
- Knowledge of the domain and the line organisation
- The ability to learn using test tools quickly
- Knowledge of project organisation and a project-based work approach
- Skills in word processing and working with spreadsheets
- Creativity and accuracy.

Test tool programmer

The test tool programmer is responsible for the technical aspect of the automated test suite. A test suite is often built with tools for executing the test (see section 8.5.3 "Types of test tools"). He translates the design of the test suite to modules in the test tool to be realised. In existing and new test tools, he realises the test suite. Within the framework of the instructions provided by the test tool consultant, the test tool programmer executes the detailed design, realisation and implementation of test suites.

Possible tasks
- Realisation, testing, management and maintenance of a test suite
- Providing support in the design of a test suite.

Required knowledge and competencies
Test-specific
- Knowledge of (the possibilities of) tools for executing the test
- Knowledge of automation of the test process.

Automation
- Knowledge of system development methods
- Knowledge of the architecture and tools for system development
- Knowledge of hardware, software and data communication resources
- Experience in structured programming (preferably in the programming language of the tool).

General
- Good analytical power
- Creativity and accuracy
- The ability to learn using test tools quickly.

Test method expert

The test method expert is a specialist in being a tester. This can be with a special test type or level (acceptance or end-to-end test) or in a specific environment (web or real-time). He is experienced and fulfils a combination of executing and advisory roles in projects. He can also act as a team lead.

Possible tasks
- The tasks as executed by the tester
- Support in creating (detailed) test plans
- Support in setting up the test organisation
- Recruiting and assessing employees from test knowledge point of view
- Executing work distribution and progress monitoring
- Development and maintenance of test training
- Teaching and coaching
- Mediation for external training
- Advice and support for the implementation of all types of test techniques
- Advising the test coordinator
- Collecting and assessing statistical data about testing.

Required knowledge and competencies
Test-specific
- Extensive, expert experience in the implementation of the TMap life cycle and techniques
- General knowledge about the deployment of test tools.

Automation
- Comprehensive automation knowledge and experience
- Expert knowledge and experience in system design and realisation
- Knowledge of architectures and tools for system development
- General knowledge of hardware, software and data communication resources.

General
- Knowledge of the domain and the line organisation
- Knowledge of project organisation and a project-based work approach
- Creative, accurate and able to work on a strictly methodical basis
- Good contact skills and a motivating personality
- Good written and spoken communication skills.

Test tool expert

An expert in being a 'test tool programmer'. This can be by means of special tools (performance test tools, automated test execution tools) or in a specific environment (interface testing, screen testing). He is highly experienced and fulfils a combination of executing and advisory roles in projects. He can also act as a team lead for test tool programmers. He helps the test tool consultant with the introduction of new tools.

Possible tasks
- The tasks as executed by the test tool programmer
- Support in creating automated test suite
- Supporting the execution of the quick scan
- Configuring test tools
- Recruiting and assessing employees
- Executing work distribution and progress monitoring
- Development and maintenance of tool training
- Teaching and coaching
- Mediation for external training
- Advising the test coordinator.

Required knowledge and competencies
Test-specific
- Comprehensive knowledge of (the possibilities of) various tools for executing the test
- Comprehensive knowledge of automation of the test process.

Automation
- Comprehensive automation knowledge and experience
- Knowledge of the architecture and tools for system development
- Knowledge of hardware, software and data communication resources
- Ample experience in structured programming (preferably in the programming language of the tool).

General
- Good analytical power
- Creativity and accuracy
- The ability to learn using test tools quickly.

Test coordinator

The test coordinator leads a team of testers, test method experts, test tool programmers and/or test tool experts. The test coordinator is responsible for the planning, management and execution of the test process, within planning and budget and at the right quality, for at most one test level or test type. He reports conformable to the test plan on the progress of the test process and the quality of the test object. This function is active throughout the TMap life cycle.

Possible tasks
- Creating, obtaining approval of and maintaining the test plan
    - Risk assessment and strategy determination
    - Creating planning and estimate
    - Specification of organisation and infrastructure
    - Specification of procedures and standards
- Executing the test plan within planning and budget
    - Recruiting and assessing employees
    - Day-to-day coordination of test activities
    - Executing work distribution
    - Establishing plans
    - Monitoring progress
- Leading internal consultations
- Creating release advice
- Participating in project meetings
- Assessment of test process.

Required knowledge and competencies
Test-specific
- Extensive experience in the implementation of the TMap life cycle and techniques
- Experience as a team lead
- Extensive knowledge about the deployment of test tools.
Automation
- Comprehensive automation knowledge and experience
- Good knowledge of system development methods
- Knowledge of architectures and tools for system development
- General knowledge of hardware, software and data communication resources.

General
- General knowledge of the domain and the line organisation
- Excellent contact skills and a motivating personality
- Excellent written and spoken communication skills.

Test consultant

The test consultant is a specialist in being a test method expert. He focuses exclusively on consulting work in relation to the aspects of testing. He provides method-oriented support for the test process in the broadest sense of the word. The test consultant supports all test activities and all members of the test team. I.e., both the test manager or test coordinator in e.g. strategy determination and the tester in specifying test cases. This function may be active throughout the TMap life cycle.

Possible tasks
- Setting up test techniques
- Development of new test techniques
- Creation of test regulations
- Development of related training
- Teaching and coaching
- Advice and support for the implementation of all types of test techniques
- Improvement of test process
- Management consulting.

Required knowledge and competencies
Test-specific
- Expert experience in the implementation of the TMap life cycle model and techniques
- Knowledge in improving test processes
- Extensive knowledge about the deployment of test tools.

Automation
- Comprehensive automation knowledge and experience
- Expert knowledge and experience in system design and realisation
- Knowledge of architectures and tools for system development
- General knowledge of hardware, software and data communication.

General
- Knowledge of the domain and the line organisation
- The ability to learn using (test) tools quickly
- Knowledge of project organisation and a project-based work approach
- Creative, accurate and able to work on a strictly methodical basis
- Good contact skills and a motivating personality
- Good written and spoken communication skills.

Test tool consultant

The test tool consultant is a specialist in being a tool expert. He focuses exclusively on consulting work in relation to the aspects of test tools. He supports the process relating to the deployment of tools in the broadest sense of the word. The test tool consultant supports all test tools and all members of the test team.

Possible tasks
- Setting up and configuring a test suite
- Development of new test suites
- Creation of regulations
- Development of related training
- Teaching and coaching
- Advice and support for the implementation of all types of tools
- Defining tool policy
- Executing quick scan
- Management consulting.

Required knowledge and competencies
Test-specific
- Expert knowledge of (the possibilities of) various types of tools
- Expert knowledge of deployment of tools.

Automation
- Comprehensive automation knowledge and experience
- Knowledge of the architecture and tools for system development
- Knowledge of hardware, software and data communication resources
- Ample experience in structured programming (preferably in the programming language of the tool).

General
- Good analytical power
- Creativity and accuracy
- The ability to learn using test tools quickly
- Good written and spoken communication skills.

Test manager

The test manager leads a team of test coordinators or test managers. He is responsible for the planning, management and execution of the test process, on time and on budget and at the right quality, for multiple test levels or test types. He reports conformable to the test plan on the progress of the test process and the quality of the test object. This function is active throughout the TMap life cycle.

Possible tasks
- The tasks as executed by the test coordinator
- Creating, obtaining approval of and maintaining the master test plan
  - Risk assessment and strategy determination
  - Creating planning and estimate
  - Specification of organisation and infrastructure
  - Specification of procedures and standards.
- Executing the master test plan within planning and budget
  - Recruiting and assessing employees
  - Day-to-day management of test activities
  - Setting up the organisation
  - The test functions and procedures are executed conformable to the structure specified in the master test plan
  - Executing work distribution
  - Establishing master test plans
  - Monitoring progress.
- Maintaining external contacts
- Internal quality management
- Acknowledging, anticipating and reporting on project risks
- Defining or advising on test policy
- Execution of test process optimizing.

Required knowledge and competencies
Test-specific
- Extensive experience in the implementation of the TMap life cycle and techniques
- Experience as a test coordinator.

Automation
- Comprehensive automation knowledge and experience
- Good knowledge of system development methods
- Knowledge of architectures and tools for system development
- General knowledge of hardware, software and data communication resources.

General
- Ample experience in leadership in projects
- General knowledge of the domain and the line organisation
- Excellent contact skills and a motivating personality
- Excellent written and spoken communication skills.

8.6.6   Training

As described earlier, test professionals must comply with high requirements. They are expected to possess knowledge and experience in:
- The discipline of testing
- Related disciplines
- IT generally
- Social and communication skills
- The domain.

Following courses is a requirement to ensure this. One important instrument for HRM is a training programme for test personnel. It can be used to determine the gap between the available and required knowledge of the test professional. We recommend ensuring that the test courses have a modular structure and are available as such. Depending on the position and the employee's existing expertise, training can then be provided more or less individually per (sub-)subject. Subjects may be:

Discipline of testing:
- Test methods and techniques
- Test environment and test tools
- Test management and control
- Test process improvement
- Product risk analysis and estimating
- Test certification.

In more detail

To have more certainty that the testers have sufficient test knowledge, one can ask for certified testers. The ISTQB (International Software Testing Qualifications Board) is responsible for an international qualification scheme for testers (www.istqb.org). EXIN (Examination Institute for Information Science, www.exin-exams.com) organises a certification scheme specifically for TMap.

Related disciplines:
- Quality management
- Requirements Lifecycle Management
- Project management.

General IT knowledge:
- Methods and tools for system development
- Planning and progress monitoring tools
- System management and operation
- Technical infrastructure.

Social and communication skills:
- Reporting and documentation techniques
- Test attitude
- Social skills in speech, writing and personality
- Effective leadership.

Domain:
- Industry-specific domain and certification
- General domain and organisation knowledge.

9   Product risk analysis

9.1   Introduction

Testing is a measure to provide insight into the quality of delivered products and the related risks when taken into production. If the quality is inadequate timely measures can be taken, such as rework by the developers. However, there is never an unlimited quantity of test resources and time. This is why it is important to relate the test effort to the expected product risks: thorough testing where great risks are discerned; light or no testing where the risks are small. The motto is:

> **"No risk, no test"**

Well-justified choices have to be made in this context. Product risk analysis (PRA) is a tool in making such choices.

> **Definition**
>
> A product risk analysis is analysing the product to be tested with the aim of achieving a joint view, for the test manager and other stakeholders, of the more or less risky characteristics and parts of the product to be tested so that the thoroughness of testing can be related to this view.

The focus in PRA is on the product risks, i.e. what is the risk to the organisation if the product does not have the expected quality. This can be because the software contains defects, but also because the AO procedures are not in line with the system or the system is not sufficiently effective or too slow for the end users.

> **In more detail**
>
> There are also (test) project risks. Examples: the system must be live on 1 January, the functional specifications are delivered too late, skilled testers are not available or the test infrastructure is not ready in time. These risks are not taken into account when establishing the test strategy, but when creating the test plan (see sections 5.2.11, 6.2.13). Www.tmap.net also contains a checklist with such risks: "Test process risks".

In practice, people are found to have highly diverging ideas of 'risks'. A PRA requires a shared reference framework, in particular as to what product risk is understood to mean.

Definition

A product risk is the chance that the product fails in relation to the expected damage if this occurs.

Product risk = Chance of failure * Damage

where Chance of failure = Chance of defects * Frequency of use

---

The Chance of failure is determined by the *Chance of defects* and the *Frequency of use*. The chance of defects is the chance that a product (component) contains a defect. The presence of a defect in the product, however, does not mean that that defect will actually manifest itself in production. When the defect is in a part of the product that is never used, the product will not fail. The more often the product component with the defect is used – or, the higher the frequency of use – the greater the chance that the product will fail.

For a proper risk analysis, the separate factors of a risk are therefore taken into consideration:

- Frequency of use

  In a system (component) that is accessed several dozens of times per day, the chance that a defect will manifest is many times bigger than in a system (component) that is accessed just once per year.

- Chance of defects

  To assess the chance of defects, the following overview of where defects often concentrate may be of assistance. This overview is based in part on [Schaefer, 1996]:

  – Complex functions (also: complex functionality, software)
  – Completely new functions
  – Often adapted functions
  – Functions for which specific tools or techniques were deployed for the first time
  – Functions that were handed over to someone else during development
  – Functions realised under extremely high time pressure
  – Functions requiring above-average optimisation (e.g. rendering a function extremely fast or economical, often because of resource restrictions, typically either machine time or memory)
  – Functions in which many defects were found earlier (e.g. in a previous release or during earlier evaluations)
  – Functions with many interfaces.

  The chance of defects is bigger as well with:

  – Inexperienced developers
  – Inadequate commitment of users

- Inadequate quality management during development
- Inadequate quality of the development tests
- New development tools and environment
- Big development teams
- Development teams with sub-optimal communication (due to geographical or personal causes).

An important point of concern in relation to the chance of defects (and therefore the chance of failure) is that it can be assessed more correctly as the development or maintenance process advances. The PRA can (and will) therefore be adjusted in the course of the test process.

■ Damage

What is the damage that will be suffered if the defect manifests itself? A distinction is to be made between direct and indirect damage for the organisation. Direct damage would involve loss of revenue, damage to third parties, economic loss, environmental or physical damage (especially with embedded systems - explosion, crash, car injury) costs for correction and repairs. Indirect damage would be e.g. damage to the image, loss of trust, damage claims from third parties, overload of the help desk or, for government institutions, social damage such as for the tax department (errors in tax refunds) and justice (formality issues due to which serious offenders are not condemned). Moreover, damage can result for third parties because the system does not function as intended. The damage usually grows when the defect has an impact on other functions or systems. An organisation can determine damage at various levels, such as at the level of business processes, business objectives, business requirements, but also systems or subsystems.

9.2   Approach

As a rule, a PRA is first performed at the master test plan level, i.e. early on in the total testing process. To ensure the PRA's usefulness, the scope of the testing process and the business requirements have to be clear and more detailed requirements, designs or acceptance criteria have to be well on their way. Insofar as necessary, supplements and further detailing are provided at the level of the separate test levels. If there is no master test plan, a PRA is performed at the level of the separate test level. The test manager must ensure that the PRA covers only the scope of the test level.

The result is incorporated in the (master) test plan and constitutes the basis for the subsequent decisions in strategy as to non, light or thorough testing of a characteristic (e.g. a quality characteristic) or object part (component) of the product to be tested.

You should realise that a PRA is a snapshot. In the course of the subsequent process, it will be found that some risks are overestimated and some have been underestimated or neglected altogether. The test manager must adjust the test strategy and associated estimated effort, as well as the planning, see sections 5.3.4 and 6.3.4.

This section describes the steps in a PRA and provides instructions.

Steps:
1. Determining participants
2. Determining the PRA approach
3. Preparing session/interviews
4. Collecting and analysing product risks
5. Completeness check.

Please note!
The description of activities below can make it appear as if the organisation and performance of a PRA are not very complicated tasks. In practice, however, many test managers struggle with the tasks. This chapter attempts to describe the process as correctly and transparently as possible, but we should emphasise that much depends on the specific *test management skills* of the test manager. For instance communication skills, diplomacy and far-reaching knowledge of the possible risks and characteristics (to be tested) and being able to make a (rough) estimate of the costs, time and practical feasibility of testing.

In more detail

Iterations
When working with iterations or increments, the question is: what is the scope of the PRA. Is this the system to be realised, or is it an intermediary product at the end of the iteration or increment? In such a case, the preferred option is to perform an initial PRA covering the definitive system, followed by a small-scale additional (mini) PRA focusing on the iteration/increment.

Example
A system will consist of 2 functional subsystems. The PRA shows that, in addition to functionality, performance and security must also be tested. Subsystem 1 is realised in iteration 1; subsystem 2 is added in iteration 2. Performance and security can be tested starting from iteration 3. The mini PRA and related test strategy for iteration 1 determine that subsystem 1 is tested thoroughly from the functional perspective. The mini PRA and the test strategy for iteration 2 determine that subsystem 2 must be tested with medium thoroughness, and subsystem 1 only with light thoroughness for regression. It is decided that for iteration 3, functional integration and regression tests plus performance and security tests will be executed.

9.3   Determining participants

Assessing product risks is difficult. You need to have knowledge of the system and the organisation, of possible damage and the chance of defects. The test manager does not possess this knowledge, or only to a limited extent. Moreover, the knowledge is usually distributed over various parties or persons. Therefore the organisation and client are responsible for the correct assessment of the product risks. In practice, the test manager is usually the facilitator and organiser of the PRA, approaching various people who can contribute knowledge about the product risks.

As a rule, the receiving parties are in the best position to estimate the damage and frequency of use, while the supplying parties can best estimate the chance of defects. Below you will find several examples of receiving and supplying parties, respectively:

- Receiving parties

   Client, (end) users, line managers, project board members, project manager and (functional and system) administrators can, in view of their knowledge of the environment in which the system will be used, provide insight into the damage due to failure and the expected frequency of use.

- Suppliers

   Architects, requirement managers, developers, designers, programmers, database administrators, quality management personnel, test managers, and project manager, in view of their knowledge of the creation process and the technical operation, can provide a good indication of the chance of defects.

In this step, the test manager estimates how many – and which - parties and persons are necessary to perform a PRA with sufficient reliability. He must take the test assignment into consideration, i.e. the fact if it is a PRA for a master test plan or a (supplementary) PRA for a system or acceptance test plan. For instance, the product risks for the system test are usually in "does the system do what is specified", while for a users acceptance test, they focus more on the question "does the system support the organisation".

The persons to be involved are not necessarily the same people listed for the activity "Understanding the assignment" (see sections 5.2.2 and 6.2.2). The PRA is intended as a further elaboration of the information obtained through the Understanding step, but is more test-specific and focused on the completeness of the product risks associated with the system.

In addition to the fact that the PRA serves as the basis for the test strategy, another advantage is that the various parties become more aware of both the risks and the contribution testing can make to make them more manageable. A shared and widely supported image of the main risks with their classifications is created. In the rest of the testing process, this helps realise commitment if decisions must be made in the relevant field.

> **Tips**
> - The complexity of the subject matter makes it difficult to ensure that a PRA is fully objective and detailed: PRAs are overall estimates. The test manager should make this clear to the participants.
> - In a PRA, the test manager requests a lot of input from different stakeholders. Because he asks for so much input, some parties may start to feel that the test manager is unable to do his work autonomously. The test manager can prevent this by explaining in advance in which period their input will be asked and making as many proposals as possible to serve as starting points.

9.4   Determining the PRA approach

The test manager determines how the PRA will be performed. This is done in parallel to or after the previous step.

Two choices must be made when determining the PRA approach:
- How will the PRA be organised, in sessions or interviews?
- Which risk classification is to be used?

These aspects are discussed in greater detail below.

9.4.1   Organisation of the PRA

The PRA can be performed in the following ways:
1. The test manager preferably organises one session – but more if needed – with all of the participants
2. The test manager takes individual interviews with the participants instead of a session.
3. There are various intermediate possibilities. The test manager may, for instance, organise a session for each group of participants (e.g. users and IT people). Another variant is to do interviews each with 2 or 3 participants instead of a session. The participants must complement each other in this case (e.g. a user and a developer).

    A session can also be held with the main participant group, and additional interviews taken with participants with specific expertise. Since a PRA can require a lot of manpower in a more complex environment, another intermediate form is to do a first session with a limited number of participants (preferably with good knowledge of the product to be discussed), after which a more complete team supplements, corrects and approves the results in a follow-up session.

A session has a maximum duration of half a day, an interview has a maximum duration of 2 hours.

In more detail

Session or interview

Generally sessions are preferred over interviews, in particular due to the shared commitment they inspire. But there are also good reasons to take interviews. Below you will find a number of aspects that have an impact on the choice:

- Need for shared commitment
  A session is greatly preferred over interviews to highlight the various perspectives of the participants and work towards a shared and widely supported vision
- (Un)familiarity with PRA and risk-based testing
  If some participants are not familiar with PRA and testing, this might disturb a session because a lot of explanation is required. A prior kick-off session to explain the PRA is necessary in this case. If this is impossible, it is better to use interviews
- Number of participants
  If there is a large group of participants (> 8), the risk that timid persons will or cannot express their view increases in a session. Doing multiple sessions or interviews is recommended in this case
- Political tension
  There are two choices when such tension exists: either the test manager and client want to make the tension visible and discussible; or they want to move around it. In the first case the session is the best option
- Group thinking versus individual thinking
  A session inspires cross-fertilisation of ideas and thoughts, with the whole being more than the sum of the parts. On the other hand, some individuals are heard insufficiently in sessions. The test manager must make a decision on the basis of the participants to be involved
- Little overhead versus thorough approach
  Sessions give an impression of a thorough approach with a lot of (too much) overhead, in view of the (large) number of participants stuck together for several hours. When the organisation has a clear preference for "lean and mean", this would be an argument to take interviews
- "Discussion culture"
  While a session always involves the risk of getting mired in discussions on minor details, the risk is higher in some organisations than in others. In these cases, interviews are the preferred option
- Personal preferences and competencies
  Does the test manager like to take interviews, or does he prefer moderating a session? An interview is easier than a session. How much experience does he have with the latter?

If the test manager opts for a session, he must select a session technique. Techniques like metaplan or the similar but somewhat less formal brown paper sessions are extremely suitable.

In more detail

Metaplan
Metaplan techniques are tools to gather ideas with a group of people in a short time. The method was initiated by Eberhard Schnelle in Hamburg. In addition to simple visual techniques, like the use of boards with cards stuck on them, the method uses moderators to facilitate the discussion and a structured preparation process (with adequate question definition being vital) through to conclusion and assessment of the results. Many years of experience with metaplan sessions are required to become an experienced moderator. Less experienced moderators (and test managers) can implement a simplified version of the technique successfully. It is characteristic of the method to collect ideas from different perspectives, focusing more on categorising and prioritising the main ideas than striving towards completeness. In a PRA, a test manager can use the metaplan technique to determine the test goals together, inventory the characteristic/object part combinations to be tested, and classify the associated risks.

A checklist for an interview agenda can be found on www.tmap.net.

Before and during the session or interview, inspiration can also be found in checklists, for instance "Checklist risk factors per quality characteristic" (see www.tmap.net) and experiences from previous tests. FMEA (Failure Mode and Effect Analysis) is a separate, formal approach in which the participants analyse, for all functions of the product, what could go wrong and what the consequences would be. Additional (test) measures are defined for major risks. See www.fmeainfocentre.com for more information.

The result of the process, which is described in more detail in section 9.6, is recorded.

In more detail

Alternative: Combining PRA with test strategy
When the number of participants involved in the PRA is limited and they already have experience with PRA, or when the product risks are fairly easy to classify, it may be efficient to combine the PRA in one session with the test strategy (see sections 5.2.4 and 6.2.5 "Determining the test strategy").

In more detail

Kick-off session for maintenance testing
When inventorying the test basis, it often happens that changes are not properly documented. In the case of ad-hoc maintenance, the concrete cause/reason may not be specified. One proven method to clarify this is to organise a kick-off session with all

relevant parties (functional and technical administrators, developers, users, testers). In this session, the PRA is preceded by an impact determination and followed by the creation or adjustment of the test strategy. Attention is also devoted to non-functional quality characteristics. Take the existing situation into account when gathering non-functional quality characteristics. For instance, toughening a performance requirement from three seconds to one second is generally difficult to realise by means of maintenance if this was not taken into account in the original design of the system.

Specifically in the case of ad-hoc maintenance, it can be discussed in a kick-off session how a defect in a test situation can be reproduced.
The challenge in organising a kick-off session is aligning the agendas of the required participants with the available – usually limited – test lead time.

9.4.2   Determining risk classification method

To determine what the more or less risky characteristics and components of the product to be tested are, a classification method is necessary to specify whether something represents a high or a low risk. The various risks can all be valued separately (absolute classification), or they can be valued in relation to each other (relative classification). These two risk classification methods are discussed in greater detail below. In most cases, we recommend that an organisation should choose one risk classification mechanism. However, when the risks of the systems are highly diversified, e.g. in administrative and safety-critical systems, it is better to make the classification application-dependent.

Absolute classification
In this classification method, it is determined for each separate risk how big the *damage in case of failure* and the *chance of failure* are. The scale of the damage and the chance are plotted against each other, resulting in the risk class. An example is the table below [Broekman and Notenboom, 2003], where A stands for a high risk, B for medium, and C for low risk.

		Chance of failure		
		High	Medium	Low
	High	A	B	B
Damage in case of failure	Medium	B	B	C
	Low	C	C	C

Table 9.1: Absolute risk classification 3 x 3

The risk classes (A, B and C) in the table above are not distributed symmetrically. Application in actual practice has shown that many organisations feel it is more important to control a risk with high damage and low chance of failure than a risk with low damage and high chance of failure. Clearly an organisation can create the table at its own discretion.

For a small test object or in an organisation that has little experience with risk analyses, a system distinguishing only between the categories High and Low is usually adequate. The associated risk classes are shown in the table below [Lyndsay, 2002]:

		Chance of failure	
		High	Low
Damage in case of failure	High	A	B
	Low	B	C

Table 9.2: Absolute risk classification 2 x 2

So-called detail risk factors can be used as a possible intermediary step to determine the damage in case of failure and the chance of failure. This means that the damage in case of failure and the chance of failure are elaborated in greater detail. It is important here to determine in advance how the scores for the detail risk factors will determine the risk class. A few examples to clarify this:

Example

The stakeholders state that for system X, the non-functioning of function Y represents a risk when the system is taken live.
Detail risk factors in relation to the damage in case of failure for function Y are:
• The output is clearly visible to the client (damage H)
• The chance of loss of image is high (damage H)
• The impact on other functions is low (damage L).

Detail risk factors in relation to the chance of failure for function Y are:
• The function is used very often (chance of failure H)
• The function is simple (chance of failure L)
• The developers are very experienced (chance of failure L).

The stakeholders have reached the following agreement:
• If a H is scored for 2 detail factors, the rating is High
• If a H is scored for 1 detail factor or an M for two detail factors, the rating is Medium
• Else the rating is Low.

For the example above, this means that the Damage in case of failure is assessed as H (High). The Chance of failure in this example is M (Medium).

These values result in a risk class B.

Example

Another organisation has based the classification on Damage categories:

High: >250,000 euros
Medium: from 50,000 to 250,000 euros
Low: < 50,000 euros

Relative classification

In this classification method, the various product risks are placed in their 'order of importance' in relation to each other.

The observed risks are analysed with a number of stakeholders. It is then determined where the risk must be placed in relation to the others. This results in a list of risks, with the importance of the risk determining the order. An example to clarify this:

Example

The stakeholders recognise the following risks for system X:
1. The performance of the night batch is too slow, meaning that employees do not have access to the system in the morning.
2. The invoices that are sent to the customers contain incorrect amounts.
3. The list of check totals for the internal accounting department contains incorrect data.

The stakeholders analyse the various risks in a meeting and agree on the order 2, 1, 3. They feel that risk 2 is the most important one.

This classification method is commonly used in practice for small test objects or in organisations with little experience in performing risk analyses.

Tip

In a situation in which many risks are discerned (e.g. 20), we recommend not using an order from 1 through 20. The danger is that the order of the risks will be subject to too much discussion. In such a case it is better to work with a number of groups. For instance three groups (high, medium and low importance) in which the risks are placed.

9.5   Preparing session/interviews

It is important that the test manager informs the participants correctly about the idea of a PRA and what is expected of them. He can do this by talking to each participant, by sending them an explanatory text, or by organising a joint kick-off beforehand. In such a session, the test manager summarises the PRA, the test strategy, the vision of testing and the upcoming test process, and allows the participants to ask questions. The test manager should avoid test jargon. The participants' familiarity with PRA is the main determinant in the selection of a method. The test manager also asks the participants to prepare for the session or interviews. Some do not need to prepare and find it easy to specify the risks; others may find it useful to think about the risks that are relevant to them in advance. The system documentation and (existing and new) business and management processes are important input, both for obtaining the test goals and for distinguishing the characteristics and object parts.

The participants then receive an invitation to the session or interview. Naturally the test manager organises (or orders) the required logistical facilities in advance. The test manager prepares by familiarising himself with the concepts used in the organisation, both business and IT. He must make sure that the risk of confusion in relation to terminology and concepts is as small as possible by allowing the participants to speak their own language as much as possible. Many test managers create a first draft of the PRA for themselves during preparation, ensuring that they are well prepared and able to get the real PRA moving or moving on if needed. Still, we recommend keeping such a first draft as a backup to avoid giving the impression that the test manager is manipulating the PRA result or has determined it in advance.

In more detail

Indirect PRA input
In addition to direct input for the PRA, such as the test basis, business and management processes, there are also various information sources representing indirect input for the PRA:
• Assignment formulation
  The assignment formulation specifies the aim and scope of testing, providing important indications to what the client believes is important. It also contains the planned test levels for the MTP.
• Project proposal and business case
  Such documents often contain the reasons why a system or package must be developed, implemented or adapted and sometimes even provide risk indications at a high level.
• Business requirements
  Requirements can be split up into business, user and system requirements. Requirements have a priority marker. This does not say much about the associated

risk – at most it says something about the potential damage, and even this can be subject to discussion. Business requirements with business objectives like X% faster, cheaper and/or more turnover can, at most, be used as background information in the PRA or test strategy. User requirements and system requirements are types of test basis and therefore constitute direct input for the PRA.

• Project risk analysis
Often such an analysis contains primarily project risks instead of product risks. Moreover there is a good chance that the risks have already been covered by other counter-measures when the PRA starts, reducing the height of the product risk. When this is taken into account, the project risk analysis constitutes a useful source of information for the PRA.

• Business risks
Business risk are the risks that play at the highest organisation level, such as the failure to take a new product to market in time, a successful product from a competitor, or disappointing sales figures. These risks can help provide background information for the PRA, but do not represent direct input. Testers are usually not at the right level in the organisation to be able to talk about business risks. Also, the risks are often not documented or at least not part of the test basis. Still, this knowledge is very valuable to make a good risk assessment of the system. Message: Find out about this to get a better understanding of the system. When the business risks are known to the PRA participants, this does not mean that the test manager must communicate and report at this level. That depends entirely on the client level and test goals.

9.6   Collecting and analysing product risks

The test manager should not forget the final goal of the PRA in this activity, i.e. that it is known:
• what must be tested (object parts)
• what must be examined (characteristics)
• the required thoroughness of testing (risk classes).
To achieve these results, this activity is split up into a number of sub-activities described below:
1. Determining the test goals
2. Determining the relevant characteristics per test goal
3. Distinguishing object parts per characteristic
4. For each characteristic, filling out the risk table for test goals and object parts. This step consists of the following sub-steps:
    a) Determining the damage per test goal
    b) Determining the chance of failure per object part
    c) Determining the risk class per test goal/object part
    d) Determining the risk class per object part
5. Aggregating characteristics/object parts/risk classes in total overview

The steps above may give rise to the impression that this is a huge and complex activity. But it is not so bad. The steps have been kept as elementary as possible to facilitate understanding. Depending on the experience of the test manager and participants, some steps can be completed very quickly or may even be combined. However, it remains important to realise that communication between the participants represents the greatest challenge.

1) Determining the test goals

The test manager wishes to achieve a risk assessment for object parts and characteristics. To this end, he needs input from the various participants in the PRA. In practice, however, talking about object parts and characteristics is often found to be too technical for the participants. As such, the test manager must start the PRA from the perception of the client and other acceptants, i.e. from the perspective of what they believe to be important. These are called the test goals.

Definition

A test goal is a goal for testing relevant to the client, often formulated in terms of IT-supported business processes, realised user requirements or use cases, critical success factors, change proposals or defined risks (to be covered).

In the first place, therefore, the test goals of the client and other acceptants are collected and established in a PRA insofar as this was not done during the "Understanding the assignment", see sections 5.2.2 and 6.2.2. The table below contains a few examples for various types of test goals.

Type of test goal	Examples
Business processes	The invoicing and order handling processes continue to function correctly with support from the new/changed system.
Subsystems	Correctly functioning subsystems Customer Management, Orders, but sometimes also at the function or screen level: adding customer, editing customer.
Product risks	1) Customer receives incorrect invoice, 2) Users cannot work with the package.
Acceptance criteria	Interface between the new Customer System and the existing Order System functions correctly.
User requirements	An automated check is used to determine credit-worthiness of the applicant.
Use cases	Entering new customer, open account.
Critical Success Factors	Online mortgage offer must appear on the intermediary's screen within 1 minute.
Quality characteristics	Functionality, performance, user-friendliness, suitability.

Table 9.3: Examples of test goals

The type of test goals chosen depends on the organisation or project. IT-focused organisations or projects often opt for use cases, user requirements, but also directly for subsystems or quality characteristics. Organisations or projects with a lot of user involvement find it easier to talk about business processes, individual product risks, or critical success factors. In maintenance, for instance, an important test goal is often that the existing functionality continues to operate correctly. Processes are often chosen as test goals for package implementations. It is a matter of selecting the test goals that make sense to the participants.

In more detail
The test manager must prevent that too many test goals are defined. A general rule of thumb is 3 to 20. When more test goals are defined – which can happen in particular if the participants choose specific product risks to be covered as test goals – it must be determined whether these separate risks can be allocated to a limited number of groups.

The definition of test goals is an essential step with which the test manager can take the participants by the hand, as it were, to move through the next steps. They may also be able to lay the bridge to the stakeholders (from the business) later on because it enables targeted reporting.

2) Determining the relevant characteristics per test goal
The participants then determine the characteristics relevant for testing for each test goal. In other words, what aspects should the test work cover to be able to realise the test goals?
Organisations generally choose to use the quality characteristics. The TMap set of quality characteristics is described in chapter 10. If the quality characteristics are difficult to understand for the participants, the test manager can also use test types, e.g. installability, multi-user, regression, etc. An installation test simply means more to some participants than the quality characteristic "continuity", of which it is a part. Www.tmap.net contains the "Overview of applied test types" that lists the various test types.
In most cases, the characteristic "functionality" is a relevant one. The test manager must make clear that other characteristics, such as performance, user-friendliness and security, can also be relevant for testing. But there are also characteristics that require *no* testing, for instance because they do not represent a risk or because they are already covered by another test.

Type of test goal	Examples	Examples of characteristics
Business processes	Invoicing, orders	Various: functionality, user-friendliness, performance, etc.
Subsystems	Subsystem Customer Management, Orders, but sometimes also at the function level: adding customer, editing customer	Various: functionality, user-friendliness, performance, etc.
Product risks	1) Customer receives incorrect invoice 2) Users cannot work with the package	1) Functionality 2) User-friendliness, suitability
Acceptance criteria	Interface between the new Customer System and the existing Order System functions correctly	Functionality, perhaps performance and security
User requirements	BKR check used to determine credit-worthiness of the applicant	Functionality
Use cases	Entering new customer, open account	Various: functionality, user-friendliness, performance, etc.
Critical Success Factors	Online mortgage offer must appear on the intermediary's screen within 1 minute	Performance
Quality characteristics	Functionality, performance, user friendliness, suitability	1-on-1

Table 9.4: Examples of characteristics per test goal

3) Distinguishing object parts per characteristic
After selecting the characteristics relevant for testing for each test goal, the characteristics are collected. The participants then split up the test object into a number of object parts for each characteristic.

Definition

An object part is a logically coherent part of the test object from the perspective of the characteristic to be tested.

The division into object parts makes it possible to realise more refinement later in selecting the test coverage. It is important to note that the division into object parts depends on the characteristic. For instance, the characteristic "functionality" will have a different division into object parts than "performance" or "security". In practice, the division into functional parts (subsystems) is most essential since this will take up most test time later. We recommend ensuring that the division coincides with the design structure unless there are good reasons to deviate from this.

Example:			
Characteristic	**Object parts**		
Functionality	Subsys1	Subsys2	Total system
Performance	Batch	Online	

From the functional point of view, the system can be split up into 2 big subsystems that can be tested separately. Furthermore an integral test of the total system is also necessary. This means a division into three object parts. The characteristic Performance distinguishes between the online and batch performance, i.e. what is the direct response to a user action and what is the time required to execute batch processes.

The division into characteristics/object parts also makes it possible to distinguish strongly deviating risk parts early on in the test process. Such a part may then be defined as a separate object part, for instance. This enables diverging approaches for testing different components.

In more detail

For a PRA as part of the master test plan, this division can sometimes not be made for many characteristics because the necessary information is lacking. In this case the PRA goes down to the level of characteristics and does not make a division into object parts. That is done later when the test plans are created for the separate test levels.

In more detail

There is no fixed guideline for the number of object parts in a test object. A division in up to 7 object parts is still manageable, but practice also shows situations with dozens of object parts where each function in the system is treated as an object part. While it is a lot of work, the advantage is that a highly detailed risk analysis is performed and that hours and techniques can be allocated per function very quickly at a later stage.

4) For each characteristic, filling out the risk table for test goals and object parts
The test goals are plotted against the object parts (functional subsystems, online/batch performance, etc.) and the participants determine the risk classification for each characteristic. This is done in the sub-steps described below. In the examples below, an absolute classification according to table 9.1 is used here:

		Chance of failure		
		High	Medium	Low
Damage in case of failure	High	A	B	B
	Medium	B	B	C
	Low	C	C	C

a) Damage per test goal

The participants first estimate per test goal what the damage will be if the characteristic is inadequate. This requires a user contribution in particular. The example below uses the business processes requiring support as test goals.

Characteristic: Functionality	
Test goals	Damage
Business process 1	H
Business process 2	H
Business process 3	L

b) Chance of failure per object part

They then estimate the chance of failure for each object part. This estimate requires more input from the technical architecture and the development process.

Functionality	**Subsys1**	**Subsys2**	**Total system**
Chance of failure	H	M	L

c) Risk class per test goal/object part

At the junctions of test goals and object parts, the participants then indicate whether the combination is relevant by assigning a risk class. The risk class is derived from the damage per test goal and the chance of failure per object part. The participiants can deviate from the general formula. One reason might be that they consider the actual risk to be much higher or smaller than the risk class that follows from the formula chance of failure x damage. If there is a deviation, a comment should always be provided.

Characteristic: Functionality	**Object parts:**	**Subsys1**	**Subsys2**	**Total system**
	Chance of failure	H	M	L
Test goals	Damage			
Business process 1	H	A	- *	-
Business process 2	H	A	A' **	C'
Business process 3	L	C	C	C

* A minus-sign indicates the combination is not relevant for testing
** A notation like ' (or capital or bold) can be used to indicate that there are some special comments on the junction. For instance that it involves a small part of the subsystem or that a different risk is associated with it than would be concluded on the basis of chance of failure/subsystem and damage/business process.

d) Determine risk class per object part

The result that must be recorded in the risk table is a risk class per object part (of a characteristic). Based on this, a choice can be made in the test strategy to test the characteristic/object part combination with light, medium or heavy thoroughness. The risk class is actually determined by the risk classes at the junctions of the object part and the test goals in the previous step c. An agreement must be reached about how the risk classes of the separate junctions together determine the risk class of the object part.

The risk class of the object part was determined, in the example below, by using the following agreement: the risk class of the object part as a whole is equal to the risk class of the junctions that occurs most often. If risk class A and C are both most common, the object part will be given risk class B. If risk classes A and B *or* B and C occur most commonly, the highest risk class is selected.

Characteristic: Functionality	Object parts	Subsys1	Subsys2	Total system
	Chance of failure	H	M	L
Test goals	Damage			
Business process 1	H	A	-	-
Business process 2	H	A	A'	C'
Business process 3	L	C	C	C
Risk class =>		A	B	C

Below you will find an example for the performance characteristic.

Characteristic: Performance	Object parts:	Online	Batch
	Chance of failure	M	L
Test goals	Damage		
Business process 1	H	B	-
Business process 2	M*	B	C
Business process 3	M	-	C
Risk class =>		B	C

*   The damage deviates from the table above. This is because the damage
      in the event of functionality that does not function correctly is valued as
      greater than the damage for inadequate performance.

These risk tables establish the relationship between e.g. test goals like business
processes, user requirements or separate product risks with the characteristics
and object parts, so that the test manager can report at the test goal level in
subsequent reports. For this reason the tables must be managed, even after
the test plan is created, and therefore throughout the test process.

Tips

Balanced risk estimation
A risk class is allocated to a characteristic/object part. The risk class represents the risk
(damage x change of failure) as estimated on the basis of test goals, characteristics
and object parts. However, the test manager must prevent that each characteristic
object part is assigned the highest risk class (A). The participants/stakeholders have
a natural tendency to assess the risks as high and therefore select A. Tips to prevent
this are:
- The starting point is that all damage and chance of failure indications start at
  "Medium"; the participants must then "demonstrate" per indication why the damage
  or chance of failure is higher than average for this aspect.
- Do not compare the characteristics against each other ("functionality is more high
  risk than performance"), because a characteristic like functionality would then always
  be assigned an A.
- Discuss the implications of a specific choice for the test effort: give a quick indication
  of what a thorough, respectively a light test of a specific characteristic would cost, in
  terms of time and money.

Test process risks
Often, various other types of risks – such as process and (test) project risks – are
listed in a PRA in addition to the product risks. The test manager must ensure that
these are recorded and submitted to the authorised party or person, such as the
project manager. Typical test process risks are included in a separate section in the
(master) test plan.

Communicate in the language of the participants.
The test manager must ensure that communication occurs as much as possible in the
terminology of the stakeholders. Put very simply, the following questions can often
be asked: "What if this [test goal/characteristic/object part] doesn't work? And what
would be the consequences?" A related tip is that the participants must continue to
probe until it is about time, money, customers or image. This means talking as little
as possible about product properties ("Consequence: invoicing program needs 4
hours instead of 2") but about what it means for the organisation ("Customer receives
invoice after 2 days instead of the next day").

New requirements
Experience shows that new requirements are "discovered" in a PRA fairly often.

> The test manager must collect these and feed them back to the project, the person responsible for the requirements, or the change control board.

5) Aggregating characteristics/object parts/risk classes in total overview
The PRA total overview is created on the basis of the separate risk tables, see below. This step is an administrative exercise and requires no input from the participants. The advantage of this step is that the participants, test manager and client achieve a total overview. The risk tables are optionally included in the (master) test plan as an annex and, in any case, managed to enable subsequent reporting on the test goals. The table below is an example of a total overview. The argumentation column summarises the reasons, related to the test goals, for assigning the relevant risk class to the characteristic or object part.

Characteristic: Functionality	Risk class	Argumentation
- subsys 1	A	high chance of failure, used in vital processes 1 and 2
- subsys 2	B	medium chance of failure, used only to limited extent in vital process 2
- total	C	if subsys 1 and 2 function correctly, the risk of integration problems is low.
User-friendliness	B	...
Performance		
- online	B	
- batch	C	
Security	A	
Suitability	B	

In more detail

In case of inadequate detail
If inadequate details are available on e.g. the object parts at the time of creating the master test plan, only the characteristics remain in the first column (see the example below).

Characteristic	RC	Argumentation
Functionality	B	...
User-friendliness	B	
Performance	B	
Security	A	
Suitability	B	
...		

The detailing required to establish a test strategy must then be elaborated further during the PRAs of the individual test plans. When in the example above, functionality and performance are allocated to the system test on the basis of the master test plan, the PRA for this could be detailed as follows.

Example of system test:

Characteristic	RC MTP	Risk class	Argumentation
Functionality	B		...
- Subsys1		A	
- Subsys2		B	
- Totalsys		C	
Performance	B		
- online		B	
- batch		C	

RC MTP = Risk class assigned to the characteristic in the master test plan
A = High risk class
B = Medium risk class
C = Low risk class

In more detail

Product risks during maintenance
Since there is a (test) difference between new build and maintenance, this has consequences for the steps of the risk analysis to be executed. The main difference between new build and maintenance for the test strategy is the *chance of defects*. For the PRA, this means that the risk classification of the characteristics/object parts for maintenance differs from a new build situation.
Maintenance means that a number of modifications, usually as a result of defect reports or change proposals, are implemented in an existing system. These modifications may be implemented incorrectly and thus require testing. The modification also involves a small chance that defects are introduced unintentionally in unchanged parts of the system, deteriorating the system's quality. This phenomenon of quality deterioration is called regression and is the reason that the unchanged parts of the system are also tested. A characteristic/object part that had a high risk during the new build, may remain unchanged in the maintenance release. Since the chance of regression is then the only risk, much less thorough testing is required. For this reason, the PRA and strategy determination can be adjusted for maintenance by distinguishing the changes as object parts. Such a form of PRA and strategy determination is often executed through a kick-off session as described in section 9.4.1. It is inventoried for each change (an accepted change proposal or solved problem report) which characteristics are relevant and which parts of the system are changed, and which

part of the system may be affected by the change.

A tip here is that the chance of defects may be different for each new release, but the damage and frequency of use factors change much less quickly. This information can therefore be reused for the PRA of each subsequent release. However, the management organisation must keep this information up-to-date.

9.7 Completeness check

The last part of the PRA is to check whether the result of session(s) or interviews is sufficiently complete. Test goals, characteristics (think of the non-functional quality characteristics!) and/or object parts can be used to this end. If a characteristic has not been addressed, is it because it is associated with very little risk or because it has been forgotten? Requirements can also be used here, but attention must be paid that the number remains controllable. User requirements are easily controllable. Business requirements are too abstract for testing ("modification in system must generate 10% more turnover") and there are probably too many system requirements.

When inventorying risks per quality characteristic, you can use the overview of quality characteristics in chapter 10 and the "Checklist of risk factors per quality characteristic". This checklist can be found on www.tmap.net.

The completeness check can be done in two ways:
1. As part of the session
2. If there is no time: in a separate session with the 2 or 3 main stakeholders, prepared by the test manager.

The complete PRA result is circulated to the participants and client for approval and with the question if there are any additional comments. The test manager incorporates these, unless he expects that they will lead to too much discussion. The client gives definitive approval and makes a decision in the event of any points of discussion.

10 Quality characteristics and test types

10.1 Introduction

In this chapter we will first name and briefly explain the quality characteristics used in TMap. Subsequently, we will discuss a few specific test types and their relationship with the characteristics indicated. This concerns the test types for the testing of:
• Regression
• Usability
• Performance
• Portability
• Information security

10.2 Quality characteristics

For purposes of testing, TMap employs the set of quality characteristics shown below. Another common set of quality characteristics can be found in the international standard ISO9126. The use of a set of quality characteristics, whether from TMap or from ISO9126, is recommended as a way to check for completeness. It allows you to check that, out of all the aspects or characteristics of a system or package under test, a careful decision has been made about whether or not to test these. It makes little difference which set is applied. Often, the organisation has already made a choice. An illustration of the TMap quality characteristics comparable to ISO9126 can be found at www.tmap.net.

In more detail

There are a number of reasons for keeping to the TMap set of quality characteristics and not changing to ISO9126:
• In many organisations, TMap is the standard for testing, including the TMap set of quality characteristics. These organisations see little need to change over to another set of quality characteristics
• The testing of functionality is one of the most important areas of focus in testing, and is discussed a lot in this book. ISO9126 sees functionality as an umbrella concept, which takes in, for example, security and suitability. Therefore, within ISO, the testing of security and suitability fall under the testing of functionality. This is confusing in a book on testing

---

- ISO9126 is not necessarily better or worse than the TMap set; it is simply different
- While ISO9126 is an international standard, in practice it appears that many organisations make their own little variant on this, which detracts from the authority of ISO9126 as a standard. Various organisations also follow old versions of ISO9126.

The quality characteristics distinguished by TMap:
- Connectivity
- Continuity
- Data controllability
- Effectivity
- Efficiency
- Flexibility
- Functionality
- (Suitability of) infrastructure
- Maintainability
- Manageability
- Performance
- Portability
- Reusability
- Security
- Suitability
- Testability
- User-friendliness.

A description of each quality characteristic is given below, with an indication of the ways in which the testing of these takes place in practice, referring where necessary to section 10.3 "Test types". There is also a table included in section 6.2.8 "Allocating test units and test techniques" that shows test design techniques that are usable for a number of quality characteristics.

Connectivity
The ease with which an interface can be created with another information system or within the information system, and can be changed.

Connectivity is tested statically by assessing the relevant measures (such as standardisation) with the aid of a checklist. The testing of connectivity therefore concerns the evaluation of the ease with which a (new) interface can be set up or changed, and not the testing of whether an interface operates correctly. The latter is normally part of the testing of functionality.

Continuity
The certainty that the information system will continue without disruption, i.e. that it can be resumed within a reasonable time, even after a serious breakdown.

The continuity quality characteristic can be split into characteristics that can be applied in sequence, in the event of increasing disruption of the information system:

- Reliability: the degree to which the information system remains free of breakdowns
- Robustness: the degree to which the information system can simply proceed after the breakdown has been rectified
- Recoverability: the ease and speed with which the information system can be resumed following a breakdown
- Degradation factor: the ease with which the core of the information system can proceed after a part has shut down
- Fail-over possibilities: the ease with which (a part of) the information system can be continued at another location.

Continuity can be tested statically by assessing the existence and setup of measures in the context of continuity on the basis of a checklist. Dynamic implicit testing is possible through the collecting of statistics during the execution of other tests. The simulation of long-term system usage (reliability) or the simulation of breakdown (robustness, recoverability, degradation and fail-over) are dynamic explicit tests.

Data controllability

The ease with which the accuracy and completeness of the information can be verified (over time).

Common means employed in this connection are checksums, crosschecks and audit trails. Verifiability can be statically tested, focusing on the setup of the relevant measures with the aid of a checklist, and can be dynamically explicitly tested focusing on the implementation of the relevant measure in the system.

Effectivity

The degree to which the information system is tailored to the organisation and the profile of the end users for whom it is intended, as well as the degree to which the information system contributes to the achievement of the company goals.

A usable information system increases the efficiency of the business processes. Will a new system function in practice, or not? Only the users' organisation can answer that question. During (user) acceptance tests, this aspect is usually (implicitly) included. If the aspect of usability is explicitly recognised in the test strategy, a test type can be organised for it: the business simulation.

During a business simulation, a random group of potential users tests the usability aspects of the product in an environment that approximates as far as possible the "real-life" environment in which they plan to use the system: the simulated production environment. The test takes place based on a number of practical exercises or test scripts. In practice, the testing of usability is often combined with the testing of user-friendliness within the test type of usability; see section 10.3.2 for further information.

Efficiency

The relationship between the performance level of the system (expressed in the transaction volume and the total speed) and the volume of resources (CPU cycles, I/O time, memory and network usage, etc.) used for these.

Efficiency is dynamically explicitly tested with the aid of tools that measure the resource usage and/or dynamically implicitly by the accumulation of statistics (by those same tools) during the execution of functionality tests. This aspect is often particularly evident with embedded systems.

Flexibility

The degree to which the user is able to introduce enhancements or variations on the information system without amending the software.

In other words, the degree to which the system can be amended by the user organisation, without being dependent on the IT department for maintenance. Flexibility is statically tested by assessing the relevant measures with the aid of a checklist. Dynamic explicit testing can take place during the (users) acceptance test, by having the user create, for example, a new mortgage variant (in the case of mortgages) or (in the case of credit cards), change the way of calculating the commission, by changing the parameters in both cases. It is often tested in this way first, before the change is actually implemented in production.

Functionality

The degree of certainty that the system processes the information accurately and completely.

The quality characteristic of functionality can be split into the characteristics of accuracy and completeness:
- Accuracy: the degree to which the system correctly processes the supplied input and mutations according to the specifications into consistent data collections and output
- Completeness: the certainty that all of the input and mutations are being processed by the system.

With testing, meeting the specified functionality is often the most important criterion for acceptance of the information system. Using various techniques, the functional operation can be dynamically explicitly tested.

(Suitability of) Infrastructure

The appropriateness of the hardware, the network, the system software, the DBMS and the (technical) architecture in a general sense to the relevant application and the degree to which these infrastructure elements interconnect.

The testing of this aspect can be done in various ways. The tester's expertise as related to the infrastructural elements concerned is very important here.

Maintainability

The ease with which the information system can be adapted to new requirements of the user, to the changing external environment, or in order to correct faults.

Insight into the maintainability is obtained, for example, by registering the average effort (in the number of hours) required to solve a fault or by registering the average duration of repair (Mean Time to Repair (MTTR)). Maintainability is also tested by assessing the internal quality of the information system (including associated system documentation) with the aid of a checklist. Insight into the structuredness of the software (an aspect of maintainability) is obtained by carrying out static tests, preferably supported by code analysis tools (see also section 7.2.8 "Test tools for development tests").

Manageability

The ease with which the information system can be placed and maintained in an operational condition.

Manageability is primarily aimed at technical system administration. The ease of installation of the information system is part of this characteristic. It can be tested statically by assessing the existence of measures and instruments that simplify or facilitate system management. Dynamic testing of system management takes place by, for example, carrying out an installation test and by carrying out the administration procedures (such as backup and recovery) in the test environment.

Performance

The speed with which the information system handles interactive and batch transactions.

Test types for performance are discussed in section 10.3.3.

Portability
The diversity of the hardware and software platform on which the information system can run, and the ease with which the system can be transferred from one environment to another.

Test types for portability are discussed in section 10.3.4.

Reusability
The degree to which parts of the information system, or of the design, can be used again for the development of other applications.

If the system is to a large extent based on reusable modules, this also benefits the maintainability. Reusability is tested through assessing the information system and/or the design with the aid of a checklist.

Security
The certainty that consultation or mutation of the data can only be performed by those persons who are authorised to do so.

Test types for information security are discussed in section 10.3.5.

Suitability
The degree to which the manual procedures and the automated information system interconnect, and the workability of these manual procedures for the organisation.

In the testing of suitability, the aspect of timeliness is also often included. Timeliness is defined as the degree to which the information becomes available in time to take the measures for which that information was intended. Suitability is dynamically explicitly tested with the aid of the process cycle test.

Testability
The ease and speed with which the functionality and performance level of the system (after each adjustment) can be tested.

Testability in this case concerns the total information system. The quality of the system documentation greatly influences the testability of the system. This is statically measured with the aid of the "testability review" checklist during the Preparation phase. Also for the measuring of the testability of the information system a checklist can be used. Things that (strongly) benefit the testability are:

- Good system documentation
- Having an (automated) regression test and other testware
- The ease with which interim results of the system can be made visible, assessed and even manipulated
- Various test-environment aspects, such as representativeness and an adjustable system date for purposes of time travel.

User-friendliness

The ease of operation of the system by the end users.

Often, this general definition is split into: the ease with which the end user can learn to handle the information system, and the ease with which trained users can handle the information system. It is difficult to establish an objective and workable unit of measurement for user-friendliness. However, it is often possible to give a (subjective) opinion couched in general terms concerning this aspect. User-friendliness is tested within the test type of Usability; see section 10.3.2 for further information.

10.3   Test types

In this section, a number of specific test types are discussed. Apart from the regression test, this concerns test types for quality characteristics other than functionality. The reason for this is that these test types are becoming more common in practice, but preparation, specification and execution of these tests demand different types of knowledge than is the case with the functional test types. Per test type, explanation is given of the aspect the test type is aimed at, the relationship with the quality characteristics previously described, the significance of the test and what test techniques are possible.
The following test types are discussed in turn:

- Regression
- Usability
- Performance
- Portability
- Information security.

10.3.1 Regression

What is regression?

A system or package is more or less always subject to changes. When it is in production, its owner will want to implement certain changes or extensions. But amendments are made even earlier, when a system is being built or a package is being implemented. This usually relates to solved defects or implemented change proposals. With iterative or agile development methods, repeated issue of new, expanded releases (also known as increments) is even inherent in the method.

With the making of the amendments (or extensions), it is possible for mistakes to be introduced into unchanged parts of the system (or package), causing the quality to deteriorate. This phenomenon of quality deterioration is called regression, and it is the reason that unchanged parts of the system also need to be tested. Although regression can relate to all the quality characteristics, the testing of it in practice is aimed primarily at functionality.

Definition

Regression is the phenomenon that the quality of a system deteriorates as a whole as a result of individual amendments.

Importance of regression testing

The chance that faults have crept into an unchanged part of the system following an amendment is smaller than if the part were to be newly built. Assuming that the risk is determined by damage x chance of failure, the testing of the unchanged parts of the system can take place with less testing effort than with a new or changed part of the system. However, this is not to say that the regression test demands little effort. In maintenance situations, in particular, the total effort for this regression test is often greater than the testing effort required for the detailed testing of the changes. The reason for this is that with maintenance, usually only a very limited number of functions change.

Definition

A regression test is aimed at verifying that all the unchanged parts of a system still function correctly after the implementation of a change.

A good regression test is invaluable. Certainly in the maintenance situation, the test offers reassurance that the new version of the system or package still operates correctly as a whole.

Test techniques

There are no prescribed fixed test design techniques for regression testing. All the existing techniques can be used to specify the test cases in the test. However, a regression test focuses mainly on the correlation between the parts of the system, since this is where the chances of regression are the greatest. This means that integration test cases and 'good path' test cases are preferable to test cases for exceptional fault-handling situations. The regression test is often initially stocked with test cases from the testing of new parts or the original new-build tests and later supplemented with test cases for testing changes. Suitable test design techniques are, for example, the data combination test, data cycle test and the process cycle test. If the product risk analysis is available for the new build, the damage factors assigned to characteristics and object parts can play a role in the constitution of this regression test. Either a limited or a full regression test can be carried out, depending on the risks and on the required test effort. For an explanation of the scalable regression test, refer to section 6.6 "Specification Phase".

The regression test is sustained by adjusting or extending the test set on the basis of changes to the system, including both functional adjustments and solved faults. This keeps the regression test continuously up to date.

Because the regression test focuses on the system as a whole, the test is executed frequently (at least once for each release), while the test rarely changes very substantively. This is in contrast to a test for validating a specific amendment – usually only carried out for the release concerned. The combination of a high frequency of use and high level of stability means that a good level of reusability of the test is very important. It is therefore essential to create and maintain a well-structured and documented test set.

In the execution of regression tests, test tools used for automated test execution come into their own. The big advantage of the automated regression test is that, for little effort, the full test can be carried out every time and no choices have to be made as to which part of the regression test will or will not be executed.

10.3.2 Usability

What is usability?
As with most IT definitions, there is a variety to be found relating to usability. Even the International Standards Organisation has two definitions:

Definition

ISO 9241-11: the extent to which a product can be used by specified users to achieve specified goals with effectiveness, efficiency and satisfaction in a specified context of use.
ISO/IEC 9126: a set of attributes that bear on the effort needed for use, and on the individual assessment of such use, by a stated or implied set of users.

From the various definitions, a number of aspects emerge that play a role in usability:

- Effectiveness
  Are users able to complete their task and achieve their goal with the system?
- Efficiency
  How much trouble and time does it cost users to do this?
- Satisfaction
  What do the users think of the ease of operation of the system?
- Ease of understanding
  How easily does the user understand what the system expects him to input, and how understandable is the output to him?
- Ease of learning
  How quick and easy is it to learn *and* remember how to operate the system?
- Attractiveness
  How attractive does the user find the system, as regards e.g. layout, use of colour, graphics, film clips and interaction?
- Robustness
  How easily can the users make mistakes in the system; how serious are these, and how easily can they be rectified?

Who the abovementioned user is, and which tasks he wants to carry out, plays an important part. Users may be customers of the organisation or users of the system within the organisation, but this also includes e.g. system administrators. A distinction should also be made between untrained and inexperienced users as against trained and experienced ones, and about the context in which the system is being used. A web application on a smart phone has other standards for usability than a web application on the PC.

The TMap quality characteristics that have most to do with usability are user-friendliness and effectivity. In respect of the latter characteristic, usability testing looks at the effectivity from the user's standpoint, not at the general effectivity for the organisation in total. Usability testing also has some overlap with characteristics such as performance (if the system is not fast enough, this detracts from the usability), functionality (often all kinds of functionality are added to a system in order to make it more user-friendly) and continuity (error-resistance).

While usability is largely a subjective concept, over the course of time a multitude of publications on this subject have appeared. The best-known person in this area is undoubtedly Jakob Nielsen [Nielsen, 1999]. In addition, the World Wide Web Consortium has set up guidelines for the accessibility of websites so that they are also suitable for visually impaired people [www.w3c.org].

Importance of usability testing

The importance of usability has increased markedly with the rise in the digitisation and computerisation of society. Via the Internet, organisations have acquired new communication channels to their customers and the market, with new kinds of services (online auctions, instant price comparison). The website has become the company's shop window and business card. Usability increases in importance when the user can purchase the same service or product for the same price, either from a competing website or through a traditional communication channel, such as a shop or telephone helpdesk.

Example

Competing with traditional communication channels
The government has a monopoly on the supply of certain services or information. With web applications, substantial cost savings could be realised if enough citizens make use of these, rather than using the telephone, sending in forms or going to the town hall. However, if people prefer not to use the website, they will continue to use the traditional channels.

Other consequences of inadequate usability are that the users:
- Make more mistakes, resulting in all kinds of reworking operations
- Work less efficiently owing to confusion and more keyboard operation
- Do not know what they have to do and so make frequent calls to the helpdesk
- Require long periods of learning.

Example

Usability of the ATM
The early ATMs in the Netherlands involved the following sequence of operations:
1. Insert PIN card in machine
2. Enter PIN code
3. Enter cash sum
4. Receive cash
5. Remove PIN card
Your aim as a user of an ATM, i.e. to withdraw cash, is achieved at step 4. Users regularly forgot to remove their cards. This has been adjusted, by switching the last two steps. Now the card is returned first, and only then is the cash delivered. In other countries, such as the US, this adjustment has not yet been entirely implemented, as one of the writers found to his dismay ...

While the usability of websites has greatly improved over recent years, this remains a risk factor for a successful site. The rise of electronic agendas and smart phones, too, is giving usability problems with websites for mobile use.

But usability problems do not only occur in relation to websites or custom applications – they also affect, for example, embedded software and standard software packages. In the latter case, however, the possibilities for improving the usability are often limited.

Test techniques

A number of techniques are available for the testing of usability. Worth noting here is that usability problems found at an advanced stage (such as the acceptance test) are often far-reaching and difficult to solve, for example because the application navigation or all the screen controls need to be changed. Usability and the testing of it should therefore be taken into consideration from the beginning of the design stage, when it is still possible to make relatively inexpensive adjustments. Possible test objects are, for example, apart from the working system, prototypes and screen designs. A few of the most important usability techniques are mentioned below. Roughly, they have the following characteristics:

- Moment of applicability
  Can the technique already be used for screen design; is a working system required or is the technique intended for a system that is already in production
- Testers
  Who evaluates the usability? This may be usability experts and/or the actual users.

Heuristic evaluation

Heuristic evaluation is one of the best-known ways of testing usability. During a heuristic evaluation, a systematic examination is carried out of the usability of the design of the user interface. The ultimate aim of heuristic evaluation is to discover problems in the design of the user interface. By finding such problems at the design stage, it is possible to solve them in time. During the process of heuristic evaluation, a group of 3-5 experts (evaluators) give their opinion on the user interface in accordance with a number of usability principles (also known as the "heuristics").

In more detail

Nielsen distinguishes 10 heuristics; see [Nielsen, 2006]:
- Visibility of the system status
- Match between the system and the real world
- User control and freedom
- Consistency and standards
- Error prevention
- Recognition rather than recall
- Flexibility and efficiency of use

- Aesthetic and minimalist design
- Help for users to recognise, diagnose and recover from errors
- Help and documentation

Usability test

In a controlled environment, a number of observers watch the way in which one or more users use the system. Besides usability experts, it is advisable to invite a number of designers for this. A few tasks are selected for the user to perform that are characteristic of the application.

In more detail

A task description typically consists of:
1. A sketch of the starting point, consisting of a description of the role that the subject assumes and their background, e.g. an inexperienced user or an experienced administrator
2. One or more tasks, e.g. check the status of the last order, compare the prices between two suppliers and order an item from the cheaper of the two. The task should indicate what has to happen, but not how the user should do it.

The subjects should read the role description and prepare themselves to carry out the tasks from that background.

During the execution of the tasks, the idea is that the subject continually thinks aloud and says what he or she is doing. For example, a reaction can be "I'm now going to the menu and opening the option of 'Information on company X', to see if I can find the route map there. Oh no, it's not here… (Etc.)".

The onlookers observe the behaviour of the user and take notes. In a so-called usability lab, the observers remain behind a one-way mirror and everything is recorded on video (both the images of the user and the images and operations on the computer). Another technique, such as eye tracking (the registering of eye movements on the screen) and other physiological measurements (heartbeat, perspiration) are possible here. Because of the infrastructure and equipment used, a usability lab is generally (very) expensive. A cheaper, but less effective, alternative to a usability lab is to have the observer sit with the user and, for example, just use a video camera or use a tool to register the user's actions on the system. The observer(s) then assess the usability of the system on the basis of e.g. the number of mistakes made, the time taken to complete a task and the navigation path followed. They also use the participants' remarks during the test in their assessment of the usability.

Questionnaires

Another means of evaluation is to request the users' opinion of the system using questionnaires. While they are also applicable to prototypes or even screen designs, questionnaires are mainly used when the system is ready, or even already in production. When the participants have completed enough questionnaires, an evaluation of the results follows. While it is a relatively cheap method of testing usability, the disadvantage is that the result will not deliver a particularly detailed impression of what is right and wrong in a system. SUMI (Software Usability Measurement Inventory, http://sumi.ucc. ie) and WAMMI (Website Analysis and Measurement Inventory, www.wammi. com) are methods that are based on the use of questionnaires.

Checklists, interviews

Cheap usability test techniques are the use of usability checklists during other (usually functional) tests, or interviewing the testers and users after working with the system concerning their experience of it.

Tools

Finally, tools are available, especially for web applications, that can carry out all kinds of checks. Examples of these checks are:

- Are the graphics and animations provided with an alternative (a text box) for supplying the same information in the event that the graphics, animations, etc. are not working? This can be the case if you use a different browser, don't have a video card or are visually handicapped
- Is the size of the graphics too big, making the site slow?
- Does every page contain a link for returning to the previous page and/or a link for continuing on to the next page?
- Are the text boxes perhaps too long in a scrolling field?
- Are all the links (still) valid?

10.3.3 Performance

What is performance?

This test type is aimed at the speed with which the test object carries out its tasks for various types of processing, such as real-time, online and batch. (Sub)types of performance tests are load, stress or benchmark testing. These test types each have their own definition: load testing checks whether and how the test object performs with normal and maximum expected usage; stress testing checks at which degree of usage the test object's performance drastically deteriorates (the breaking point); benchmark testing carries out the same performance test on various configurations of the system under test and measures the results. In practice, these names tend to be intermixed; this book employs the collective name of 'performance testing'.

To be able to test performance, the requirements must be known: what is fast enough, and under which circumstances is that to be? In practice, this appears to be rather problematic and there is a lack of concrete requirements that the performance should meet and should be requested from within the testing. For that reason, the performance tester often has the role of catalyst in the clarification of these requirements.

Examples of possible requirements are:

- The 6-seconds rule (the web page should load within 6 seconds)
- 200 mortgages should be processed within one hour
- With 1,000 users, the web server should have generated and sent page WX003 within 5 seconds
- Transaction A.01 should be processed within 20 seconds when there are 100 users using the database.

None of these requirements is complete. Additional information is always necessary concerning the situations in which the requirement should be met (size of database / number of simultaneous users / hardware used). Does the requirement, for example, also apply to a user with a slow Internet connection, during peak hours and when other applications are active on the same hardware?

It should be noted that the total performance is often dependent on a large number of links, not all of which can by any means be controlled: size of database, network, application and, with the Internet, the user's computer and connection (including the intervening infrastructure). However, there are many ways of improving the performance. Performance testing offers information for choosing between the purchase of additional hardware or software adjustments, such as upgrading the software, changing the settings of the database and network parameters and the optimisation of large-scale transactions.

Example

A website has an overview page containing all the products available for ordering, with brief explanations and photographs. When the user clicks on a photograph, he goes through to a detailed page containing further information on the product and a large photograph. The performance of the overview page was very poor. Investigation revealed the cause. The photographs on the overview page were the same as those on the detailed pages. These were sizeable photographs of high resolution, and all of them had to be loaded for the overview page. The solution was to use separate, low-resolution photographs for the overview page.

Importance of performance, load and stress testing

The rise in browser-based systems with large numbers of users is an important reason for organisations to test systems on performance. Irrespective of whether the systems are accessed via Internet, intranet or extranet, the communication between the system and its users operates across a large number of components, each of which has certain limits as regards capacity and processing speeds. Moreover, the unpredictable numbers and behaviour of Internet users in particular exert an influence on the performance. Organisations have often observed to their consternation that the attraction of the system was so great that it crashed. In some cases, this has hit the headlines. What has happened in those cases is that, while up to a certain level of usage, the response times increased only slowly, after that point (the so-called breaking point) they have shot up. See also the description of load profiles in section 14.3.8 "Statistical usage: operational profiles and load profiles".

The question may be asked as to what stress testing adds in respect of a load test. The answer to this is that the knowledge of the breaking point of the system or package enables the organisation to estimate whether the system will reach breaking point in the near future, and if so, when it is going to be reached. The organisation can then take timely measures by, for example, purchasing extra hardware.

Apart from the Internet, performance testing is important in many other areas. For example, from safety-critical embedded software that is required to respond in real time within a number of milliseconds, to weighty batch processes that have a maximum run time of just a few hours.

Test techniques

The starting point for the performance test is the set performance requirements. The lack of these may result in an unstructured approach to testing and lack of clarity with regard to the results to be obtained. Sometimes the tester has to restrict himself to measuring the performance instead of testing it: "In this and that situation, the response time is 20 seconds. We do not know whether that is acceptable or not ..."

The testing of performance can be done dynamically implicitly by collecting statistics during the execution of other tests. Static testing is possible by having the performance of system components (configurations), such as DBMS and network, calculated by infrastructure specialists. The most thorough form is dynamic explicit testing, which is further explained below.

Depending on the requirements, the situations to be tested can be built up, for example, as follows:

- Simulation of one user/transaction
- Simulation of the average number of users/transactions expected
- Simulation of the maximum number of users/transactions that the system should be able to cope with
- Loading the system heavier than this maximum usage, in order to observe at which point the system response times start to deteriorate significantly (breaking point).

An important part of performance testing is that a balance should be found between representativeness, risk-bearing components and necessary time and finances:

- Representativeness:
  In what way can the system be loaded to compare as closely as possible with the future production situation
- Risk-bearing components:
  Which transactions or system components are the most vulnerable as a result of requirements or hardware limits with an increasing load
- Time and finances:
  Within what budget and timeline should a judgement be given on the performance.

Technically approaching the closest possible simulation of reality costs a lot of time and money. Focusing on the most risk-related components can also result in a non-representative situation because certain high-volume but low-priority transactions are being kept out of the performance test.

The basis for a structured performance test is formed by the creation of a:

- Load model
- Iteration model
- Measuring plan.

In this, the use of test tools (load & stress, monitoring) is more or less indispensable. The deployment of a large number of "real" users to obtain a representative situation will usually succeed after much effort once, but not usually a second time. And practice shows that these tests are repeated periodically, because adjustments in hardware and software are always having to be made during maintenance.

In more detail

Load model
The load model describes at a logical level how the test object will be loaded and how the performance will be measured. The load model is comparable with the logical test design and consists of the following parts:

- Performance requirement(s)
  The requirements are inventoried and, if necessary, detailed. A requirement in terms of the number of simultaneous users, for example, is inexact as a result of a variable pace of working and because it is not known how often a user carries out a transaction. Therefore extra information is required, preferably the number of transactions/hits per unit of time.
- Test object
  On the basis of the requirements and the risk estimate, the tester decides what the test object is (the system as a whole, or e.g. just a database or application server). This has a direct impact on the required test environment (see later in the book).
- Load to be generated
  The eventual aim of a load model is to generate a representative loading of the system (see also section 14.3.8 "Statistical usage: operational profiles and load profiles"). This loading consists of a number of users, who each carry out certain tasks/transactions. The tester differentiates various types of transactions (search task, filling a shopping cart, making a purchase) and various types of users (seekers, buyers). Subsequently, he determines the frequency with which the transactions are being carried out and the number of users required, and relates the transactions and users to each other until a representative picture emerges.

Example

Number of transactions per hour:
Transaction 1:   500 x home page
Transaction 2:   50 x search / browse task
Transaction 3:   20 x filling shopping cart
Transaction 4:   10 x making purchase

For the generation of this load, it could be decided to use 500 unique users (some of whom will therefore perform very few actions), but it is also possible to have only 50 active users (for e.g. search tasks and making selections and ordering now and then) while 50 other users do nothing other than repeatedly open and close the home page, which will result in the desired number of transactions per hour.

- Test environment
  The test environment to be used is determined based on the defined test object and the load to be generated
- Indicators
  The parts to be measured, such as processor usage, memory usage, disk usage and network traffic
- Description of required initial situation
  The initial situation that is required in order to be able to perform the test. Usually, this should be representative of the production situation as regards scope
- Graphic reproduction of the test object architecture
  Although optional, this makes the testing clearer and more accessible.

Particularly when choosing the test object, determining which transactions will make up part of the test and defining the test environment, the balance between risks and representativeness on the one hand and time and money on the other plays an important part. With this, the costs of the tools required to simulate large numbers of users and perform measurements should not be underestimated.

Iteration model

The iteration model describes at a technical level how the test object will be loaded and how the performance will be measured. A load model describes the required loading. In practice, that should be achieved through a spread of users who will gradually generate the desired level of traffic. For if all the users were to start at precisely the same moment, their actions would run concurrently over a long period. If, for example, something has to be downloaded, all the users will do it at the same moment. This is not realistic users' behaviour. An iteration model describes the (technical) way in which the loading is spread out, so that a dynamic mix of actions can be achieved quickly that can then be maintained for a certain length of time. An iteration model is dependent on the performance test tool, since it describes how various tool scripts and users operate in relation to each other

Measuring plan

The measuring plan indicates on which parts of the test environment measuring is being performed during the test execution. It is indicated per part which measurements are being performed, at which intervals and how the information will be secured and presented after completion.

10.3.4 Portability

What is portability?

Some systems are required to be able to run on a number of various configurations of hardware and (system) software. The best-known example of this is that a web application has to be capable of working with various browsers. Despite standards with which web pages are required to comply, every browser deals with them differently. Moreover, the browsers have a large variety of settings, which can also disrupt the proper operation of the web application.

Within TMap, all of this falls under the quality characteristic of portability: the diversity of the hardware and software platforms on which the information system can run, and the ease with which the system can be transferred from one environment to another. Another term often used in this connection is compatibility. Compatibility concerns the first part of the definition of portability: the degree to which the information system can operate in various environments.

Importance of portability testing

If a system has portability problems on one or more of the agreed configurations, this is often apparent from the distorted screen, or worse, the crashing of the system. Staying with the example of web applications, this can lead to annoyance on the part of the user, extra workload for the helpdesk, wrong information provision and even the loss of turnover because users are unable to place orders.

Test techniques

Testing portability is done by repeating a (limited) part of the previously executed functional testing for other configurations to be supported. The selection and size of the part of the tests to be repeated involves a consideration of risk. The use of checklists is popular as well. A tip is, during the testing of various browsers, to change the standard parameter settings (colours, fonts, Java Y/N). Wrong constructions, such as hard-coded settings in the software are then revealed more quickly. This makes the testing of portability as such simple but labour-intensive. If a large number of configurations have to be supported, the number of tests to be carried out can spiral out of hand quickly. If, for example, 6 browser versions and 4 operating systems have to be supported, this delivers 24 possible combinations. In order to avoid this explosion, only the most important combinations should be tested. This can be done by setting out the configurations to be supported in a matrix. The browser versions are shown vertically, the operating systems horizontally. Place crosses at the users' most common combinations, plus a number of others. The requirement is that every browser version and every operating system should appear at least once, without each combination of browser/OS having to be tested. In making the selection, consider any expected problems. The table below shows an example of such a matrix. The 'X's represent the configurations to be tested.

	Win 2000	WinXP	MacOS9	MacOS X
Internet Explorer 6	X	X	X	
Internet Explorer 7		X	X	X
Opera 8.5		X		
Firefox 1.5		X	X	X

 Tip

For these types of situations, the coverage forms/basic techniques of "equivalence classes" and "pair-wise testing" are ideally suited; see also section 14.3.4 "Equivalence classes" and 14.3.5 "Orthogonal arrays and pairwise testing".

It can also be difficult to obtain the right configurations. For example, it takes a lot of effort to organise a PC with Windows 2000 and a Netscape browser, and then it is an even bigger challenge to get it connected to the company network. While it is often possible to install several configurations on one machine (dual boot, several browsers), supporting a large number of configurations can mean a big investment in infrastructure. In order to organise all this, an early start on the preparations is necessary.

Tip

Research bureaus have lists available of the most commonly used software/hardware combinations. These can serve as input for the selection of configurations

10.3.5 Information security

What is information security?

'Information security is aimed at guaranteeing the availability, exclusivity and integrity of all the forms of information with the purpose of securing the continuity of the organisation and limiting any consequences of security incidents to an acceptable level. Besides the TMap quality characteristic of security, information security is also explicitly concerned with aspects such as availability (continuity), integrity (accuracy, completeness) and confidentiality (exclusivity).

The setup of information security consists of taking adequate measures (focusing on the above criteria) and the activation of a quality-evaluation mechanism (Information Security Management System).

It is a complex field that should not be underestimated. For example, at network level, 8 dimensions of security are distinguished (ISO/IEC 18028-2) in respect of which measures can be taken against threats:

- Authorisation
  orders the access to functions, applications, network, etc.
- Authentication
  confirms the identity of the communicating party
- Non-repudiation
  lays down an audit trail so that the origin of data or the cause of events or actions cannot later be denied
- Data confidentiality
  protects data from unauthorised access
- Communication security
  ensures that information only moves between authorised points without being diverted or intercepted

- Data integrity
  monitors the accuracy of the data and protects against unauthorised creation, amendment, deletion or replication
- Availability
  ensures that authorised access to network components, stored information, information flows, services and applications is not refused
- Privacy
  protects information that can be obtained by observing the network activities.

At a technical level, the following layers of security can be distinguished:
- Network & infrastructure
  This layer consists of elements such as servers, firewalls, gateways, proxy servers and routers, both hardware and software. Good (security) architecture is necessary in order to align these elements in such a way that a satisfactory balance is created between layered security and the need to make the applications accessible to a range of parties
- System software
  This covers things such as the operating system and the DBMS. Access codes, passwords and authorisations can be managed here. The components in this layer often have all kinds of possible settings in order to increase the security. Unfortunately, not enough use is made of them in practice
- Applications
  These are the applications to which the users have access, whether or not across the Internet. Security aspects are, for example, Internet cookies (small information files that are lodged with the user) with unencrypted information, unspecified and unprotected navigation possibilities whereby a user can access parts of the application for which he is not authorised, (un)encrypted data, unsafe scripts, non-valid input in the system whereby the application crashes or gets into an unstable, unexpected condition.

It should be clear that a wide range of measures is necessary for information security, both preventive and detective. Good information security also has multiple layers, so that breaking through the first layer does not directly lead to the entire opening up of all the data. Types of measures include special tools (firewalls, virus-detection programs, encryption programs), settings of hardware and software components, norms and standards for system administration, but also for system development, procedural measures and physical security measures. The developments surrounding information security are fast-moving. Moreover, a balance always has to be found between the degree of security and other aspects, such as accessibility, user-friendliness and speed. An organisation is therefore well advised to inspect the security policy periodically: does the actual degree of security still accord with the required degree of security?

Importance of testing information security

Information security has taken off markedly in recent years. This has been caused by:

- Media attention to damage caused by hacking attempts
- Scandals surrounding the bookkeeping of large organisations
- Requirements (safety guarantees) set by suppliers and customers
- Availability of relevant standards (ISO2700x, NEN7510)
- Various legislation for organisations concerning internal checks, financial reporting, dissemination of information and protection of personal data.

With this, the testing of information security (measures) is becoming an increasingly important field. Keeping knowledge up to date in this area requires an almost continuous investment. New security leaks are being found all the time that malicious hackers can exploit. Www.tmap.net contains a number of links to sites that provide the latest information in this area.

What and when to test?

There are various reasons for testing the level of information security (see summary in the previous section), for which the most important reason is to obtain insight into the performance of the implemented measures. This is essential, in order to be sure that the measures adopted meet the requirements set by the organisation. Certifying bodies also make pronouncements on this, whereby organisations can obtain norm accreditation in respect of particular compliance or legislative issues. The point at which it is decided to carry out testing varies. This depends on the status of an organisation at the time when attention is drawn to the issue of information security. No two organisations are the same, and information security is always present at a certain level (network and application login, firewalls, badges etc.). There is also a distinction to be made between this security of the organisation and the security of the individual applications that the organisation administers, sells or makes available to suppliers and purchasers, whether or not via a web application. With the previously mentioned security environment, the measures focus mainly on the availability and confidentiality of information. This is also important, of course, in respect of the applications, but the integrity of the information is also an issue. The testing approach for the various quality aspects is also different.

Testing availability

With the aspect of availability, the testing mainly concerns whether the hardware and software (containing the information) is operational at the times required by the organisation. This includes, for example, protection against Denial-of-Service attacks. With this, hackers attempt to make a site unavailable by overloading it with false requests for information. These tests are usually a focus of IT departments, supplemented with specialists in the area of penetration testing and infrastructures (explained later in the book). Network and infrastructure testing is increasingly seen as an area of focus that is also suitable for tackling via (adjustments to) standard testing methods such as TMap.

Testing confidentiality and integrity

The testing of confidentiality and integrity of information concerns issues such as: "Who is allowed access" and "What is the status of the integrity of data input". This is supplemented with "Is previously entered information (still) manipulable".

Although a world of administrative measures lurks behind the first question (including access and authorisation management), the accuracy can be tested in a fairly standardised manner, e.g. with the semantic test technique. The question of whether the data input is correct has long been a part of functional testing and can be tested with many of the test design techniques described in Chapter 14. The possibility of manipulating information after input, other than via authorised/permitted changes, is handled (at present) by specialised companies that carry out in-depth security audits in this connection. A familiar test type for this is the so-called penetration testing, or ethical hacking. This exploits known weaknesses in the software used, system information that can be obtained from e.g. cookies and various types of tools that "real" hackers use. It should be assumed that the test hackers will break through the security. Particularly in the case of externally hired employees, this should be agreed in advance with, for example, the legal affairs department, for the tester who succeeds in breaking through the security may be in a position to view all kinds of sensitive information, or his breakthrough may result in unexpected damage. These testers should have extensive technical knowledge of the various levels and dimensions of security. (See next page 'in more detail').

One of the more difficult aspects of security testing in respect of an application is that the test should focus on whether the application does things that are *not* specified. With the more conventional functional tests, this is reversed: the tests are based on the specifications and it is checked whether the application works in accordance with the specifications. For example, from the point of view of security, an application should not crash due to incorrect input and (interim) data should not be visible and able to be manipulated (unless it is specified that this be allowed).

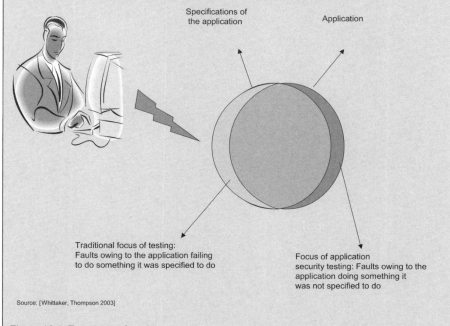

Specifications of the application

Application

Traditional focus of testing: Faults owing to the application failing to do something it was specified to do

Focus of application security testing: Faults owing to the application doing something it was not specified to do

Source: [Whittaker, Thompson 2003]

Figure 10.1: Two types of errors

For further information on security testing, refer to [Splaine, 2002] and [Whittaker, Thompson, 2003].

11   Estimation techniques

There are various techniques to create an estimate. This chapter begins with an explanation of the different levels at which estimates can be done and an overview of the suitable techniques for estimating specific quality characteristics. The following estimating techniques are then discussed:

- Estimation based on ratios
- Estimation based on test object size
- Work Breakdown Structure
- Evaluation estimation approach
- Proportionate estimation
- Extrapolation
- Test point analysis.

11.1   Estimating

Estimates can be made at a number of levels, as shown in the figure below.

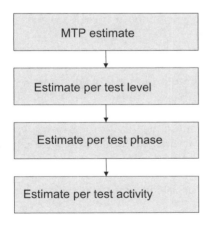

Figure 11.1: Estimation levels

Estimates for a MTP are created early on in the project. Often, not all knowledge of the test object is available at this point. As a consequence, the accuracy of the estimate is limited. The size and complexity of the test object may change during the project. It is important for the test manager to make it clear to the stakeholders that the estimate is based on a number of assumptions and therefore details will have to be added later. A possible solution is to use margins to represent the initial estimate for an MTP.

The estimate in the MTP constitutes the framework for the estimates per test level (e.g. system test, user acceptance test, and production acceptance test). The required time for the various phases – Control, Setting up and maintaining infrastructure, Preparation, Specification, Execution and Completion – is then established for the test level. Separate test activities are estimated within the test phases. The time necessary to create the MTP (Planning) is not included in the estimates. A fixed number of hours is usually estimated for this. After all, establishing the plan consists of executing clearly defined activities. The impact of e.g. the test object size on the time required to create the MTP is limited in this context. If there is an impact, it will be noticeable in particular during the activities "Analysing product risks" and "Determining test strategy". In practice, some 60 to 160 hours are usually invested in creating the MTP.

As the estimate is made later in the test process and therefore at a lower level, more knowledge of the test object is available. Moreover, experiences from earlier on in the process can be used, making the estimate more accurate.

Independent of the level, creating the plan consists of the following generic steps:
1. Inventory the available material that can serve as a basis for the estimate.
2. Select (a number of) estimating techniques.
    We recommend using multiple techniques in parallel. This makes it possible to compare the outcome of the various techniques. In addition to estimating techniques, it is worthwhile asking an experienced employee to make an estimate of the required time (expert estimate).
3. Determine the definitive estimate.
    The aim of this step is to combine the outcomes of the previous step into one single estimate. If the outcomes vary little, taking an average will work. In other cases the differences have to be analysed. If an adequate estimate cannot be made after analysing the differences, the client must be consulted. The test manager explains the problems and makes proposals to achieve a correct estimate.
4. Present the outcome.
    The aim of presenting the outcome is to provide insight to the business into the consequences of the selected test strategy and approach. It is important to show clearly which assumptions were made. Especially with an estimate created very early on in the process, assumptions will be involved that will become more concrete later on in the process.

As discussed earlier, there are various estimating techniques to create an estimate. Choosing the right ones in particular is a step requiring experience.

The sections below describe the estimating techniques, based on the following assumptions:

- Estimating the test activities in the development phase (unit test and unit integration test) is an integrated component in estimating the realisation project and is not taken into consideration unless explicitly specified.
- Where possible, experience figures are mentioned for the specified techniques. We explain the background of these figures. The figures shown must always be considered within the described context. They do not necessarily apply in a different situation.
- One retest is included in all of the experience figures mentioned in subsequent sections.
- Please refer to chapter 13, "Metrics", for the structured collection and analysis of test estimating figures.

An adequate choice from the various techniques can be made with the use of two tables. These tables answer the following two questions:

- Which technique is suitable for which level of estimating?
- Which techniques are suitable for estimating which quality characteristics?

The answers to these questions are shown in the tables below.

	Master test plan	Detailed test plan	Test phase	Test activity
Estimating based on ratios	X	X	X	(X)
Estimating based on size	X			
Work Breakdown Structure (WBS)	X	X	X	X
Evaluation estimating techniques	X			
Proportionate estimation	X	X	X	(X)
Extrapolation			X	X
Test point analysis (estimating based on size and strategy)	X	X		

The possible estimating techniques are shown per quality characteristic in the table below. The table distinguishes between three different levels of testing depth for dynamic tests, i.e. •, •• and ••• (low, medium and high).

	Evalua-tion	Statisti-cal test	UT	UIT	Implicit test	Dynamic test	Dynamic test	Dynamic test
Depth of testing →	●	●	●	●		●	●●	●●●
Quality characteristic↓	No. of pages 1)		2)	2)	3)			
Connectivity		TPA-s				-	-	-
Continuity		TPA-s				Time-box7) week	Time-box7) month	Time-box7) quarter
Data controllability		TPA-s				-	-	-
Effectivity		TPA-s				TPA6)	TPA6)	WBS
Efficiency		TPA-s				-	WBS	-
Flexibility		TPA-s				-	-	-
Functionality		TPA-s	Hour box7)	Hour box7)		TPA	TPA	TPA
Infrastructure		TPA-s				-	-	-
Manageability		TPA-s 4)				WBS5)	-	-
Maintainability		TPA-s				-	-	-
Performance Batch Online		TPA-s				TPA WBS	TPA WBS	TPA WBS
Portability		TPA-s				WBS	TPA	TPA
Reusability		TPA-s				-	-	-
Security		TPA-s				TPA	TPA	WBS
Suitability		TPA-s				TPA6)	TPA6)	TPA
Testability		TPA-s				-	-	-
User-friendliness		TPA-s				WBS	WBS	WBS

Comments on the table:

- It is not possible to indicate a specific estimating technique for this level of depth.

1) Several pages must be read when verifying a quality characteristic. Quality characteristics that have to do with functionality require a study of the pages on which the functionality is described. Other quality characteristics are generally described on other pages. This results in a varying number of pages per quality characteristic for verification.

2) It is assumed that the estimate of the standard test activities in the UT and UIT is part of the estimate of the realisation. If desirable, extra attention to testing during the UT and UIT can be specified. The estimating technique for this is an hour box, in which e.g. a supplement rate is added to the

build effort (e.g. 10%) or part of the effort for the ST.

3) TPA-i is the component for implicit testing of a quality characteristic during dynamic testing of another quality characteristic. In TPA, this results in an additional supplement of 0.02 when determining the Q_d. Please refer to section 11.8 for a more detailed description of TPA.

4) TPA-s is the statistical component of TPA. Please refer to section 11.8 for a more detailed description of TPA.

5) WBS = Work Breakdown Structure.

6) If effectivity and suitability are tested with the same test type/test technique, the effort is included once.

7) The time box and hour box are determined by factors outside the test process. Time box week in the table above means that testing takes a period of one week.

11.2 Estimation based on ratios

To use ratios as a basis to create an estimate, it is important to collect the greatest possible amount of experience figures. This makes it possible to derive 'standard' ratios for similar projects. Similar projects are projects that are the same in terms of certain key properties. For instance the same development method, the same development platform, the same software environment, the same experience level of the developers, etc.

Naturally, the own ratios of an organisation generally are the best ones to use within that organisation. Ratios can be used at all estimation levels. At the level of test activities in test phases however, the ratios are so specific that they can only be used within one organisation and often even within the area of application (project or system).

Below please find a number of ratios between tests and other development activities from actual practice. An organisation can use these observations as a starting point. By then keeping track of its own experience figures, the organisation can match the ratios more and more adequately to its own practice.

The various observations are based on the following standardisation of terms:

■ Functional design (FD) = functional detailed design.
■ Realisation, consisting of the technical design (TD), programming (P), unit and unit integration test (UT and UIT).
■ Functional test. This concerns the testing of the functionality quality characteristic, with the FD as the test basis. The ST and AT test levels are used for this purpose.

Observed ratios in an average risk profile are as follows:
- FD : Realisation : Functional test = 2 : 5 : 3
  In an environment with a formally complete FD, waterfall development method, 3GL programming language, and a structured test approach. These figures were found to apply for the activities in the maintenance phase as well, with testing only involving a test of the change.
- (FD+TD) : (P + UT + UIT) : Functional test = 1 : 3 : 3
  In an environment with an incompletely detailed FD, experienced builders who fill the FDs themselves, and a starting test approach.
- FD : Realisation : Functional test = 1 : 2 : 1.2
  In a test environment with a formally complete FD, waterfall development method, experienced builders, and a functional test that does not have maximum test coverage but is driven by risk, and a maximised budget. The test approach is structured.

Within a test level, ratios can be used to estimate the various phases. Here, too, observations from actual practice are available:
- For a system test with good but complex specifications, the observed ratio is as follows: Preparation 6%, Specification 54%, Execution 21%, Completion 2%, and 17% for Control and Setting up and maintaining infrastructure taken together.
- The following ratio was observed for a system with an inadequate test basis: Preparation 21%, Specification 33%, Execution 24%, Completion 5%, and 17% for Control and Setting up and maintaining infrastructure taken together.

Note: in both cases, 160 hours were spent on creating the MTP.

11.3   Estimation based on test object size

The size of the test object can be established in different ways. The term Test Object Size Meter (TOSM) is used to indicate the size of a test object in a uniform manner. Based on a test object size determined this way, the following number can be used to estimate the functional test even without the strategy being known (yet).

1.5 to 4 hours per size unit (TOSM)

The actual number for a specific area of application depends on:
- type of environment (web, database)
- support provided
- quality of the test basis
- size of the project, towards factor 2 for very small and very big projects

- required reporting
- experience of testers.

Organisations can maintain experience figures to make ever more reliable estimates.

The size of a test object (and therefore the number of TOSMs) can be established in the following ways:
- Detailed functional description
  A function point analysis can be performed on a detailed functional description (e.g. a functional design). The result of the function point analysis is a number of function points (FP). One function point is then equalled to one TOSM, making the size of the test object (= number of TOSMs) the same as the number of function points.
- Data model
  If a data model is available, the following approach can be used to establish the size of the test object: determine the number of logical data collections (LDCs) and estimate the complexity. The size of the test object is found by multiplying the number of data collections by the value in the table below.

Number of LDCs	Complexity		
	Low	Medium	High
< 10	25	28	35
10 - 25	28	35	42
> 25	35	42	47

- Requirement pages
  The literature contains experience figures to relate the size of the test object to the number of requirement pages. Generally speaking, this means that not all information concerning the conditions under which the data were measured is available.
  - 1 A4-sized page of requirements without diagrams = 15 TOSMs [Collard, 1999].
  - In a large classical project in which a highly detailed functional design without illustrations was available, the following experience figure was measured: 1 A4-sized page of requirements = 2.5 to 3 TOSMs.
- Number of screens
  If the number of screens is a determinant for the size of the application, the following derivation can be used [Collard, 1999]: 1 screen (window/webpage) = 8 TOSMs.
- Program source code
  For a new development project, clearly the program source code is not

available until after the realisation process. For a migration or maintenance project, for instance, the derivations below may be applicable:

- 1 kilo lines of code (3 GL) = 17 TOSMs [Collard, 1999].
- [Jones, 1996]

1 KLOC (kilo lines of code)	number of TOSMs
C	6.6
Algol, Cobol, Fortran	10
PL/1	12
Lisp, basic	16
4GL database	25
Objective C	39
Smalltalk	49
Query languages	60

11.4 Work Breakdown Structure

The Work Breakdown Structure (WBS) is an estimating approach based on splitting up the activities into partial activities up to a level of detail at which the required time per activity can be estimated. By adding the time required for the partial activities, the total required time is calculated.

The table below shows the number of hours per quality characteristic. For quality characteristics where the strategy matters, this is shown. The hours are derived from actual practice. Please note that the experience base and therefore the how hard the figures are differs. Levels of hardness are:

- Hard: experience from multiple projects, confirmed on the basis of multiple sources
- Experience: based on a few sources
- Soft: an estimate by experienced test consultants.

Practice demonstrates which factors have the greatest impact on the definitive number of hours. These factors are shown.

Quality characteristic	Strategy	Hardness estimation	Hours	Important factors for variation in size
Manageability Installability		soft	24	
Security	●●●	experience	80	Minimal, hour box
Effectivity	●●●	soft	350	Incl hours of users
Continuity	●●●	N/A		Depends on the duration of shadow production
User-friendliness	●	hard	70	Size of application (limit 15/100 screens) Scope of research question (limit: several subjects)
User-friendliness	●●	hard	80	
User-friendliness	●●●	hard	130	
Performance, online	●●	hard	192 tot 224	Low: 15 user tasks High: 40 user tasks Complex database
Portability	●	soft	28	
Economy	●●	soft	28	

Please note: The table above does not include hours for e.g. setting up a usability lab or selecting test-support packages. The starting point is that the required facilities must be available.

11.5   Evaluation estimation approach

One of the size bases for evaluations often mentioned in the literature is the number of pages of the document that is being evaluated.

Figures from the literature: 1-4 pages per hour per evaluator per size unit, depending on:
- the number of quality characteristics looked at
- the evaluator's experience
- the required depth
- the formality of the evaluation type – the more formal the evaluation, the more time it takes.

11.6 Proportionate estimation

This estimating technique is based on a total quantity of budget to test the entire test object. The total amount is divided over the distinguished components. When dividing the total budget over the various components, the allocated risk class (for a test strategy) and the size of the components are taken into account. A factor is chosen for each risk class (in the test strategy) that enables a weighted distribution. For example:

■ Risk class A is allocated a factor 1.5
■ Risk class B is allocated a factor 1
■ Risk class C is allocated a factor 0.6.

The steps to derive an estimate are as follows:
5. Calculate the product of the size of the object part to be tested with the factor associated with the risk class of that object part. Do this for all object parts.
6. Add the outcomes from step 1.
7. Determine the scaling factor by dividing 100 by the result of step 2.
8. Calculate the number of hours per object part by multiplying the results of step 1 by the scaling factor.

An example to clarify this:
100 hours are to divided over 5 object parts. The size and a risk class have been determined for each object part. The number of hours per object part is then established following the steps above.

Object part	Size	Risk class	Factor	Size x Factor	Scaling factor	Number of hours
1	10	C	0.6	6		7.86
2	15	A	1.5	22.5		29.48
3	7	B	1	7		9.17
4	25	A	1.5	37.5		49.12
5	5	C	0.6	3		3.93
Total				76	100/76=1.31	100 (100.56)

11.7   Extrapolation

In this estimating method, measurements are made as early on in the project as possible to build experience figures. Once it is known what percentage of the work was done in how much time, it can be established (on approximation) how much time is required for the remainder of the work. This method is used a lot in practice to estimate test activities within a test level. It is also very suitable to estimate test activities in incremental development methods.

11.8   Test point analysis

This section describes the test estimating technique test point analysis (TPA). Test point analysis makes it possible to estimate a system test or acceptance test in an objective manner. Development testing is an implicit part of the development estimate and is therefore outside the scope of TPA. To apply TPA, the scope of the information system must be known. To this end, the results of a function point analysis (FPA) are used. FPA is a method that makes it possible to make a technology-independent measurement of the scope of the functionality provided by an automated system, and using the measurement as a basis for productivity measurement, estimating the required resources, and project control. The productivity factor in function point analysis does include the development tests, but not the acceptance and system tests.

Test point analysis can also be used if the number of test hours to be invested is determined in advance. By executing a test point analysis, any possible risks incurred can be demonstrated clearly by comparing the objective test point analysis estimate with the number of test hours determined in advance. A test point analysis can also be used to calculate the relative importance of the various functions, based on which the available test time can be used as optimally as possible. Test point analysis can also be used to create a global test estimate at an early stage (section 11.8.8).

Philosophy
When establishing a test estimate in the framework of an acceptance or system test, three elements play a role (see figure 11.2 "Estimating basic elements"):
- The size of the information system that is to be tested.
- The test strategy (which object parts and quality characteristics must be tested and with what thoroughness, what level of depth?).
- The productivity.

The first two elements together determine the size of the test to be executed (expressed as test points). A test estimate in hours results if the number of test points is multiplied by the productivity (the time required to execute a specific test depth level). The three elements are elaborated in detail below.

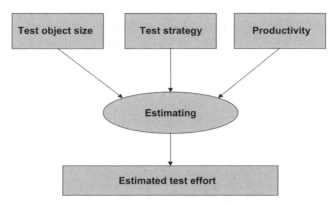

Figure 11.2: Estimating basic elements

Size
Size in this context means the size of the information system. In test point analyses the figure for this is based primarily on the number of function points. A number of additions and/or adjustments must be made in order to arrive at the figure for the test point analysis. This is because a number of factors can be distinguished during testing that do not or barely play a part when determining the number of function points, but are vital to testing. These factors are:

- Complexity
  How many conditions are present in a function? More conditions almost automatically means more test cases and therefore greater test effort.
- System impact
  How many data collections are maintained by the function and how many other functions use them? These other functions must also be tested if this maintenance function is modified.
- Uniformity
  Is the structure of a function of such a nature that existing test specifications can be reused with no more than small adjustments. In other words, are there multiple functions with the same structure in the information system?

Test strategy
During system development and maintenance, quality requirements are specified for the information system. During testing, the extent to which the specified quality requirements are complied with must be established.

However, there is never an unlimited quantity of test resources and test time. This is why it is important to relate the test effort to the expected product risks. We use a product risk analysis (chapter 9) to establish, among other things, test goals, relevant characteristics per test goal, object parts to be distinguished per characteristic, and the risk class per characteristic/object part. The result of the product risk analysis is then used to establish the test strategy. A combination of a characteristic/object part from a high risk class will often require heavy-duty, far-reaching tests and therefore a relatively great test effort when translated to the test strategy. The test strategy represents input for the test point analysis. In test point analysis, the test strategy is translated to the required test time.

In addition to the general quality requirements of the information system, there are differences in relation to the quality requirements between the various functions. The reliable operation of some functions is vital to the business process. The information system was developed for these functions. From a user's perspective, the function that is used intensively all day may be much more important than the processing function that runs at night. There are therefore two (subjective) factors per function that determine the depth: the user importance of the function and the intensity of use. The depth, as it were, indicates the level of certainty or insight into the quality that is required by the client. Obviously the factors user importance and intensity of use are based on the test strategy.

The test strategy tells us which combinations of characteristic/object part must be tested with what thoroughness. Often, a quality characteristic is selected as characteristic. The test point analysis also uses quality characteristics, which means that it is closely related to the test strategy and generally is performed simultaneously in actual practice.

Tip

Linking TPA parameters to test strategy risk classes
TPA has many parameters that determine the required number of hours. The risk classes from the test strategy can be translated readily to these parameters. Generally, the TPA parameters have three values, which can then be linked to the three risk classes from the test strategy (risk classes A, B and C).
If no detailed information is available to divide the test object into the various risk classes, the following division can be used:
• 25% risk class A
• 50% risk class B
• 25% risk class C.

This division must then be used as the starting point for a TPA.

Productivity
Using this concept is not new to people who have already made estimates based on function points. Productivity establishes the relation between effort hours and the measured number of function points in function point analysis. For test point analysis, productivity means the time required to realise one test point, determined by the size of the information system and the test strategy. Productivity consists of two components: the skill factor and the environment factor. The skill factor is based primarily on the knowledge and skills of the test team. As such, the figure is organisation and even person-specific. The environment factor shows the extent to which the environment has an impact on the test activities to which the productivity relates. This involves aspects such as the availability of test tools, experience with the test environment in question, the quality of the test basis, and the availability of testware, if any.

Overall operation
Schematically, this is how test point analysis works:

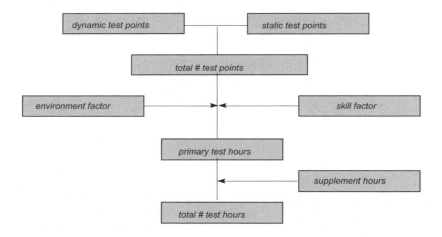

Figure 11.3: Schematic representation of test point analysis

Based on the number of function points per function, the function-dependent factors (complexity, impact, uniformity, user importance and intensity of use), and the quality requirements and/or test strategy relating to the quality characteristics that must be measured dynamically, the number of test points that is necessary to test the dynamically measurable quality characteristics is established per function (dynamically measurable means that an opinion can be realised on a specific quality characteristic by executing programs).

Adding these test points over the functions results in the number of dynamic test points.

Based on the total number of function points of the information system and the quality requirements and/or test strategy relating to the static quality characteristics, the number of test points that is necessary to test the statically measurable quality characteristics is established (static testing: testing by verifying and investigating products without executing programs). This results in the number of static test points.

The total number of test points is realised by adding the dynamic and static test points.

The primary test hours are then calculated by multiplying the total number of test points by the calculated environment factor and the applicable skill factor. The number of primary test hours represents the time necessary to execute the primary test activities. In other words, the time that is necessary to execute the test activities for the phases Preparation, Specification, Execution and Completion of the TMap life cycle.

The number of hours that is necessary to execute secondary test activities from the Control and Setting up and maintaining infrastructure phases (additional hours) is calculated as a percentage of the primary test hours.

Finally, the total number of test hours is obtained by adding the number of additional hours to the number of primary test hours. The total number of test hours is an estimate for all TMap test activities, with the exception of creating the test plan (Planning phase).

Principles
The following principles apply in relation to test point analysis:
- Test point analysis is limited to the quality characteristics that are 'measurable'. Being measurable means that a test technique is available for the relevant quality characteristic. Moreover, sufficient practical experience must be available in relation to this test technique in terms of the relevant quality characteristic to make concrete statements about the required test effort.
- Not all possible quality characteristics that may be present are included in the current version of test point analysis. Reasons for this vary – there may be no concrete test technique available (yet), or there may be insufficient practical experience with a test technique and therefore insufficient reliable metrics available. Any subsequent version of test point analysis may include more quality characteristics.
- In principle, test point analysis is not linked to a person. In other words, different persons executing a test point analysis on the same information system should, in principle, create the same estimate. This is achieved by

letting the client determine all factors that cannot be classified objectively and using a uniform classification system for all factors that can.

- Test point analysis can be performed if a function point count according to IFPUG [IFPUG, 1994] is available; gross function points are used as the starting point.
- Test point analysis does not consider subject matter knowledge as a factor that influences the required quantity of test effort in test point analysis. However, it is of course important that the test team has a certain level of subject matter knowledge. This knowledge is a precondition that must be complied with while creating the test plan.
- Test point analysis assumes one complete retest on average when determining the estimate. This average is a weighted average based on the size of the functions, expressed as test points.

Tip

From COSMIC full function points (CFFP) to function points (FP)
To estimate the project size, the COSMIC[1] Full Function Points (CFFP) approach is used more and more often in addition to the Function Point Analysis (FPA) approach [Abran, 2003]. FPA was created in a period in which only a mainframe environment existed and moreover relies heavily on the relationship between functionality and the data model. However, CFFP also takes account of other architectures, like client server and multi tier, *and* development methods like objected oriented, component based, and RAD. The following rule of thumb can be used to convert CFFPs to function points (FPs):
- if CFFP < 250   : FP = CFFP
- if 250 ≤ CFFP ≤ 1000   : FP = CFFP / 1.2
- if CFFP > 1000   : FP = CFFP / 1.5

TPA, the technique in detail

11.8.1 Input and starting conditions

To perform a test point analysis, one must have a functional design. The functional design must include detailed process descriptions and a logical data model, preferably including a CRUD matrix. Moreover a function point count must have been executed according to IFPUG. These function point methods can be used as input for TPA. It is important to use only one of these function point methods when determining the skill factor, not multiple methods combined. In a function point count, the number of gross function points is taken as the starting point. Which function point method is used is not important when determining the test points. It will, however, have an impact on the skill factor.

The following modifications must be made to the function point count for TPA:

---

[1]COSMIC: COmmon Software Measurement International Consortium.

- The function points of the (logical) data collections distinguished in the function point count must be allocated to the function(s) that handle(s) the input of the relevant (logical) collection.
- The function points of the interface data collections distinguished in the function point count must be allocated to the function (or possibly functions) that use(s) the relevant interface data collection.
- For FPA functions in the clone class, the number of function points that applies to the original FPA function is used. A clone is an FPA function that has already been specified and/or realised in another, or the same, user function in the project.
- For FPA functions in the dummy class, the number of function points is determined if possible. Else this FPA function is given the qualification average complexity and the corresponding number of function points. A dummy is an FPA function if the functionality does not have to be specified and/or realised, but is already available because it was specified/realised outside the project.

Tip

Estimating guideline for counting function points
If no function point count is available and you wish to make one (for TPA), the following guideline can be used to determine the time required to count the function points:
Determine the number of TOSMs using one of the methods described in section 11.3 and divide it by 400. The outcome represents an estimate of the number of days necessary to count the function points.
Note: as a rule, 350 to 400 function points can be counted in a day.

Calculation example (1): Number of function points (FP$_f$)

An information system has two user functions and one internal logical data collection:
Registration (11 function points), with as underlying FPA functions:

Entry	3 function points
Editing	4 function points
Deleting	4 function points

Processing (12 function points), with as underlying FPA functions:

Overview 1	5 function points
Overview 2	7 function points

The internal logical data collection 'data' has 7 function points and is allocated to the entry function in the context of test point analysis.

FP$_f$ Registration 18 function points
FP$_f$ Processing   12 function points

(**FP$_f$** = function points per function)

11.8.2   Dynamic test points

The number of dynamic test points is the sum of the number of test points per function in relation to dynamically measurable quality characteristics.

The number of test points is based on two types of factors:
- function-dependent factors (D_f)
- factor representing the dynamically measurable quality characteristics (Q_d).

The FPA function is used as a unit of function. When determining the user importance and intensity of use, the focus is on the user function as a communication resource. The importance the users attach to the user function also applies to all of the underlying FPA functions.

Function-dependent factors

The function-dependent factors are described below, including the associated weights. Only one of the three described values can be selected (i.e. intermediate values are not allowed). If too little information is available to classify a certain factor, it must be given the nominal value (in bold print in this section).

User importance
User importance is defined as the relative importance the user attaches to a specific function in relation to the other functions in the system. As a rule of thumb, around 25% of the functions must be in the category "high", 50% the category "neutral", and 25% in the category "low". User importance is allocated to the functionality as experienced by the user. This means allocation of the user importance to the user function. Of course, the user importance of a function must be determined in consultation with the client and other representatives of the user organisation.

Weight
3   low: the relative importance of the specific function in relation to the other functions is low
6   Neutral: the relative importance of the specific function in relation to the other nfunctions is neutral
12 high: the relative importance of the specific function in relation to the other functions is high.

Intensity of use
Intensity of use is defined as the frequency at which a certain function is used by the user and the size of the user group that uses that function. As with user

importance, intensity of use is allocated to functionality as experienced by users, i.e. the user functions.

Weight
2   low: the function is executed by the user organisation just a few times per day or per week
4   neutral: the function is executed by the user organisation many times per day
8   high: the function is executed continuously (at least 8 hours per day).

System impact
System impact is the level at which a mutation that occurs in the relevant function has an impact on the system. The level of impact is determined by assessing the logical data collections (LDCs) to which the function can make mutations, as well as the number of other functions (within the system boundaries) that access those LDCs. The impact is assessed using a matrix that shows the number of LDCs mutated by the function on the vertical axis, and the number of other functions accessing these LDCs on the horizontal axis. A function counts several times in terms of impact when it accesses multiple LDCs that are all maintained by the function in question.

Number of LDCs	Functions		
	1	2 - 5	> 5
1	L	L	M
2 - 5	L	M	H
> 5	M	H	H

Explanation: L = Low impact, M = Medium impact, H = High impact.

If a function does not mutate any LDCs, it has a low impact. A CRUD matrix is very useful when determining the system impact.
Weight
2   the function has a low impact
4   the function has a medium impact
8   the function has a high impact.

Complexity
The complexity of a function is assessed on the basis of its algorithm. The global structure of the algorithm may be described by means of pseudo code, Nassi-Shneidermann or regular text. The level of complexity of the function is determined by the number of conditions in the algorithm of that function. When counting the number of conditions, only the processing algorithm must be taken into account. Conditions resulting from database checks, such as validations by domain or physical presence, are not included since they are

already incorporated implicitly in the function point count.

As such the complexity can be determined simply by counting the number of conditions. Composite conditions, such as IF a AND b THEN count double for complexity. This is because two IF statements would be needed without the AND statement. Likewise, a CASE statement with n cases counts for n-1 conditions, because the replacement of the CASE statement by successive IF statements would result in n-1 conditions. In summary: count the conditions, not the operators.

Weight
3   a maximum of 5 conditions are present in the function
6   6 to 11 conditions are present in the function
12   more than 11 conditions are present in the function.

Uniformity
In three types of situation, a function counts for only 60%:
- A nearly unique function occurring a second time – in this case, the test specifications that are to be defined can be largely reused.
- Clones – in this case, too, the test specifications that are to be defined can be reused.
- Dummy functions – but only if reusable test specifications for the dummy exist.

The uniformity factor is given the value 0.6 if one of the above conditions is met, otherwise it is given the value 1.

In an information system, there can be functions that have a certain level of uniformity in the context of testing, but are marked as unique in the function point analysis. In the function point analysis, being unique means:
- A unique combination of data collections in relation to the other input functions.
- Not a unique combination of data collections, but another logical processing method (e.g. updating a data collection another way).

In addition, there are functions in an information system that are said to be fully uniform in the context of function point analysis and are therefore not allocated any function points, but must be counted in the testing because they do require testing. These are the clones and dummies.

Calculation method
The factor (D_f) is determined by establishing the sum of the values of the first four function-dependent variables (user importance, intensity of use, system impact and complexity) and dividing it by 20 (the nominal value). The result

of this calculation must then be multiplied by the value of the uniformity factor. The D_f factor is determined per function.

$$D_f = ((Ui + Iu + Si + C) / 20) * U$$

D_f	= weight factor of the function-dependent factors
Ui	= user importance
Iu	= intensity of use
Si	= system impact
C	= complexity
U	= uniformity

Standard functions
If functions for error messages, help screens and/or menu structure are present in the function point count – which often is the case – they must be valued as follows:

Function	FPs	Ui	Iu	Si	C	U	D_f
Error messages	4	6	8	4	3	1	1.05
Help screens	4	6	8	4	3	1	1.05
Menu structure	4	6	8	4	3	1	1.05

Calculation example (2): Determining the function-dependent variables (D_f)

	Registration	Processing
User importance	6	12
Intensity of use	8	2
System impact	2	2
Complexity	3	6
Uniformity	1	1
$D_f =$	19/20 * 1 = 0.95	22/20 * 1 = 1.10

(In this example, it is assumed that the valuation of the factors system impact and complexity are identical for the FPA functions in a user function).

Dynamically measurable quality characteristics

Below, we describe how the requirements specified for the dynamically measurable quality characteristics are incorporated into the test point analysis. In relation to the dynamically measurable quality characteristics, TPA distinguishes between quality characteristics that can be measured explicitly and/or implicitly.

The following can be measured dynamically explicitly:
- functionality
- security
- effectivity/suitability
- performance
- portability.

The weight of the quality requirements must be valuated for each quality characteristics in the context of the test to be executed, by means of a score, possibly by sub-system.

Weight
0   not important – not measured
3   low quality requirements – attention must be devoted to it in the test
4   regular quality requirements – usually applicable if the information system relates to a support process
5   high quality requirements – usually applicable if the information system relates to a primary process
6   extremely high quality requirements.

The quality characteristics that are measured dynamic explicit have the following weight factors:

Functionality   0.75
Security   0.05
Effectivity   0.10
Performance   0.05
Portability   0.05

Which relevant quality characteristics (distinguished in the test strategy) will be tested dynamic implicit must be determined. A statement about these quality characteristics can be made by collecting statistics during test execution. E.g. performance can be measured explicitly, by means of a real-life test, or implicitly, by collecting statistics.

The quality characteristics to be measured dynamic implicit must be specified. The number of quality characteristics can then be determined. The weight is 0.02 per characteristic for Q_d. In principle, every quality characteristic can be tested dynamic implicit.

Calculation method (Q_d)
The score given to each dynamic explicit measurable quality characteristic is divided by four (the nominal value) and then multiplied by its weight factor.

The sum of the figures obtained this way is calculated. If certain quality characteristics were earmarked for dynamic implicit testing, the associated weight (0.02 per characteristic) must be added to the above sum. The figure obtained this way is the Q_d factor. Usually, the Q_d factor is established for the total system once. However, if the strategy differs per sub-system, the Q_d factor must be determined per sub-system.

Calculation example (3):
Determining the dynamically measurable quality characteristics (Q_d)

Functionality	5	(5/4) * 0.75 = 0.94
Security	4	(4/4) * 0.05 = 0.05
Effectivity	0	(0/4) * 0.10 = 0
Performance	0	(0/4) * 0.05 = 0
Portability	0	(0/4) * 0.05 = 0

The following are measured dynamic implicit:

Performance	= 0.02
Efficiency	= 0.02
Maintainability	= 0.02

Q_d = 0,94 + 0,05 + (3 * 0,02) = 1,05

Formula for dynamic test points

The number of dynamic test points is a sum of the number of test points per function. The number of test points per function can be established by entering what is now known in the formula below:

$$TP_f = FP_f * D_f * Q_d$$

TP_f = the number of test points per function
FP_f = the number of function points per function
D_f = weight factor of the function-dependent factors
Q_d = weight factor of the dynamic quality characteristics

Calculation example (4):
Calculation of total number of dynamic test points ($\sum TP_f$)

	FP_f *	D_f *	Q_d	=	TP_f
Registration	18	0,95	1,05	=	18
Processing	12	1,10	1,05	=	14 +
Total number of dynamic test points					32

11.8.3 Static test points

The number of static test points naturally depends on the quality characteristics that require static testing (the Q_s factor), but also on the total number of function points of the system. A static assessment of a large-scale information system simply takes more time than one of a simple information system.

For the relevant quality characteristics, it must be determined whether or not they will be tested statically. A statement about these quality characteristics is arrived at by means of a checklist. In principle, *all* quality characteristics can be tested statically with the aid of checklists. E.g. security can be measured either dynamically, with the aid of a semantic test, or statically, by assessing the security measures on the basis of a checklist.

Calculation method (Q_s)
If a quality characteristic is tested statically, the factor Q_s will have a value of 16. For each subsequent quality characteristic to be included in the static test, another value of 16 is added to the Q_s factor rating.

Calculation example (5): Calculation of static test points (Q_s)

The following quality characteristics are measured statically (using a checklist):
Continuity
Q_s = 16

11.8.4 Total number of test points

The number of test points of the total system can be established by entering what is now known in the formula below:

$$TP = \Sigma TP_f + ((FP * Q_s) / 500)$$

TP	=	the number of test points of the total system
ΣTP_f	=	the sum of the number of test points per function (dynamic test points)
FP	=	number of function points of the total system (minimal value 500)
Q_s	=	weight factor of static quality characteristics

Calculation example (6): Calculation of total number of test points (TP)

$TP = 32 + ((500 * 16) / 500) = 48$

11.8.5 Primary test hours

The formula in the section above results in the total number of test points. This is the measure for the scope of the primary test activities. These primary test points are multiplied by the skill factor and the environment factor to obtain the primary test hours. This represents the time that is necessary to execute the test activities for the Preparation, Specification, Execution and Completion phases of the TMap model.

Skill factor

The skill factor indicates how many hours of testing are required per test point. The higher skill factor, the greater the number of hours of testing.

The productivity with which the test object is tested on the basis of the test strategy depends primarily on the knowledge and skills of those executing the tests. It is also relevant to know if people are testing part-time or full-time. Testing users that are deployed for test work only part of the workday, have a lot of switch moments between their day-to-day work and the test work, which often results in reduced productivity.

In practice, the following basic figures are used per test point:
- 1-2 hours for a tester, depending on knowledge and skills
- 2-4 hours for a user, depending on experience.

The skill factor naturally varies per organisation and within that even per department/person. A factor can be obtained by analysing completed test projects. To make such an analysis, one must have access to experience figures for the test projects already realised.

Calculation example (7): Skill factor

For the relevant organisation, a skill factor of 1.2 applies.
$S = 1.2$

Environment factor

The number of required test hours per test point is influenced not only by the skill factor, but by the environment factor as well. A number of environment variables are used to calculate this. The environment variables are described below, including the associated weights. Again, only one of the available values may be selected. If too little information is available to classify a certain variable, it must be given the nominal value (in bold print).

Test tools
The test tools factor involves the level to which the primary text activities are supported by automated test tools. Test tools can contribute to executing part of the test activities automatically and therefore faster. Their availability does not guarantee that, however - it is about their effective use.

Weight
1   the test uses support tools for test specification, and a tool is used for record & playback
2   test execution uses support tools for test specification, or a tool with record & playback options is used
4   no test tools are available.

Previous test
For this factor the quality of the test executed earlier is important. When estimating an acceptance test this is the system test, when estimating a system test, the development test. The quality of the previous test is a co-determinant for the quantity of functionality that may be tested at a more limited level as well as for the lead time of the test execution. When the previous test is of a higher quality, fewer progress-hindering defects will occur.

Weight
2   a test plan is available for the previous test, and the test team also has insight into the concrete test cases and test results (test coverage)
4   a test plan is available for the previous test
8   no test plan is available for the previous test.

Test basis
The test basis is awarded a factor representing the quality of the (system) documentation on which the test for execution must be based. The quality of the test basis has an impact in particular on the required time for the Preparation and Specification phases.

Weight
3   standards and templates are used to create the system documentation. The documentation is also subject to inspections
6   standards and templates are used to create the documentation
12   no standards and templates are used to create the system documentation.

Development environment
The environment in which the information system is realised. Of particular interest here is to what extent the development environment prevents errors and/or enforces certain things. If certain errors can no longer be made, clearly they do not require testing.

Weight
2   the development environment contains a large number of facilities that prevent errors being made for example by executing semantic and syntactic checks and by taking over the parameters
4   the development environment contains a limited number of facilities that prevent errors being made for example by executing a syntactic check and by taking over the parameters
8   the development environment contains no facilities that prevent errors being made.

Test environment
The extent to which the physical test environment in which the test is executed has proven itself. If an often used test environment is used, fewer disturbances and defects will occur during the Execution phase.

Weight
1   the environment has already been used several times to execute a test
2   a new environment has been set up for the test in question, the organisation has ample experience with similar environments
4   a new environment has been set up for the test in question that can be characterised as experimental for the organisation.

Testware
The level to which existing testware can be used during the test to be executed. The availability of effective testware has a particular impact on the time required for the Specification phase.

Weight
1   a usable general central starting situation (tables etc) is available, as well as specified test cases for the test to be executed
2   a usable general central starting situation (tables etc) is available
4   no usable testware is available.

Calculation method
The environment factor (E) is determined by establishing the sum of the values of the environment variables (test tools, previous test, test basis, development environment, test environment, and testware) and dividing it by 21 (the nominal value). The environment factor E can be established for

the total system once, but also per sub-system if necessary.

Calculation example (8): Environment factor (E)

The various environment variables were given the score below:

Test tools	4 (no test tools)
Previous test	4 (a test plan is available of the previous test)
Test basis	3 (documentation templates and inspections)
Development environment	4 (Oracle in combination with COBOL)
Test environment	1 (tested environment)
Testware	4 (no usable testware available)

E = 20/21 = 0.95

Formula for primary test hours

The number of primary test hours is obtained by multiplying the number of test points by the skill and environment factors:

$$PT = TP * S * E$$

PT	= the total number of primary test hours
TP	= the number of test points of the total system
S	= skill factor
E	= environment factor

Calculation example (9): Calculation of primary test hours (PT)

PT = 48 * 1.2 * 0.95 = 54.72 (55 hours)

11.8.6 The total number of test hours

Since every test process involves secondary activities from the Control phase and the Setting up and maintaining infrastructure phase, a supplement must be added to the primary test hours for this. This will eventually result in the total number of test hours. The number of supplemental hours is calculated as a percentage of the primary test hours.

The supplemental percentage is often determined by a test manager on the basis of experience or using historical data. Some organisations use a fixed percentage. The percentage is nearly always in the range of 5 to 20%.

If no experience, historical data or fixed percentages are available, a supplemental percentage can be estimated in the following way. A standard (nominal) supplemental percentage of 12% is used as the starting point. We must then look at factors that may increase or reduce the percentage. Examples of such factors are:
- Team size
- Management tools
- Permanent test organisation.

These factors are explained below. Since there is a great variety of test projects, we have not used seemingly certain absolute percentage figures to determine the impact of these factors on the percentage, but have chosen to indicate whether the impact will increase or reduce the percentage.

Team size
The team size represents the number of members in the test team (including the test manager and a test administrator, if any). A big team usually results in greater overhead and therefore a higher supplemental percentage. However, a small test team results in a reduced percentage:
- Reduction
  Test team consists of maximum 4 persons
- Neutral
  Test team consists of 5 - 9 persons
- Increase
  Test team consists of at least 10 persons.

Management tools
For management tools, it is considered to what extent automated tools are used during the test activities for Control and Setting up and maintaining infrastructure. Examples of these tools are an automated:
- planning system
- progress monitoring system
- defect administration system
- testware management system.

If little use is made of automated tools, certain activities will have to be done manually. This increases the supplement percentage. If intensive use is made of automated tools, this will reduce the percentage:
- Reduction
  At least 3 automated tools are used
- Neutral
  1- 2 automated tools are used
- Increase
  No automated tools are used.

Permanent test organisation

There are many kinds of permanent test organisation (section 8.3). If an organisation has one of these permanent test organisations, lead time reduction, cost savings and/or quality improvement are often realised in a test process that uses it.

- Reduction
  Test team uses the services of a permanent test organisation
- Neutral
  Test team does not use the services of a permanent test organisation.

Calculation example (10): Determining supplement for Control and Setting up and maintaining infrastructure (C and S&MI)

Historical data show the supplement percentage for such test projects to fluctuate around 15%. The test manager decides to use this percentage.

Supplement percentage C and S&MI = 15%

Calculation method

The supplemental percentage is used to calculate the supplement (in hours) on the basis of the number of primary test hours. The total number of test hours is then obtained by adding the supplement calculated for Control and Setting up and maintaining infrastructure to the total number of primary test hours.

Calculation example (11): Calculation of total number of test hours

Primary test hours	55
Supplement C and S&MI	55 * 0.15 = 8.25 (rounded down: 8)

Total number of hours   55 + 8 = 63

Figure 11.4 shows the TPA calculation example as a whole.

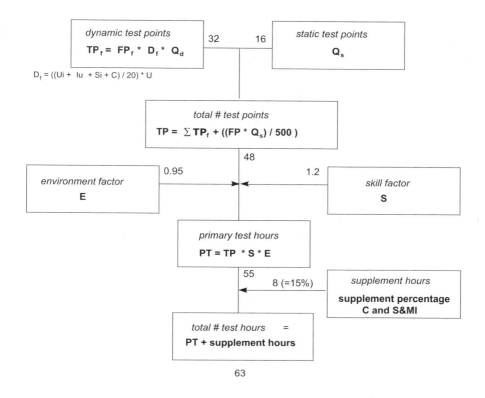

Figure 11.4: Schematic representation of calculation example

11.8.7 Distribution over the phases

When using TMap, the test process is split up into seven phases, and many clients will be interested in the estimate per phase in addition to the estimate for the entire test process.

TPA gives an estimate for the entire test process, with the exception of test plan creation (Planning phase).

In principle, for the phases Control and Setting up and maintaining infrastructure, the number of hours is estimated that was calculated on the basis of the number of primary test hours using the supplement percentage (supplement hours). These supplement hours must be divided between the two phases.

The primary test hours are divided over the other phases (Preparation, Specification, Execution, and Completion). The distribution of the primary test hours over the phases may naturally vary per organisation, and even within one organisation. A distribution applicable to the organisation can be obtained by analysing completed test projects. To make such an analysis, one must have access to experience figures for the test projects already realised.

Distribution of primary test hours

Practical experience with test point analysis in combination with TMap yields the following distribution of the test effort over the various phases:

Preparation	10%
Specification	40%
Execution	45%
Completion	5%

Please refer to section 11.2 for other distributions based on practical experience.

11.8.8   TPA at an early stage

Often, a project estimate for testing must be made at an early stage. In this case, it is not possible to establish factors like complexity, impact and so on, because no detailed functional specifications are available. However, there are approaches that can often be used to perform a rough test point analysis. By using one of the approaches below, the total number of (gross) function points can be estimated:
- on the basis of very rough specifications, perform a so-called rough function point analysis
- determine the number of function points by determining the number of TOSMs (for more information, see section 11.3).

One function is then defined for the purpose of a rough test point analysis. This function has the size of the total number of defined (gross) function points. In principle, all function-dependent factors (user importance, intensity of use, complexity, impact and uniformity) are given the neutral value, so that $D_f = 1$. A test point analysis can then be made as described in the previous sections. Usually assumptions will have to be made when determining the environment factor. When presenting the test estimate, it is important to describe these assumptions clearly.

12 Defects management

12.1 Introduction

Many people see the finding of defects as the purpose of testing. While it should be clear that the purpose of testing is much more, i.e. the provision of information and advice concerning risks and quality, the fact remains that finding defects is one of the most important activities of testing.

A defect is also termed a 'fault'. Confusion sometimes arises concerning the various terms, such as errors, faults and failures. In this book, the following distinction is made:

- Error
  Human mistake; this action takes place prior to any faults and/or failures
- Fault
  Results from an error. Fault is the view from inside the system. Fault is the state where mistake or error exists. Developers will see the fault
- Failure
  When the system is performing differently from the required behaviour, from a viewpoint outside the system. Users will see the failure.

In this book, the following definition of defect is used:

Definition

A defect (fault) is the result of an error residing in the code or document.

Testers should realise that they are a) judging another's work, and b) that the final product is the result of cooperation between all parties. It is more considerate towards the other party to find a discrepancy between what the software does and what the tester expects, based on the available information, than if the tester immediately exclaims that he has caught the developer out in a mistake. The latter has a polarising effect and quickly becomes a discussion on who has made the mistake, instead of a discussion on how best to solve the defect. In some cases, the testers employ terms such as "issues", "problems" or "findings" rather than defects. The tester should adopt as neutral an attitude as possible in connection with defects. Another good reason for adopting this attitude is that the cause of the defect often turns out not to lie with the developer, but with the tester himself. In a situation in which developers and testers stand opposite each other instead of side by side, a number of unjustified defect reports can destroy the testers' credibility entirely.

Administering and monitoring the defects also involves the solving of them. This is actually a project matter and not specifically a matter for the testers, although testers have the greatest involvement here. Good administration should be able to monitor the life cycle of a defect and also deliver various overviews, which are used, among other things, to make well-founded decisions on quality. This management is sometimes assigned to a dedicated role: defects administrator (see section 16.3 "Roles not described as a position").

From within the test process, the testers are the submitters of defects, and they check the solutions of these. The test manager communicates with the other parties concerning (the handling of) the defects. The choice may also be made to place this task within a separate role in the team: the intermediary. The purpose of this is to channel the defects and the associated solutions effectively. In this regard, the intermediary maintains external contacts at the level of staff doing the actual work. This person has an overview of all the defects and acts as a relay and inspection post for the defects on the one hand, and the solutions on the other. Advantages of this are that the quality of the defects and solutions is monitored better and that communication is streamlined.

There are great advantages to be gained in organising one single defects administration and defects procedure for the entire project or the entire line department. All the parties involved – developers, users, testers, QA people, etc. can deposit both their defects and solutions here. Communication on the handling of the defects is thus considerably simplified. A central administration also offers extra possibilities of obtaining information. The authorisations are a point to note here; it should not be possible for unauthorised persons to be able to amend or close defects by this means.

The rest of this chapter is divided into a number of sections that collectively reflect the life cycle of a defect:
- Finding a defect (section 12.2)
- Reporting a defect (section 12.3)
- The procedure surrounding the handling of the defect (section 12.4).

12.2   Finding a defect

Defects may be found practically throughout the entire test process. The emphasis, however, is on the phases of Preparation, Specification and Execution. Since, in the Preparation and Specification phases, the test object is normally not yet used, in these phases the testers find defects in the test basis. During the Execution phase, the testers find differences between the actual and the expected operation of the test object. The cause of these defects, however, may still lie within the test basis.

The steps that the tester should perform when a defect is found are described below:
- Collect proof
- Reproduce the defect
- Check for your own mistakes
- Determine the suspected external cause
- Isolate the cause (optional)
- Generalise the defect
- Compare with other defects
- Write a defect report
- Have it reviewed.

The steps are in a general order of execution, but it is entirely possible to carry out certain steps in another sequence or in parallel. If, for example, the tester immediately sees that the defect was found previously in the same test, the rest of the steps can be skipped.

Collect proof

At a certain point, the test object produces a response other than the tester expects, or the tester finds that the test basis contains an ambiguity, inconsistency or omission: a defect. The first step is to establish proof of this anomaly. This can be done during the test execution, for example, by making a screen dump or a memory dump, printing the output, making a copy of the database content or taking notes. The tester should also look at other places where the result of the anomaly could be visible. He could do this, for example, in the case of an unexpected result, by using an Edit function to see how the data is stored in the database and a View function to see how it is shown to the user. If the defect concerns a part of the test basis, other related parts of the test basis should be examined.

Reproduce the defect

When a defect is found during test execution, the next step is to see whether it can be reproduced by executing the test case once more. The tester is now on guard for deviant system behaviour. Besides, executing the test again helps with recognising any test execution errors. If the defect is reproducible, the tester continues with the subsequent steps. If the defect is not reproducible and it is not suspected to be a test execution error, things become more difficult. The tester executes the test case again. He then indicates clearly in the defect report that the defect is not reproducible or that it occurs in 2 out of 3 cases. There is a real chance that the developers will spend little or no time on a non-reproducible defect. However, the point of submitting it as a defect is that this builds a history of non-reproducible defects. If a non-reproducible defect occurs often, it may be expected to occur regularly in production as well and so must be solved.

Example

During a system test, the system crashed in a non-reproducible way a couple of times a day. The test team reported this each time in a defect report, but the development team was under pressure of time, paid no attention to this defect, and dismissed it as an instability of the development package used. By reporting the large number of non-reproducible defects and indicating that a negative release advice would result, they were finally persuaded. Within a relatively short time, they found the cause (a programming mistake) and solved the problem.

In more detail

In some cases, such as with performance tests and testing of batch software, it costs a disproportionate amount of time to execute the test again. In those cases, the test to see whether the defect is reproducible is not repeated.

Check for your own mistakes

The tester looks for the possible cause of the defect, first searching for a possible internal cause. The defect may have been caused, for example, by a error in:

- The test specification or (central) starting point
- The test environment or test tools
- The test execution
- The assessment of the test results.

The tester should also allow for the fact that the test results may be distorted by the results of another test by a fellow tester.

If the cause is internal, the tester should solve this, or have it solved, for example by amending the test specification. Subsequently, the tester repeats the test case, whether in the same testing session or in the following one.

Determine the suspected external cause

If the cause does not lie with the testing itself, the search has to widen externally. External causes may be, for example:

- Test basis
- Test object (software, but also documentation such as user manuals or AO procedures)
- Test environment and test tools.

The tester should discover the cause as far as possible, as this would help in determining who should solve the defect and later with discerning quality trends.

Because the tester compares his test case against the test object, there is the inclination in the event of an anomaly to point to the test object as the primary cause. However, the tester should look further: perhaps the cause lies with the test basis? Are there perhaps inconsistencies in the various forms of test basis?

As well as the formal test basis (such as e.g. the functional design or the requirements), the tester regularly uses other, less tangible forms of test basis. These may include the mutual consistency of the screens and user interface, the comparison with previous releases or competing products, or the expectations of the users. See also section 6.5 "Preparation Phase". In describing a defect, it is thus important to indicate which different form of test basis is used, and whether or not the test object corresponds with the formally described test basis, such as the requirements or the functional design. If the test object and the formal test basis correspond, the cause of the defect is an inconsistency between the informal and formal test basis and not the test object.

Example

During an exploratory test, the tester discovers that the position of the operating buttons vary on many screens. Further investigation shows that the cause lies with the screen designs and not with the programming. The tester submits the defect, citing the test basis as the cause.

An external defect is always managed formally. This may be in the form of the defect report and defects procedure described in the sections below. Where reviews are concerned, a less in-depth form may be chosen in which the defects are grouped into a review document and passed to the defect solver; see also Chapter 15 "Evaluation Techniques".

Isolate the cause (optional)

While the suspected cause is often apparent, in the case of a defect in the test object or the test environment, it is often insufficiently clear to the defect solver. The tester therefore looks at surrounding test cases, both the ones that have been carried out successfully and the ones that have not. He also makes variations where necessary to the test case and executes it again, which often results in indicating a more exact cause or allows further specification of the circumstances in which the defect occurs. This step is optional, since it lies on the boundary of how far the tester should go in respect of development in seeking the cause of a defect. It is important to make agreements with the developer on this beforehand. This can avoid discussions on extra analysis work later on, when test execution is on the critical path of the project.

Generalise the defect

If the cause appears sufficiently clear, the tester considers whether there are any other places where the defect could occur. With test object defects, the tester may execute similar test cases in other places in the test object. This should be done in consultation with the other testers, to prevent these tests from disrupting those of his colleagues. With test basis defects, too, the tester looks at similar places in the test basis ("In the functional design, the check for overlapping periods for function A has been wrongly specified. What is the situation as regards other functions that have this same check?").

Example

During a Friday-afternoon test, the parallel changing of the same item by two users in function X produced a defect. Further testing on other functions showed that the multi-user mechanism had been wrongly built in structurally.

The tester need not aim for completeness here, but should be able to provide an impression of the size and severity of the defect. If the defect is structural, it is up to the defect solver to solve it structurally. This step also has the purpose of building up as good a picture as possible of the damage that the defect could cause in production.

Compare with other defects

Before the tester writes the defect report, he looks to see whether the defect has been found previously. This may have been done in the same version of the test object by a fellow tester from within a different test. It is also possible for the defect to have been reported in an earlier release. The tester consults with the defects administration, his fellow testers, the test manager, defects administrator or the intermediary to find out.

There are a number of possibilities:

- The defect was found in the same part of the current release. The defect need not be submitted. The test case in the test execution report may refer to the already existing defect.
- A similar defect has already been found in another part of the current release. The defect should be submitted and should contain a reference to the other defect.
- The defect has already been found in the same part of the previous release. If the old defect was to have been solved for this release, it should be reopened or resubmitted with reference to the old defect, depending on the agreement. If the old defect is still open, the tester need not submit a new one.

Tips

- The test manager, defects administrator or intermediary would be well advised to send frequent overviews of found defects to the testers. This keeps the testers abreast of found defects and prompts them to look within their own test for similar defects. Alternatively, the testers could regularly consult the defects administration concerning found defects.

- It may also be agreed that the testers *do not* look at duplicate defects, to avoid disrupting the progress of the test execution. Checking for duplicate defects is then done by the intermediary, who would be empowered to combine duplicate defects. In cases of doubt, the intermediary should of course consult with the testers involved.

Write a defect report

The tester documents the defect in the defects administration by means of a defect report. In this, he describes the defect and completes the necessary fields of the report; see section 12.3. The description of the defect should be clear, unambiguous and to the point. The tone should remain neutral, and the tester should come across as impartial, being conscious of the fact that he is delivering bad news. Sarcasm, cynicism and exaggeration are obviously to be avoided.

Ideally, the tester makes clear what the consequences are in the event of the defect not being solved, or what the damage might be in production. This determines the chances of the defect being solved after all. In some cases, the damage is very clear ("Invoices are wrongly calculated") and little explanation is necessary; in other cases, it is less clear ("Wrong use of colour in screens") and the tester should clearly indicate what the consequences could be ("Deviation from business standards means that the External Communication department may obstruct release of the application"). Otherwise, it is by no means always possible for the tester to estimate the potential damage, as he lacks the necessary knowledge. The final responsibility for estimating the damage lies with (the representatives of) the users and the client in the defects consultation, which is discussed later. A difficult question is always how much information the description should contain. The guideline for this is that the defect solver should be reasonably able to solve the defect without further explanation from the tester.

> **In more detail**
>
> 'Reasonably' in the above sentence is a difficult concept. The developer would prefer the tester to indicate which statement is wrong in the software. However, this is debugging and comes under the responsibility of the developer. The situation should be avoided in which the tester regularly sits with the programmer to search together for the cause of the defect. This indicates poorly written defects rather than collaborative testing. The tester is at that point no longer involved in testing operations, as the test manager expects of him. If this happens regularly, it will render the plan of the test process unmanageable.

In some cases, the tester finds many small defects in a particular part, e.g. a screen. The inclination is then to keep the administration simple by grouping all these defects into one collective defect report. There is sometimes pressure from the developers to do this, either for the same reason or to make the number of defects appear lower. This is rarely advisable. The chances are that, out of such a collection, a number of defects will be solved in the subsequent release, a number will be solved in the release following, and a number will not be solved at all. Following and monitoring such a collective defect thus becomes an administrative nightmare.

Have it reviewed

Before the defect formally enters the defects procedure, the tester has the report reviewed for completeness, accuracy and tone. This may be done by a fellow tester, the test manager, defects administrator or the intermediary. After processing their comments, the defect is formally submitted. This is performed in accordance with the procedure described in section 12.4.

For more information on handling a defect, see [Black, 2004].

12.3 Defect report

A defect report is more than just a description of the defect. Other details on the defect need to be established (e.g. version of the test object, name of the tester). In order to do this in a structured manner, a defect report is often divided into several 'fields', in which the various details can be laid down that are necessary for the management of the defect and for obtaining meaningful information from the administration. The most important reasons for including separate fields, rather than one large free-text field, are:

- The fields compel the defect information to be entered as completely as possible
- It is possible to create reports on selections of defects.

For example, it is easy to select all the outstanding defects, all the defects with the test environment as a cause or all the defects in a particular part of the test object.

Defect reports are almost impossible now without automated support. This may be a simple spreadsheet or database package, but there are also various freeware or commercial tools available. The latter group of tools often has the advantage that the defects administration is integrated with testware management and plan and progress monitoring. Attention should be paid to the matter of authorisations with the tools. It should not be possible for a developer to change or close a tester's defect, but it should be possible for the developer to add a solution to the defect.

Tip

If testers and other parties are geographically far removed from each other, as is often the case with outsourcing or offshoring, it is advisable to purchase a web-enabled defects tool. This allows all the parties to directly view the current status of the defects administration and significantly eases communication on defects.

In more detail

In some organisations, the defects administration is placed within the incidents registration system of the production systems. While this is possible, such a system contains many more information fields than are necessary for a defect. Sometimes this can be adjusted, but sometimes the testers have to learn to deal with the complex system and ignore all the superfluous fields on the screen. This requires decidedly more training time and involves a greater likelihood of incorrect input of defects than with a standard defects administration.

If the defects are stored in an automated administration, a range of reports can be generated. These are very useful for observing certain trends concerning the quality of the test object and the progress of the test process as early as possible (see sections 5.3.2 and 6.3.2 "Monitoring"). For example, ascertaining that the majority of the defects relates to (a part of) the functional design, or that the defects are concentrated in the screen handling. Such information can be used again for purposes of timely intervention and adopting measures.

The success of the defects administration is determined to a significant degree by the testers' discipline in completing the fields. To this end, the testers should first be sure of the content of each field and how it should be filled in. Particularly in the beginning, there is a need for guidance and monitoring of the completion of defect reports. This is usually a role for the test manager, defects administrator or intermediary, and forms part of the step "Have it reviewed" in section 12.2.

The uniformity and consistency of a defect report can be improved by restricting the possible input values for the fields, instead of using free-text boxes. For example, for the cause of a defect, a choice can be made between test basis, test object or test environment. This prevents all kinds of synonyms from being entered ('software', 'code', 'programming', 'program', 'component') that severely obstruct or render impossible any later selection of cause of defect.

A description is first given below of what a defect report should minimally contain. Subsequently, various recommendations are given as regards expanding on this.

Minimum fields in a defect report

A defect report contains the following fields at minimum:

- *Project or system name*
  The name of the (test) project or of the system under test.
- *Unique identification of the defect*
  A unique identity, usually in the form of a (serial) number of the defect report, for purposes of management and tracking progress.
- *Brief characterisation*
  A brief characterisation of the defect in a limited number of words, maximum one sentence that preferably also clearly indicates the consequence of the defect. This characterisation is printed in defects overviews and makes the defect more communicable.
- *Submitter*
  The name of the individual who has submitted the defect.
- *Identification of phase/test level*
  The phase or test level in which the defect was found, e.g. design,

development, development test, system test, acceptance test or implementation.
- *Severity*

  The severity category proposed by the tester. This categorisation reflects the damage to the business operations. For example:
  - Production-obstructive: involves (high) costs, e.g. because the defect will shut down operations when the system goes into production
  - Severe: (less) costs involved, e.g. because the user has to rework or add items manually
  - Disruptive: little or no costs involved, e.g. chopping of alphanumeric data on the screen or issues relating to user-friendliness
  - Cosmetic: wrong layout (position of fields; colours) which is not a problem for the external client, but can be disturbing to the internal employee.
- *Priority*

  The priority of the solution proposed by the tester. Possible classification:
  - Immediate reworking required, e.g. a patch available within 48 hours that (temporarily) solves the problem. The test process or the current business operations (if it concerns a defect from production) are seriously obstructed
  - Reworking required within the current release. The current process can continue with work-arounds, if necessary, but production should not be saddled with this problem
  - Reworking required eventually, but is only required to be available in a subsequent release. The problem (currently) does not arise in production, or else the damage is slight.

In more detail

At first sight, it does not appear important to make a distinction between severity and priority. These usually run in sync, so that a high level of severity implies a high priority of solving. However, this is not always the case and that is the reason for distinguishing both categories. The following examples illustrate this:

1) With a new release, the internally allocated nomenclature in the software has been amended. The user will not be aware of this, but the automated test suite will suddenly stop working. This is a defect of low severity, but test-obstructive and therefore of very high priority.

2) The user may find a particular defect so disturbing that it may not be allowed to occur in production. This may be, for example, a typo in a letter to a customer. This, too, is a defect of low severity that nevertheless needs to be reworked before going into production.

3) A potentially very serious defect, e.g. the crashing of the application with resulting loss of data, only occurs in very specific circumstances that do not arise often. A work-around is available. The severity level is high, but the priority may be lowered because of the work-around.

- *Cause*
  The tester indicates where he believes the cause to lie, for example:
  TB: test basis (requirements, specifications)
  S: software
  DOC: documentation
  TIS: technical infrastructure.
- *Identification of the test object*
  The (part of the) test object to which the defect relates should be indicated in this column. Parts of the test object may be e.g. object parts, functions or screens. Further detail may be supplied optionally by splitting the field into several fields, so that e.g. subsystem and function can be entered. The version number or version date of the test object is also stated.
- *Test specification*
  A reference to the test case to which the defect relates, with as much relevance to the test basis as possible.
- *Description of the defect*
  The stated defect should be described as far as possible in accordance with the guidelines in section 12.2.
- *Appendices*
  In the event that clarification or proof is necessary, appendices are added. An appendix is in paper form, such as a screen printout or an overview, or a (reference to an) electronic file.
- *Defect solver*
  The name of the individual who is solving the defect, has solved it or has rejected it.
- *Notes on the solution*
  The defect solver explains the chosen solution (or reason for rejection) of the defect.
- *Solved in product*
  Identification of the product, including version number, in which the defect should be solved.
- *Status + date*
  The various stages of the defect's life cycle are managed, up to and including retesting. This is necessary in order to monitor the defect. At its simplest, the status levels of "New", "In process", "Postponed", "Rejected", "Solved", "Retesting" and "Done" are used. The status also displays the date.

Possible extensions

Besides the above fields, various other fields may be added to the defect report. The advantages of including one or more of the fields below are better management and more insight into the quality and trends. The disadvantages are the extra administration and complexity. Experience shows that the advantages far outweigh the disadvantages in medium-sized and big tests or in cases in which a lot of communication on the defects between various parties is necessary.

- *Identification of the test environment*
  The test environment used, with identification of the starting situation used.
- *Identification of the test basis*
  The test basis used: name of the test basis document, including version number, supplemented if necessary with specific-requirement number.
- *Provisional severity category*
  Provisional: the severity category proposed by the tester.
- *Provisional priority*
  Provisional: the priority of solution proposed by the tester.
- *Provisional cause*
  Provisional: the cause of the defect as estimated by the tester.
- *Quality characteristic*
  The quality characteristic established by the tester, to which the defect relates.

In connection with the solution:
- *Definitive severity*
  The definite category of severity as determined by the defects consultation.
- *Definitive priority*
  The definite priority of solution as determined by the defects consultation.
- *Definitive cause*
  The definite cause of the defect as determined by the defects consultation. Besides the categories mentioned for the minimum defect report, the category of "Testing" is added here.
- *Deadline or release for required solution*
  A date or product release is set, by which the defect should be solved.

In connection with retesting:
- *Retester*
  The name of the tester who carries out the retest.
- *Identification of the test environment*
  The test environment used, with identification of the starting point used.
- *Identification of test basis*
  The test basis used: name of the test basis document, including version number, if necessary supplemented with specific-requirement number.
- *Identification of test object*
  The (part of the) test object that was retested. The version number or version date of the test object is also stated.

In addition, test, defects consultation, retest and comments fields may be added, with which extra information may be optionally supplied, e.g. on corresponding defects or the identification of the change proposal by which the handling of the defect is brought within another procedure.

12.4   Procedure

When a defect is taken into the administration, it enters the defects procedure.

Progress of the solving of defects is discussed in a periodic defects consultation. During the preparation and specifying of tests, this consultation is usually held once or twice a week. During test execution, it often increases to once a day. Participants in the consultation are representatives of the parties who submit and/or deal with the defects. From within the testing, this is the test manager, defects administrator or the intermediary. Sometimes a tester is invited to explain a defect. Other parties may be the user organisation, functional management, system development and system management. The defects consultation is also sometimes combined with the handling of the change proposals in, for example, a Change Control Board.

> **Tips**
>
> • Conference call
>   If the parties are spread over different locations (around the world), this is no reason not to carry out a defects consultation. Conference calls or video conferencing facilitate this.
> • Ensure that each participant is well informed of how the defects procedure works and what his or her tasks and responsibilities are. For example, who updates the status of the defects following the defects consultation?

In order of priority, the participants discuss each new defect and decide whether it should be solved, and if so, by whom. In this consultation, the correctness, cause, priority and severity of the defects, as well as the costs of solving them, are discussed. A familiar humorous reaction of developers in this connection is "It's a feature, not a bug". The representative of the testing also has the job of ensuring that the importance of a defect (severity and priority) becomes sufficiently clear to all the parties. The consultation may also request the submitter of the defect to provide additional information or carry out further investigation. The participants in the consultation determine, after carrying out the necessary discussions, the definitive values for cause, priority and severity of a defect.

If the defects consultation agrees that it is a valid defect and the costs of solving it are acceptable, the defect is assigned to a defect solver. If the consultation agrees that it is not a valid defect or that the costs, lead-time or regression risks of solving it are too high, it is rejected. A valid defect that is nevertheless rejected is also known as a 'known error'. In the event of rejection, it may be decided to submit the defect via another channel as a formal change proposal or to devise a procedural solution. Examples of procedural solutions are notes in the help text, instructions to the helpdesk assistants or amendment to the AO procedures. If the consultation does not agree, then the defect is escalated to the decision forum. Representatives of the parties with decision-making powers sit in this forum, such as the client and project manager, who decide on whether or not (and when) the defect is to be solved. The decision forum is not necessarily an independent consultation, but is often the project management meeting or the project board meeting.

The diagram below shows the relationship between the defects consultation and decision forum:

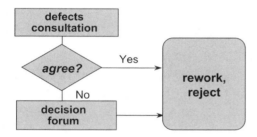

Figure 12.1: Defects procedure

The defect solver investigates the defect and solves it. Or it may emerge that the defect has been incorrectly identified as such (a testing mistake) or should be handled by another defect solver. In the latter cases, the defect goes back for discussion. If it is solved, it can be transferred at any time to the test environment to be (re)tested. The tester, preferably the original submitter, carries out the test and checks whether the defect is solved. If so, the defect is closed. If it appears that the defect is not (adequately) solved, then its status is reset and it again undergoes the defects procedure. The retesting of the defect is an essential step in order to be able to close it. It is unacceptable for the defect solver to solve the defect, test it himself and then close it. Checking whether the defect is solved is the task of the submitter (or his replacement).

Figure 12.2 shows the life cycle of a defect according to the above procedure, in which the texts in the rectangles show the status of the defect. The diamonds refer to the actors. The dotted line from "Postponed" to "Allocated" means that the defect is postponed in the current release, but should be solved in a future release.

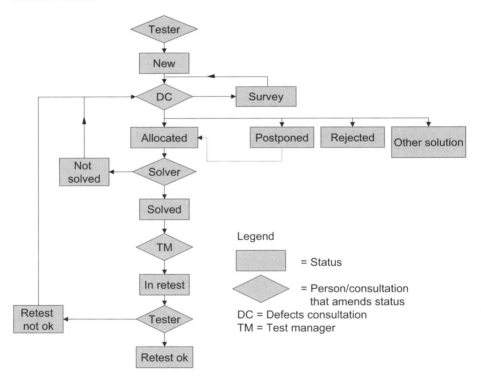

Figure 12.2: Life cycle of a defect

13 Metrics

13.1 Introduction

Quite often, test managers are expected to answer such questions as:
- Why does testing take so long?
- Why has the test process not been completed yet?
- How many defects can I still expect during production?
- How many re-tests are still required?
- When can testing be stopped?
- When will the test team start the execution of the test?
- Tell me what exactly you are up to!
- What is the quality of the system that you have tested?
- When can I start production?
- How can it be that the previous test project was much faster?
- What did you actually test?
- How many defects have been found and what is their status?

Answering these types of questions with well-founded, factually based answers is not easy. Most questions can be answered with reference to the periodic reports as described in Section 6.3.3 "Reporting". Such reports can only be created on the basis of correctly recorded relevant data, which is converted into information and then used to answer the above-mentioned questions.

Metrics on the quality of the test object and the progress of the test process are of great importance to the test process. They are used to manage the test process, to substantiate test advice and also to compare systems or test processes with each other. Metrics are important for improving the test process, in assessing the consequences of particular improvement measures by comparing data before and after the measures were adopted.

To summarise, a test manager should record a number of items in order to be able to pass well-founded judgement on the quality of the object under test as well as on the quality of the test process itself. The following sections describe a structured approach for arriving at a set of test metrics.

13.2   GQM method in six steps

There are various ways of arriving at a particular set of metrics. The most common is the Goal-Question-Metric (GQM) method [Basili, 1994]). This is a top-down method in which one or more goals are formulated. For example: what information should I collect in order to answer those questions posed in the introduction? These goals include questions that constitute the basis for the metrics. The collected metrics should provide the answers to those questions, and the answers will indicate among other things whether the goal has been achieved or not. The summary of the GQM method described below focuses in particular on the test aspect. The GQM process is described in six steps. This is a concise description that includes only those items that are relevant to the test manager. For a more detailed description, please refer to the aforementioned GQM literature.

Step 1: Defining the goals
Measuring purely for the sake of measuring is pointless. Clear and realistic goals should be set beforehand. We distinguish two types of goals:
- Knowledge goals (knowing where we are now). These goals are expressed in words such as evaluate, predict, or monitor. For example, "Evaluate how many hours are actually spent on re-testing" or "Monitor the test coverage". The goal here is to gain insight.
- Improvement goals (where do we want to go). These goals are expressed in words such as increase, decrease, improve, or achieve. Setting such goals suggests that we know there are shortcomings in the present test process or the present environment and that we want to improve these.

An example of such an improvement goal is obtaining a 20% saving on the number of testing hours at a constant test coverage within a period of 18 months.
In order to ascertain this, the following two knowledge goals should be aimed at:
- Insight into the total number of testing hours per project.
- Insight into the achieved test coverage per project.

It is important to investigate whether the goals and the (test) maturity of the organisation match. It is pointless to aim at achieving a certain test coverage if the necessary resources (knowledge, time and tools) are not available.

Example: Knowing where we are now.

> Goal: Provide insight into the quality of the test object

Step 2: Asking questions per goal

For each goal, several questions have to be asked. The questions are formulated in such a way that they act as a specification of a metric. It can also be asked, for each question, who is responsible for the test metrics supplied. From the above goal, various questions can be derived. We will limit the number of questions in this example to three.

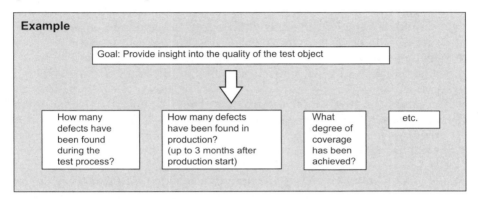

Step 3: From questions to metrics

The relevant metrics are derived from the questions, and form the full set of metrics, gathered during the test process.

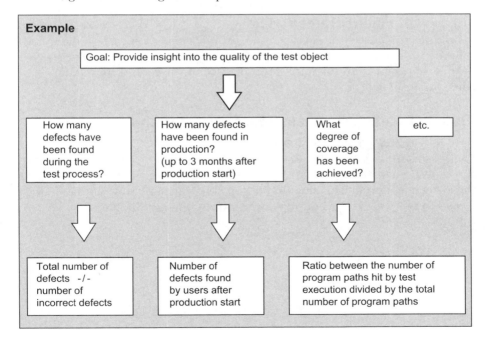

By asking the right questions, we arrive at the correct set of metrics for a certain goal. It is important to define and specify each metric correctly. For example, what exactly is a defect?

Step 4: Data collection and analysis

During the test process a variety of data is collected. One way of keeping things simple is to use forms/templates (if possible in electronic form). The data should be complete and easy to interpret. In the design of these forms, attention should be paid to the following points:

- Which metrics are collected on the same form.
- Validation: how easy is it to check whether the data is complete and correct.
- Traceability: forms supplied with the date, project ID, configuration management data, data collector, etc. Take into consideration that it is sometimes necessary to preserve this data for a long time.
- Possibility of electronic processing.

As soon as the data is collected, it should be analysed. At this point it is still possible to make corrections. Waiting too long decreases the chance of restoring the data. Bear in mind possibilities, for example, of booking time with the incorrect activity code.

Step 5: Presentation and distribution of the measurement data

The collected measurements are used both in the test reports on the quality of the product under test and in those on the test process. Proper feedback is also of importance to the motivation of those involved and the validation of the measured data.

Step 6: Relating the measurement data to the questions and goals

This last step is used to investigate to what extent the indicators (answers to the questions) offer sufficient insight into the matter of whether the goals have been achieved. This situation may be the starting point for a new GQM cycle. In this way, we are continually improving the test process.

13.3   Hints and tips

When metrics are being collected, the test manager should take the following issues into account:
- Start with a limited set of metrics and build it up slowly.
- Keep the metrics simple. The definition should appeal to the intuition of those involved. For example, try to avoid the use of a variety of formulas. The more complicated the formulas, the more difficult they are to interpret.
- Choose metrics that are relatively simple to collect and easily accepted. The more difficult it is to collect data, the greater the chance that it will not be accepted.
- Collect data electronically as much as possible. This is the quickest way of data collection and avoids the introduction of manual errors into the data set.
- Keep an eye on the motivation of the testers to record accurately. In the case of time registration, for example, it sometimes happens that incorrect (read: not yet fully booked) codes are used.
- Avoid complicated statistical techniques and models during presentations. Allow the type of presentation to depend on the data presented (tables, diagrams, pie charts, etc.).
- Provide feedback to the testers as quickly as possible. Show them what you do with the information.

13.4   Practical starting set of test metrics

Below is an indication of what test managers embarking on a "metrics programme" should start with. The metrics set described is a starting set that can be used in practice with little cost and effort. Section 6.3.3 "Reporting" lists a number of more specific test statistics and progress reports.
- Registration of hours, using activity codes. Register the following for each tester: date, project, TMap phase, activity and number of hours. A "Comments" field is recommended, making it possible to check whether the data has been entered correctly. Registering the hours in this way enables you to obtain insight into the time spent on each TMap phase (see figure 13.1). It also enables the client to check the progress of the test process. It is advisable to compile this type of timesheet on a weekly basis for projects that last up to three or four months. For projects that last longer than half a year, this can be done on a fortnightly basis. For projects that last longer than a year, it is best to report on a monthly basis.
- Collect data about the test deliverables (test plans, test scripts, etc.), the test basis and test object. Record the following: document name, delivery date, TMap phase upon delivery, version and a characteristic that says something

about the quantity. This may be the number of test cases for the test scripts, or the number of pages for the other documents. For the test basis, the number of user requirements can be taken as a quantity characteristic.

■ Report on the progress of the defects. Chapter 12 "Defects management" describes how a defect administration can be set up. An example of this type of reporting is shown in figure 13.2.:

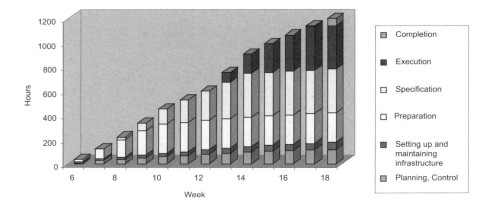

Figure 13.1: Example of hours spent on test process, per TMap phase

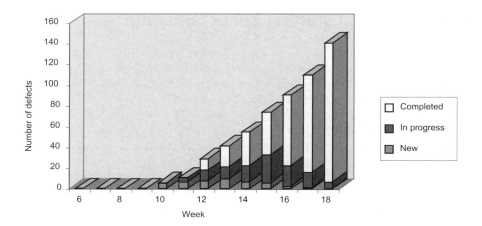

Figure 13.2: Example of a progress overview of defects

These elementary metrics (hours, documents and defects) can be used to assess the productivity of the test process. Note that this productivity should be seen in relation to the required effort and size of the test project. Example:

in the first ten hours of testing we may find more defects per hour than in 400 hours of further testing, simply because the first defects are found more quickly than the last ones.

The following metrics regarding productivity can be derived from this elementary set:
- number of defects per hour (and per hour of test execution)
- number of test cases carried out per hour
- number of specified test scripts per hour (and per hour of test specification)
- number of defects per test script
- ratio of hours spent over the TMap phases.

If the number of function points or the number of 'kilo lines of code' (KLOC) of the object under test is known, the following numbers can be calculated:
- number of test hours per function point (or KLOC)
- number of defects per function point (or KLOC)
- number of test cases per function point (or KLOC).

For the test basis we can establish the following metrics:
- number of test hours per page of the test basis
- number of defects per page of the test basis
- number of test cases per page of the test basis
- number of pages of the test basis per function point.

When it is known how many defects occur in production during the first three months, the following metric can be determined:
- Defect-detection effectiveness of a test level: number of found defects in a test level divided by the total number of defects present. This metric is also called the Defect Detection Percentage (DDP). In calculating the DDP, the following assumptions are applied:
  - all the defects are included in the calculation
  - the weighed severity of the defects is not included in the calculation
  - after the first three months of the system being in production, barely any defects are present in the system.

The DDP can be calculated both per test level and overall. The DDP per test level is calculated by dividing the number of found defects from the relevant test level by the sum of this number of found defects and the number of found defects from the subsequent test level(s) and/or the first three months of production. The overall DDP is calculated by dividing the total number of found defects (from all the test levels together) by the sum of this number of found defects and the found defects from the first three months of production.

Example

DDP calculations

Test level	Found defects
System test (ST)	100
Acceptance test (AT)	60
3 Months of production	40

DDP ST (after the AT is carried out)   : (100   /   100+60   ) = 63%
DDP ST (after 3 months of production) : (100   /   100+60+40) = 50%
DDP AT (after 3 months of production) : (60   /   60+40   ) = 60%
DDP overall   : (100+60 /   100+60+40) = 80%

Some causes of a high or low DDP may be:
- High DDP
  - the tests have been carried out very accurately
  - the system has not yet been used much
  - the subsequent test level was not carried out accurately.
- Low DDP
  - the tests have not been carried out accurately
  - the test basis was not right, consequently nor were the tests derived from it
  - the quality of the test object was wrong (containing too many defects to be found during the time available)
  - the testing time has been shortened.

By recording the above-mentioned metrics, supplemented here and there with particular items, we arrive at the following list of metrics.

13.5   Metrics list

In the following (non-exhaustive) list of metrics, a number of commonly used metrics are mentioned, which can be used as indicators for pronouncing on the quality of the object under test or for measuring the quality of the test process and comparing against the organisation's standard. All the indicators can of course also be used in the report to the client:
- *Number of defects found*
  The ratio between the number of defects found and the size of the system per unit of testing time.
- *Executed instructions*
  Ratio between the number of tested program instructions and the total

number of program instructions. Tools that can produce such metrics are available.

■ *Number of tests*
Ratio between the number of tests and the size of the system (for example expressed in function points). This indicates how many tests are necessary in order to test a part.

■ *Number of tested paths*
Ratio between the tested and the total number of logical paths present.

■ *Number of defects during production*
This gives an indication of the number of defects not found during the test process.

■ *Defect detection effectiveness*
The total number of defects found during testing, divided by the total number of defects – estimated partly on the basis of production data.

■ *Test costs*
Ratio between the test costs and the total development costs. A prior definition of the various costs is essential.

■ *Cost per detected defect*
Total test cost divided by the number of defects found.

■ *Budget utilisation*
Ratio between the budget and the actual cost of testing.

■ *Test efficiency*
The number of required tests versus the number of defects found.

■ *Degree of automation of testing*
Ratio between the number of tests carried out manually and the number of tests carried out automatically.

■ *Number of defects found (relative)*
The ratio between the number of defects found and the size of the system (in function points or KLOC) per unit of testing time.

■ *Defects as a result of modifications that are not tested*
Defects because of modifications that are not tested, as a part of the total number of defects arising as a result of changes.

■ *Defects after tested modifications*
Defects because of modifications that are tested, as a part of the total number of defects arising as a result of changes.

■ *Savings of the test*
Indicates how much has been saved by carrying out the test. In other words, what would the losses have amounted to if the test had not been carried out?

14   Test design techniques

14.1   Introduction

Why test design techniques?

The aim of testing is to provide advice on quality and risks. To do this, the tester needs to collect information about the system behaviour. The most important means to achieve this is to execute test cases. The big questions in this context are: 'Which test cases? How many? And how do we get these test cases?' Test design techniques play an important part in answering these questions.

> **Definition**
>
> A test design technique is a standardised method to derive, from a specific test basis, test cases that realise a specific coverage.

Designing test cases is the vital link between the test strategy and the concrete test cases that are used to implement that test strategy. This is realised in the context of test assignment to test cases (see section 6.2 'Phase Planning'), the theme of which can be outlined as follows (see figure 14.1):

- It is not possible to test everything within the confines of the preconditions of time and costs defined in the *job specification*. Choices will have to be made as to the lengths one wishes to go to in testing.
- The more important something is, the more intensive the tests required. Something is very important if its failure would result in severe damage to the business or client. This is mapped by means of a *risk analysis*.
- A *test strategy* is used to create an overview of what will be tested and how intensively, such that the risks defined earlier are covered as adequately as possible.
- The decisions concerning intensive and less intensive testing are translated to concrete statements about the targeted *coverage*.
- Depending on the available *test basis*, among other things, appropriate *test design techniques* are selected to achieve said coverage.
- The implementation of these techniques eventually results in the set of *test cases* that is needed to execute the test assignment satisfactorily.

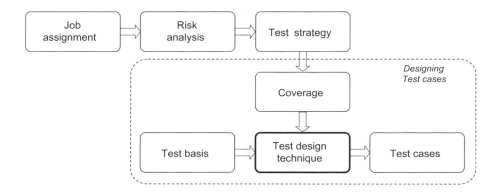

Figure 14.1: Test design techniques within the context of 'assignment definition' to 'test cases'.

Importance of test design techniques

You will find several arguments below that indicate the importance and benefits of using test design techniques and their definition in the test specifications.

- It provides a justified elaboration of the test strategy: the agreed coverage in the agreed place
- Because a test design technique focuses on achieving a specific coverage to detect specific types of defect (e.g. in the interfaces, the input checks or the processing), such defects are detected more effectively then by specifying ad hoc test cases
- The tests are reproducible because the order and content of the test execution are described in detail
- The standardised method ensures that the test process is independent of the individual who specifies and executes the test cases
- The standardised method ensures that the test specifications are transferable and maintainable
- It becomes easier to plan and manage the test process because the processes of test specification and execution can be split up into clearly definable blocks.

Reading guide

The remainder of this chapter is structured as follows:

Section 14.2 discusses several essential concepts relating to test design techniques in greater detail. It explains the terms 'test situation', 'test case' and 'test script' and their interrelationships. It then details the phenomenon of 'coverage' and explains why there are multiple types of coverage and therefore the need for multiple test design techniques.

Section 14.3 then provides an overview of the main types of coverage, related to the type of information available in the test basis. The associated basic techniques are explained to achieve the required coverage type.

Finally section 14.4 describes a number of test design techniques, including examples. Where a test design technique uses one or more basic techniques, these are not described every time. Please refer to section 14.3 for more information. It is a varied set of test design techniques with which the tester can tackle a broad range of real-life situations.

Readers with a purely pragmatic perspective, who are interested exclusively in learning some specific test design techniques, may initially wish to limit their reading to section 14.4. They will be referred automatically to section 14.3 for an explanation of the basic techniques required for the specific test design technique.

Readers who are also interested in the principles underpinning test design and the wider range of options for designing test cases will want to examine sections 14.2 and 14.3 as well.

14.2 Essential test design concepts

14.2.1 Test situation, test case and test script

In the ideal case, testing would give us the certainty that the system behaved as required or desired *under all circumstances*. In reality, not every circumstance can be tested – only a subset that is a direct result of the decisions and choices made during the test design phase.

The test design leads to a hierarchical structure of test situations – test cases – test scripts. These terms are discussed in detail further on in this section. The relationship between the concepts is shown in figure 14.2 and can be summarised as follows:

- Every test situation occurs in at least 1 test case
- A logical test case covers 1 or more test situations
- Every logical test case is worked out concretely into 1 physical test case
- Every physical test case occurs in 1 test script.

The figure on the next page also shows the distinction between the logical and physical parts of the test design:

The *logical test design* consists of the test situations and the logical test cases. This is the part that demonstrates that the required coverage is achieved, thereby complying with the test strategy.

The *physical test design* consists of the concretely created physical test cases, laid down in test scripts. This guarantees a thorough preparation of the 'Execution' phase. The physical creation of test cases therefore adds nothing to the thoroughness of the test.

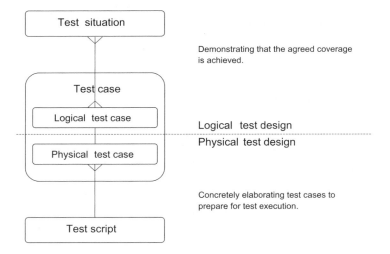

Figure 14.2: Relationships between the terms test situation – test case – test script.

Test situations

Definition

A test situation is an isolated condition under which the test object displays a specific behaviour that needs to be tested.

For example:
'an order of more than 1 book'
Another test situation that is closely related would be:
'an order of exactly 1 book'
And if, for instance, a discount on an order would not be offered until the order price exceeds a specific threshold value, the following test situations would be logical:
'order price above threshold value', and
'order price below threshold value'

The targeted **coverage** and the test design technique chosen to achieve it determine which test situations are defined exactly.

Test cases

Definition

A test case is used to examine whether the system displays the desired behaviour under specific circumstances.

A test case must therefore contain all of the ingredients to cause that system behaviour and determine whether or not it is correct. A well-known way to describe system behaviour is 'Input → Processing → Output'. To be able to test the system behaviour, a test case must match this perfectly and 'embrace' it, as it were (see figure 14.3). Therefore the following elements must be recognisable in *every* test case regardless of the test design technique used:

- Initial situation
  This covers everything that is needed to prepare the system for receiving the required **input**. This includes not only the data that are needed for the processing, but also the condition in which the system and its environment must be. For instance, one might think of setting a specific system date, or running specific week and month batches that bring the system to a specific status.

- Actions
  This means all of the activities that must be executed to activate the system to the **processing**. It might be a simple command ('Run …') or entering specific data on a screen. But it can also be a complex sequence of entering parameters, activating a specific function, manipulating other data, starting up another function, etc.

- Predicted result
  This covers all of the results that the tester must check to establish whether the system behaviour conforms to the expectations. Often, predicted result is incorrectly thought to be limited to the output that appears on screen or is stored in databases. But the system can also produce **output** that is transmitted to other systems or peripheral equipment. Furthermore, more than just output data may have to be checked to established that the system is working correctly. For instance: 'How quickly should the output appear?', 'What is the maximum allowed memory load and is it released afterwards?', or 'Should the system produce interim signals or messages, such as the hourglass or beeps?'

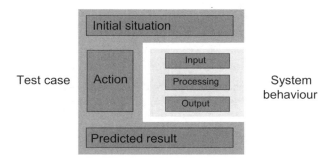

Figure 14.3: Generic structure of a test case in relation to the system behaviour to be tested.

In other words, executing a test case roughly goes through the following steps: 'Prepare this → Do this → Check that.' Contrary to a test situation – which addresses an isolated aspect – a test case is a *complete unit* that can be executed as a separate test.

When designing test cases, we first create *logical test cases* that are then worked out into *physical test cases*. Both terms are explained in further detail below.

Logical test cases

Definition

A logical test case describes, in logical terms, the circumstances in which the system behaviour is examined by indicating which test situations are covered by the test case.

Take, for instance, the 4 test situations described earlier about ordering books and obtaining a possible discount:
   order of more than 1 book (A1)
   order of exactly 1 book (A2)
   order price above threshold value (B1)
   order price below threshold value (B2)
These test situations are covered by, for instance, the following 2 logical test cases:
• TC-1: Order for more than 1 book, with the order price remaining below the threshold value.
• TC-2: Order for 1 book, with the order price above the threshold value.

Clearly this small, simple example is very trivial. And it can probably be described much more practically and compactly. (E.g. TC-1 = A1+B2) But the point is that the logical test cases show, in a clearly structured manner:
- What the test situations are
- That the set of test cases covers all defined test situations.

Physical test cases

Definition

A physical test case is the concrete elaboration of a logical test case, with choices having been made for the values of all required the input and settings of the environmental factors.

The physical test case describes in practical terms what has to be done. The 3 basic elements of a test case are recognisable: What needs to be prepared? (Initial situation) What does the tester have to do? (Action) What is the expected result? (Predicted result).

For instance, the 2 logical test cases described above can be rendered physical as follows:

Initial situation (valid for both test cases):

Threshold price = € 50.00
discount   = 10%
price book-01 = € 18.50
price book-02 = € 25.50
price book-03 = € 65.00

TC-1:
Action: Order book-01 and book-02
Predicted result: No discount will be given.
                  Order price = € 44.00

TC-2:
Action: Order book-03
Predicted result: A 10% discount will be given.
                  Order price = € 58.50 (€ 65.00 - € 6.50)

The step from logical to physical test case is more than just inserting concrete values. It is also a step from 'theoretical' to 'practical'. In this step, the tester needs to look beyond the system specifications on which the logical test cases were based and ask himself: 'Do I now know everything I need to execute this test case in the Execution phase?' For instance:

- In the *initial situation:*
  Is the tester allowed to determine himself what data are entered in the test database? Or is use of existing test databases required?
- In the *predicted result*:
  How will it be established that the requirements are complied with? Is it sufficient that the datum appears on screen correctly, or must it (also) be retrieved from the database via a Read function?

Choices in the elaboration of the physical test design
The elaboration of the logical test design into a physical test design is an investment made in the Specification phase – outside the project's critical path – to result in a saving in the Execution phase, which is on the critical path. The test organisation needs to decide:

- How far the tester must go in the physical elaboration of his test cases.
  Two extremes exist in this respect:
  In the extreme situation, the test case is not worked out concretely, but remains described in abstract terms. It is left to the tester to work out the correct concrete content 'on site' when the test is executed. In the other extreme, it is described to the lowest level of detail what the tester needs to do exactly: Which value should be where on the screen and which key then needs to be pressed.

- In what form the result must be registered.
  The most common ways to register test cases and test scripts are: text document, spreadsheet, database, in a test management tool. It might also be a mix. For example: the logical test design (test situations and logical test cases) is described in a text document while a spreadsheet elaborating the physical test cases is created for each individual test script.

Some considerations in the choice as to in how far the test cases need to be elaborated physically:
- Knowledge and experience of the testers.
  This mainly involves expertise on the subject matter and knowledge about how the automated system works. The less knowledge and experience, the more the tester needs to be told what to do exactly when executing the test.
- Time pressure in the Execution phase.
  The less the test cases are elaborated and prepared concretely in advance, the more 'time to think' the tester needs when executing the test (and vice versa). Normally, the Execution phase is on the critical path of the project. The higher the time pressure in that phase, the greater the necessity to have to do as little as possible in this phase – and therefore to have prepared the maximum properly.
- Transferability to other testers.
  A tester who has himself designed the test cases will require less comprehensive information to know exactly how to execute the test. However, if it must be possible for the test to be executed by people who were not involved in the creation of the test cases, the physical test cases and test scripts must contain more extensive information.

Some considerations when selecting in what form the result is to be registered:
- Availability of tools and knowledge about their use.
  This is a trivial point. It is no use prescribing the form in which the test cases and test scripts need to be registered if the testers do not have access to the tool required or do not know how to use it.
- Transferability to other environments.
  This is an important consideration if there are several environments on which the test products must be installed and used. Text documents are easily exported to other environments. Spreadsheets and databases are a bit more difficult. And transferring test products embedded in a test management tool often requires having an identical installation of exactly the same tool in the other environment.
- Interface with automated test execution.
  In case of far-reaching test automation, the tests are executed by an automated test suite that uses a specific test tool (see section 8.5.3

"Types of test tools"). This means that the physical test cases and test scripts must be recorded in a way that *that tool can read*. Often it is decided to register in spreadsheets, databases or the tool itself.

Test scripts

> **Definition**
>
> In a test script, multiple physical test cases are combined to be able to execute them in an efficient and simple manner.

There are no strict rules that say which test cases must be combined in a test script or how many test scripts are allowed. The tester has full freedom provided that the test scripts together contain all the test cases. The reasons to combine specific test cases into one test script are of a purely practical nature. For example:

- They use the same initial situation
- The same time-consuming actions must be executed for all test cases
- They all have to do with the same exceptional situation. For example: the test script contains all test cases about clients abroad
- There are timeline-dependent test cases. Before specific test cases can be executed, other test cases must have been completed first.

From a test-management perspective, test scripts are excellent, manageable units. Planned hours can be linked to each test script. Progress can be measured and reported in terms of test scripts.

14.2.2 Coverage, coverage type and coverage ratio

There are a lot of definitions relating to coverage. The definition below is a simple one, but it reflects the essence perfectly well:

> **Definition**
>
> Coverage is the ratio between that which can be tested and that which is tested with the test set.

In other words, coverage says something about how many of 'all possibilities that can be tested' are actually tested. This means that there are 2 phenomena that together determine the coverage (see 14.4):

- Which possibilities are distinguished?
  This is termed **coverage type**. It indicates what type of possibilities are involved. These are subsequently elaborated into the required *test situations*.

For instance, it is possible to look at the possible combinations of paths in an algorithm. But in that same algorithm, you can also look at the possibilities to cover one outcome or the other within each decision point. These are 2 different forms of coverage (i.e. 'coverage types').

> **Definition**
>
> Coverage type is the form in which the covering of test situations deducible from the test basis, is expressed.

- How many of these possibilities are tested?
  This is called the **coverage ratio** and is generally expressed as a percentage. It shows which part of all of the alternatives have actually been tested. The number (percentage) does not have meaning until it is clear which possibilities are involved, i.e. when it is associated with the coverage type.

> **Definition**
>
> Coverage ratio is the percentage of test situations, as defined by the coverage type, that is covered by the test.

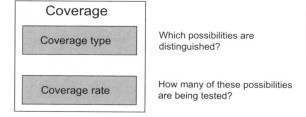

Figure 14.4: Components of the concept of 'coverage'.

This chapter discusses the how and why of coverage, coverage type and coverage ratio in detail. It first discusses why coverage is a useful and practical concept for testers. It then explains, using a comprehensive example, why it is necessary to distinguish several types of coverage. Finally, it describes how test design techniques constitute the link between test cases and the coverage they achieve.

Why coverage?

'Coverage' is a useful concept that helps testers with complex questions, such as:

- Since it is impossible to test everything and we are therefore forced to test only a subset of all of the possibilities, what is the best subset?
- What is the difference between 'elementary testing' and 'thorough testing'? What does it mean concretely for the test cases we need for this?

Coverage has everything to do with the wish to find the most possible defects with the fewest possible test cases. Instead of simply testing 'just any' subset of options, we aim to compile a set of test cases that create *the greatest possible change* of finding the defects that are there.

We can *never be certain* that all defects have been found or even that 60% of all defects has been found. After all, we do not know how many defects there actually are. What we can demonstrate, is the coverage realised by the test. And this confers a certain level of *confidence* that the chance of any defects remaining in the tested system is small. In summary: the higher the coverage realised, the smaller the chance that any unknown defects remain in the system.

The decision to 'test more thoroughly' concretely translates to a decision to achieve more extensive coverage. In principle, there are 3 options in this respect:
- A more thorough coverage type
- Multiple coverage types
- A higher coverage ratio of a specific coverage type.

One type of coverage or more?

It should be clear by now that a statement like 'I want to test with a 75% coverage ratio' does not say much, for the following reasons:
- What type of coverage are we talking about?
- Why does 25% (and which) not require coverage? (In other words: Why not simply cover 100%?)

This section will discuss these issues in greater detail and explain
- that we cannot talk about *the* coverage, but talk of many forms of coverage (i.e. 'coverage types')
- that the choice for more thorough testing must be worked out primarily with the choice for another coverage type
- that the use of a coverage type implies that one aims for a coverage ratio of 100%
- that generally speaking, the various coverage types CANNOT be compared in terms of 'X is better than Y'. Different coverage types tend to supplement rather than replace each other.

To explain this, we will use the following example about a system to order books via the Internet. It describes only a fraction of what such a system could do in reality, but it will suffice for our purposes.

Example

The chart below describes the process to order books in our example system. We have used an intuitive diagram technique with decision points (A, B, and C) and paths (1 through 7). In reality a lot is happening on the paths of the process, but this is not relevant to the example. It is mainly about the fact that the process includes *different* possibilities and the question which different aspects should or can be tested.

The ordering process looks like this. The numbers and letters in parentheses refer to the decision points and paths in the diagram:

After the general details of the ordering party are entered (1), it is decided (A) whether to continue with an existing order (2) or initiate a new order (3). An order may contain more than one book.

After the required books are ordered, it is decided (B) whether to continue to payment (4) or change the order by cancelling ordered books (5), after which the order can continue.

When determining the final price, it is checked if the customer is a 'good customer' (C) and is entitled to extra discount (6) or not (7).

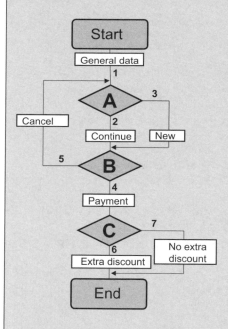

Figure 14.5: Chart of the process 'ordering books'.

Discussion on test cases and coverage ratio

Say that the system component described above requires **thorough** testing. What does that mean exactly? Which test cases are required?

A test case runs through the process to be tested from start to end, covering various decision points and going through different paths. For a thorough test, we must look for a set of test cases that responds to the objective in the best possible way: 'If there is a defect in the process, then this set of test cases will find it.'

Now look at the following set of 2 test cases, which are described by a series of numbers that shows which paths are followed consecutively:

TC-1 = 1 2 5 3 4 6
TC-2 = 1 3 4 7

Thanks to the loop in the chart, test case TC-1 covers virtually all of the paths. Only path 7 is not covered. This is why TC-2 has been added.

So do these 2 test cases achieve a coverage ratio of 100%? If a coverage tool were used to measure the coverage, it would indeed report that 100% coverage is achieved. Still, many testers would say that these 2 test cases test far from everything... that many defects may exist in the system that would slip through these test cases. Are they right? Absolutely! For instance, look at this:

Say that there is a defect in the system in path 5. When an ordered book is cancelled, a related discount must be cancelled as well – but the system *incorrectly retains the discount.*

Is this defect found with the set of 2 test cases described above? No! While test case TC-1 does cover path 5 and will therefore receive an excessive discount, the latter then disappears when the test case continues through path 3 and starts a new order from scratch with discount=0. This defect *would* be found with a test case that continues with path 2 after completing path 5. In this case, the same order would be continued and the excessive discount would be visible on payment.

In other words, this is a defect type that does not 'occur in a path' randomly, but occurs only in case of a special combination of 2 successive paths. So the 2 test cases TC-1 and TC-2 do have a coverage ratio of 100% in the sense of 'covering all paths', but they do not cover 'all combinations of 2 successive paths'. For a set of test cases that does cover this, we speak of achieving 'test depth level 2'.

> Test depth level 2 = the certainty that all combinations of 2 successive paths are covered.

For '100% of test depth level 2', path combinations 2-4 and 3-5 must also be covered. This can be achieved by adding the following test case:

TC-3 = 1 3 5 2 4 7

(Please note that this eliminates the need for test case TC-2.)

It is a very common phenomenon that paths affect each other, so that defects do not occur until paths are combined in certain ways. This influence may be functional (such as in the above example of excessive discount), but it may also be technical. An example of the latter is:

When cancelling an earlier discount in path 5, a buffer overflow occurs, overwriting the memory location of the variable 'extra discount'. When a test case going through path 5 then runs through path 7 (where no extra discount is given), this defect will not be noticeable. However, if the test case would continue with path 6, a bizarre extra discount would be allocated or the application might even crash.

Naturally there may also be defects that do not occur unless a specific combination of 3 successive paths is followed. This defect type cannot be found *for certain* unless the set of test cases achieves test depth level 3. And so on... The higher the test level achieved, the greater the certainty that the more *exceptional* defects are found.

The concept of 'test depth level' and its application is explained in greater detail in the section on 'Path coverage'.

So is this it: The higher the test depth level, the more thorough the test? The maximum test depth level is 'infinite', but this is clearly not practically feasible. But could one (theoretically) conclude that with test depth level 'infinite' one will find all defects? No! Not even that! The example below shows a defect that cannot be found with certainty even with a test set of test depth level 'infinite'. And the defect described is not even farfetched:

A 'good customer' is given an extra discount. This is established in decision point C, where the system checks whether the customer has ordered a lot of books or for a high amount. More precisely:

IF (number of books > 8 OR amount ≥ €250) THEN extra discount

There are therefore 4 possible situations in which extra discount will or will not be given. These are shown below.

number of books	> 8 ; amount	≥ 250 →	YES extra discount	(1)
	>	<	YES	(2)
	≤	≥	YES	(3)
	≤	<	NO	(4)

Say there is a defect in the system, so that you do not get the extra discount in situation (3). So, if you order few books but they are expensive, you will not get the discount – incorrectly.

The problem described above (situation 3) occurs in path 6, where you ARE supposed to get the extra discount. But there are 2 other situations also associated with path 6. Our test set of test depth level 'infinite' may have passed path 6 many times, but that does not guarantee that at least 1 test case has actually tried situation 3. It might *accidentally* be true, but we *cannot be certain* that situation 3 will be covered. Why not? Because the test set of test depth level 'infinite' *is not designed* for this purpose. The test set was designed to cover path combinations, but this defect has nothing to do with that. The defect would have been found with certainty if a test set was used with a *different coverage type*, i.e. a coverage that focuses on how a complex decision point handles the various options. E.g. by covering all possible combinations of all conditions. In the example above, this amounts to all 4 specified situations. Such a *coverage type* is called 'multiple condition coverage'. Another coverage type is 'decision coverage', which covers only the 2 possible outcomes of the decision point (YES or NO extra discount). This is less thorough coverage than multiple condition coverage, which would *not* detect the above defect with certainty.

So what is best? Do we choose covering paths or covering decision points? Clearly doing both achieves the highest level of thoroughness. But say that this is not allowed (e.g. because it is too costly). Say that we **have to choose**, then what would be best? Or more concretely:

Which coverage type is better: 'test depth level 2' or 'multiple condition coverage'?

This question may seem simple, but it isn't. One coverage type could only be called 'better' with any practical use if it would find at least all of the defects found by the other coverage type plus some additional defects. But the example above demonstrated that multiple condition coverage finds a specific defect that is **not** found with test depth level 2 (i.e. the extra discount for few but expensive books). But the reverse is true as well (i.e. the discount that is given incorrectly in case of cancellation). So the best answer is:

We cannot unequivocally talk about 'better'!

The various coverage types find *different* defects.

Tip:

If multiple coverage types can be used from which a choice has to be made, consult with the client. Analyse where the highest risks are located and select the coverage type that matches this area most adequately. Then make sure that the client is aware of the fact that there are risks in the area relating to the coverage type that was not selected.

For instance, the tester and client must typically ask themselves the following for the earlier question whether to choose test depth level 2 or multiple condition coverage: Is it a process in which many different types of actions are executed whose consequences might affect each other? In this case, path coverage test depth level 2 would be a good choice. But in case of a process where a specific discount is given or not after every decision point, path combinations are not that interesting because the discounts do not have a mutual impact. However, the client might consider the possible situations in which the discount is given or not given extremely important. In this case, coverage type multiple condition coverage might be the wiser choice.

14.2.3 Test design technique and basic technique

Techniques as a link between coverage and test cases

A test design technique is used to derive the necessary test cases that achieve the required coverage from a specific test basis. Such deriving from test cases is not a direct process – it occurs by determining the required **coverage type(s)** and deriving the **test situations** to achieve that coverage type (see figure 14.6 on the next page). This is explained further below.

The required coverage is expressed concretely in the selected coverage types. Each **coverage type** requires a specific type of information in the test basis, e.g. a structured flow chart with paths and decision points. A standard method to derive the required test situations can be created for a specific coverage type. This is called a **basic technique** in this document.

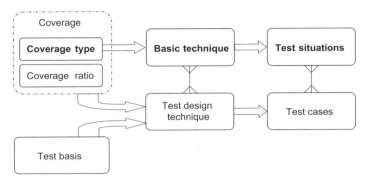

Figure 14.6: Deriving test situations from coverage type.

Definition

Basic technique is the method of deriving test situations from the test basis to achieve the required coverage type.

Please note that for some basic techniques, a tool can be used to derive the required test situations.

Section 14.3 will discuss the main coverage types and available basic techniques in greater detail.

How are techniques related to quality characteristics/test types?

The **test design technique** is closely related to the **test type** that is executed and thereby the **quality characteristic** that is tested with that test type. A test design technique describes the required test basis, the intended coverage types, and the basic techniques applied to achieve these coverage types. Section 14.4 will describe the most common and practical test design techniques and give examples.

A **basic technique** is NOT, in principle, related to a quality characteristic. For instance, path coverage with test depth level 2 (a coverage type) can be used to test functionality but also e.g. security, provided that the security specifications are described in terms of paths and decision points.

To clarify the distinction and relationship between test design technique, basic technique and quality characteristic, consider the following two test design techniques:

- The Process Cycle Test (see section 14.4.8) is a test design technique to test the 'suitability' quality characteristic. The required test basis is the description of the AO (Administrative Organisation) in terms of paths and decision points. The intended coverage type is 'path coverage test depth level 2'.

- The Algorithm Test (see www.tmap.net) is a test design technique to test the 'functionality' quality characteristic. The test basis is the algorithm description of a piece of program code in terms of paths and decision points. The intended coverage type is 'path coverage test depth level 2'.

These two test design techniques each have a different aim (a different quality characteristic is being tested) and work with completely different test objects (AO procedures and program code). But both test design techniques aim for the same coverage type (path coverage test depth level 2) and therefore use the same basic technique. In fact a tester only needs to learn one single basic technique (path coverage test depth level 2) to be able to use both test design techniques.

14.3 Coverage types and basic techniques

14.3.1 Introduction

This section provides an overview of the most important types of coverage. The table below gives a brief description of each type of coverage discussed in this chapter. Where applicable, a key word indicates how the depth of coverage can vary according to the type of coverage. Another way of increasing the depth of coverage is to combine different types of coverage. This is explained further at the end of this section. See the table on the next page.

Coverage type	Description	Variation in depth
Paths	Coverage of the variations in the process in terms of combinations of paths. A scheme of decision points and paths is required as a test basis.	Test depth level N
Decision points	Coverage of the various possibilities within a decision point with the purpose of arriving at the outcomes of TRUE and FALSE. As a test basis, a formal description of the decision point is required, in which the conditions within the decision point are linked with AND, OR and NOT.	Condition/ decision Modified condition/ decision Multiple condition
Equivalence classes	The value range of a parameter is divided into classes in which different system behaviour takes place. The system is tested with at least 1 value from each class.	--
Pairwise testing	Combining an existing set of test situations, which are created, e.g. from "equivalence classes" or "decision points". Pairwise testing combines all the possibilities from every set of 2 parameters.	N-wise testing
Orthogonal arrays	See "pairwise testing"	Strength N
Boundary value analysis	A boundary value determines the transfer from one equivalence class to the other. Boundary value analysis tests the boundary value itself plus the value directly above it and directly below it.	Boundary plus one or plus two values around the boundary
CRUD	Coverage of all the basic operations (Create, Read, Update, Delete) on all the entities.	--
Operational profiles	Simulation of the realistic use of the system, by carrying out a statistically responsible *sequence of transactions*.	--
Load profiles	Simulation of a realistic loading of the system in terms of *volume* of users and/or transactions.	--
Right paths/Fault paths	Coverage of the right path and the fault path in every defined fault situation	Only right paths or only fault paths
Checklist	Checking off an unstructured list. Each element in the list is directly tested by at least one test case.	--

Table 14.1: Brief description of the most important coverage types.

These coverage types are explained in more detail in the following sections. Where necessary, the basic technique is explained for deriving the required test situations for the relevant coverage type.

The intention is not to produce an exhaustive list of coverage types and associated basic techniques. For example, there is also the coverage of "state transition diagrams" and the application of "evolutionary algorithms". These, however, are mainly applicable to embedded systems and are described in the book "Testing Embedded Software" [Broekman, 2003] and elsewhere.

Reinforcing the coverage by combining coverage types

The required coverage of a test can be reinforced by combining several coverage types in the test.

Boundary value analysis and **pairwise testing** are typical coverage types that are used to provide an applied coverage type with extra reinforcement. They are particularly suitable when combined with the coverage of decision points and of equivalence classes.

Other coverage types, too, can be combined, if the necessary information is available as a test basis. Each coverage type individually delivers a number of test situations, which are collectively covered in the test cases. A few examples of usable combinations of coverage types are:

- Paths + Equivalence classes

  Example: The process of "Orders–Delivery-Payment" is specified in a process scheme. This is tested with *path coverage of test depth level 2*. Variations in types of orders and in means of payment are designed with the aid of *equivalence classes*. This can be reinforced again by applying boundary value analysis and/or pairwise testing.

- CRUD + Decision points

  Example: A CRUD matrix of the data "order", "delivery" and "payment" is compiled. This is used to test the life cycle of these data. There are integrity rules specified for the possible processing of the data. These are described formally, as, for example

  "IF condition A OR (condition B AND condition C) THEN processing not permitted".

  These integrity rules are covered by the application of modified condition/ decision coverage.

14.3.2 Paths

The coverage of paths is applicable if the system behaviour is described with the aid of decision points and paths. Figure 14.7 shows an example, which is also used in section 14.2.2.

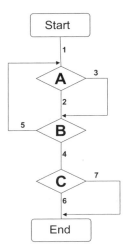

Figure 14.7: Example of a specification of the system behaviour in terms of decision points and paths.

Such a chart of decision points and paths shows, in a structured way, how the process runs from start to end and what the various possibilities in the course of the process are: At each decision point, the process can go various ways, indicated by the various paths that continue from the particular decision point. The conditions under which it takes one path or another are described in the decision points themselves.

The aim of the coverage type described here is to cover the *variations in the process run* that are possible according to the chart. The **test situations** are described in this case by indicating which paths in the chart should be followed consecutively.

Keep in mind that such charts with decision points and paths do not necessarily have to be about the *functionality* of the system. Security processes or work procedures in business processes can also be described with such charts, which makes the basic technique described here applicable to other test types.

Neither is the abstraction level relevant: it is applicable at both detailed level (algorithm code) and at overall system level, as long as the information on the required system behaviour is provided in the structured form of decision points and paths.

Levels of coverage: the test depth level

In the coverage of paths, various levels are possible. The more thorough the level, the greater the probability of finding defects. This is explained below. The most elementary form of path coverage only provides the guarantee that each path has been travelled once. The **test situations** consist in this case of every individual path. In our example (Figure 14.7), these are the test situations:

1; 2; 3; 4; 5; 6; 7

A **test case** is a completed whole that goes through the process run from "Start" to "End". The above-mentioned test situations can, for example, be covered with the following 2 logical test cases:

TC1 = 1 2 5 3 4 6
TC2 = 1 3 4 7

This finds all the faults that will always occur in a particular path. However, it is not for certain that faults that only occur with a specific combination of process steps will be found in this way. In our example, therefore, a particular fault may be present, which only occurs if path 2 is carried out immediately after path 5 (see also the example set out in 14.2.2). That is equal to a "5-2" test situation and is *not* covered by the above two test cases. This type of fault is only found if the variations in the process run are covered in a more *thorough* way. Usually this means that additional, or more complex, test cases are necessary. And suppose that a fault exists that only occurs when "path 2 is carried out immediately after path 5, which in turn is carried out immediately after path 3". That is equal to a "3-5-2" test situation. In order to find this type of fault, testing has to be more thorough.

The depth of coverage is reflected in the concept of test depth level:

Definition

Test depth level N = the certainty that all the combinations of N consecutive paths are covered.

The test depth level in principle runs from 1 to unlimited. The higher the test depth level, the greater the certainty that even faults that occur in complex compositions of process steps will be found. A higher test depth level implies a lower test depth level. In other words, a higher test depth level will at any rate find all the faults that can be found with a lower test depth level, plus possible additional faults.

Deriving the test situations for test depth level 1 is easy. The basic technique for obtaining test depth level 2 is described below. Subsequently, it is explained how higher test depth levels can be derived simply from test depth level 2.

Technique for obtaining test depth level 2

Irrespective of the test depth level, the starting point for this technique requires a **test basis** that describes the system behaviour in terms of decision points and paths. The following steps are then carried out:

1. Decision points & paths

   Nominate the decision points in the process scheme (A, B, etc.) and number the paths, as in Figure 14.7.

   Sum up, per decision point, the:

         a. Incoming paths ("IN")

         b. Outgoing paths ("OUT")

2. Path combinations

   Working out all the combinations of "IN" and "OUT" at each decision point. With a number of incoming P paths and outgoing Q paths, this leads to P times Q path combinations.

3. Logical test cases.

   Creation of logical test cases, until all the path combinations are covered. Each logical test case begins at "Start" and finishes at "End", running through various path combinations.

The first 2 steps lead to the **test situations** in the test design. They are all the variations (in this case, path combinations) that have to be tested in order to reach test depth level 2.

Step 3 leads to a set of **logical test cases** that are guaranteed to cover all the test situations. The tester is free to create a set of test cases that comply with this. If necessary, it can be shown with the aid of a cross-reference matrix that all the test situations are covered with the chosen set of test cases. In principle, there are two ways of arriving at a covering set of test cases:

- Working from the process chart, define a test case by running through the process in a particular way from "Start" to "End". The tester is in principle free to choose the exact way of going through the process. Cross out of the list of path combinations every combination that occurs in this test case. Repeat this process until the list of path combinations is completely crossed out.

- Working from the list of path combinations, start with a path combination that begins at "Start" (e.g. "1-3"). Seek a subsequent path combination that starts with the path with which the previous one ends (e.g. a "3-5") – like setting down domino tiles, in fact. Continue seeking a subsequent path combination until "End" has been reached. Obviously, previously unused path combinations should be used as much as possible.

The steps are now explained using the example in Figure 14.7.

In more detail

Breakdown of test depth level 2 for the scheme from Figure 14.7

1.   Decision points & paths

        A: IN: 1, 5
                   OUT: 2, 3
        B: IN: 2, 3
                   OUT: 4, 5
        C: IN: 4
                   OUT: 6, 7

2.   Path combinations

        A: 1-2; 1-3; 5-2; 5-3
        B: 2-4; 2-5; 3-4; 3-5
        C: 4-6; 4-7

3.   Logical test cases

        TC1 = 1-2-5-3-4-6 (Cross out the path combinations covered here)
        TC2 = 1-3-5-2-4-7 (Simply follows from the remaining path combinations.)

Cross-reference matrix (optional)

	TC1	TC2
1-2	X	
1-3		X
5-2		X
5-3	X	
2-4		X
2-5	X	
3-4	X	
3-5		X
4-6	X	
4-7		X

Deriving test situations for higher test depth levels

For higher test depth levels, the following simple mechanism is used:

- Use the list of path combinations of the preceding test depth level as a basis
- Extend each path combination by every possible subsequent step in the course of the process. So, suppose that after path P there are three possible subsequent steps, let us say Q, R and S. Then every path combination that ends at P is extended to three new 'higher' path combinations: ..PQ and ..PR and ..PS.

It may be formulated as:

Test depth level (N+1) = Test depth level N + "1 step further in the course of the process"

This is broken down in the example below.

In more detail

Test depth level 3 from the chart in Figure 14.7
It is simple to deduce the following from the scheme:
Path 1 is the starting point for every test case
Paths 2 and 3 are followed by paths 4 and 5
Path 5 is followed by paths 2 and 3
Path 4 is followed by paths 6 and 7
Paths 6 and 7 are end paths and have no sequel.
This can directly extend the path combinations of test depth level 2 to test depth level 3:

Path combinations from test depth level 2		Extended to test depth level 3
A:	1-2	1-2-4; 1-2-5
	1-3	1-3-4; 1-3-5
	5-2	5-2-4; 5-2-5
	5-3	5-3-4; 5-3-5
B:	2-4	2-4-6; 2-4-7
	2-5	2-5-2; 2-5-3
	3-4	3-4-6; 3-4-7
	3-5	3-5-2; 3-5-3
C:	4-6	No extension and already covered.
	4-7	No extension and already covered.

In the same way, the test situations of test depth level 3 can be extended to test depth level 4.

14.3.3 Decision points

Introduction – basic principles of Boolean algebra

With almost every system, there are *decision points*, where the system behaviour can go in *different directions*, depending on the outcome of such a decision point.

Definition

A decision point is a combination of one or more conditions that define the conditions for the various possibilities in the subsequent system behaviour.

The various conditions collectively determine the outcome of the decision point. The way in which a condition contributes to the outcome is reflected in terms such as "AND" or "OR". There is a special kind of mathematics – Boolean algebra, or proposition logic – for the manipulation of these types of constructions. This chapter employs the theory of Boolean algebra, but the intention is not to instruct on this, and the interested reader is referred to the countless books on this subject. Below are the most important basic principles of Boolean algebra that are necessary for the techniques for covering decision points.

Take, for example, the following decision point that consists of only one condition:

IF (number of books > 8) THEN extra discount

Decision points that consist of such **singular conditions** lead to two test situations, namely the situation in which the condition is true and the situation in which the condition is false. In Boolean algebra, 0 is used to indicate that something is false; 1 is used if something is true. In our example, this refers to the following test situations:

Test situation	1	2
Number of books	> 8	≤ 8
Result	True (1)	False (0)

Decision points can also consist of combinations of conditions, the so-called **compound condition**. Compare the following compound conditions:

IF (Number of books > 8 OR sum ≥ €250) THEN extra discount
and
IF (Number of books > 8 AND sum ≥ €250) THEN extra discount

Often an abbreviation is used by replacing the conditions by a capital letter (A, B, etc.) The two decision points mentioned above are thus abbreviated to:

A OR B   and
A AND B

A compound condition is also either true or false, depending on the truth values of the individual conditions and the way in which the conditions are connected (the so-called **operators**): by an AND or an OR. With two conditions, the following combinations are possible:

A	B
1	1
1	0
0	1
0	0

This is called the **complete decision table**.

In the 0-0 situation, both statements are false. In the 0-1 situation and the 1-0 situation, only one of the two statements is true and in the 1-1 situation, both are true. The end result in each of the 4 situations depends on the operator

"AND" or "OR": with an "AND" the end result of two conditions is only true if both individual conditions are true; in all the other cases, the end result is false. With an "OR" the reverse is the case: the end result is only false if both individual conditions are false; in all the other cases the end result is true.

A common way of demonstrating the outcomes of all the situations of a complete decision table is the **truth table**. Below shows the truth tables for the compound conditions "A OR B" and "A AND B".

A	B	A OR B
1	1	1
1	0	1
0	1	1
0	0	0

A	B	A AND B
1	1	1
1	0	0
0	1	0
0	0	0

For a decision point that consists of, not two, but three conditions, the complete decision table is as follows:

A	B	C
1	1	1
1	1	0
1	0	1
1	0	0
0	1	1
0	1	0
0	0	1
0	0	0

Clearly, the number of situations increases exponentially with the number of conditions. With 6 conditions, there are already 64 situations.

Where there is a mixture of operators (AND and OR) in a compound condition, the outcome depends on which operator is executed first. To avoid confusion, it is best to indicate this by using brackets. In the absence of brackets, the rule is that the AND goes before the OR. As an example, the truth table is shown below for the compound condition "(A OR B) AND C".

A	B	C	(A OR B) AND C
1	1	1	1
1	1	0	0
1	0	1	1
1	0	0	0
0	1	1	1
0	1	0	0
0	0	1	0
0	0	0	0

Although many different Boolean operators exist, it appears that every operator can be brought back to a combination of 3 elementary operators: AND, OR and NOT. That means that if the tester knows how to deal with these 3 operators, he can tackle *every decision point*. (The operator "NOT" is not dealt with here; the effect of this operator is insignificant: the outcome "1" is converted to "0" and vice versa.)

The commonest coverage types in relation to decision points

The complete decision table defines all possible combinations of the individual conditions. Therefore, the testing of all these possibilities is the most thorough coverage type in respect of a decision point, and is known as "multiple condition coverage". In addition, there are various coverage types with which a subset of the complete decision table is tested. This does not refer to a random subset, but to a subset with a specific goal. Table 14.2 describes in brief the commonest coverage types and their comparative degree of thoroughness. A more thorough coverage type 'implies' a less thorough coverage type, i.e.: one that covers minimally all the test situations of the elementary coverage type.

Condition coverage	The possible outcomes of ("true" or "false") for each condition are tested at least once.
Decision coverage	The possible outcomes of the decision are tested at least once.
Condition/decision coverage	The possible outcomes of each condition *and* of the decision are tested at least once. This implies both "condition coverage" and "decision coverage".
Modified condition/ decision coverage	Every possible outcome of a condition determines at least once the outcome of the decision. This implies "condition/decision coverage".
Multiple condition coverage	All the possible combinations of outcomes of conditions in a decision (therefore the complete decision table) are tested at least once. This implies "modified condition/decision coverage".

Table 14.2: Overview of the commonest coverage types in relation to decision points.

The example below illustrates the differences between the coverage types mentioned.

In more detail

Take the following decision point as an example:
  IF (number of books > 8 OR sum ≥ €250) THEN extra discount
The tables below show with which situations the relevant coverage type is obtained.

Condition coverage

Number of books >8	Sum ≥ €250	Outcome
1	0	1 (extra discount)
0	1	1 (extra discount)

Decision coverage

Number of books >8	Sum ≥ €250	Outcome
0	1	1 (extra discount)
0	0	0

Condition/decision coverage

Number of books >8	Sum ≥ €250	Outcome
1	1	1 (extra discount)
0	0	0

Modified condition/decision coverage (see next section)

Number of books >8	Sum ≥ €250	Outcome
1	0	1 (extra discount)
0	1	1 (extra discount)
0	0	0

Multiple condition coverage

Number of books >8	Sum ≥ €250	Outcome
1	1	1 (extra discount)
1	0	1 (extra discount)
0	1	1 (extra discount)
0	0	0

With some coverage types, other choices of situations are possible that lead to the same goal. For example, condition coverage is also achieved with the 2 situations "1 1" and "0 0". And decision coverage is also achieved with "1 0" and "0 0" (and also with "1 1" and "0 0").

For the most elementary coverage type, the best choice is "condition/decision coverage", which fulfils both "condition coverage" and "decision coverage", and requires the same number of test situations.

The coverage type "modified condition/decision coverage" is a very powerful means of obtaining thorough coverage with a small number of test situations. This coverage type is not readily mastered by everyone. For that reason, it is explained in depth in the following section.

Modified condition/decision coverage

> **Definition**
>
> Modified condition/decision coverage (abbreviation: MCDC) is the coverage type that guarantees the following:
>
> Every possible outcome of a condition is the determinant of the outcome of the decision at least once.

The important concept in this definition is "determinant". If the outcome of the condition changes (from 0 to 1 or vice versa) then the outcome of the whole decision point changes with it. The meaning of MCDC can be explained as follows:

If a decision point consists of the conditions A, B and C, then MCDC guarantees:

- That there is at least 1 test situation in which the outcome is TRUE, owing to the fact that condition A is TRUE
- That there is at least 1 test situation in which the outcome is FALSE, owing to the fact that condition A is FALSE
- Ditto for condition B and ditto for condition C

This is a thorough level of coverage, with which the following faults, for example, would be detected in the system under test:

- There is a condition missing that should be present
- The "AND" was wrongly implemented as an "OR", and vice versa
- A condition has been inverted, such as "<" instead of ">" or "≠" instead of "=".

The big advantage of this coverage type is its efficiency: with a decision point that consists of N conditions, usually only **N+1 test situations** are required for MCDC. Compared with the maximum number of test situations (the complete decision table) of 2^N, that is a considerable reduction, particularly if N is large (complex decision points). This combination of "thorough coverage" with "relatively few test situations" makes this coverage type a powerful weapon in the tester's arsenal.

According to the definition of MCDC, every condition should *determine* the outcome of the decision once. Then all the other conditions in that situation should be given a value that has *no influence* on the outcome of the decision. This value is called the "neutral value" and is further explained below.

> **In more detail**
>
> Take, for example, the complex decision (R), which consists of a combination of two conditions (A, B). The outcome of the decision is only true if both conditions are true. In other words:

R = A AND B
Now suppose that condition B is FALSE (or value 0). Then it no longer matters what A is; the outcome of R is always FALSE. In other words:
    A AND 0 = 0
However, if condition B is TRUE (or value 1), the R outcome of the decision depends entirely on the outcome of A. In other words:
    A AND 1 = A
This last is exactly what should be achieved with MCDC:
If condition A should determine the outcome of the decision (in this 'AND combination'), then the other condition should be set at value 1. We are talking here about the **neutral value**, since value 1 has no influence on the final outcome.
Similarly, we can talk of the neutral value for the 'OR combination', which is 0 in this case, since:
    A OR 0 = A

In summary:
The neutral value with AND = 1
The neutral value with OR = 0

6-step plan for deriving test situations for MCDC

Employing the concept of "neutral value", achieving MCDC can be translated in concrete terms into the requirements:

- Let every condition within the decision be TRUE once and FALSE once,
- With all the *other* conditions in that test situation being given a *neutral value.*

There are various ways of deriving the necessary test situations. The 6-step plan is a technique that very directly follows on the definition of MCDC and with which a table is simply created with all the necessary test situations. The 6-step plan is explained below with a relatively simple example. Subsequently, it is explained how this technique works for more complex combinations of conditions.

Take as an example the following decision point, which describes how good customers receive an extra discount:

    IF (Number of books > 8 OR Sum ≥ €250) THEN extra discount

The decision point here is made up of 2 conditions with the structure: R = A OR B.

The 6-step plan is set out below, giving the test situations with which this decision point is covered by MCDC.

1. Create a table with 3 columns.
   Fill in the first row as follows:

R = A OR B	1	0

2. Add 1 row for every condition in the decision.
   This row will contain the 2 test situations in which the relevant condition determines the outcome of the decision point. The condition will decide the outcome "1" once and the outcome "0" once. In the first column, enter the description of every condition.

R = A OR B	1	0
A: Number of books > 8		
B: Sum ≥ €250		

3. Fill in the rest of the cells in the table with a number of dots equal to the number of conditions in the decision.
   Each cell is a test situation, which should indicate which combination of TRUE/FALSE applies to the conditions.

R = A OR B	1	0
A: Number of books > 8	. .	. .
B: Sum ≥ €250	. .	. .

4. Enter "1" diagonally in the second column and "0" in the third column. This is actually entering the **determining values** for every condition. The meaning of e.g. the cell that belongs to row "A" and column "1" is: "This is the test situation in which condition A determines an outcome of 1."

R = A OR B	1	0
A: Number of books > 8	1 .	0 .
B: Sum ≥ €250	. 1	. 0

5. Over the remaining dots, enter a **neutral value**.
   In this case, both A and B will contribute to the outcome via an OR combination. So for both, the neutral value is 0.

R = A OR B	1	0
A: Number of books > 8	1 0	0 0
B: Sum ≥ €250	0 1	0 0

6. Score out duplicates of test situations.

R = A OR B	1	0
A: Number of books > 8	1 0	0 0
B: Sum ≥ €250	0 1	~~0 0~~

In more detail

Each test situation can be further worked out, by indicating which requirements are set on the parameters of the decision point to arrive in this test situation. This is particularly useful if the tester is dealing with many decision points and so with many test situations that have to be combined into test cases.

In the above example, the 3 test situations can be worked out as follows:

Test situation	10	01	00
Number of books	> 8	≤ 8	≤ 8
Sum	< €250	≥ €250	< €250

The 6-step plan described above works for every compound condition, however complex. With compound conditions in which both "AND" and "OR" occur, care should be taken at step 5 (entering the neutral values). The example below will explain this.

Take as an example the decision point R = (A OR B) AND C.
After the first 4 steps, the table of test situations looks as follows:

R = (A OR B) AND C	1	0
A	1 . .	0 . .
B	. 1 .	. 0 .
C	. . 1	. . 0

Now the neutral values should be entered for each of the 6 situations. With the top 2 situations (A is the determining value), the neutral values can immediately be determined: B is connected to A via the operator "OR" and should therefore be given the neutral value "0". C is connected with A via the operator "AND" and should therefore be given the neutral value "1".

The same applies to the middle 2 situations (B is the determining value). However, for the bottom situation (C is the determining value) an interim step is necessary: it is not A that is directly connected with C, nor is it B. It is the combination "(A OR B)" that is connected with C, via the operator "AND". Thus "(A OR B)" should assume the neutral value of "AND", and that is "1". In other words: (A OR B) = 1. For the values for A and B there are 3 possibilities of achieving this, i.e. "1 1", "1 0" or "0 1". Only 1 of the 3 need to be selected to reach the goal of MCDC. In principle, it does not matter which. The only difference in the 3 possibilities is that in selecting "1 0" or "0 1" a test situation can be scored off, while that is not possible with the choice of "1 1".

If the neutral value of "1 0" is selected for (A OR B), then after the 6 steps, the table looks as follows:

R = (A OR B) AND C	1	0
A	1 0 1	0 0 1
B	0 1 1	~~0 0 1~~
C	~~1 0 1~~	1 0 0

This phenomenon, that several possibilities exist for neutral values, *always* occurs in cases of an operator between brackets.

14.3.4 Equivalence classes

The covering of equivalence classes is a powerful means of achieving a relatively high fault-detection rate with a limited set of test situations. The principle is simple and is applied by most experienced testers automatically and intuitively.

Definition

In the application of equivalence classes, the entire value range of a parameter is partitioned into classes, in which the system behaviour is similar (equivalent).

These are called equivalence classes. Other terms used to refer to the design of test cases based on equivalence classes are "equivalence partitioning" and "domain testing".

In more detail

The following example is by way of clarification:

In the decision of whether or not to issue a loan, many parameters play a role. One of those parameters is the *age* of the borrower. In the lending system, the age can vary between 0 and 100. As regards the age, the rules for granting or refusing the loan are as follows:

Younger than 18	Refuse loan
From 18 to 55	Issue standard loan
Older than 55	Issue more expensive loan

Suppose that 3 test cases are being executed, with the following consecutive values for age: 16, 32 and 44. This is not a good choice, for several reasons:

- There is no single test case in which a more expensive loan is issued. Any mistake in the issue of more expensive loans will therefore not be found
- If the system works correctly in respect of age = 32, then it is highly unlikely that a mistake will occur in respect of age = 44. The last test case is therefore superfluous.

In this example, for the parameter "Age" there are 3 equivalence classes, namely:

0 - 17, 18 - 55 and 56 - 100.

The various types of system behaviour in respect of this parameter are covered with 1 test case from each equivalence class.

The principle behind the application of equivalence classes is that each value taken from a class has the same chance of finding a fault *and* that testing with several values from the same class barely increases the chances of fault detection. It should be realised that this is an *assumption*. If, with a random value in an equivalence class the correct system behaviour occurs, it is in principle still possible for a fault to occur with another value. For example:

- Fraudulent system behaviour
  For example, if a programmer with fraudulent intent has added into the code: "IF name = [my name] THEN discount = [ridiculously high]" In principle, this cannot be found in any structured manner – only by sheer coincidence or by inspecting the source code itself.
- Landing in the wrong equivalence class
  In certain situations, system behaviour can occur that belongs to another equivalence class. This usually concerns boundary values that were assigned to the wrong equivalence class. See more about this in section 14.3.6 "Boundary value analysis".

Even though the underlying principle is an assumption, it is a usable and useful one. By basing test cases on these equivalence classes instead of on every possible input value, the number of test cases is restricted, while a satisfactory coverage is obtained of the possible variations in the system behaviour.

Sometimes a distinction is made between valid and invalid equivalence classes: input values from the invalid equivalence class result in error messages. Input values from a valid equivalence class are processed as intended. This special form of coverage falls under the coverage of "Right paths / Fault paths" (see section 14.3.9).

Equivalence classes are applicable to both input parameters and output parameters.

14.3.5 Orthogonal arrays and pairwise testing

'Orthogonal arrays' is a fairly recent mathematical theory that is attracting increasing interest. It concerns the mathematical properties in the combining of factors, so-called "Combinatorics". It has countless interesting applications in science, industry and... testing.

Combinations are also employed in testing. Consider that system behaviour in general is determined by several parameters, each of which can assume various values. In order to create a test case, the tester chooses one of the possible values for each parameter. In fact, he is creating a *combination of parameter values* that is going to be tested. The testing of all the possible combinations soon becomes unfeasible in practice. If, for example, there are 8 parameters, each of which have 3 possible values (or equivalence classes), then there are already $3^8 = 6,561$ possibilities! Of necessity, only a subset can be tested. But what is a sensible subset to use? This is where orthogonal arrays and pairwise testing can offer a solution.

This chapter first explains the principle of pairwise testing, to familiarise the reader with the meaning and result of such techniques that are based on combinatorics. Subsequently, the more complex material of orthogonal arrays is explained along general lines. The latter is not necessary in order to be able to apply the basic technique of pairwise testing, but is intended for those interested in deeper theory.

Pairwise testing

Pairwise testing is based on the phenomenon that most faults in software are the consequence of one particular factor or the combination of 2 factors. The number of faults that are caused by a specific combination of more than 2 factors becomes exponentially smaller. Instead of testing *all* the possible combinations of *all* the factors, it is very effective if every combination of 2 factors is tested.

Definition

The aim of pairwise testing is to test all the possibilities of any combination of 2 factors.

This delivers an enormous reduction in the number of required test cases, yet still gives a good fault-detection result.

The following example illustrates the meaning of pairwise testing.

In more detail

In the system under test (for ordering books via the Internet), the following 3 parameters play a role. For each parameter, there are 2 equivalence classes to be tested:

Number of books   Few; many
Sum   Low; high
Membership card   None; Gold card

In order to test all the combinations relating to these 3 parameters, 2x2x2=8 test cases are required, namely:

	Number of books	Sum	Membership card
1	Few	Low	None
2	Few	Low	Gold card
3	Few	High	None
4	Few	High	Gold card
5	Many	Low	None
6	Many	Low	Gold card
7	Many	High	None
8	Many	High	Gold card

For pairwise testing, as few as 4 test cases will suffice, as shown below:

	Number of books	Sum	Membership card
1	Few	Low	None
2	Few	High	Gold card
3	Many	Low	Gold card
4	Many	High	None

Of the 2 parameters [Number of books, Sum], all 4 existing combinations are tested (Few/Low; Few/High; Many/Low; Many/High). The same applies to the other combinations of 2 parameters, so for [Number of books, Membership card] and [Sum, Membership card]. Check it for yourself.

What is the point of this? If a fault exists in the system that occurs when one of the possible values of one of the parameters is combined with a particular value of one of the other parameters, then this fault is *always* found with these 4 test cases. That is the strength of pairwise testing.

Deriving test cases for pairwise testing

If there is a pair of parameters with only 2 equivalence classes, the test cases necessary for pairwise testing can be derived manually. In most situations in practice, however, there are more parameters and equivalence classes and it is not possible to do this manually. In that case, there are 2 ways of solving this:

- Application of orthogonal arrays (see following subsection)
- Use of tools (discussed further in this section).

The number of necessary test cases, and how exactly they are combined, depends on the tool that is used. Various tools are available, both commercially and free via the Internet (freeware). In the example below, the result of 2 freeware tools is described.

Take, for example, the following more extended version of the "book-ordering system". The previously mentioned parameters now have more equivalence classes, and another parameter: "Ordering period", has been added:

Number of books	1; 2-8; >8
Sum	<100; 100-250; >250
Membership card	None; Silver; Gold; Platinum
Ordering period	Weekday; Weekend; Public holiday

For the testing of all possible combinations in this case, 3x3x4x3=108 test cases are necessary. For pairwise testing, a fraction of these will suffice. Below, the results are shown that were obtained with 2 freeware tools:

Results with tool "Pict33"

This is a tool from Microsoft® and can be downloaded via their site or via www. pairwise.org . This tool generates the following 14 test cases:

	Number of books	Sum	Membership card	Ordering period
1	1	<100	None	Public holiday
2	1	>250	Platinum	Weekday
3	1	>250	Silver	Weekday
4	1	100-250	Gold	Weekend
5	>8	<100	Silver	Weekend
6	>8	>250	None	Weekday
7	>8	>250	Gold	Public holiday
8	>8	100-250	Platinum	Public holiday
9	>8	100-250	Platinum	Weekday
10	2-8	<100	Platinum	Weekday
11	2-8	<100	Gold	Weekday
12	2-8	>250	Platinum	Weekend
13	2-8	100-250	Silver	Public holiday
14	2-8	100-250	None	Weekend

Result with "Allpairs" tool

The creator of this tool is James Bach. It may be downloaded from www. satisfice.com. This tool generates the following 13 test cases:

	Number of books	Sum	Membership card	Ordering period
1	1	<100	None	Weekday
2	2-8	100-250	None	Weekend
3	>8	>250	None	Public holiday
4	1	100-250	Silver	Public holiday
5	2-8	<100	Silver	Weekday
6	>8	<100	Silver	Weekend
7	1	>250	Gold	Weekend
8	2-8	<100	Gold	Public holiday
9	>8	100-250	Gold	Weekday
10	2-8	>250	Platinum	Weekday
11	1	<100	Platinum	Weekend
12	>8	100-250	Platinum	Public holiday
13	~1	>250	Silver	~Weekday

The symbol "~" in the last test case means that the value makes no difference here. A different equivalence class might have been selected. The test case is solely required to complete the coverage of the other parameters.

Stronger variants, such as triplewise testing
The principle of pairwise testing can be extended to the combination of more than two factors. For example, the testing of all the possibilities of any **three** random factors is known as 'triplewise testing'. A general definition is as follows:

Definition

N-wise testing has the aim of testing all the possibilities of any random combination of N factors.

The maximum value for N is equal to the number of parameters. In that case, the result is equal to the testing of the complete decision table: all the combinations of all the values of all the parameters. In practice, a value of 4 or higher is seldom applied.
The previously mentioned "Pict33" tool can tackle a randomly given strength. For triplewise testing of the previously given example, this tool calculates 43 test situations. Application of N=4 would deliver the maximum number of 108 test situations.

Orthogonal arrays
The first example of pairwise testing deals with 3 parameters, each with 2 equivalence classes. If, for each parameter, the equivalence classes are numbered, i.e. "1" and "2", then the 4 test cases for pairwise testing are described by the following 2-dimensional array:

	param-1	param-2	param-3
TC1	1	1	1
TC2	1	2	2
TC3	2	1	2
TC4	2	2	1

This is an example of an orthogonal array and is noted as $L_4(2^3)$. The meaning of the different symbols here is:

4 = The number of rows (therefore the number of test cases that appear to be required)

3 = The number of columns (therefore the parameters that together form a test case)

2 = The maximum value in each column (therefore the number of equivalence classes of each parameter)

The interesting property of this array is that every combination of 2 columns contains all the possible combinations of the values "1" and "2". The term for this is that it is an orthogonal array of "**strength 2**". This exactly fits the purpose of pairwise testing, in which "all the combinations of equivalence classes of TWO random parameters" are tested.

Another special property of orthogonal arrays is that they are **balanced**. That means that each combination of parameter values *occurs with equal frequency* to any other combination of parameter values. This property distinguishes orthogonal arrays from pairwise testing. With the test cases that are created through the application of pairwise testing, certain equivalence classes usually occur more frequently than others do. With orthogonal arrays, all the equivalence classes (even each combination of equivalence classes) occur with equal frequency.

For deeper testing than pairwise testing, an orthogonal array with a higher strength is necessary. For the testing of all the combinations of equivalence classes of *three* random parameters, an orthogonal array of "**strength 3**" will be required. Below is an orthogonal array of strength 3 for 4 parameters, each of which can have 2 values:

1	1	1	1
1	1	2	2
1	2	1	2
1	2	2	1
2	1	1	2
2	1	2	1
2	2	1	1
2	2	2	2

This array has the property that every combination of 3 columns contains all the possible combinations of the values 1 and 2, namely (1 1 1), (1 1 2), (1 2 1), (1 2 2), (2 1 1), (2 1 2), (2 2 1) and (2 2 2).

The notation for this orthogonal array is $L_8(2^4, 3)$, in which the number 3 indicates the strength of the array. In the literature, there are various ways of noting orthogonal arrays. The most usual ways of notation are:

- $L_8(2^4, 3)$,
- $OA(8, 2^4, 3)$,
- $OA(8, 4, 2, 3)$

If the value for strength is omitted, the default value of strength 2 is assumed.

All of the foregoing can be summarised in the following complicated definition:

Definition

An orthogonal array $L_N(s^k, t)$ is a 2-dimensional array of N rows and k columns consisting of elements that can assume s values, whereby every combination of t columns contains all the combinations of the s values in equal proportion.

An orthogonal array does not exist for every value of "s" and "k". In practice, such a situation uses a 'too big' array, with the superfluous columns being ignored in its application.

So far, orthogonal arrays have been described in which the possible values for the elements of all the columns are equal. There are also orthogonal arrays in which columns can have varying possible values. An example of this is $L_8(2^4, 4^1, 2)$. The array of strength 2 contains 4 columns, each of which have 2 possible values, plus 1 column with 4 possible values. Such an array is set out below:

0	0	0	0	0
1	1	1	1	0
0	0	1	1	1
1	1	0	0	1
0	1	0	1	2
1	0	1	0	2
0	1	1	0	3
1	0	0	1	3

How do you get orthogonal arrays?

The creation of an orthogonal array is not simple. If there are several columns that can assume more than 2 values, it is more or less impossible to do manually. Fortunately, there is extensive literature on the subject, including books, articles and websites, with many examples and worked-out arrays that the tester can employ.

The book "Orthogonal arrays: Theory and Applications" [Hedayat, 1999] is generally accepted as the standard work on orthogonal arrays.

One of the most extensive collections of orthogonal arrays on the Internet can be found on the site of N.J.A Sloane. An Internet search for "orthogonal arrays" will undoubtedly lead to this and many other useful sites.

Deriving test cases with orthogonal arrays

The application of pairwise testing (and stronger variants) is simple, thanks to the available tools that quickly generate the necessary test cases. Deriving the test cases using orthogonal arrays involves more work and is more complicated, but gives the extra advantage of the "balanced test cases": every combination of equivalence classes occurs with equal frequency. The tester will have to consider whether this extra advantage is worth the additional effort necessary.

For the enthusiasts, it is explained below how orthogonal arrays can be applied in order to derive a balanced set of test cases for N-wise testing:
1. Determine the parameters of which the test case consists.
2. Determine the equivalence classes of each parameter.
3. Select the strength of the orthogonal array, based on the required strength of the test.
4. Find a fitting orthogonal array.
   An orthogonal array does not exist for every quantity of parameters and equivalence classes. In that case, one has to be found that is 'just a bit too big'. This can be done in 2 ways and should then be used as follows:
   • There are too many columns (more columns than parameters).
     The relevant columns can simply be omitted. This has no influence on the orthogonality of the array
   • The maximum value of a column is too great. (The maximum value of "s" is greater than the number of equivalence classes of the parameter.) Here, the rows that contain the too-great value may not be casually omitted. These rows are necessary to realise the obligatory combinations of the other parameters. In this case, a too-great value in the column should be construed as "don't care value". A random equivalence class can therefore be selected
5. Translate the orthogonal array into test cases.

Example

In order to explain this, the same example is used as worked out with pairwise testing, concerning the "book-ordering system":
Suppose that this system is to be tested with an average strength. The 5 steps for deriving the test cases proceed as follows:
Step 1: Determine the parameters of which the test case consists.
There are 4 parameters: "Number of books", "Sum", "Membership card", "Ordering period".
Step 2: Determine the equivalence classes of each parameter.
The parameters are arranged in ascending order according to the number of equivalence classes. This simplifies the search for a suitable orthogonal array (step 4).

Number of books	1; 2-8; >8
Sum	<100; 100-250; >250
Ordering period	Weekday; Weekend; Public holiday
Membership card	None; Silver; Gold; Platinum

Step 3: Select the strength of the orthogonal array.
Since the system is to be tested with average strength, strength 2 is selected. For stronger testing, a higher strength can be selected. This mainly affects the search for a fitting orthogonal array (step 4). Otherwise, the 5 steps remain unchanged in this technique.

Step 4: Find a fitting orthogonal array.
There are 3 parameters with 3 equivalence classes and 1 parameter with 4 equivalence classes. This means that an orthogonal array must be found that approximates as far as possible:

$$L_N(3^3, 4^1, 2)$$

Unfortunately, this orthogonal array does not exist. Therefore, one must be found that is just a bit bigger. The following 2 orthogonal arrays could be considered:

- $L_{18}(3^6, 6^1, 2)$
  This consists of 18 rows and 7 columns. Of the first 6 columns (that can assume 3 values), 3 are superfluous and can be scrapped. The last column can assume 6 values, but of those, only 4 are required for our test. The column therefore has 2 superfluous values that may be entered randomly (the "don't-matter values").
- $L_{16}(4^5, 2)$
  This consists of 16 rows and 5 columns. One column is superfluous and can be scrapped. The first 3 columns of the remainder of the table then contain 1 possible value too many, which counts among the "don't-care values".

The second array is selected, since it delivers the lowest number of required test cases. The $L_{16}(4^5, 2)$ looks as follows:

1	1	1	1	1
1	2	2	2	2
1	3	3	3	3
1	4	4	4	4
2	1	2	3	4
2	2	1	4	3
2	3	4	1	2
2	4	3	2	1
3	1	3	4	2
3	2	4	3	1
3	3	1	2	4
3	4	2	1	3
4	1	4	2	3
4	2	3	1	4
4	3	2	4	1
4	4	1	3	2

Step 5: Translate the orthogonal array into test cases

The selected orthogonal array is now cut to size and then filled in with the real values of the test parameters.

The last column of the array is removed. The first 3 parameters have only 3 possible values. For that reason, of the first 3 columns, the value "4" is replaced by a "~" , indicating that the value does not matter. The array then looks as follows:

1	1	1	1
1	2	2	2
1	3	3	3
1	~	~	4
2	1	2	3
2	2	1	4
2	3	~	1
2	~	3	2
3	1	3	4
3	2	~	3
3	3	1	2
3	~	2	1
~	1	~	2
~	2	3	1
~	3	2	4
~	~	1	3

Finally, the test parameters should be allocated to the columns of the array and the values in the columns replaced by an equivalence class. Which value is linked to which equivalence class is irrelevant, as long as they are consistently applied. As a reminder, the parameters are repeated below with their equivalence classes summed up.

Number of books	1; 2-8; >8
Sum	<100; 100-250; >250
Ordering period	Weekday; Weekend; Public holiday
Membership card	None; Silver; Gold; Platinum

In our example, the final result then looks as follows. A "~" still indicates that a random selection of the available values may be made.

	Number of books	Sum	Ordering period	Membership card
1	1	<100	Weekday	None
2	1	100-250	Weekend	Silver
3	1	>250	Public holiday	Gold
4	1	~	~	Platinum
5	2-8	<100	Weekend	Gold
6	2-8	100-250	Weekday	Platinum
7	2-8	>250	~	None
8	2-8	~	Public holiday	Silver
9	>8	<100	Public holiday	Platinum
10	>8	100-250	~	Gold
11	>8	>250	Weekday	Silver
12	>8	~	Weekend	None
13	~	<100	~	Silver
14	~	100-250	Public holiday	None
15	~	>250	Weekend	Platinum
16	~	~	Weekday	Gold

14.3.6 Boundary value analysis

If the system behaviour changes as soon as the value of a parameter exceeds a particular boundary, this is called a 'boundary value'. The following example demonstrates this:

> "As regards age, the rules pertaining to the issue or non-issue of a loan are as follows:
>
> | | |
> |---|---|
> | Younger than 18 | Refuse loan |
> | From 18 to 55 incl. | Issue standard loan |
> | Older than 55 | Issue more expensive loan" |

In this example, there are 3 equivalence classes for the age parameter. The values of 18 and 55 are the boundaries for this parameter. Both boundaries belong in this case to the middle equivalence class of "standard loan", as illustrated in figure 14.8.

Figure 14.8: Example of 2 boundaries and their position in the equivalence classes of the parameter "Age"

In practice, it appears that many faults are connected with boundaries. Usually these are simply 'sloppy programming mistakes' in which the programmer, for example, has accidentally programmed a ">" instead of a "≥", or a "=" instead of a "≥". In the above example, somewhere in the code, the condition "IF age ≤ 18 THEN ..." could have been programmed accidentally. In that case, the age of 18 could suddenly be allocated to the first equivalence class ("Refuse loan") instead of to the middle one ("Standard loan").

Apart from in the equivalence classes, boundaries also often occur in the coverage of conditions and decision points. For example, in the lending system the following condition could be defined:

IF (loan sum > salary) THEN ...

Here, the "loan sum" is the parameter with the boundary of "salary".

The testing of whether the boundary values have been allocated to the appropriate equivalence class (or outcome of the condition) is a separate test goal that is achieved by means of "**boundary value analysis**".

The technique for carrying out boundary value analysis is simple in the extreme:

■ Determine the boundaries of the relevant equivalence class or condition

- Define the following **3 test situations**: exactly on the boundary, directly above it, directly below it.

The precise significance of "directly above it" or "directly below it" depends on the unity and precision with which the value of that parameter is expressed. If the salary and loan sum are expressed in cents, then the previous example, the following loan sums should be tested:
- Loan sum == salary
- Loan sum == salary + € 0.01
- Loan sum == salary - € 0.01

However, if the system calculates to 4 decimal points, the difference should be tested to € 0.0001 instead of to € 0.01.

There is also a slight variant of boundary value analysis, with which only 2 test situations are tested: the boundary itself plus the adjacent values in the *other* equivalence class. This can be illustrated using the example at the start of this section (see figure 14.8). The parameter of Age has 3 equivalence classes and 2 boundaries (18 and 55). The number of test situations with No, Normal and Slight boundary value analysis is then as follows:
- No boundary value analysis   → 3 test situations: e.g. 12, 32, 64
- Normal   "   → 6 test situations: 17, 18, 19 and 54, 55, 56
- Slight   "   → 4 test situations: 17, 18 and 55, 56

If boundary value analysis has not been opted for explicitly, experienced testers will often intuitively apply the slight variant. Indeed, if it is a requirement to test a value from both equivalence classes (above and below the boundary), then "exactly on" and "adjacent to" the boundary value can be selected without any extra effort.

A disadvantage of the slight variant is that this will not uncover certain faults that are found using standard boundary value analysis. An example of this is the previously mentioned fault, in which a "=" has been programmed instead of a "≥".

Boundary value analysis is *not always applicable* to equivalence classes or conditions. Boundaries are not always present. Take, for example, the parameter "Gender" with the values (and therefore equivalence classes) of "M" and "F". There is no such thing as a boundary between the "M" and the "F". This applies also, for example, to all those parameters in a system that belong to 'codes' and 'types'.

Boundary value analysis is not only applicable to the *input side* of a system, but also to the *output side*. Suppose that a sales quote page should contain a maximum of 10 lines. This is then tested using boundary value analysis by printing out an offer with 9 lines, with 10 lines (all the lines on one page) and with 11 lines (eleventh line on second page).

14.3.7 CRUD

The data that are stored and maintained in the system under test have a *life cycle*. This starts when an entity is created and ends when it is removed. In between, the entity is used by updating it or consulting it.

An overview of the life cycle of the data, or entities, is obtained with the aid of a "*CRUD matrix*". This is a matrix in which the entities are shown horizontally on the axes and the functions vertically. The matrix is filled in using the letters C(reate), R(ead), U(pdate) and D(elete). If a function executes a particular action in connection with an entity, this is shown in the matrix by means of a C, R, U and/or D. This is illustrated in figure 14.9.

	Invoice	Article	...
Management of articles	-	C, U, D	...
Create invoice	C	R	...
Desk payment	C, R, D	-	...
...	...	...	...

Figure 14.9: Example of a CRUD matrix.

Creating a CRUD matrix

In order to create the CRUD matrix, *all the* functions in the system are reviewed. For each recognised function, one needs to determine:
- Which entities are used by this function
- Which actions (C, R, U and/or D) are carried out on these entities.

The result of this is entered in the matrix.

In more detail

Often, a special structure is visible that is connected with 2 groups of data and of functions:

• Master data with management functions.

Master data are the basic data in the system. For example, "article" and "customer". They are usually maintained independently of the other data with the aid of the management functions linked to them. This generally has the following effect on the CRUD matrix: with a management function, only the column for the relevant master data is completed, and with all the actions: C, R, U and D. If the master data and management functions are defined first (and in the same sequence) in the CRUD matrix, this part of the CRUD matrix will be filled in solely on the diagonal (with "CRUD")

• Derived data with processing functions

Derived data are data that are produced by the specific business processes, in which master data is used. For example, "Quote" and "Invoice". It is the processing functions that manage the specific business processes and produce and amend the derived data. This generally has the following effect on the CRUD matrix:

> processing functions only execute the action "R" on the master data. All the actions
> can be carried out on the derived data. With the derived data, the management
> function rows are empty. All the actions (C, R, U and D) are carried out by 1 or more
> processing functions.
> In practice, it is of course permitted to deviate from this, but the reason for doing so
> would at least merit investigation.

The use of the CRUD matrix is preferably not delayed until during the testing, but should be delivered as part of the system development by the developer, for the creation of a CRUD matrix is not only useful to testers, but also to the developers themselves: the designing of an information system is usually reasoned from within the functions. Per function, it is described which data will be used. In the creation of a CRUD matrix, reasoning takes place from within the data. Per entity, it is described which functions will use the relevant entity in which way. By creating such a cross-reference table (CRUD matrix) anomalies and/or incomplete areas are sometimes brought to light that would probably not be found with a function-orientated approach, whereas they are now found at an early stage.

Testing the life cycle

The testing of the life cycle consists of 2 parts: the completeness check and the consistency test. These are explained below:

Completeness check

This is a *static* test, in which it is examined in the CRUD matrix whether all 4 possible actions (C, R, U and D) occur with every entity. In other words, has the entire life cycle been implemented for every entity? The lack of an action does not necessarily mean that the system is wrong. However, the reason for it at least requires investigation.

Consistency test

This is a *dynamic* test aimed at integration of the various functions. This checks whether the various functions use an entity in a consistent way. In other words, is the relevant entity being corrupted by one function in such a way that it can no longer be used by the other functions correctly?

Test cases are derived by putting together an entire life cycle of an entity. This is done as follows:

- Every test case starts with a "C", followed by all the possible "U"s and ending with a "D". If there are further possibilities of creating or removing an entity, additional test cases are designed
- After every action (C, U or D), an "R" is carried out once or more. This is to establish that the entity has been correctly processed and is usable for the other functions (has not been corrupted)
- In respect of the relevant entity, all the occurrences of actions (C, R, U and D) in all the functions should be covered by the test cases.

With this, CRUD is fully covered in principle.

More thorough coverage of CRUD can be achieved by requiring that combinations of actions also be fully covered. For example, by requiring that after each "U" *all* the functions with an "R" should be carried out.

The example below illustrates this:

In more detail

Suppose that the entity "Order" is processed as follows by the following functions:
    Create order (C); Cancel order (D); Part-delivery (U); Overview of orders (R);
    Stock control (R)
The standard coverage of CRUD is then achieved with the following test case:

Create order	(C)
Stock control	(R)
Part-delivery	(U)
Overview of orders	(R)
Cancel order	(D)
Overview of orders	(R)

However, with this, the following fault would not be found: after a part-delivery, the stock control is no longer correct, because it is (wrongly) treating the whole order as having been delivered. This fault would have been found with the more thorough variant, which gives the result with the following test case:

Create order	(C)	
Overview of orders	(R)	
Stock control	(R)	
Part-delivery	**(U)**	**(Causes fault in "Stock control")**
Overview of orders	(R)	
Stock control	**(R)**	**(Fault is found)**
Cancel order	(D)	
Overview of orders	(R)	
Stock control	(R)	

14.3.8 Statistical usage: Operational profiles and Load profiles

With this coverage type, it is not the intention to test the system behaviour in separate situations, but to simulate the use of the system in a *statistically responsible* way. In order to test whether the system is proof against the realistic operation of it, that realistic operation needs to be specified one way or another. Such specifications are often called "profiles". The 2 best-known are:

- Operational profiles

  These describe which transactions are carried out by a user and with what frequency. The testing of operational profiles has the aim of examining whether: "The system continues to work correctly when transactions have been carried out *often and over a long time*"

- Load profiles
  These describe the loading under which the system operates in terms of how many users are operating the system at once. The testing of load profiles has the aim of examining whether: "The system works correctly when *many* transactions are carried out by *many* users at once"

Both profiles are further explained below.

Operational profiles

An operational profile describes in quantitative terms how the system is used by a particular type of user. This concept was introduced by John Musa; you are referred to his work [Musa, 1998] for a more comprehensive discussion of operational profiles. Below is a brief explanation.

An operational profile describes the realistic usage by answering the question: "When the system is in *this condition*, how great is the *chance* that *this action* will be carried out by the user?" In the literature, instead of *condition* and *action*, reference is usually made to *history class* and *event*. An operational profile provides a statistical average of how 'the user' handles the system. If various types of users are distinguishable who display significantly varied static average behaviour, it is advisable to create a separate operational profile per user type.

In more detail

For example, for a system on "Internet banking" the following types of users could be distinguished:
- School pupils
- Adult consumers
- Business users

For the creation of an operational profile, the following steps are gone through:

1. Determine the list of possible events
   This covers, in principle, all the actions and events with which the system functionality is activated. These are usually the functions that are carried out by users or connected systems. If various functions have been defined that have a lot to do with each other and which also have the same likelihood of being executed, it is advisable to group these functions. This keeps the operational profile clear.

2. Determine the history classes of the system
   A history class describes the condition in which the system finds itself. It says something about what has happened (the history) with the system. The occurrence of an event (execution of a function) usually results in the system arriving in a different history class.

For example, for a DVD recorder the history classes defined are "Standby", "Record", "Play", "Fast Forward", and "Fast Rewind". If, in the history class of "Play" the user presses the "Forward" button (an event), the system moves into the history class of "Fast Forward". However, if the user presses this button in the history class of "Record", this has no effect and the system remains in the same history class.

In general, it is advisable to nominate a new history class if the probability distribution in respect of the occurrence of the subsequent event changes significantly. It is usual for the first history class to select the initial condition of the system.

3. Determine for each history class the probability distribution of the events
   In other words: how great are the chances that this event will be executed if the system is in this history class. In every history class, the sum of all the probabilities should come out as 1 (or 100%).

The result of these steps can be reproduced in the form of a matrix, as illustrated in figure 14.10. In this, for example, the term $P_{2,1}$ means "the chances that event 1 will be executed by the user in history class 2".

	Event 1	Event 2	...	Event m
History class 1	$P_{1,1}$	$P_{1,2}$	...	$P_{1,m}$
History class 2	$P_{2,1}$	$P_{2,2}$	...	$P_{2,m}$
...	...	...	...	...
History class n	$P_{n,1}$	$P_{n,2}$	...	$P_{n,m}$

Figure 14.10: General content of an operational profile.

There are various ways of obtaining the information required for an operational profile, for example:

- Copying an existing operational profile of a system with similar functionality (e.g. the preceding system)
- Maintaining data (logging) on how often each function is used
- Interviewing users.

It is important here to realise that this does not concern '100% accurate measurements', but estimates that provide a realistic impression of the average use of the system.

Testing operational profiles

A test case consists in this instance of a chain of events that are carried out by the user. The length of a test case is up to the tester, but typically is in the order of some tens of events in sequence. The test case starts in the initial condition (history class 1). Subsequently, the system will move into other history classes, depending on the events that are carried out.

For the creation of each test case, the following steps are performed:

1. Start in history class 1
2. Select the following event to be carried out.

   This is derived directly from the operational profile. With the aid of a random generator, a figure between 0 and 100% is generated and the corresponding event from the operational profile is determined. This results in events occurring in a statistically responsible manner in the test set with large numbers of test cases (in accordance with the probability distribution in the operational profile).
3. Determine into which subsequent history class the system consequently arrives.

   This is determined by how the system functions. It should therefore be derived from the functional specifications of the system.
4. Repeat steps 2 and 3 until the required length of the test case has been reached.

In order to test the realistic usage in a statistically responsible way according to the operational profile, a large number of test cases is required, each carrying out a large number of actions (events). This is more or less impossible to do manually. It is advisable to generate the required test cases automatically. This is not further discussed here, but more information on it can be found in the book "Testing Embedded Software" [Broekman, 2003], among other sources.

Load profiles

Load profiles show the degree to which the system resources (CPU, memory, network capacity) are loaded in reality. The loading is usually shown in terms of the number of users or number of times that a transaction is carried out in a particular period. Usually, the loading of a system is not continuously even, but varies over a period of time: there are peaks and valleys within a 24-hour stretch. Often, weekends will show a different loading from weekdays. And during holiday periods and public holidays, the loading of a system may look different again. In figure 14.11, an example is shown of a load profile over the course of 24 hours.

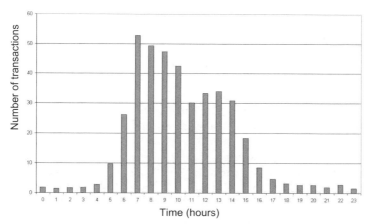

Figure 14.11: Example of a load profile, showing the number of transactions per hour over a full 24-hour period.

For the creation of a load profile, information from the following sources is combined:

- Measuring the loading of the system using specific tools (monitors).
  The responsibility for this usually resides with a department for "Technical System Administration"
- Interviewing users
  In fact, this amount to the following questions: "Which transactions do you carry out? How often, and when?"

Testing load profiles
The testing of load profiles comes under the category of "performance testing" (see also section 10.3.3 "Performance") and is a testing specialism in itself. While it is possible to do manually, tools are usually employed that generate a particular loading of the system. Using the tools, a realistic loading is *simulated*, such as:

- Creation of virtual users
  A virtual user is a small program that simulates a user. On one PC, many such programs can run at once. This avoids the need for the physical presence of a separate PC for each user. This is mainly applied for subjecting the entire system, including the network, to a particular loading
- Offering transactions via the database-management interface
  This creates a certain loading of the back-end of the system without overloading the front-end or the network. It facilitates direct measurement of whether the database server has the appropriate dimensions.

There are various types of performance tests that each have a different goal. The most common are:

- Testing with normal or average usage
  The aim here is to examine whether the available system resources are adequate for the 'usual' circumstances. The idea here is, that it can be commercially advantageous to deploy extra resources for the rare occasions that 'exceptionally heavy loading' takes place
- Testing with peak loading
  The aim here is to examine whether there are sufficient system resources for even the most demanding circumstances that may arise in practice
- Measuring the breaking point
  This is also known as "stress testing". The aim here is to examine what the maximum load is under which the system will still perform acceptably. With a particular system configuration, the loading is stepped up, while the response time is measured. This can be shown in a graph. At the point when the graph shows a sharp incline, the response time increases disproportionately fast (the response 'collapses') and the breaking point has been reached. See also figure 14.12.

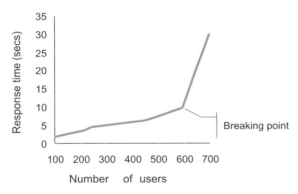

Figure 14.12: Example of the measurement of the breaking point: the maximum load at which the system still performs at an acceptable level.

14.3.9 Right paths / Fault paths

In well-designed systems, checks are built in that protect the system against invalid situations, such as:
- Offering invalid input
- Executing an action without the associated preconditions being met.

In such situations, the system has to carry out correct error handling. That means that the system may not produce unpredictable or undesired results, but should discontinue its processing in a controlled manner.

The aim in the testing of right paths/fault paths is to test both the valid and invalid situations in every defined error situation. An invalid situation should lead to correct error handling, while a valid situation should be accepted by the system without error handling.

The aim is not to test all the possible variations within the valid situations. For example, in the testing of the function "Create order", it is sufficient to establish one time that the system creates a permitted order correctly. If you also wish to test how the tens of variations in permitted orders are handled by the system, other coverage types for this can be applied, such as equivalence classes, modified condition/decision coverage, pairwise testing, etc.

Inventorying test situations: right paths/fault paths

The test situations are the collection of all the right paths and fault paths with every defined error handling. To inventory which error processings are to be tested, in principle 2 sources can be drawn on:

- From the data
  "Are there certain values or combinations of values defined that are not permitted for the relevant functionality?"
  In fact, this refers to a special application of the principle of *equivalence classes*: Each considered entity is divided into one valid and one or more invalid equivalence classes
- From the process steps
  "Have specific control steps been nominated in the process or algorithm that precede the processing?"
  In fact, this refers to decision points with the standard outcomes: Continue with the processing steps (right path); produce error message and discontinue processing (fault path).

Points of focus in the coverage of the fault paths

With an error processing, several conditions may play a role in determining whether the relevant situation is permitted or not. That means that several fault paths also exist, namely one for every condition that is not met. However, there is only one right path, namely if all the conditions are met.

With the testing of the fault paths, it should be ensured that *no more than one invalid situation at a time* is tested. If several invalid test situations are combined on one test case, there is the risk of "masking" faults: in the processing of the first invalid situation, the system correctly discontinues processing and consequently the second invalid situation is not tested. This is illustrated by the following example:

In more detail

For the issue of a loan, the following 2 conditions must be met:
- Age should be greater than or equal to 18
- Loan sum may not be higher than the annual salary.
Suppose that both error processes were to be tested with one test case, in which the

age is lower than 18 and the loan sum greater than the annual salary. The system
rightly produces an error message after it has established that the age does not meet
the condition. The check on the loan sum is now skipped. If in the system the error
processing of the loan sum is wrong or even not implemented at all, this will not be
found with the one test case.

An additional disadvantage of test cases with more than one invalid situation
is that if the error message does not explicitly state what is wrong, it cannot be
determined which invalid situation has caused the error message.

14.3.10 Checklist

Definition

With the coverage type "Checklist", all the situations are tested that are summed up
in an unstructured list.

This coverage type is applicable to, for example:
- Testing requirements
  The requirements describe what is required of the system, without going into
  detail about how exactly they are realised. For example: "Payment should
  also be possible in foreign currency." In principle, for every requirement
  1 or more test cases are created to test that precise requirement. Some
  requirements are not testable and should then be removed from the
  checklist. For example: "With this system, the company's market share
  should increase by 20%."
- Testing use cases
  The same largely applies here as to requirements, except that this concerns
  user scenarios instead of system requirements.
- Testing user-friendliness aspects
  Examples of this are: understandable error messages; possibility of "undoing"
  the last action; maximum of 10 fields per screen. See also Nielsen's ten
  heuristics in section 10.3.2 "Usability". This delivers a checklist of things
  to be tested with every function or screen in the system and that can be
  checked off during the testing.

It is a very simple coverage type in which the test cases are derived directly with
no interim steps. Because there is no structure (therefore no dependencies
between the defined situations), every line on the checklist can be checked
separately and directly, and the sequence of the test cases is not important.
However, the concrete working out into physical test cases is not always simple
and can involve a lot of work. In addition, it should be realised that the
checklist generally only achieves elementary coverage. For example, in the

testing of requirements it only provides the certainty that every requirement has been tested once. This is not to say that it proves that the requirements have been correctly implemented in all the expected situations.

It is also a coverage type that has little trouble with any changes in the test basis (and so the checklist itself). If a line is added to the checklist, a test case is added with which the relevant line is tested.

This coverage type also offers the possibility of directing in a simple way how far the testing should go, and of measuring how far the testing has progressed:

- In the planning or preparation phase, the lines in the checklist are prioritised, e.g. with H(igh) - M(edium) – L(ow). Another common means of notation of priorities is the MOSCOW notation: Must have; Should have; Could have; Would have. In the execution phase, the lines (and so the associated test cases) are then executed in order of priority
- During test execution, the degree of coverage so far obtained can be reported on. This is measured as follows:
  Degree of coverage = (Number of tested lines) / (total number of lines)
  This strongly corresponds with progress (and is even exactly equal if test cases are 1-to-1 with the lines of the checklist):
  Progress = (Number of test cases executed) / (total number of test cases).

14.4 A basic set of test design techniques

14.4.1 Introduction

The place of test design techniques in the test process

Definition

A test design technique is a standardised method of deriving test cases from a particular test basis that will achieve a certain coverage.

In the "Planning" phase, it is determined for every test type whether test design techniques will be applied, and if so, which ones. This is described in depth in the sections 6.2.5 "Determining the test strategy" and 6.2.8 "Allocating test units and test techniques". The choice of a particular test design technique mainly depends on:

- The system characteristics (usually the quality characteristics) that are to be tested
- The depth of testing to which these system characteristics will be subjected

- The available relevant information on the system characteristics. This defines the test basis for the test design technique
- The appropriate coverage types – together with the basic techniques – that can be applied to the test basis.

Test design techniques are applied in the "Specification" phase, in which the test cases and test scripts are specified in five generic steps (see section 6.6.1 "Creating test specifications"):

1. Identifying test situations
2. Creating logical test cases
3. Creating physical test cases
4. Establishing the starting point
5. Creating the test script

The first two steps result in the logical test design, with which the required coverage is guaranteed. The last three steps result in the physical test design that will provide sound preparation for the test execution. See also section 14.2.1 "Test situation, test case and test script".

Setup and structure of this section

This section offers a varied set of test design techniques that most organisations can apply immediately. The list is not exhaustive. To supplement it, a test organisation could consult the literature, such as [Beizer, 1990] and [Copeland, 2003], or even create new techniques, as described at the end of this introduction.

The description of each test design technique in this section covers the following subjects:

- *Description*
  This provides a concise impression of the technique by means of a brief sketch of the most important features, such as
  - The goal of the test
  - The test basis required
  - The basic techniques applied
  - Tips for variations in the technique.
- *Points of focus in the steps*
  This explains how the generic steps are specifically elaborated for the relevant test design technique.

The emphasis is on the first two steps, in which the test situations and logical test cases are designed, since this is where the biggest distinction exists between the various test design techniques.

The next two steps, in which the logical test cases are translated into physical test cases, are generally the same for most test design techniques and therefore are given less emphasis. They have already largely been described in the sections 6.6.1 "Creating test specifications" and 14.2.1 "Test situation, test case and test script".

The final step, "Creating the test script", is not set out in this section, since the process is too organisation-specific and does not vary per test design technique. More on this has been provided in the previously mentioned sections 6.6.1 and 14.2.1.

Where possible, a concrete example has been set out in detail. This can be used as a test-specification template for the relevant test design technique.

For a detailed explanation of the applied basic techniques, section 14.3 "Coverage types and basic techniques" should be consulted.

Creating new test design techniques

Test design techniques exist in many variants and combinations. A test design technique is a specific application of the general basic techniques to a company-specific situation. Depending on which system characteristics a company attaches importance to, and how the system behaviour is defined, a company can formulate its own tailor-made test design technique. In creating such a 'new' test design technique, the following questions should be answered:

- What is to be tested?
  This says something about the quality characteristics or test type for which the test design technique is intended.
- What information is available for this?
  All the available relevant information should be sought out and collected. This defines the test basis for the test design technique.
- What kind of situations are to be tested, and how thoroughly should they be covered?
  This should be expressed in the definition of one or more coverage types and associated basic techniques.
- In which form should the test design be documented?
  Are the test specifications to be established as text, in tables or spreadsheets, or in a specific test tool?

Overview of the test design techniques

Table 14.3 summarises the most important features of the test design techniques discussed here. This can be of assistance in comparing the techniques and in selecting the most suitable ones.

Test design technique	Coverage types / basic techniques	Test basis	Quality characteristic / Test type
Decision Table Test	Multiple condition coverage	Individual conditions of decision tables, without structure	Detail functionality
Data Combination Test	Equivalence classes and (Multiple condition coverage or pairwise testing)	All types of test basis	Overall functionality Detail functionality
Elementary Comparison Test	Modified condition / decision coverage	Structured functional specifications, such as pseudo-code	Detail functionality
Error Guessing	--	All types of test basis	Diverse
Exploratory Testing	Diverse, according to choice	All types of test basis	Diverse
Data Cycle Test	CRUD and Decision coverage	CRUD matrix Data-integrity rules	Overall functionality Connectivity Suitability
Process Cycle Test	Path coverage test depth level 2	Structured description of business or operating processes	Suitability
Real-Life Test	Statistically responsible simulation	Operational profiles Load profiles	Effectivity Connectivity Performance
Semantic Test	Modified condition / decision coverage	Input and output specifications Business rules	Functionality / Validation test
Syntactic Test	Checklist	Input and output specifications Descriptions of attributes	Functionality / Validation test User-friendliness
Use Case Test	Checklist	Use cases	Suitability Effectivity User-friendliness

Table 14.3: Overview of the most important features of the described test design techniques.

14.4.2 Decision Table Test (DTT)

Description

The decision table test is a thorough technique for the testing of detail functionality. The required test basis contains conditions or decision tables. The type and structure of this test basis is of minor importance to the application of the decision table test technique.

The decision table test is aimed at the thorough coverage of the conditions and not at combining functional paths. The basic technique used here is:

- Decision points: multiple condition coverage

Variations on the decision table test can be created by applying the basic technique:

- Decision points: condition coverage, decision coverage or condition/ decision coverage. With these, decision points can be tested in *less depth*
- Boundary value analysis
  With this, the possibilities of a condition can be tested in *more depth*.

It is a preferred technique for the testing of functions and/or complex calculations considered to be very important.

Points of focus in the steps

In this section, the decision table test is explained step by step, taking the generic steps as a starting point (see 14.4.1 "Introduction"). An example is also set out showing at every step how this technique works.

The test basis consists of decision tables, pseudo-code, a process description or other (functional) descriptions, in which conditions occur. The conditions *and* the results are put into a decision table. The general shape of a decision table after step 2 – "Creating logical test cases" is shown in table 14.4.

Identification table				
Test situations	1	2	..	n
Condition 1	0	0	..	1
Condition 2	0	~	..	0
Condition ..	0	..	~	0
Condition n	0	1	..	0
Result 1	X	..	..	..
Result ..	..	..	..	..
Result n	..	..	..	..
Not possible	..	..	X	..

Table 14.4: Decision table.

Each column of the decision table forms a test situation. The part above the double line forms the situation description and the part below the line reflects the consequences, or the results.

The conditions can have the values of "0" or "1" (see also section 14.3.3). The value "1" means that the condition is true; the value "0" means that the condition is false. The value "~" can also be allocated. This means that the value of the condition is not important. Below the double line, the cells contain an "X", or are empty. Where there is an "X", the relevant result occurs in that test situation; if a cell is empty, the relevant result does not occur in that test situation. Several results are possible per test situation. "Not possible" indicates that the test situation is not physically executable, for example because certain values of conditions exclude each other.

Example

When ordering coffee capsules via the Internet, the shipping costs are calculated. These consist of the standard shipping costs, plus a long-distance supplement. The text below shows the associated process description.

Shipping costs calculation:
Calculation of standard shipping costs
If 200 or more capsules are ordered and if the form of payment is "direct debit", then no shipping cost is applied. If fewer than 200 capsules are ordered, or if the form of payment is other than "direct debit", then a shipping cost of €10 is applied.
Calculation of long-distance supplement
If the delivery address for the capsules is within a radius of 50 km of Utrecht, no long-distance supplement is applied. If the delivery address is 50 km or more from Utrecht, but still in the Netherlands, then a long-distance supplement of €5 is applied. If the delivery address is outside of the Netherlands, then a long-distance supplement of €15 is applied. (The highest sum is applied.)

Below, each step is set out showing how the decision table test is applied to this process:

1- Identifying test situations
To fill in the table, in step 1 "Identifying test situations" the following activities are carried out:
- Find conditions in the test basis
- Create a conditions list
- Find results in the test basis and add these to the conditions list
- Fill in the decision table.

The activities are explained below:
The finding of conditions involves a degree of detective work. Often, a condition in the test basis is preceded by words such as "if" and "then" and can be looked for by this means.

Example

The tester has underlined the conditions in the process description.
Shipping costs calculation:
Calculation of standard shipping costs
If 200 or more capsules are ordered *and* if the form of payment is "direct debit", then no standard shipping costs are applied. If fewer than 200 capsules are ordered or if the form of payment is other than "direct debit", then a standard shipping cost of €10 is applied.
Calculation of long-distance supplement
If the delivery address for the capsules is within a radius of 50 km from Utrecht, then no long-distance cost is applied. If the delivery address is 50 km or more from Utrecht, but still in the Netherlands, then a long-distance supplement of €5 is applied. If the delivery address is outside of the Netherlands, then a long-distance supplement of €15 is applied.

Subsequently, a conditions list is created. If the test basis is a decision table, the conditions can often be copied one for one. In creating the list, the following rules are applied. These rules are created in order to keep the decision tables clear and intelligible:

- A condition is singular (therefore without "AND" or "OR" constructions)
- A condition is formulated positively (in order to avoid "not not" combinations)
- Try to keep the number of conditions per table to five or lower (that is maximum $2^5 = 32$ test columns). If there are more conditions, split the table into several tables.

Example

Concerning the shipping costs calculation, the tester arrives at the following conditions list:
Calculation of standard shipping costs
C1 order ≥ 200 capsules
C2 form of payment = "direct debit"
Calculation of long-distance supplement
C3 distance < 50 km from Utrecht
C4 country = The Netherlands

Creating a conditions list may require some interpretation of the description. There often appears to be more conditions necessary in order to reach a particular situation. In that case, investigate whether there is indeed a supplementary condition or if a particular situation can be realised by one or more of the recognised conditions being false.

When the conditions list is known, the results are added to it. The tracing of the results also involves some detective work. A result is often preceded in the test basis by words such as "then" and "else".

Example

The tester has underlined the results in the process description.

Shipping costs calculation:
Calculation of standard shipping costs
If 200 or more capsules are ordered *and* if the form of payment is "direct debit", <u>then no standard shipping costs are applied</u>. If fewer than 200 capsules are ordered or if the form of payment is other than "direct debit", <u>then a standard shipping cost of €10 is applied</u>.

Calculation of long-distance supplement
If the delivery address for the capsules is within a radius of 50 km from Utrecht, <u>then no long-distance supplement is applied</u>. If the delivery address is 50 km or more from Utrecht, but still in the Netherlands, <u>then a long-distance supplement of €5 is applied</u>. If the delivery address is outside of the Netherlands, <u>then a long-distance supplement of €15 is applied</u>.
The tester adds the results to the conditions list:

Calculation of standard shipping costs:
C1 Order ≥ 200 capsules
C2 Form of payment = "Direct debit"
R1 Standard shipping costs := 0
R2 Standard shipping costs := 10

Calculation of long-distance supplement
C3 Distance < 50 km from Utrecht
C4 Country = The Netherlands
R3 Long-distance supplement := 0
R4 Long-distance supplement := 5
R5 Long-distance supplement := 15

Now that both conditions and results are known, the decision table is filled in in accordance with multiple condition coverage.

Example

Since the total number of conditions amounts to four, the tester has decided to include these in one table[1]. The conditions list and the filling in of the tables according to multiple condition coverage deliver table 14.5 with test situations for the shipping costs example.

---

[1] This is irrelevant to the final number of combinations. Consider: in the shipping costs example, one table is created with four conditions in total. This leads to one table with maximum $2^4 = 16$ combinations. In the example, the table could be split into two tables ("Calculation of standard shipping cost" and "Calculation of long-distance supplement"). Both tables would then consist of $2^2 = 4$ test columns. Those, in combination with each other, would give 4*4, or 16 combinations. Since splitting or nor splitting the table makes no difference to the final result, it is advisable to split tables with more than five conditions into several tables, since this makes the individual tables clear and intelligible.

Shipping costs calculation (test situations)																
Std. shipping costs / Long-distance supplement	1	2	3	4	5	6	7	8	9	10	11	12	13	14	15	16
C1 Order ≥ 200 capsules	0	0	0	0	0	0	0	0	1	1	1	1	1	1	1	1
C2 Form of payment = "direct debit"	0	0	0	0	1	1	1	1	1	1	1	1	0	0	0	0
C3 Distance < 50 km from Utrecht	0	0	1	1	1	1	0	0	0	0	1	1	1	1	0	0
C4 Country = The Netherlands	0	1	1	0	0	1	1	0	0	1	1	0	0	1	1	0
R1 Std. shipping cost := 0									X	X	X	X				
R2 Std. shipping cost := 10	X	X	X	X	X	X	X	X					X	X	X	X
R3 Long-distance supplement := 0		X	X	X	X						X	X	X	X		
R4 Long-distance supplement := 5		X					X			X					X	
R5 Long-distance supplement := 15	X			X	X			X	X				X	X			X

Table 14.5: Table with test situations filled in using multiple condition coverage.

Reading a table is often thought to be difficult. Test situation 7, for example, is read as follows:
The customer has ordered fewer than 200 capsules AND has selected the "direct debit" payment form AND the delivery address is 50 km or more from Utrecht AND the delivery address is in the Netherlands. The shipping costs amount to €10 standard cost plus €5 long-distance supplement, equals €15.

Filling in a table with ones and zeros can be done in many ways. The manner of doing so in the above "Shipping costs calculation" table simplifies the creation of physical test cases (see "In more detail" below for explanation).

In more detail

Note the handy way of filling in the "Shipping costs calculation" decision table. This causes only one condition to change in value per column (referred to in the literature under the name of: "Gray-code"). This is helpful for the creation of the physical test cases: copy and paste and change one value. For the filling in, we begin at the bottom row of conditions with one 0 followed by, consecutively, two times 1, two times 0 and so on until the last, which is given the value 0. In the row second from the bottom, we begin with two times 0 followed by, consecutively, four times 1, four times 0, and so on until the last two, which are given the value 0. We continue like this with the whole table; in every row the zero and one sets are twice as long as in the previous row.

In more detail

Instead of filling in the decision table according to the basic technique of multiple condition coverage, a (more elementary) variant could be chosen at the stage when the strategy is being determined. This technique is applied both to the conditions and to the results. As an example, the "shipping costs calculation" table 14.6 has been filled in according to the condition/decision coverage.

Shipping costs calculation (test situations)			
Std. shipping costs / long-distance supplement	**1**	**2**	**11**
C1 Order ≥ 200 capsules	0	0	1
C2 Form of payment = "direct debit"	0	0	1
C3 Distance < 50 km from Utrecht	0	0	1
C4 Country = The Netherlands	0	1	1
R1 St. shipping costs := 0			X
R2 St. Shipping cost := 10	X	X	
R3 Long-distance supplement := 0			X
R4 Long-distance supplement := 5		X	
R5 Long-distance supplement := 15	X		

Table 14.6: Table with test situations, filled in using condition/decision coverage.

With the three columns, all the possible outcomes of each condition *and* of each result are covered at least once. The columns 1 and 11 cover all the conditions, and column 2 is necessary to cover result 4 as well.
Several combinations of columns are possible that meet with the condition/decision coverage (e.g. 3, 9, 10 and 2, 11, 16).

In more detail

Besides conditions that can only assume the values of true or false, parameters also exist with more than 2 possible values (i.e.: equivalence classes). There are two ways of dealing with these:
1. Split the parameters into several conditions that can only be true or false. The approach described in this section can then be used.
2. Add as many columns as there are possible equivalence classes, whereby the content of the other rows of conditions does not change. Suppose that in the example there is a choice of three forms of payment: direct debit, giro transfer and cash. Then, as an example, the 'old' test situation 1 would lead to the following 3 'new' test situations in this approach:

Std. shipping costs / long-distance supplement	1	2	3
C1 Order ≥ 200 capsules	0	0	0
C2 Form of payment	"direct debit"	"Giro tr."	"Cash"
C3 Distance < 50 km from Utrecht	0	0	0
C4 Country = The Netherlands	0	0	0
R2 St. Shipping cost := 10	X	X	X
R5 Long-distance supplement := 15	X	X	X

For more information on this, refer to "N-wise testing" in section 14.3.5 "Orthogonal arrays and pairwise testing" and to books on theory, such as [Copeland, 2003].

2- Creating logical test cases

The test situations (columns) in step 1 now constitute the logical test cases. However, a logical test case must not contain 'mutually exclusive conditions', since that would make the test case inconsistent in itself, and therefore unexecutable. In the step from test situations to logical test cases, any unexecutable test cases should be traced. These test cases are marked "Not possible" in the table.

Example

In the shipping costs example, the conditions C3 and *not*-C4 exclude each other. There are no foreign locations within a radius of 50 km from Utrecht. Therefore, 4 of the 16 logical test cases are unexecutable, see table 14.7 (next page).

Shipping costs calculation (logical test cases)																
Std. shipping costs / long-distance supplement	1	2	3	4	5	6	7	8	9	10	11	12	13	14	15	16
C1 Order ≥ 200 capsules	0	0	0	0	0	0	0	0	1	1	1	1	1	1	1	1
C2 Form of payment = "direct debit"	0	0	0	0	1	1	1	1	1	1	1	1	0	0	0	0
C3 Distance < 50 km from Utrecht	0	0	1	1	1	1	0	0	0	0	1	1	1	1	0	0
C4 Country = The Netherlands	0	1	1	0	0	1	1	0	0	1	1	0	0	1	1	0
R1 Std. shipping cost := 0									X	X	X					
R2 St. Shipping cost := 10	X	X	X			X	X	X						X	X	X
R3 Long-distance supplement := 0			X			X					X			X		
R4 Long-distance supplement := 5		X					X			X					X	
R5 Long-distance supplement := 15	X							X	X							X
Not possible				X	X							X	X			

Check for yourself that the logical test cases 4, 5, 12 and 13 are not executable.
Table 14.7: Table with logical test cases.

For the logical test cases with the result of "Not possible", no physical test case exists. Ideally, these columns should not be removed, so that no misunderstanding can arise as to why no physical test case is present for a particular logical test case.

3- *Creating physical test cases*
With a physical test case, all the data that play a part in the conditions are translated into concrete terms. To this end, the table of logical test cases can simply be adapted for making the test cases physical. In the table of physical test cases, each numbered column describes a physical test case and the last row(s) contain(s) the predicted result(s). For the entries:
- The "0" or the "1" is replaced in the table with a physical value
- The physical value is entered in the place of an "X".

A point of focus with the first bullet is that in the table of physical test cases, no conditions remain, only data. A particular data attribute can occur in several conditions. In logical test cases, they occur in several rows, while that particular data naturally only occurs once in the table for physical test cases. Besides this, it is possible that additional refinements are required. For example, by putting derived data into concrete terms (see example below):

Example

For the creation of physical test cases, the "Place of delivery" has to be derived from "Distance from Utrecht". This delivers the table 14.8 (as an example, 8 of the 12 logical test cases are shown):

Shipping costs calculation (physical test cases)								
	1	**2**	**6**	**7**	**9**	**10**	**11**	**16**
Number of capsules	199	199	199	199	200	200	200	200
Form of payment	cash	cash	dir.dbt.	dir.dbt.	dir.dbt.	dir.dbt.	dir.dbt.	cash
Distance from Utrecht	178	182	10	182	178	182	10	178
Place of delivery	Brussels	Heerlen	Zeist	Heerlen	Brussels	Heerlen	Zeist	Brussels
Country	B	NL	NL	NL	B	NL	NL	B
St. shipping cost	10	10	10	10	0	0	0	10
Long-distance suppl.	15	5	0	5	15	5	0	15
Total shipping costs	25	15	10	15	15	5	0	25

The logical test cases 4, 5, 12 and 13 are not executable and can therefore not be made physical.

Table 14.8: Table with physical test cases.

In more detail

The decision table test can be reinforced by the application of a boundary value analysis. This option is included as an extra condition in the creation of the logical test cases. In the example, this condition could be included in respect of the number of capsules and the distance. The requirement then is that for the "number of capsules" at least the values of 199, 200 and 201 should occur (e.g. in columns 9, 10 and 11) and for "distance" at least the values of 49, 50 and 51 (e.g. in columns 1, 2 and 7).. The number of test cases does not change with this approach.

Another possibility is to include a separate column for each value. This is a thorough method that tests all the combinations, but it is labour-intensive. The number of test cases increases with this approach.

4- Establishing the starting point
No remarks.

Example
The customer's details that are relevant to the placing of an order should be present in the information system.

14.4.3 Data Combination Test (DCoT)

Description

The data combination test (DCoT) is a versatile technique for the testing of functionality both at detail level and at overall system level. In the embedded world, this technique is also known as the "Classification Tree Method". It was developed by Grochtmann and Grimm, and is described in "Testing Embedded Software" [Broekman, 2003] and elsewhere.

For the DCoT, no specific test basis is required. All types of information on the functionality of the system are usable:

- Formal system documentation, such as functional design, logical data model and requirements
- Informal documentation, such as manuals, folders, pre-surveys and memos
- Domain expertise that is not documented, but resides 'in the experts' heads'.

The fact that domain expertise is usable as a test basis also makes this technique suitable for situations in which specifications are incomplete or out of date, or even unavailable altogether.

Because of the strongly informal character of this technique, the quality of the test cases designed with it is largely determined by the expertise and skill of those involved. For that reason, the DCoT is preferably carried out by a team of 2 to 5 persons with a *mix of expertise*: test, domain and system expertise.

Tip
Organise a 'creative session', such as brainstorming or meta-planning, in which the tester acts as moderator of the process. Invite one expert to this session from every relevant discipline, e.g. a user, an administrator and a system developer or system architect. The experts will supply the substantive information, which can be structured by the tester and converted into test situations and test cases.

With the DCoT, the test situations are determined by reasoning from within the data attribute as to which variations should be tested. The basic technique used here:

- Equivalence classes

Depending on the agreed depth of the test, the coverage can be extended by fully combining the equivalence classes of two or more different data. In this, the following basic techniques can be used:

- Pairwise testing
- Complete decision table (multiple condition coverage) on selected data attributes.

Besides these, there is the option of reinforcing the test by applying *boundary value analysis*. This can also be applied selectively, by defining the boundary values for specific data attributes as a separate equivalence class.

Thanks to its versatility, the data combination test is suitable both for testing those functions that are deemed very important, and for testing system parts that 'just need a quick test'.

Points of focus in the steps

In this section, the data combination test is explained step by step. In this, the generic steps (see 14.4.1 "Introduction") are taken as a starting point. An example is also set out, showing at each step how this technique works.

Example

This example concerns a function for creating flight reservations:

With this function, the user enters a number of details concerning the nature of the group (adults, children and babies) and the trip (such as date and destination). The user can then select the search criteria relating to a suitable flight. The system displays the list of possible flights, or reports if no flight exists that meets the criteria and still has the required places available.

The function should be tested to average depth using the DCoT.

1- Identifying test situations

Identifying test situations is the creative step in the process and is ideally carried out by a team in which various forms of expertise are represented. During this step, the following activities are carried out:

- Determine the data attributes that influence the functionality

  This does not automatically mean all the data attributes that are *used* by the function. It concerns the data attributes that are of influence on *variations* in the system behaviour. This includes the data attributes for which equivalence classes can be determined. The defined data can consist

of entities, attributes or functional concepts in a general sense.
- Determine the equivalence classes for each data attribute
See section 14.3.4. for this.
- Determine the relationships between the data attributes
Some data attributes are only of influence on the system behaviour under certain conditions, namely if another data attribute has a value from a specific equivalence class. That means that the possible variations of the first-mentioned data attribute *must* be combined with the specific value of the last-mentioned data attribute. In the example set out, such a relationship is visible between the data attributes "search criterion" and "flies to that destination".
The result can be illustrated in a 'classification tree':
- Data attributes that logically belong together can be grouped under an overall title, such as "personal details" or "employer types"
- Under every data attribute the equivalence classes are hung, like branches on the tree
- Relationships between the data can be shown simply by hanging the relevant parts of the classification tree directly under the relevant equivalence class.

The creation of the classification tree with which the test situations are identified is an iterative and interactive process, in which the parties involved inspire, correct and complement each other. How far this process will go is the choice and responsibility of the team. A test manager who wishes to keep this well under control will provide a concrete job description for the team and request regular feedback on the results.
If required, it is defined which data attributes are eligible for 'fully combined testing'. That means that all the possible combinations of all the equivalence classes of those data attributes should be tested. How many of such combinations can be defined depends on the agreed depth of testing.

Tip

The following can serve as a guideline:

Elementary	None, or only one data pair.
Average	Two or more data pairs. This offers a scale of increasing depth of testing that ends with "pairwise testing".
Thorough	Average depth + boundary value analysis.

Instead of combinations of two data (data pair), it can also be defined that all the combinations of three data (data triplet) should be tested. This should be treated as an increase in the depth category.

Example
For the function of "flight reservation", the team has worked out the classification tree in figure 14.13.

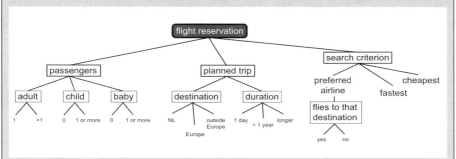

Figure 14.13: Example of a classification tree.

In this, the following aspects, among others, are important:
- A passenger may be an adult, child or baby. A baby does not get its own seat on the plane
- A planned trip that takes longer than a year could lead to confusion in regard the return date
- An airline may or may not fly to the intended destination. This is solely relevant under the condition that this company is offered as a search criterion.

Two data pairs have been defined, fitting the agreed average depth of testing, which should be tested in total combination:
- Child – baby (4 mandatory combinations)
- Destination – flying to that destination (6 mandatory combinations)

2- Creating logical test cases
With a logical test case, precisely *one* of the equivalence classes is covered for *each* data attribute in the classification tree. Collectively, the logical test cases should at any rate cover all the equivalence classes of all the data attributes. Depending on the chosen depth of testing, they should also cover all the combinations of equivalence classes of particular data attributes, if necessary. In principle, there are two ways of demonstrating this clearly:

- In table form
  This method is usually employed where the "pairwise testing" option has been adopted (see section 14.3.5). Tools for pairwise testing normally deliver their results directly in table form.
- Graphic depiction of a 'classification tree'
  This is particularly useful if the most elementary form of testing (without combinations) has been chosen, or for the selective application of "complete decision table" coverage. Ideally, a graphic tool should be used

here. The freeware tool "Classification Tree Editor", which was specially developed for this purpose by DaimlerChrysler, can be downloaded via the Internet (www.systematic-testing.com).

Example

The logical test cases are shown with the aid of the classification tree, see figure 14.14.

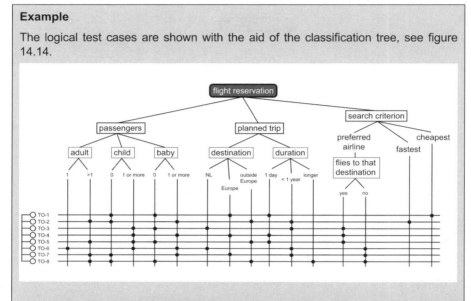

Figure 14.14: Example of a classification tree with logical test cases.

Allowance is made here for the two data pairs that are to be tested in full combination. Test cases TC1 to TC4 incl. cover the data pair "Child - Baby", while the data pair "Destination – Flies to destination" is covered by the test cases TC3 to TC8 incl.
N.B. To obtain the minimum coverage, in which all the equivalence classes are solely covered without combinations of data pairs, 4 logical test cases are sufficient here, e.g. TC1, TC2, TC3 and TC8.

3- Creating physical test cases

In creating the physical test cases, concrete values should be chosen for all the input data. These input data do not always correspond exactly with the concepts maintained in the classification tree. For example, the classification tree may contain the concept of "duration", while the function to be tested expects the data "Start date" and "End date".

Every physical test case should have a concrete predicted result. However, this generally depends on the other data and system settings that belong with the chosen starting point.

Example

In order to illustrate the principle, 4 test cases are made physical in figure 14.9. With every test case, the physical values are defined for all the necessary input data and the predicted result is described in concrete terms.

	TC1	TC2	TC3	TC6
Customer name	Jansen	Breugel	Voort	Hansma
#Adults	1	2	3	1
#Children	0	0	1	4
#Babies	0	2	0	1
Destination	France-CdG	Singapore	The Netherlands-Eindhoven Airport	The Netherlands-Eindhoven Airport
Departure date	12-02-2006	14-02-2006	15-02-2006	16-02-2006
Return date	12-02-2006	15-02-2006	15-04-2006	23-02-2006
Search criterion	Cheapest	Fastest	KLM	Senegal Airlines
Predicted result				Message: "Airline does not fly to chosen destination"
Airline	Korean Air	Canada Air	KLM	
Flight number	KA0455	CA0833	KL1288	
Price	€ 44	€ 865	€ 83	

Table 14.9: Physical test cases for "flight reservation".

In order to predict the results of every physical test case, it is necessary to know exactly which flights and prices are stored in the database. This step goes hand-in-hand with the next step, "Establishing the starting point".

4- Establishing the starting point
No remarks.

Example

The following database has to be loaded:"TST_RES_03". This contains in particular the situation that the company "Senegal Airlines" exists, but does not recognise "Eindhoven Airport" as a destination.
Set the system date to 01-02-2006(1 February 2006).

14.4.4 Elementary Comparison Test (ECT)

Description

The elementary comparison test (ECT) is a thorough technique for the detailed testing of the functionality. The necessary test basis is pseudo-code or a comparable specification in which the decision points and functional paths are worked out in detail and structurally.

The ECT aims at thorough coverage of the decision points and not at the combining of functional paths. The basic technique used here is:

- Decision points: modified condition/decision coverage

Variations on the ECT can be created by the application of the following basic techniques:

- Decision points: multiple condition coverage
  With this, the possibilities within the decision points (specifically selected, if necessary) can be tested in more depth.
- Boundary value analysis
  With this, the possibilities within the decision points (specifically selected, if necessary) can be tested in more depth.
- Pairwise testing
  With this, the testing of possible combinations of functional paths is added.

It is a preferred technique for testing functions deemed very important and/or complex calculations.

Points of focus in the steps

In this section, the elementary comparison test is explained step by step. In this, the generic steps (see 14.4.1 "Introduction") are taken as a starting point. An example is also set out, showing at every step how this technique works.

Example

In this example, we take a function (task) in which the data referring to the car owner are entered in a screen and subsequently, upon request, a calculation is made of the premium that the car owner should pay for his vehicle insurance. Depending on a number of variables, the level of the premium is established. The pseudo-code below gives a detailed functional description of this:

```
IF              Age < 18 years OR driving licence suspended
THEN            Error message
ELSE    IF      Age < 25 years AND years holding driving licence < 3
        THEN            Premium := 1,500
        ELSE            Premium := 800
        ENDIF
        IF      Car age < 2 OR (car age ≥ 5 AND damage in last 3 years ≥ 2,500)
                OR age ≥ 70
```

	THEN	Increase premium by 500
	ENDIF	
ENDIF		

It is set out per step below how the elementary comparison test is applied to this function:

1- Identifying test situations

The test basis consists of pseudo-code or a comparable formal function description which can be copied directly in this step. If not, an extra activity should be carried out in order to convert the existing specifications into pseudo-code.

The decision points in the pseudo-code are provided with unique identification. It is usual to use the codes D1, D2, etc. for this (or D01, D02, etc. if there are many decision points).

Example
There are three decision points, which are shown structurally below:

D1	IF	Age < 18 years OR Driving licence suspended
	THEN	Error message
D2	ELSE IF	Age < 25 years AND number of years holding driving licence < 3
	THEN	Premium := 1,500
	ELSE	Premium := 800
	EINDIF	
D3	IF	Car age < 2 OR (car age ≥ 5 AND damage in 3 years ≥ 2,500) OR Age ≥ 70
	THEN	Increase premium by 500
	ENDIF	
	ENDIF	

Per decision point, the basic technique for MCDC (modified condition/ decision coverage) is applied. The resulting test situations are numbered. The combination of this number and the decision point provides a unique identification of the test situations (such as D1-1, D1-2, etc.). The numbering begins with the test situations from column "1" (True) and then from the column "0" (False).

For each decision point, the test situations are worked out in detail in a separate table. The rows of the table contain the data or parameters that occur in the conditions of the decision point. A column then indicates which requirements are set on each parameter for the relevant test situation.

Example

D1 A OR B	1 Error message	0
A: Age < 18	<u>1</u> 0 (1)	<u>0</u> 0 (3)
B: Driving licence suspended	0 <u>1</u> (2)	~~0 0~~

D2 A AND B	1 Premium = 1,500	0 Premium = 800
A: Age < 25	<u>1</u> 1 (1)	<u>0</u> 1 (2)
B: # years with driving licence< 3	~~1 1~~	1 <u>0</u> (3)

D3 A OR (B AND C) OR D	1 Premium + 500	0
A: Car age < 2	<u>1</u> 0 1 0 (1) (or 1 **1** 0 0, but that gives a logical contradiction, or 1 **0** 0 0)	<u>0</u> 0 1 0 (4)
B: Car age ≥ 5	0 <u>1</u> 1 0 (2)	~~0 0 1 0~~
C: 3 years-damage ≥ 2,500	~~0 1 1 0~~	0 1 <u>0</u> 0 (5)
D: Age ≥ 70	0 **1** 0 **1** (3) (of 0 **0** 1 1, or 0 **0** 0 1)	~~0 1 0 0~~

NB! In D3, the combination "A = true and B = true" gives a logical contradiction and therefore may not occur in the test situations: Car age should be simultaneously lower than 2 and higher than, or equal to, 5. This contradiction would otherwise show up when the test cases are made physical.

Detailed working out of the derived test situations:

Test situations D1	D1-1	D1-2	D1-3
Age	< 18	≥ 18	≥ 18
Driving licence suspended	N	Y	N

Test situations D2	D2-1	D2-2	D2-3
Age	< 25	≥ 25	< 25
# years with driving licence	< 3	< 3	≥ 3

Test situations D3	D3-1	D3-2	D3-3	D3-4	D3-5
Car age	< 2	≥ 2	≥ 2	≥ 2	≥ 2
Car age	< 5	≥ 5	≥ 5	< 5	≥ 5
3 years-damage	≥ 2,500	≥ 2,500	< 2,500	≥ 2,500	< 2,500
Age	< 70	< 70	≥ 70	< 70	< 70

NB! The parameter "Age" occurs in the decision points D1, D2 and D3. This leads to the following mutually exclusive test situations: D2-1 with D3-3; D2-3 with D3-3.

Graphic demonstration of test situations
For some testers, the creation of logical test cases is made easier with the aid of a graphic demonstration of the test situations – a Graph.
With this, each decision point and end point is represented by a circle and each test situation by a line that goes from one circle to another.
A logical test case runs through the graph from beginning to end, linking a chain of test situations. The graph also supplies insight into the minimum number of test cases necessary to cover all the test situations. This is determined by the maximum number of parallel lines in the graph.

Example

The test situations are reproduced in figure 14.15.

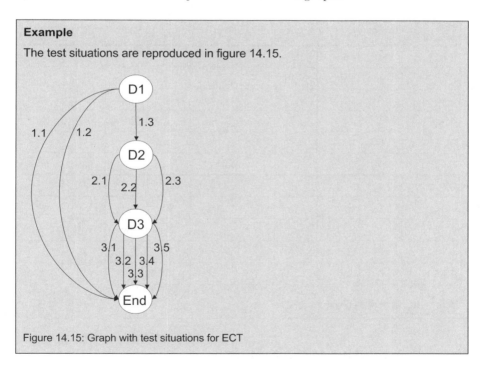

Figure 14.15: Graph with test situations for ECT

2- Creating logical test cases
A test case runs through the functionality from start to end and will come across one or more decision points on its path. With each decision point, the test case will test one of the defined test situations.
The logical test cases are combined with the aid of a matrix. The rows contain the test situations and the columns contain the logical test cases. With each

test case, it is indicated by one or more crosses which test situations should be tested by this test case. This matrix simultaneously serves as a check on the complete coverage of test situations.

In order to take account of the nesting of decision points, the columns "Value" and "Next" have been added. These indicate for each test situation what the outcome of the decision is (directly obtainable from the tables in step 2) and to which subsequent decision point (or end process) this leads. This helps to prevent the tester from placing a cross at a test situation where the test case does not go.

Example

Table 14.10 describes test cases TC1 to TC7 incl., which give the required coverage:

Test situation	Value	Next	TC1	TC2	TC3	TC4	TC5	TC6	TC7
D1-1	1	End	X						
D1-2	1	End		X					
D1-3	0	D2			X	X	X	X	X
D2-1	1	D3				X			X
D2-2	0	D3			X		X		
D2-3	0	D3						X	
D3-1	1	End			X				
D3-2	1	End				X			
D3-3	1	End					X		
D3-4	0	End						X	
D3-5	0	End							X

Table 14.10: Logical test cases for ECT.

Mutually exclusive test situations

Each test situation sets particular requirements on one or more parameters. If a parameter occurs in several decision points, it is possible that a test situation in one decision point sets requirements on that parameter that conflict with the requirements of a test situation in another decision point. For example, test situation D2.1 requires "Age < 25" and test situation D3.3 requires "Age ≥ 70". These test situations are mutually exclusive.

A logical test case may not contain "mutually exclusive test situations", for that makes the test case inconsistent and therefore unexecutable. Such a test case will be discovered automatically, as soon as the test case has to be made physical (see next step). The problem can then be simply resolved, by replacing one of the "mutually exclusive test situations" with a non-conflicting test situation. In this connection, it can be advantageous to first translate each logical test case into a physical test case in order to discover possible mutually exclusive test situations, before starting on the following logical test case.

In order to reduce the probability of test cases occurring with mutually exclusive test situations, the optional step of an extra analysis could be carried out in advance:

- Inventory which parameters occur in several decision points, and (per parameter) which decision points they are
- Sum up the combinations of mutually exclusive test situations.

3- Creating physical test cases
With a physical test case, all the parameters (data) have to be given concrete substance, so that the relevant test situations are covered by this.

Physical test cases can be handily described with the aid of a matrix that is built up as follows:

- Each column describes a physical test case.
- The first row indicates per test case which test situations should be covered.
- Thereafter, there is a row for each parameter of which the test case consists.
- Finally, one or more rows are added with which the predicted result is described in concrete terms.

Example

In table 14.11 the physical test cases are shown, including the predicted results:

Test case	TC1	TC2	TC3	TC4	TC5	TC6	TC7
Contains test situations	D1-1	D1-2	D1-3 D2-2 D3-1	D1-3 D2-1 D3-2	D1-3 D2-2 D3-3	D1-3 D2-3 D3-4	D1-3 D2-1 D3-5
Age	16	33	35	19	72	24	20
Driving licence suspended	N	Y	N	N	N	N	N
# years with driving licence			2	0	1	5	2
Car age			1	12	6	3	20
3 years-damage			6000	4300	50	2700	2200
Result:							
Error message	X	X					
Premium			1300	2000	1300	800	1500

Table 14.11: Physical test cases for ECT.

4- Establishing the starting point
No remarks.

Example

The premium sums should be entered in the database.
The details of the car owner are entered online and the premium is then calculated immediately.

14.4.5 Error Guessing (EG)

Description
The value of Error Guessing (EG) lies in the unexpected: tests made up by guessing would otherwise not be considered. Based on the tester's experience, he goes in search of defect-sensitive spots in the system and devises suitable test cases for these.

Experience here is a broad concept: it could be the professional tester who 'smells' the defects in certain complex screen processes, but it could also be the user or administrator who knows the exceptional situations from practice and wishes to test whether the new or amended system is dealing with them adequately.

Together with exploratory testing (section 14.4.6), error guessing is rather a strange technique among test design techniques. Neither technique is based on any of the described basic techniques and therefore does not provide any specifiable coverage.

This very informal technique leaves the tester free to design the test cases in advance or to create them on the spot during the test execution. Documenting the test cases is optional. A point of focus when they are not documented is the reproducibility of the test. The tester often cannot quite remember under which circumstances a defect occurred. A possible measure for this is the taking of notes (a 'test log') during the test. Obviously, defects found with the test are documented. In those cases, great attention should be paid to the circumstances that have led to the defect, so that it will be reproducible.

Tip

An aid for reproducing a defect is the activation of logging during the test, documenting the actions of the tester. A tool for automated test execution can be used for this.
The considerable freedom of the technique makes the area of application very broad. Error guessing can be applied to the testing of every quality characteristic and to every form of test basis.

Tip

Error guessing can also be used, for example, to instil (or restore) users' or administrators' confidence in a system, in the spirit of 'If these situations are processed satisfactorily, then the rest will probably also be all right'.

In more detail

Error guessing is sometimes confused with exploratory testing (section 14.4.6). The table 14.12 sums up the differences:

Error guessing	Exploratory testing
Does not employ the basic techniques	Employs the most suitable basic technique, depending on the situation
Suitable for testers, users, administrators, etc.	Suitable for experienced testers with knowledge of the basic techniques
The test cases are designed in the Specification phase or during test execution	The test cases are designed during test execution
Focuses on the exceptions and difficult situations	Focuses on the aspect to be tested in total (screen, function)
Not systematic, no certainty at all concerning coverage	Somewhat systematic

Table 14.12: Differences between error guessing and exploratory testing.

In more detail

In practice, error guessing is often cited for the applied test technique in the absence of a better name - 'It's not a common test design technique, therefore it is error guessing'. In particular, the testing of business processes by users, or the testing of requirements is often referred to as error guessing. However, the basic technique of "checklist" is used here, while with error guessing no specific basic technique is used.

The fact that tests are executed that otherwise would not be considered makes error guessing a valuable addition to the other test design techniques. However, since error guessing guarantees no coverage whatsoever, it is not a replacement.

By preference error guessing takes place later in the total testing process, when most normal and simple defects have already been removed with the regular techniques. Because of this, error guessing can focus on testing the real exceptions and difficult situations. From within the test strategy, the test manager would normally provide some direction to the aim of error guessing, so that duplication of other tests can be avoided. The test manager also makes a certain amount of time (time box) and resources available.

Points of focus in the steps

The steps can be performed both during the Specification phase and during the test execution. The tester usually does not document the results of the steps, but if great value is attached to showing evidence or transferability and reusability of the test, then this should be done.

1- Identifying test situations

Prior to test execution, the tester identifies the weak points on which the test should focus. These are often mistakes in the thought processes of others and things that have been forgotten. These aspects form the basis of the test cases to be executed. Examples are:

- Exceptional situations: rare situations in the system operation, screen processing or business and other processes
- Fault handling: forcing a fault situation during the handling of another fault situation, interrupting a process unexpectedly, etc.
- Non-permitted input: negative amounts, zeros, excessive values, too-long names, empty (mandatory) fields, etc. (only useful if there is no syntactic test carried out on this part)
- Specific combinations, for example in the area of:
  - Data: an as-yet untried combination of input values
  - Sequence of transactions: e.g. "change – cancel change – change again – cancel – etc." a number of times in succession
- Claiming too much of the system resources (memory, disk space, network)
- Complex parts of the system
- Often-changed parts of the system
- Parts (processes/functions) of the system that often contained defects in the past.

2- Creating logical test cases

This step normally takes place only with more complex test cases. The tester may consider creating a logical test case that will cover the situation to be tested.

3- Creating physical test cases

This step normally only takes place with more complex test cases. The tester may consider creating a physical test case for the logical test case.

4- Establishing the starting point

During this activity, it may emerge that it is necessary to build a particular starting point for purposes of the test.

14.4.6 Exploratory Testing (ET)

Description
Exploratory testing was founded and described as a concept and an approach a number of years ago by James Bach. What is exploratory testing?

Definition according to James Bach [Bach, 2002]

Exploratory testing is the simultaneous learning, designing and executing of tests, in other words every form of testing in which the tester designs his tests during the test execution and the information obtained is reused to design new and improved test cases.

This means that the tester is always exploring a piece of the system under test, thinking about what should or could be tested (test design) and subsequently carrying it out (test execution). In doing so, the tester gathers new knowledge of the system, considers what to test next, carries this out, etc. This means that the design and subsequent execution of the tests take place in close succession. Documenting the test case is not necessary. In exploratory testing, therefore, test design does indeed take place, in contrast to ad hoc or unstructured testing. The tester employs the most applicable basic technique, depending on the features to be tested and the information available on these. This places high demands on the tester, since he must be able to apply a large collection of basic techniques without explicitly formulating each step in the techniques.

In more detail

When a tester executes a test script, from time to time he comes up against 'suspicious system behaviour', i.e. when the system looks different or responds differently from what is expected. This does not have to be written into the test script as such, and the expectation does not even need to be justified by particular system documents. When the tester examines this suspicious behaviour more closely, he is engaged in exploratory testing. Most testers, however, will exclaim that this is obvious and they will not themselves have the impression they are applying exploratory testing. It is not so much a question of whether someone is testing exploratively, but more of the degree to which he does this. This makes it difficult to distinguish what precisely to call or not to call 'exploratory testing'.

As with error guessing (section 14.4.5) exploratory testing is rather difficult to line up with the other test design techniques. It is not based on any of the described basic techniques, it leaves a free choice of basic techniques to be applied and it provides no guaranteed coverage. It is even debatable whether it really is a test design technique. Mainly for practical reasons, in this book the decision has been made to include exploratory testing among these.

> **In more detail**
>
> In practice, exploratory testing is sometimes confused with error guessing. In section 14.4.5, the differences between them are set out.

Exploratory testing is often associated with testing in the absence of a formal test basis, such as a functional design. However, this is not necessarily true. It is entirely possible to apply it with a well-described system. Having said that, the technique lends itself very well to situations in which no described test basis is present. Exploratory testing puts less emphasis on a described test basis and more on other ways of assessing the adequacy of the test object, such as by familiarisation with the system in the course of the test execution.

> **Tip**
>
> There is a risk attached to the use of forms of test basis other than the formal system documentation. This is that the tester becomes so trusting of these other sources of information that testing against the system documentation disappears into the background. An undesirable end result can be that the system and documentation are running out of sync. If the work is based on contracts, this could lead to contractual difficulties. If the system is correct and the documentation not, it can result in maintenance or administrational problems. For that reason, where a defect is concerned, the relationship between software and formal test basis should always be taken into consideration.
>
> By contrast, it is possible that (complex) functionality is described in the documentation that has been implemented incorrectly in the system, so that when testing is carried out based on sources other than the system documentation, defects will not be found. Another undesirable result may be that, owing to the lack of clarity on the scope, the testers will generate an endless stream of change requests under the disguise of possible defects. Both are points of focus for the test manager.

When to apply or not to apply

The great freedom of the technique makes for a very wide area of application. It can be applied to the testing of every quality characteristic and with every form of test basis. There are, however, varying circumstances in which the application of exploratory testing is or is not a good idea. This is indicated below.

Apply:
- *Where experienced and trusted testers with domain knowledge are available.*
  If testers are not required to document what they are doing, it is cheaper than when they are required to do so. The downside of this choice is a greater risk of insufficient test quality, longer lead-time of testing on the critical path of the project and lower levels of transferability and reusability of the tests (possibly leading to higher test costs in the long term). The

preconditions and downsides are explained in the other points in this section

■ *Where testing as cheaply as possible is by far the biggest consideration.*
Since this is usually the case, exploratory testing would appear to be almost always applicable. This does not hold true, however. The technique can be employed from the point of view of costs, but there are some important preconditions: you must have good and experienced testers, and have complete faith in them, without requiring proof of the coverage and depth of testing. The downside of this option is a greater risk of inadequate quality of the test, longer lead-time of testing on the critical path of the project and lower levels of transferability and reusability of the tests (possibly leading to higher test costs in the long term). The preconditions and downsides are explained in the other points in this section

■ *Where there is an insufficiently documented test basis.*
Through exploration, the tester automatically acquires a perspective on the test object. Since emphasis is placed on the inventiveness and intuition of the tester, it is more suitable for use where there is little system documentation at the start of testing or when the documentation strongly deviates (reads: is out of date) with regard to the required operation of the system. This also makes the technique very suitable with 'documentation-light' and agile methods such as Extreme programming, DSDM and (to a lesser degree) with the Rational Unified Process. Points of focus here are that the lack of system documentation is a risk that the use of exploratory testing cannot dispel and that the testers should possess a lot of system and domain knowledge, since there is no frame of reference in the form of system documentation

■ *As an addition to testing according to more formal techniques, to encourage creative testing.*
Defects often exist in unexpected places in the software, and they also tend to cluster together. Formal test design techniques are aimed at finding certain types of defects. The use of these techniques can be seen as a filter on the software. With each filter (test design technique), certain types of defects are found. It is then a question of whether many other kinds of defects remain and how severe these are. Exploratory testing can provide additional insight here. By its informal nature, it is less focused on particular types of defects. Therefore, in the case of a defect that is found by exploratory testing, the tester should consider carefully whether the defect is unique and isolated, whether it occurs in various other places, or indicates a cluster. This makes it a good addition to the other more formal techniques. Figure 14.16 demonstrates this.

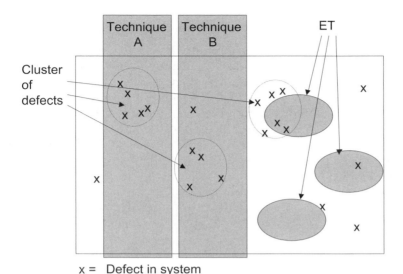

x = Defect in system

Figure 14.16: Exploratory testing as an addition to testing according to more formal techniques

■ *Where there is no time available to prepare the tests.*
Although this is no ideal situation – and one in which the risks should certainly be highlighted from within the testing – nevertheless it is a common occurrence. Exploratory testing is then a means of achieving the maximum amount of testing in the short time that remains and of obtaining a general insight into the product quality. Suppose that the tester has 8 hours in which to test a particular group of functions or screens. What is then more productive: 8 hours of going through the functions in all kinds of explorative ways, using checklists, zooming in on anything that looks suspicious, or spending half the time on specifying a number of test cases in a reusable and verifiable way, before carefully executing them during the remainder of the time?

Other circumstances for which the technique lends itself are when the testers want to learn quickly how the system works, to assess the quality of someone else's testing with a short test, for gaining a first impression of the quality of the system or to examine a specific defect or possible fault source.
This is not to say that, in the event of any of the above situations, exploratory testing is straightaway the best solution. There are various situations in which its application is less suitable.

Do not apply:
- When higher requirements are set as regards the demonstrability/reporting of the testing, for example by imposed standards.
  The testing process is less manageable, less measurable and less auditable, because no test cases are defined and low requirements are set as regards the logging of tests. It is not known what the tester will do and how he will do it. It is almost impossible to check in retrospect what has been done.
- With critical functionality, failure of which can cause severe damage.
  Because little is documented, the technique leans heavily on trust in the individual tester. The potential damage when this trust turns out to be unfounded may be so great for certain systems or system parts that the organisation cannot or will not accept this risk.
- For inexperienced testers, as they will lack the knowledge and experience necessary for creating good test cases without the explicit support of a technique.
- If test cases are required to be executed by a tester other than the creator or by a test tool. Or if the test cases are required to be reused, e.g. in future maintenance.
- If there is no direct feedback from test execution, so that the test results are not directly available, e.g. in the case of test runs of batch software at night.
- In tests that require a lot of preparation, such as the testing of complicated calculations, performance tests, the testing of security or of usability. These preparations, which may involve test cases, starting points, reference tables as well as test environments, can best take place well in advance of test execution in order to avoid a lot of time being wasted during test execution.
- When the testing has to be on the critical path of the project as briefly as possible.
  The tester starts exploratory testing at a late stage, after the test object has been delivered, and carries out both design and the execution of tests during the Execution phase. This is usually on the critical path of the project, requiring more lead-time than when the tests have already been designed before delivery of the test object, in the form of test scripts or checklists. It is important here that the test scripts *can* be prepared, i.e. that there is a sufficiently documented test basis. It should also be said that the maintenance of test scripts during the test execution usually costs extra time, thus somewhat reducing the time advantage of the test script in respect of the critical path.

Whether the technique can be usefully applied therefore depends on various factors. It is up to the test manager to judge this. In view of the high demands placed on the tester, exploratory testing should be applied in test teams in which professional testers participate. In practice, this concerns the system and acceptance tests.

Points of focus in the steps

The generic steps (see 14.4.1 "Introduction") are in principle also applicable to exploratory testing. The substance of the steps, however, depends on which basic techniques the tester selects and applies during the test execution. For this reason, the steps are not further substantiated in this section.

In addition, the generic steps are normally only implicitly applicable and are not documented. When explicit requirements are set for evidence or transferability, it can be agreed that the tester will explicitly document the test cases. This takes place at the same time as the test execution. The variant of session-based test management is also an option.

In more detail

Session-based test management

The unmanageability of exploratory testing is often cited as a big disadvantage. To obviate this, Jonathan Bach introduced session-based test management as an approach [Bach, 2000]. In this, the (part of the) system under test is divided into a number of test charters. A test charter can be anything, e.g. a function, screen, menu, user transaction, user-friendliness or performance, or very generally an area with possible instability, such as memory usage. Thus, a test charter is something different from a test case or a test script. With the testing of a test charter, various test cases are often executed. Criteria set for a test charter are:

- It sets a test goal
- It proposes a unit of work, which will take roughly between half an hour and four hours
- It is independently testable, i.e. a tester can start or finish with any test charter.

The test charters are tested in testing sessions. A session is a period of time, usually between half an hour and four hours, in which the tester can test one or more test charters without interruption. During testing, the tester documents his/her actions (along general lines) in the form of notes on the session paper. This renders the tests reusable to a certain degree, since the retesting of a test charter can take place based on the notes of the previous session(s). It is then up to the tester to repeat the previous session as much as possible, or to try other variations of it.

In contrast to the test charters that can be tested several times, the test sessions are one-offs: you start and end a session at a certain point. If you have to test a test charter again at a later stage, this takes place in a new session. The advantage of sessions is that they are restricted in time and thus more manageable. After the session has ended, the test manager runs through the session with the tester in a debriefing to determine the priorities of the found defects, share points of learning and estimate (remaining) risks.

During the session, the tester can create new test charters, which are then added to the list of test charters. By administering sessions and test charters, the progress of the test process can be monitored and the outside world can obtain insight into what has happened and what still has to happen in the testing.

14.4.7 Data Cycle Test (DCyT)

Description

The data cycle test (DCyT) is a technique for testing whether the data are being used and processed consistently by various functions from within different subsystems or even different systems. The technique is ideally suited to the testing of overall functionality, suitability and connectivity.

The primary aim of the data cycle test is not to trace functional defects in individual functions, but to find integration defects. The test focuses on the link between various functions and the way in which they deal with communal data. The DCyT is most effective if the functionality of the individual functions has already been sufficiently tested. That is also an important reason why this test is usually applied in the later phases of acceptance testing.

The most important test basis is the CRUD matrix (see section 14.3.7) and a description of the applicable integrity rules. The latter describe the preconditions under which certain processes are or are not permitted, such as, for example, "Entity X may only be changed if the linked entity Y is removed from it". Besides this, functional specifications or detailed domain expertise is necessary in order to be able to predict the result of each test case.

The basic techniques used are:
- CRUD, for coverage of the life cycle of the data
- Decision coverage, for coverage of the integrity rules.

Reinforcement of the test can be achieved by the application of, e.g.:
- A more extended variant of the CRUD
- Modified condition/decision coverage or multiple condition coverage of the integrity rules.

Points of focus in the steps

In this section, the data cycle test is explained step by step. In this, the generic steps (see 14.4.1 "Introduction") are taken as a starting point. An example is also set out that demonstrates, up to and including the designing of the logical test cases, how this technique works.

1- Identifying test situations

The test situations are created from the coverage of the CRUD and from the integrity rules. Both will be further explained here.

Test situations in connection with CRUD

The following activities should be carried out:
- Determine the entities of which the life cycle is to be tested.
  Usually, this concerns all the entities that are used by the system or subsystem

(created, changed, read or removed). If there are too many enitities, a cohesive subset of entities may be selected

- Determine the functions that make use of these entities.
  Here, too, the scope of the test should be determined: all the functions of the system under test, a cohesive subset of this, functions from other systems that are linked to the system under test
- Fill in the CRUD matrix (see section 14.3.7).
  If the CRUD matrix is delivered as a test basis, the relevant part should be selected from this, based on the previous two activities. If it was not possible to get the CRUD matrix delivered as a test basis, the test team may decide to create this themselves, based on the functional specifications. This is obviously undesirable, but is a last resort
- Each process (C, R, U or D) that occurs in the CRUD matrix is a separate test situation that has to be tested.

Test situations in connection with integrity rules
The following activities should be carried out:
- Gather the integrity rules on the selected entities.
  These are the rules that define under which conditions the *processing* of the entities is valid or not. Integrity rules are usually specified within the functional specifications, database models or in separate business rules
- Apply decision coverage. That means that for each integrity rule, two test situations are derived:
  - Invalid
    The integrity rule is disobeyed. The process is invalid and should result in correct error handling.
  - Valid
    The integrity rule is obeyed. The process is valid and should be executed.

In more detail

Integrity rules should not be confused with semantic rules, which define the conditions under which the value of the data themselves is valid or not. For example:
- The rule "When creating an order, the value of quantity should not be below the boundary that is set in product" – is a semantic rule
- The rule "The creation of an invoice is only permitted if the order concerned has already been approved" – is an integrity rule.

Therefore, the integrity rule determines whether the function is permitted in the first place. Thereafter, the semantic rules determine whether the input data offered to that function are valid.

Example

The data cycle test is applied to a subsystem that invoices orders and processes payments. The relevant part of the CRUD matrix is shown in table 14.13.

	Item	Payment agreement	Invoice	Ledger
Item management	C, R, U, D	-	-	...
Payment agreement man.	-	C, R, U, D	R	...
Ledger management	-	-	R	C, R, U, D
Invoice creation	R	R	C	U
Cash payment	-	-	C, U, D	U
Bank transfer	-	-	U, D	U
...	...	...	...	...

Table 14.13: Example of a CRUD matrix.

For this part of the CRUD matrix, there is one relevant integrity rule: A payment agreement may not be removed as long as there is an outstanding invoice with the relevant payment agreement.
This leads to two test situations:
IR1-1: Delete (D) payment agreement, while an invoice is outstanding with the relevant payment agreement
IR1-2: Delete (D) payment agreement, without there being an outstanding invoice with the with the relevant payment agreement
A brief overview notation for this type of test situation is, for example:

Test situation	Process	Entity	Condition	Valid Y/N
IR1-1	D	Payment agreement	Outstanding invoice	N
IR1-2	D	Payment agreement	No outstanding invoice	Y

The initials "IR" here stand for "Integrity rule".

2- Creating logical test cases
Create 1 or more logical test cases in such a way that:
- Each entity goes through a full life cycle (beginning with 'C' and ending with 'D')
- All the test situations from the CRUD matrix (every C, R, U and D) are covered
- All the test situations of the relevant integrity rules are covered.
See also section 14.3.7.
A test case thus describes a complete scenario consisting of several actions, each of which perform a process on a particular entity.

Example

In table 14.14 and 14.15 the logical test cases for the entities "Item" and "Payment agreement" are set out, to illustrate the principle.

The table describe at each row which function should be used, which process (CRUD) on the relevant entity is covered by this and a brief explanation with additional information on the action to be performed.

LTC01: "Item"

Function	CRUD	Action / Notes
Item management	C	Create new item ITM-01
Item management	R	Check ITM-01
Create invoice	R	Create invoice INV-01 in which ITM-01 occurs
Ledger management	-	Check INV-01
Item management	U	Change ITM-01 (e.g. price) in ITM-01B
Item management	R	Check ITM-01B
Ledger management	-	Check INV-01 is unchanged
Item management	D	Remove ITM-01B
Item management	R	Check ITM-01B (is removed)

Table 14.14: Logical test case for "Item".

LTC02: "Payment agreement"

Function	CRUD	Action / Notes
Payment agreement mgt.	C	Create new payment agreement PAG-01
Payment agreement mgt.	R	Check PAG-01
Payment agreement mgt.	U	Change PAG-01 (e.g. period) in PAG-01B
Payment agreement mgt.	R	Check PAG-01B
Create invoice	R	Create invoice INV-02 containing agreement PAG-01B
Ledger management	-	Check INV-02
Payment agreement mgt.	D	IR1-1. Error handling!
Payment agreement mgt.	R	Check PAG-01B still exists
Cash payment	-	Full payment of INV-02 so that INV-02 is removed (no longer outstanding)
Payment agreement mgt.	D	IR1-2. Permitted
Payment agreement mgt.	R	Check that PAG-01B is removed

Table 14.15: Logical test case for "Payment agreement".

A "-" in the column "CRUD" means that the relevant function is required in order to carry out a certain action, but that this does not perform any processing on the tested entity. For example:

With LTC01, "Ledger management" is used to be able to check that the correct item

appears on the invoice, but does not perform any processing itself on "Item".
With LTC02, "Cash payment" is used to close invoice INV-02 so that integrity rule
IR1-2 is complied with, but does not perform any processing itself on "Payment
agreement".

3- Creating physical test cases

In the translation of logical test cases to physical test cases, the following
details are added:

- (Optional) Exactly how the relevant function is activated. This is usually
  clear enough, but sometimes it requires a less obvious sequence of
  actions.
- The data to be entered with that function. If the logical test case indicates
  that a certain entity has to be changed, then the physical test case should
  indicate unequivocally which attribute is changed into which value.
- A concrete description with each predicted result of what has to be checked
  concerning a particular entity.
- Extra actions that are necessary to facilitate subsequent actions in the test
  case. E.g., the changing of the system date or the execution of a particular
  batch process in order to give the system a certain required status.

4- Establishing the starting point

The DCyT typically operates at overall system level, possibly across several
systems. That means an extensive starting point has to be prepared that is
complete and consistent across all the systems. The following, in particular,
should be organised:

- All the necessary databases for all the systems involved, in which all the
  data is consistent
- A configuration (possibly a network) in which all the necessary systems
  are connected and in which all the necessary users are defined with the
  necessary access rights.

Such a starting point approximates the production situation and is complicated
to put together. Ideally, an existing real-life test environment is used. See also
section 6.6.2 "Defining central starting point(s)".
In particular, attention should be paid to the data in the starting point that
are only valid for a limited time. At the start of each test execution, it should
be checked whether these time-dependent data are still valid and whether, on
the basis of this, changes should be made in the starting point.

14.4.8 Process cycle test (PCT)

Description

The process cycle test is a technique that is applied in particular to the testing of the quality characteristic of Suitability (integration between the administrative organisation and the automated information system). The test basis should contain structured information on the required system behaviour in the form of paths and decision points. The process cycle test digresses on a number of points from most other test design techniques:

- The process cycle test is not a design test, but a structure test: the test cases issue from the structure of the procedure flow and not from the design specifications.
- The predicted result in the process cycle test is simple: the physical test case should be executable. This checks implicitly that the individual actions can be carried out. In contrast to other test design techniques, no explicit prediction is made of the result, and so this does not have to be checked.

The process cycle test focuses on the coverage of the variations in the processing. The basic technique used in this is:

- Paths: test depth level 2

Variations on the process cycle test can be created by applying the basic technique:

- Paths: test depth level 1, test depth level 3 and higher
  With this, paths can be tested in respectively *more* or *less depth.*

Points of focus in the steps

In this section, the process cycle test is explained step by step, taking the generic steps (see 14.4.1 "Introduction") as a starting point. An example is also set out, showing at each step how the technique works. In the example, a certain drawing technique is used to represent a detailed process diagram. Since no uniform agreements exist concerning the use of the technique and the use of the symbols, the meanings of the symbols are stated next to the diagram.

Example

Claim forms come into the claims handling department. After someone in the department has entered the claim details into the system, a process is begun to check the completeness of the details. In the event of incompleteness, the employee contacts the insured party, after which the details can be re-entered. When the details are complete, a process is begun to determine the claim sum and the number of claims submitted by the insured party over the previous year. If the claim sum is higher than €2,500, or if in the previous year more than 2 damages claims have been submitted, the head of the department then assesses whether or not the claim should be met. In the event of rejection by the head of department, a rejection letter is created; if it has been approved, a letter of approval is created. With 2 or fewer claims in the previous year and a damages claim of €2,500 or less, a letter of approval is always created.

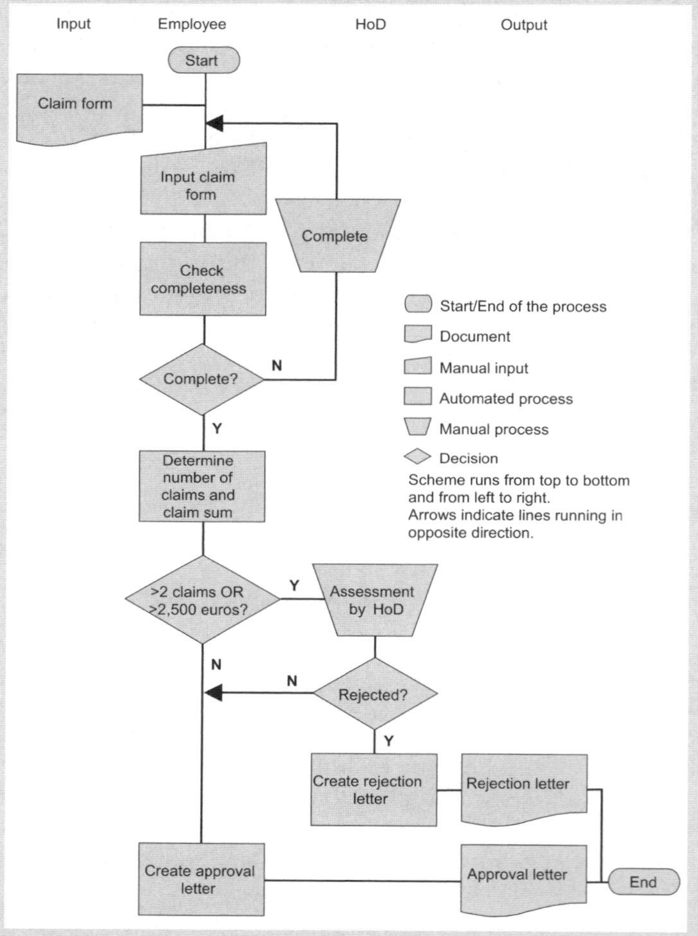

Figure 14.17: Part of the detailed process diagram of "claims handling".

Below, it is set out per step how the process cycle test is applied to this process:

1- Identifying test situations
In order to apply the process cycle test, a process diagram is required. This

diagram should contain, besides a start and end point, decision points and paths. If the test basis already contains a diagram, then for the sake of clarity it is often useful to 'undress' it, so that it only contains the above-mentioned aspects. If there is no diagram present in the test basis, the tester will have to distil the decision points and paths from the test basis himself in order to create a diagram. Subsequently, the test situations are derived from the diagram in accordance with the technique described in section 14.3.2 for the coverage type "paths".

Example

The tester has removed the information in the "claims handling" detailed process diagram that is surplus to the process cycle test, and numbered the paths.

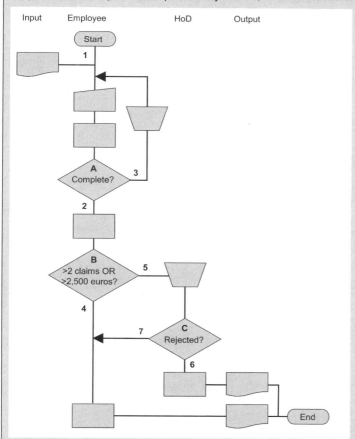

Figure 14.18: Simplified reproduction of the process diagram.
Check for yourself that application of the coverage type "paths" delivers the following

test situations (path combinations) with test depth level 2:
A: 1-2; 1-3; 3-2; 3-3
B: 2-4; 2-5
C: 5-6; 5-7

2- Creating logical test cases
The creation of the logical test cases is divided into two activities:
- Creating a set of logical test cases
- Describing the consecutive actions per logical test case.

In the creation of the set of logical test cases, all the test situations should be covered. A test case is defined by going through the process in a certain way from "Start" to "End" (see section 14.3.2, "Paths"). The tester is free to choose the way in which the process is followed, as long as all the test situations are covered at least once.

Example

For the process of claims handling, the tester arrives at the following set of logical test cases:
TC1 = 1-2-4
TC2 = 1-2-5-6
TC3 = 1-3-3-2-5-7
Check for yourself that the following set is also one of the possible sets:
TC1 = 1-3-3-2-4
TC2 = 1-2-5-6
TC3 = 1-2-5-7
If test depth level-1 had been used, for example, it would have led to the following set of logical test cases (check for yourself that several sets are possible here):

TC1 = 1-2-4
TC2 = 1-2-5-6
TC3 = 1-3-2-5-7

The logical test cases should then be written out. This means that for each test case a row of consecutive actions should be described, in such a way that the execution of these actions will touch on all the test situations from the test case. This activity requires inventiveness and is therefore rather difficult to describe in general terms. See the concrete terms of the example.

Example

The tester has described the following actions in respect of TC3 (1-3-3-2-5-7):

A3-1	Create claim form	(Insured)
A3-2	Enter claim form details into the system (incomplete)	(Employee)
A3-3	Start the process "Check for completeness"	(Employee)
A3-4	Contact the insured party to complete the details	(Employee)
A3-5	Enter claim form details including one additional detail into the system (incomplete)	(Employee)
A3-6	Start the "Check for completeness" process	(Employee)
A3-7	Contact the insured party to complete details	(Employee)
A3-8	Enter claim form details including additional details into the system (complete, claim sum > €2,500)	(Employee)
A3-9	Start "Check for completeness" process	(Employee)
A3-10	Start "Determine number of claims and claim sum" process	(Employee)
A3-11	Assess notification of claim	(Head)
A3-12	Claim is accepted	(Head)
A3-13	Start "Create letter" (approval letter) process	(Employee)
A3-14	End process	

3- Creating physical test cases

Besides the previously mentioned differences from the other test design techniques, there is another difference to note. With the test execution, there is more required in the process cycle test than just the technical test infrastructure on which the automated part of the information system runs. The manual procedures mainly have to be carried out by various types of employees, which means that several testers are required to play particular roles in the test execution. It is of course also possible to have the test executed by one tester who possesses several user IDs, repeatedly logging in and out during the test execution. In addition, the required data are only partly present in the database of the automated part of the information system, and the rest is outside the system, for example in the form of completed forms. That, too, is different from the other test design techniques.

In the creation of the physical test cases, a physical formulation of the logical test cases is supplied. With this, the actions described serve as a starting point.

Example

The tester has described the physical formulation of TC3 (1-3-3-2-5-7) as follows:

Insured party:

A3-1   Create claim form with following details:

Name	: Janssen, J.
Address	: Amsterdamstreet 7, Utrecht
Date of loss	: <empty>
Description of loss	: <empty>
Cause of loss	: Theft from home
Claim sum	: €4,250

Employee (EMP_01):

A3-2   Enter claim form details into the system (without "Date of loss" and
        without "Description of loss")

A3-3   Start "Check for completeness" process (form is incomplete)

A3-4   Contact insured party to obtain "Date of loss"

A3-5   Enter claim form details in the system ("Date of loss" is 1 December 2006)

A3-6   Start "Check for completeness" process (form is incomplete)

A3-7   Contact insured party to obtain "Description of loss"

A3-8   Enter claim form details in the system ("Description of loss" is
        "Stolen necklace")

A3-9   Start "Check for completeness" process (form is complete)

A3-10   Start "Determine number of claims and claim sum" process (claim sum
        > 2,500, therefore assessment by HoD)

Head of Department (HEAD_01):

A3-11   Assess notification of claim

A3-12   Accept claim

Employee (EMP_01):

A3-13   Start "Create letter" process (approval letter is created)

A3-14   End process

4- Establishing the starting point
No remarks.

Example

In order to execute the test cases from the claim example, the following is
necessary:

• The insurance details pertaining to the insured party must be present in the
  database

• The user IDs of an employee and the head of department with relevant
  authorisation(s) should be known by the system

• The claim forms must be completed.

As an example, the starting point for TC3 is provided here:

Insurance details:

Name   : Janssen, J.

Address   : Amsterdamstreet 7, Utrecht

Number of claims in 2006   : 2

User IDs:

The user IDs "EMP_01" and "HEAD_01" should be present in the system with the
associated authorisation(s).

> **Claim form:**
> Name   : Janssen, J.
> Address   : Amsterdamstreet 7, Utrecht
> Date of loss   : <empty>
> Description of loss : <empty>
> Cause of loss   : Theft from home
> Claim sum   : €4,250

14.4.9 Real-Life Test (RLT)

Description

With the real-life test (RLT), it is not the intention to test the system behaviour in separate situations, but to simulate the realistic usage of the system in a statistically responsible way. This test mainly focuses on characteristics, such as effectivity, connectivity, continuity and performance of the system under test. Many defects that are found with a real-life test are connected with a system's use of resources:

- Crashing of transactions following lengthy use
- Crashing of transactions that are carried out in a particular sequence
- Inadequate response times and speed of processing
- Insufficient memory or storage space available
- Insufficient capacity of peripherals and data-communication network.

To be able to test whether a system can handle realistic usage of it, that usage should be somehow specified. This also serves as a test basis and, in this context, is often referred to as the profile. The two most common types are:

- Operational profile
  Simulation of the realistic usage of the system, by carrying out a *sequence of transactions*, which is compiled in a statistically responsible way.
- Load profile
  Simulation of a realistic loading of the system in terms of *numbers of* users and/or transactions.

The basic technique used here is:

- Statistically responsible simulation

For further explanation of these profiles and their simulation, refer to section 14.3.8 "Statistical usage: Operational profiles and load profiles".
In practice, in a real-life test a mix of these profiles is often used. A particular loading of the system is simulated by carrying out realistic scenarios.
A profile is used in the setting out of one or more test goals of the real-life test. Examples of test goals are:

- Testing with normal or average usage

The aim here is to examine whether the available system resources are sufficient for the usual circumstances. This often involves a test with an average number of users who carry out interactive work, run overviews and carry out a number of small batch functionalities.

- Testing with intensive usage
  The aim here is to examine whether there are sufficient system resources for even the most stressful, but realistic, circumstances. This often involves a test with a maximum number of users who carry out interactive work (peak loading) or a test in which certain transactions are carried out often and at length.
- Measuring the breaking point (stress testing)
  The aim here is to examine what the maximum load is under which the system will still perform to an acceptable level. This often involves a test with an increasing number of (simulated) users.
- Testing daily batches
  The aim here is to examine whether the available system resources are sufficient for the combination of a normal number of interactive users with the simultaneous execution of relatively demanding batch jobs.
- Testing nightly batches
  The aim here is to examine whether both the available system resources and the available time are sufficient for the (nightly / weekend) execution of big batch jobs.

Execution of the real-life test is usually more complicated than that of other tests. In an environment in which the number of end users is not too great, you can have everyone work overtime for a weekend and carry out a previously established test scenario. However, use is increasingly being made of tools that simulate a realistic load in various ways. These are tools that simulate, for example, the number of users through the creation of virtual users, or tools that simulate a particular loading of the back-end of the system by offering transactions directly via the database management interface (hence without the use of the front-end or network).

It should be clearly determined in advance what and how measuring is to be done during the real-life test. Sometimes the measuring in itself also puts demands on the system, which can lead to distortion of the results. On the other hand, sufficient data is required to be able to carry out a satisfactory analysis in retrospect.

It can sometimes be difficult to assess the results of a real-life test. Occasionally, tests are not reproducible, because defects are often found that are caused by insufficient memory, lengthy use, etc. These kinds of defects (e.g. memory leaks) are difficult to reproduce, because there are almost always outside influences at play, which are impossible, or almost impossible, to control, such as the memory management of the operating system. In tracing the causes of any defects, logging and monitoring facilities could be used.

Points of focus in the steps

For the real-life test, the creation or establishing of correct profiles is the most important step. This takes place within step 1 "Identifying test situations". The exact content of the test cases is less relevant than with most other test design techniques. The most important criterion is that reality regarding the size and frequency of use is approximated as closely as possible. This means that there is usually no point in creating logical test cases. The physical translation can often be made immediately to cover the required test situations.

1- Identifying test situations
The profiles can be seen as the situations to be tested. These indicate along general lines which types of actions (functions) are carried out over a particular period and the number of active users. This may be a number of daily cycles, e.g. a minimum, average and maximum cycle. A daily cycle consists, for example, of logging on, intensive use, lighter use during the lunch break, intensive use, logging out, backup and daily batches. Besides these, there could also be comparable weekly, monthly and annual cycles and specific processes, such as backup and recovery. There are various ways of obtaining the necessary information for the creation of an operational profile, load profile or a mix of these. Below are a number of them in random order:

- Derive the profile from the current system or release
- Copy an existing profile of a system with comparable functionality
- Copy an existing profile with comparable load of the system resources
- Log how often each function is used
- Measure the load of the system with the aid of specific tools (monitors)
- Interview users, in which the key question is: "Which transactions do you carry out, how often and when, or which transactions do you expect to carry out on the new system?"

An important consideration in creating a profile is the degree of detail. A more extensive and detailed profile will of course give a better reflection of reality, but will also lead to an increase in the testing effort for the specification and realisation of test cases and the execution of the real-life test. It should be ensured that in the profile all the system resources are used realistically. It is pointless to simulate significantly heavier usage than is usual in reality, as the result of such a test will tell us nothing. If, for example, the system is too slow under those circumstances, it does not mean that the system is unsatisfactory. If the system is not too slow, that only tells us that it is over-configured, but not by how much. Simulating significantly heavier usage is useful, of course, if the aim of the test is test is to determine the maximum load under which the system still performs acceptably.

To obtain further detail on the profile and the parts of the system-resource load to be tested, the following activities can be carried out. This takes in a number of the above-mentioned methods of obtaining information for creating a profile:

• Identifying user groups

Identifying the user groups can take place, for example, on the basis of descriptions of the Administrative Organisation(AO), analysis of the target groups for whom any output is intended or security overviews at job level as user groups are usually strongly related to organisational positions and tasks. For the sake of the backup and recovery processes, the system administrators should not be forgotten

• Overview of tasks per user group

A task is defined as a number of successive actions that a user carries out in dialogue with the system for a particular purpose. The functional specifications are probably the most important source of information for this activity. Alternatives are the business processes, AO descriptions, the user manual, a prototype of the system, and any previous version of the information system. It is advisable to carry out this activity by means of direct contact (interviews) with users. Involving them during this activity usually clarifies things and provides all kinds of additional information.

• Determine the frequency per task per time unit

Data relating to frequency are often already present from previous systems with comparable functionality. If not, they should be collected, for example, by keeping track in the present system of how often a particular function is started or executed, or by interviewing users. It is important here to bear in mind that it concerns estimates of the frequency and not precise measurements of a hundred percent accuracy.

• Determine the relative frequency

The relative frequency is determined by dividing the number of occurrences of a particular task within a particular time unit by the total number of occurrences of all the tasks executed in the same period. The test cases are realised to correspond with the tasks and the relative frequency.

Example

In an organisation that processes bank transactions for various banks, 275,000 transactions are processed per hour with normal usage. These are divided into transaction types as follows (see table 14.16):

Transaction type	Frequency(#/hr)	Relative frequency
Point of Sale transactions	150,000	0.55
Direct debits	90,000	0.33
ATM transactions	20,000	0.07
Credit transfers	15,000	0.05
Total	275,000	1.0

Table 14.16: Example of a frequency distribution of transaction types.

The test cases are realised to correspond with the tasks and the relative frequency. For the example, this means the following spread across the test cases: 55% point of sale transactions, 33% direct debits, 7% ATM transactions and 5% credit transfers.

> Possible aims of the test are:
> • What is the maximum number of transactions that can be processed per second?
> • What is the average lead-time of a transaction under normal or intensive usage, and does this fall within the agreed limits?
> • Is the system proof against lengthy uninterrupted use?

2- Creating logical test cases
The creation of physical test cases is often started at once.

3- Creating physical test cases
For the real-life test, the exact content of the physical test cases is less relevant than for most other test design techniques. The only criterion is that reality regarding size and frequency of use is approximated as closely as possible. This sounds easier than it actually is. It has to be carefully considered *how* a particular usage or loading of the system can be realised or simulated. Additionally, test cases should be gathered or created for some tests, which have then to be carried out with the test execution. In contrast, in the execution of other tests the system has to be prepared with content *in advance.*

The creation of test cases can be done, for example, by physically setting out user scenarios, or, if an operational system already exists, by 'tapping' a representative test set.

For the testing of particular aspects of the system usage, the test cases can be realised by preparing a daily production (after processing) as real-life input. When using production data, bear in mind the privacy aspects. The devised user scenarios and actions that form part of the real-life test should also be distributed as realistically as possible among the users (testers) participating in the test.

The use of a tool, for example to simulate users or transactions, does not mean that user scenarios not need to be worked out. Even when a tool is used, these user scenarios form the basis of the test. In addition, the tool will have to be programmed or set so that it can carry out the user scenarios.

Example

In the example of the transaction processing, the following physical features have been given to the point of sale transactions (see table 14.17):

Nr	Transaction type	Parameters*	Goal and expectation
1	Point of sale transactions	Let number of transactions in 90 minutes rise from 5 tr/sec to 450 tr/sec.	Determine breaking point (stress test). Expectation: ≥ 350 tr/sec.
2	Point of sale transactions	42 tr/sec (over 5 minutes)	Determine lead time of a transaction with normal use
3	Point of sale transactions	120 tr/sec (over 5 minutes)	Determine lead time of a transaction with intensive use
With test cases 2 and 3, besides the point of sale transactions, the fixed system load consists of 25 direct debits/sec, 5 cash withdrawals/sec and 4 credit transfers/sec. The transaction should be carried out to 95% < 5 sec, to 99% < 7 sec and to 100% < 10 sec.			
4	Point of sale transactions	42 tr/sec (over 7 days)	Test whether the system crashes with lengthy use

* The point of sale transactions amount to an average of €100.00 and are spread over 4 banks.

Table 14.17: Physical test cases for point of sale transactions .

4- Establishing the starting point

As with most other tests, the creation of an appropriate starting point for a real-life test is often a challenge. However, with the real-life test, often there are additional points of focus:

- The test environment should be representative of the production situation
- Sizeable files are used
- Many users (testers) perform the testing
- A 'real' network should be available.

For more information, refer to section 6.6.2 "Defining central starting point(s)", in which this matter is discussed extensively.

14.4.10 Semantic Test (SEM)

Description

The semantic test (), together with the syntactic test, belongs among the *validation tests*, with which the *validity of the data input* is tested. In practice, the semantic test is often executed in combination with the syntactic test (see section 14.4.11).

The test basis consists of the semantic rules that specify what a datum should comply with in order to be accepted by the system as valid input. Semantic rules are connected with the *relationships between data*. These relationships may be between the data within a screen, between data on various screens and between input data and existing data in the database. Semantic rules may be established in various documents, but are usually described in:

- Functional specifications of the relevant function or input screen
- The business rules that apply to the functions overall

If the semantic rules describe the conditions for meeting security requirements, the SEM can also be applied to the "Security test" test type

With the semantic test, user-friendliness aspects can also be tested, by assessing the messages that occur in invalid situations thus:

• Are they understandable and unambiguous?

• Do they offer clear indications of how the invalid situation can be resolved?

Since the semantic rules can be specified as decision points that consist of compound conditions, one of the coverage types for the semantic test is selected from the area of decision points. The default choice for the semantic test is:

- Modified condition/decision coverage

Variants can be realised simply by replacing this with:

- Condition/decision coverage, for a more lighter variant
- Multiple condition coverage, for a more thorough variant.

Points of focus in the steps

In principle, for the SEM, too, the generic steps (see 14.4.1 "Introduction") are carried out. However, the formulation of a semantic test is very simple: each semantic rule is tested separately. Each rule leads to one or more test situations and each test situation generally leads to one test case.

For that reason, this section is restricted to explaining the first step "identifying test situations". This will be explained and expanded on through an example.

1- Identifying test situations

A semantic rule that describes the conditions of validity can generally be set out as follows:

> IF (semantic rule)   THEN   valid input or processing
> ELSE   error message

In the event that the semantic rule describes the *in*valid situations in which an error message should occur, this becomes:

> IF (semantic rule)   THEN   error message
> ELSE   valid input or processing

The semantic rule is a decision point that consists of one or more conditions connected by AND and OR. A single condition has only two test situations, one for valid input and one for invalid input. For compound conditions, the test situations are derived by applying modified condition/decision coverage (MCDC), as explained in section 14.3.3.

Example

Suppose that the following semantic check is specified:
"IF customer lives in the Netherlands AND (postcode does not comply with Netherlands format OR country code is different from 31) THEN this results in an error message."
The following occurs after applying MCDC:

D1 A AND (B OR C)	1 Error message	0 Valid input
A: Customer in NL	<u>1</u> 1 0 (1)	<u>0</u> 1 0 (3)
B: Postcode not in NL	~~1 1 0~~	1 <u>0</u> 0 (4)
C: Country code ≠ 31	1 0 <u>1</u> (2)	~~1 0 0~~

In more detail

In practice, semantic rules are sometimes described in the form:
"IF item X meets condition A, THEN condition ... should also be met"
The pitfall here is that it appears as though the semantic rule only consists of the condition "IF item X meets condition A". However, that is not the case. Everything that comes after the "THEN" also describes the conditions that should be met. In fact, this way of writing the semantic rule is an example of the "imply operator" in Boolean algebra. The truth table for this operator, which is shown by the symbol "→", is:

A	B	A → B
1	1	1
1	0	0
0	1	1
0	0	1

Now, a condition that is described by the imply operator can be converted simply into a compound condition with the same truth table:

"A → B" is equivalent to "(NOT A) OR B"

The basic technique of modified condition/decision coverage can be applied to the resulting compound condition – that contains only the operators AND, OR and NOT – without difficulty.

The example below explains this further.

Suppose that the following semantic rule is specified:

"When code_contribution = V THEN code_employment
must be = F AND Age ≥ 55"

An imply operator has been applied here, whereby the rule actually looks like this:

"code_contribution = V → (code_employment = F AND Age ≥ 55)"

This can be converted into the following compound condition:

"(NOT code_contribution = V) OR (code_employment = F AND Age ≥ 55)"

or

"code_contribution ≠ V OR (code_employment = F AND Age ≥ 55)"

Application of the basic MCDC technique delivers the following four test situations:

D1 A OR (B AND C)	1 Valid input		0 Error message	
A: code_contribution ≠ V	1 1 0	(1)	0 1 0	(3)
B: code_employment = F	0 1 1	(2)	0 0 1	(4)
C: Age ≥ 55	0 1 1		0 1 0	

2- Creating logical test cases

The test situations from step 1 at once form the logical test cases.

Example

The formulation of the four test situations from our example immediately gives us the four logical test cases:

Test cases/Test situations	D1-1	D1-2	D1-3	D1-4
Customer	in NL	in NL	not in NL	in NL
Postcode	not in NL	in NL	not in NL	in NL
Country code	31	≠ 31	31	31
Expected result	Error message	Error message	OK	OK

3- Creating physical test cases
No remarks.

4- Establishing the starting point
No remarks.

14.4.11 Syntactic Test (SYN)

Description
The syntactic test, together with the semantic test, belongs to the *validation tests*, with which the *validity of the input data* is tested. This establishes the degree to which the system is proof against invalid, or 'nonsense' input that is offered to the system wilfully or otherwise. This test is also used to test the validity of *output data*.

Validation tests focus on *attributes*, which should not be confused with *data*. An input screen or other random interface contains attributes that are (to be) filled with input values. If the sections contain valid values, the system will generally process these and create or change certain data within.

The test basis for the syntactic test consists of the syntactic rules, which specify how a attribute should comply in order to be accepted as valid input/output by the system. These rules actually describe the value domain for the relevant attribute. If a value outside this domain is offered for the attribute, the system should discontinue the processing in a controlled manner – usually with an error message.

Syntactic rules may be established in various documents, but they are normally described in:

- The 'data dictionary' and other data models, in which the characteristics of all the data are described
- Functional specifications of the relevant function or input screen, containing the specific requirements in respect of the attributes.

The syntactic rules may take a random order and be tested independently of each other. The coverage type applied here is:
- Checklist.

Usually, in practice, the input screens of data are used to test the syntactic checks. For practical reasons, this is often combined with the *presentation tests*, which test the layout of the screens. Presentation tests can be applied to both input (screens) and output (lists, reports).

Layout rules may be established in various documents, but are usually described in:

- Style guides, which often contain guidelines or rules for the whole organisation, concerning matters such as use of colour, fonts, screen layout, etc.
- Specifications for the layout of the relevant list or screen.

With both the validation test and the presentation test, checklists are used in which the checks are described that apply to each attribute or screen and that can be tested.

Points of focus in the steps

For the SYN, too, in principle the generic steps (see 14.4.1 "Introduction") are carried out. However, the construct of a syntactic test is very simple: Each attribute check and layout check is tested separately. Each check leads to one or more test situations, and each test situation generally leads to one test case.

For that reason, this section is restricted to the explanation of the first step, "Identifying test situations". This will focus on the compiling of the relevant checklists and the organisation of the test based on these.

1- Identifying test situations

With the syntactic test, two kinds of checks may be applicable:

- Attribute checks, for the validation test
- Layout checks, for the presentation test.

An overview is given below of the commonest types of checks in respect of both kinds. These can be used to compile a checklist that can be applied to every attribute/screen to be tested.

Overview of attribute checks

- Data type
  E.G. numeric, alphabetical, alphanumeric, etc.
- Field length
  The length of the input field is often limited. Investigate what happens when you attempt to exceed this length. (Press the letter key for a some time.)
- Input / Output
  There are 3 possibilities here:
  I: No value is shown, but may be or must be entered
  U: The value is shown, but may not be changed
  UI: A value is shown, and may be changed.
- Default
  If the attribute is not completed, the system should process the default value.
  If it concerns a UI field (see above), the default value should be shown.
- Mandatory / Non-mandatory

A mandatory attribute may not remain empty.

A non-mandatory attribute may remain empty. In the processing, either the datum is left empty or the default value for this datum is used.

- Selection mechanism

    A choice has to be made from a number of given possibilities. It is important here whether only one possibility may be chosen or several. This is particularly the case with GUIs (Graphical User Interface), e.g. with:

    - Radio buttons (try to activate several)
    - Check boxes (try to activate several)
    - Drop-down box (try to change the value or make it empty).

- Domain

    This describes all the valid values for this attribute. It can, in principle, be shown in two ways:

    - Enumeration

        For example {M, F, N}.

    - Value range

        All the values between the given boundaries are permitted. The value boundaries themselves, in particular, should be tested. For example, [0, 100>, where the symbols indicate that the value range is from 0 to 100, *including* the value 0, but *excluding* the value 100.

Tip

In practice, the value 0 (zero) can cause problems in input fields. It is advisable to try out the value 0 at *every* input field.

- Special characters

    Is the system proof against special characters, such as quotes, exclusive spaces, question marks, Ctrl characters, etc.?

- Format

    For some attributes, specific requirements are set as regards format, e.g.:

    - Date

        Common formats, for example, are YYYYMMDD or DD-MM-YY,

    - Postcode

        The postcode format in principle varies from country to country. In the Netherlands, the format for this is "1111 AA" (four digits followed by a space and two letters).

Overview of format checks

- Headers / Footers

    Are the standards being met in this regard? For example, it may be defined that the following information must be present:

    - Screen name or list name
    - System date or print date

- Version number.
■ Attributes
  Per attribute, specific formatting requirements are defined. For example:
  - Name of the attribute
  - Position of the attribute on the screen or overview
  - Reproduction of the attribute, such as font, colour, etc.
■ Other screen objects (optional)
  If necessary, such checks as are carried out on "Attributes" can be applied to other screen objects, such as "push buttons" and "drop-down lists".

The checklist describes in *general terms* the type of check that should be carried out on a particular attribute or screen. The *concrete requirements* in respect of the attribute or format that are related to this kind of check are described in detail in the relevant system documentation, such as screen descriptions and the data dictionary.

The syntactic test is adequately specified if there is an overview of:
■ All the attributes and screens that are to be tested
■ All the checks (checklist) that are to be tested in the relevant attribute/ screen.

During the test execution, the tester should keep the relevant system documentation to hand for the exact details of the checks. This method has the added advantage that with changes in the system documentation, the test specifications do not require to be changed.
An alternative option is to copy the details from the system documentation into the test specifications. The advantage of this is that there is no need to search for details in the system documentation during the test execution. On the other hand, it has the disadvantages that it requires disproportionately more work to specify the test and that there is a risk that the test specifications will be out of step with the system documentation.

If there is a large number of attributes and screens, there is a risk of the number of checks to be carried out becoming too high. In addition, the severity of the defects that are generally found with the syntactic test is quite low. It can therefore be useful to restrict the testing effort by prioritising:
■ Determine all the attributes/screens that are to be tested and sort them according to priority
■ Determine all the checks that have to be applied to the attributes/screens and sort them according to priority
■ First, carry out the tests with the highest-priority checks and attributes/ screens. Depending on the number and severity of the found defects, it can be decided whether to continue with lower-priority tests.

Such a mechanism at once offers excellent possibilities for managing the test and for reporting on progress, coverage and risks.

An overview can be shown in a matrix of which checks are to be carried out on which attributes and which priority they have. Each cell in the matrix represents a test situation to be tested. It can be indicated by a "-" or shading that the relevant check does not apply to that attribute.

Table 14.18 provides an example for the syntactic test of the function "Input booking". The matrix can simply be expanded for each function/screen for which a syntactic test is required.

The priorities are indicated by H(igh), M(edium) and L(ow). In this example, the priority is determined at function level and all the attributes of the selected function are tested. However, another option is to allocate different priorities to the attributes within one function. Such a refinement of course means a considerable amount of extra work.

		Data type	Format	Domain	I/U	Selection	Mandatory	Field length	Special characters	Default
Input booking	**H**	H	H	H	M	M	M	L	L	L
Booking ID			-			-				-
Destination			-							-
Airline			-							-
Date of travel						-		-		
No. of passengers			-			-				
Class			-							
...	...									

Table 14.18:Matrix of fields versus attribute checks for SYN.

During test execution, the same matrix can be used to indicate which test situations are tested and if necessary which findings have been made.

2- Creating logical test cases
The test situations from step 1 at once form the logical test cases.

3- Creating physical test cases
If desired, physical test cases and a test script can be created. This is particularly useful if the testing is to be carried out by inexperienced testers.

In table 14.19 is an example of physical test cases. It shows 3 groups of test situations: the "always wrong" situations; situations that can sometimes be wrong and sometimes be right; the "always valid" situations.

Screen 2.6	Always Wrong				W/V	W/V	Always Valid	
Value Field	Too many symbols	Too few symbols	Wrong symbols	Value outside of range	Leave field empty	Value zero	Min. value	Max. value
Bank group	> 5	< 5	¬ num	n.a.	EM	EM	00001	55555
Expiry date	> 4	< 4	¬ num	¬ **01-**12	OK	EM	0001	9912
Postcode	> 6	< 6	¬ alphanum	¬ 9999XX	EM	EM	1000AA	9999ZZ
Pin ind	> 1	< 1	¬ alpha	¬ {Y,N}	EM	EM	Y	N

The abbreviation "EM" stands for "error message". The symbol "¬" stands for "not".
Table 14.19: Example of physical test cases for SYN.

However, the description of each test situation usually provides sufficient information for executing the test. In that case, it is advisable during the test execution somehow to establish in concrete terms what has been tested, for purposes of reproducibility of the test. In the cases in which a defect is found, this is even a condition.

Tip

The syntactic test is ideally suited to automation. Besides the advantage of reproducibility, the automated test in itself offers detailed documentation on what exactly has been tested and which situations have been right or wrong.

4- Establishing the starting point
No special requirements are normally set as regards the starting point.
An exception to this is perhaps the testing of the syntax and layout of *output* such as lists and reports. This can prevent a particular list with a particular value in a particular field from only being produced after a complex and lengthy series of actions.

Tip

Combine the syntactic tests of lists and reports as far as possible with the functional tests (that produce the necessary variations of lists and reports), or do them at the end of such tests, so that the database is already maximally filled with lists and reports.

14.4.12 Use Case Test (UCT)

Description

The use case test is a technique that is applied in particular to the testing of the quality characteristics of Suitability, Effectivity and User-friendliness. The test basis contains at least the use cases and preferably also the associated use-case diagram. There are various definitions of the concept of use case in circulation. In this section, the following definition is used:

Definition

A use case contains a typical interaction between a user and a system. The use case describes a complete piece of functionality that a system offers to a user and that delivers an observable result for the user.

Besides various use case definitions, there are also various types of use case descriptions. The type can vary from organisation to organisation and even from project to project. The variations relate to the abstraction level, the scope and the degree of detail, with which a use case is described. Since a use case can be described in various ways, it makes sense to carry out a check before applying the use case test in order to examine whether the use case description employed contains sufficient information to be used for the use case test. The simplest way to perform this check is with a checklist (see the tip "Use cases checklist").

Tip

Use cases checklist
The detail content of a checklist for determining whether a use case is usable for the application of the use case test depends on the way in which a use case is described. Below are some checks that can be used as a basis for creating your own checklist:
- Is the (standard for the project/organisation) use case template filled in completely?
- Is the use case diagram available?
- Is the use case a separate task in itself?
- Is the aim of the use case clear?
- Is it clear for which actors the use case is intended?
- Does the use case relate to the functionality (and not to the screens sequence)?
- Have all the foreseen alternative possibilities been described?
- Have all the known exceptions been described?
- Does the use case contain a complete step-by-step plan?
- Has each step in the scenario(s) been clearly, unambiguously and completely described?
- Are all the actors and steps cited in the use case relevant to the execution of the task?
- Are the described steps executable?
- Is the result of the steps verifiable?
- Do the pre- and post conditions correspond with the use case?

The use case test focuses on the coverage of the interactions between the user and the system. The basic technique used here is:

- Checklist

Variations on the use case test can be created by applying other basic techniques, such as:

- Paths
- Decision points: modified condition/decision coverage
- Pairwise testing

The basic technique "checklist" is almost always usable. The effectiveness of the alternative basic techniques is strongly dependent on the content of the use case descriptions. In this section, the "checklist" basic technique is employed in an example. For an explanation of the other techniques, see section 14.3 "Coverage types and basic techniques".

In more detail

Use case diagram

A use case describes a (part of the) functionality. A use case diagram indicates the system boundaries, reflects possible mutual relationships between use cases, and especially shows which relationships there are between the actors (users) and the use cases.

A use case diagram is relatively simple. The three most important symbols are:

- A 'doll' to indicate an actor
- An oval, to indicate a use case
- A line between actor and use case, or between use cases (see explanation below).

Use cases can have two types of connections: "extend" or "include":

- Extend

  An extend relationship is used when a use case present corresponds with another use case, but does something extra. This 'something extra' is removed from the use case and placed into a separate use case

- Include

  If a particular behaviour occurs in several use cases, this is usually modelled, rather than repeated in each use case. In this way, a use case is created that is used (include relationship) by other use cases. A simple example is a use case that looks up the marital status of an individual. This can be used by both the use case "Determine tax rate" and the use case "Amend marital status". This is then often modelled into the use case "Determine marital status".

The correspondence between extend and include is that, in both cases, similar behaviour is removed to avoid repetition. The difference between them is that an include relationship, in contrast to the extend relationship, often does not involve an actor. Furthermore, the include use case is always executed, whereas the extend use case is executed optionally.

For more information on use cases/models, refer to the official Unified Modelling Language (UML) documentation of the Object Management Group (http://www.omg.org).

Points of focus in the steps

In this section, the use case test is explained step by step. In this, the generic steps (see 14.4.1 "Introduction") are taken as a starting point. An example is also provided, showing at each step how the technique works. A use case diagram is set up in the example according to the above description. Since no uniform agreements exist concerning a description of a use case, only relevant use case components have been used in the example.

Example

Figure 14.19 shows a use case diagram in which the student ("actor") can start an application ("TestDesignTechniqueAssessment"). After going through the logging-in procedure, the student selects a particular test design technique on which he wishes to be assessed.

During the assessment, there is the possibility of giving the student an explanation when a wrong answer is given. There is also a possibility of providing an interim score relating to the number of correct answers given. After a certain number of questions have been posed, the application stops. The tutor ("actor") can follow the student's progress and results.

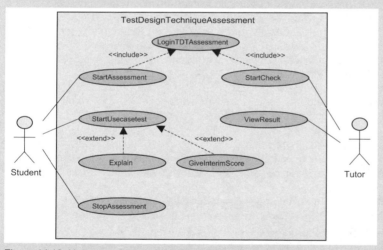

Figure 14.19: Use case diagram "TestDesignTechniqueAssessment".

As an example, some use case descriptions are provided:

Name	StartAssessment
Actor	Student
Preconditions	Student has followed test design technique training
Primary scenario	1. The student starts the "TestDesignTechniqueAssessment" program 2. Include <LoginTDTAssessment> 3. The student chooses from the available test design techniques 4. The student may choose the option "Explain" 5. The student may choose the option "Provide interim score" 6. The program is ready for the first question
Postconditions	The student can start the selected test

Name	StartUsecasetest
Actor	Student
Preconditions	Student has followed test design technique training

Primary scenario	1. The use case starts when the student presses the question button for the first time
	2. While fewer than 10 questions have been set
	  2.1 The computer will generate a question concerning the use case test
	  2.2 The student will read the question, think of the answer and type it in
	  2.3 After checking, the student presses "Enter"
	  2.4 The computer reads the answer
	  2.5 If the answer is processable, then
	    2.5.1 The assessment "Right" is given if the answer corresponds with that of the computer
	    2.5.2 The assessment "Wrong" is given if the answer does not correspond with that of the computer
	  2.6 Else, the student receives the message: "Answer is not processable and therefore counts as wrong" <GiveInterimScore>
	  2.7 The student thinks about a wrong answer <Explain>
	  2.8 The student presses the question button
	3. The student receives an assessment in the form of a score after 10 questions
	4. The program stops

Exceptions	1. Student presses the question button, while the previous question has not been answered 2. Student types something in the input field, while the question has already been answered 3. Student stops before 10 questions have been answered
Postconditions	The student is given a score for the test

Name	GiveInterimScore
Actor	Student
Preconditions	At start of assessment, the student has opted for receiving the interim score
Primary scenario	• The right answer increases the number of right answers by one. An interim score is generated based on this number • The interim score is provided in a status line

In more detail

Besides the above-mentioned components (name, actor, preconditions, primary scenario, exceptions and postconditions) use-case components that are often used in use-case templates are:
• Scope (does it for example concern a system or a subsystem)
• Level (does it for example concern a primary task or a subfunction)
• Stakeholder (concerns the party/parties involved: e.g. student, tutor, employer and/or customer)
• Trigger (the 'event' that ensures that the use case starts is also shown as the first step in the use-case scenario)
• Priority (degree of importance of the use case)
• Response time (the time available for executing the use case)
• Frequency (number of times that the use case is executed)
• Secondary actors (other actors involved in the use case)
The use of the above-mentioned use case components is not imperative. Depending on the nature of the use case, components are added or left out. Naturally, basic component, such as "Name", "Actor", "Preconditions", "Primary scenario" and "Postconditions" are almost always present in a use case description.

Below, it is set out step by step how the use case test is applied in this example:

1- Identifying test situations

Deriving test situations from the use case is largely dependent on the level of detail to which the use case is described. When there is little detail, it may be the case that only one test case can be described for a use case (e.g. the purpose of the use case). Under such circumstances, no logical test cases can be created for these test situations, since not enough information is present. If the use case contains more detail, then of course detailed test situations can be distinguished, which can immediately be seen as the logical test cases. In all cases, the recognised test situations are included on a checklist, so that it will be possible at the next stage to check off whether at least one logical test case has been created for each test situation.

Since no uniform description exists for use cases, it is not possible to provide a formal way of deriving test situations. Depending on the knowledge and expertise of the testers, one will find it easier than another (see also the tip).

Tip

Depending on the way in which a use case is described, carrying out the following steps can help to get thoughts in order for identifying and describing test situations:
1. Look for variables that result in a reaction of the system or the environment. Examples of variables are input data, output data, environment variables that force the actor into certain behaviour, status of the system, etc.
2. Determine the domain of the variables.
3. Determine which variables have a relationship with each other.
4. Combine related variables into a test situation and describe this.
   A test situation contains at least the relationship between the variables, certain value(s) from the domain, the starting situation and a specific described result.

The result of the first three steps for the use case "StartUsecasetest" may look as follows:

Variable	Domain	Relationship with
Give interim score	{Y, N}	Given answer
Explain	{Y, N}	Given answer
Given answer	(Right, Wrong)	Processable answer, Give interim score, Explain
Processable answer	{Y, N}	Given answer
No. of answers given	{0 - 10}	Program

With the aid of the above table and the use case description, test situations can be identified and described (step 4).

Example

Suppose that the use cases from the example "TestDesignTechniqueAssessment" were to contain almost no details; a checklist with test situations (these are *not* logical test cases) might look like this:
Use case "StartAssessmentt"
1a. The student should be able to log on with his 'own' settings on the assessment application.
1b. The student should be able to select a test for a test design technique.
Use case "StartUsecasetest"
2a. The student should be able to take the "use case test" test.
2b. The student should have the option of obtaining an explanation with a wrong answer.
2c. The student should have the option of getting an interim score.
Use case "StartCheck"
3. The tutor should be able to log in with his 'own' settings to the test (check) application.
Use case "ViewResult"
4. The tutor should be able to follow a student's progress and results.

However, as the example does contain more detail, the test situations description does not have to be restricted to a checklist. In the table below, a few example test situations for the use case "StartUsecasetest" are described. These test situations *are* at once the logical test cases. For the description of a test situation, a layout that is similar to the use case description has been chosen.

Use Case Name	StartUsecasetest
Test case ID	1
Test case purpose	Check whether the computer generates a question the first time the question button is pressed
Priority	Medium
Actor	Student
Precondition	Select "Usecasetest" at the start of the test
Trigger	Press the question button
Postconditions	The first question about the "Usecasetest" is shown.
Test case ID	2
Test case purpose	Check whether an interim score is given with a right answer.
Priority	Low
Actor	Student
Precondition	At the start of the test, select the option "Give interim score". The given answer is processable.
Trigger	Type right answer and press "Enter".
Postcondition	The message "Right" is shown and an interim score is shown.
Test case ID	3
Test case purpose	Check that no explanation is given with a wrong answer.
Priority	High
Actor	Student
Precondition	At the start of the test, do not select the option "Explain". The given answer is processable.
Trigger	Type wrong answer and press "Enter'.
Postcondition	The message "Wrong" is shown and no explanation is given.
Test case ID	4
Test case purpose	Check that the program stops if the question button is pressed after 10 answers are given.
Priority	Medium
Actor	Student
Precondition	10 answers have been given.

Use Case Name	StartUsecasetest
Trigger	Press the question button.
Postcondition	A final score is shown and the program stops.

The component "Priority" can be used to indicate whether it is mandatory or optional to execute the test case. It can also be used to determine the sequence of execution.

2- Creating logical test cases

If step 1 "Identifying test situations" has resulted only in a checklist, no logical and physical test cases can (at the moment) be created on the basis of the use cases. In that case, other parts of the test basis should be searched for additional information to enable the creation of the test cases. If step 1 has delivered detailed test situations, these are at once the logical test cases.

In a UCT test case traceability matrix, a track is kept (by checking off) of whether at least one logical test case has finally been made for all the recognised test situations.

Example

With the checklist example, it will still be possible at a given point, on the basis of information from other parts of the test basis, to start creating logical test cases. The UCT test case traceability matrix (here completed with fictional values) might look as follows:

Test situation	Logical test case								
	TC1	TC..	TC..	TC..	TC..	TC..	TC..	TC..	TCn
1a	√		√						
1b							√		
2a									
2b				√					
2c								√	
3									
4		√			√				

It can be seen from the matrix that no logical test cases (TCs) have yet been created for test situations 2a and 3. It can also be seen, for example, that test situation 1a occurs in various logical test cases.

The simple UCT test case traceability matrix for the example with the detailed test situations (which are at once the logical test cases) looks as follows:

Test situation	Logical test case			
	TC1	TC2	TC3	TC4
1	√			
2		√		
3			√	
4				√

3- Creating physical test cases
No remarks.

4- Establishing the starting point
No remarks.

15 Evaluation techniques

15.1 Introduction

The result of an evaluation depends heavily on the attitude of the evaluator(s). After all, an evaluation often assesses documents created by someone else. It usually results in a list of findings intended for the author of the document in question. Depending on how the findings are recorded or communicated, the author may feel 'attacked'. Chances are that this will result in a negative perception of the evaluation process. As such, it is important to realise that the author did not intend to write things down 'incorrectly' on purpose. It is also important to be aware that the evaluation process' final goal is to deliver the best possible end product together. Evaluation techniques are very well suited to improve the quality of products. This applies not only to the evaluated products themselves, but also to other products. For instance, the findings from the evaluation process may cause the development process to implement process improvements.

Research has shown, however, that evaluation processes – despite their proven value – are not always implemented or executed seamlessly. A few causes that a survey brought to light:
- 56% of the authors found it hard to disengage from their work
- 48% of the evaluators had not received the correct training
- 47% of the authors were afraid that the data would be used against them.

After a general description of evaluation, this chapter discusses three techniques in greater detail: inspections, reviews, and walkthroughs. The last section of this chapter contains an evaluation technique selection matrix that can be used to choose a technique.

"IEEE Std 1028-1997 Standard for Software Reviews" [IEEE, 1998] was used as a basis for this chapter, supplemented with experiences from practice.

> **Tip**
>
> Evaluation is one of the points of concern in the "test process improvement" (TPI) model [Koomen, 1999]. The TPI book contains some suggestions for implementing and improving the evaluation process (section 7.19 "Evaluation").

15.2   Evaluation explained

Intermediary products

Various intermediary products are developed in the course of the system development process. Depending on the selected method, these have a certain form, content and inter-relationship, on the basis of which they can be evaluated (see section 2.3.3 "Test and system development process").

> **Definition**
>
> Evaluation is assessing the intermediary products in the system development process.

The evaluation of intermediary products does not have to limit itself to the development documents. Evaluation can occur at all levels of documentation:

- Functional/ technical design
- Requirements document
- Management plan
- Development plan
- Test plan
- Maintenance documentation
- User/Installation manual
- Software
- Release note
- Test design
- Test script
- Prototype
- Screen print
- Etc.

Evaluation site

Beside the quality improvement described earlier, another important aspect of evaluation is that defects can be found much earlier in the (development) process than by testing (see figure 15.1). This is because evaluation assesses intermediary products and not, as testing does, the end products. And the earlier a defect is found, the more easily and economically it can be repaired [Boehm, 1981].

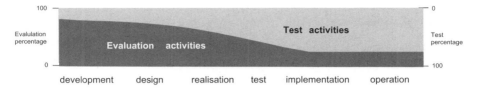

Figure 15.1: Evaluation and testing versus system development phasing

Evaluation has demonstrated time and again to be the most efficient and effective way to eliminate defects from the intermediary products of a system (see the practical examples in section 6.5 "Preparation phase"). Evaluation is also a process that is easy to set up because, for instance, no software has to be run and no environment has to be created. As such, there are adequate reasons to set up an evaluation process.

In practice, however, good intentions can become mired in practical execution problems: "Can you have a look at these 6 folders with the functional specifications? Please get them back to us the day after tomorrow, because that is when we start programming."

Formal evaluation techniques in the form of process descriptions and checklists, help get this under control. A formal evaluation technique is characterised by the fact that several persons evaluate as a team, defects are documented (see tip), and there are written procedures to execute the evaluation activities.

Tip

The evaluators detect many defects; often it is decided to enter these in a defect administration. At the end of the evaluation meeting, rubrics such as status, severity, and action have to be updated for the defects. These are labour and time-intensive activities that can be minimised as follows:
• Evaluators record their comments on an evaluation form.
• These comments are discussed during the evaluation meeting.
• At the end of the meeting, only the most important comments are registered in the defect administration as a defect. Please refer to chapter 12, "Defects management", for more information on the defect procedure.

An evaluation form contains the following aspects:

Per form
• Identification of evaluator
  ◦ name
  ◦ role
• Identification of the intermediate product

> - document name
> - version number/date
> - Evaluation process data
>   - number of pages evaluated
>   - evaluation time invested
> - General impression of the intermediate product
>
> **Per comment**
> - unique reference number
> - Clear reference to the place in the intermediate product to which the comment relates (e.g. by specifying the chapter, section, page, line, requirement number)
> - Description of the comment
> - Importance of the comment (e.g. high, medium, low)
> - Follow-up actions (to be filled out by the *author* with e.g. completed, partially completed, not completed)
>
> Note: This form is useful for reviewing documents in particular. When reviewing software or for a walkthrough of a prototype, the aspects on the form need to be modified.

There are various evaluation technique intensities. This is important because not every intermediary product needs to be evaluated equally intensively. This is why an evaluation strategy is often included in the master test plan. Like a test strategy, an evaluation strategy is extremely important when aiming to deploy the effort in an optimal way, as well as a means of communication towards the client. While establishing the strategy, it is analysed what has to be evaluated where and how often in order to achieve the optimal balance between the required quality and the amount of time and/or money that is required. Optimisation aims to distribute the available resources correctly over the activities to be executed.

Structure of evaluation technique sections

After a few general tips, the sections below describe the techniques according to the following structure:
- Introduction
  Description of the goal of the technique and the products to which the technique can be applied.
- Responsibilities
  Description of which roles are allocated to participants.
- Entry criteria
  Description of the necessary products and conditions that must be met before evaluation can begin.
- Procedures
  Description of:
  - How to organise an evaluation (planning)

- The method to be used
- The required preparation of the participants
- How evaluation results are discussed and recorded
- How rework is done and checked.
- Exit criteria
  Description of the deliverable documents and the conditions under which the product can exit the evaluation process.

Tips

When using an evaluation technique, practice has shown that there are several critical success factors:

- The author must be released from other activities to participate in the evaluation process and process the results.
- Authors must not be held accountable for the evaluation results.
- Evaluators must have attended a (short) training in the specific evaluation technique.
- Adequate (preparation) time must be available between submission of the products to the evaluators and the evaluation meeting (e.g. two weeks). If necessary, the products can be made available during a kick-off. See figure 15.2 for a possible planning of the evaluation programme.
- The minutes secretary must be experienced and adequately instructed. Making minutes of all defects, actions, decisions and recommendations of the evaluators is vital to the success of an inspection process. Sometimes the author takes on the role of minutes secretary, but the disadvantage is that the author may miss parts of the discussion (because he must divide his attention between writing and listening).
- The size of the intermediary product to be evaluated and the available preparation and meeting time must be tuned to each other.
- Make clear follow-up agreements. Agree when and in which version of the intermediary product the agreed changes must be implemented.
- Feedback from the author to the evaluators (appreciation for their contribution).

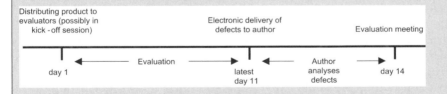

Figure 15.2: Possible planning of an evaluation programme

The planning above does not keep account of any activities to be executed after the evaluation meeting. These might involve: modifying the product, re-evaluation, and final acceptance of the product. If relevant, such activities must be added to the planning. The activities 'modifying the product' and 're-evaluation' may be iterative.

Practical example

In an organisation in which the time-to-market of various modifications to the information system had to be short, the modifications were implemented by means of a large number of short-term increments.

The testers were expected to review the designs (in the form of use cases). A lead time of two weeks for a review programme was not a realistic option. To solve the problem, the Monday was chosen as the fixed review day. The 'rules of the game' were as follows:
- The designers delivered one or more documents for review to the test manager before 9.00am (if no documents were delivered, no review occurred on that Monday).
- All documents taken together could not exceed a total of 30 A4-sized pages.
- The test manager determined which tester had to review what.
- The review comments of the testers had to be returned to the relevant designer before 12.00pm.
- The review meeting was held from 2.00pm to 3.00pm.
- The aim was for the designer to modify the document the same day (depending on the severity of the comments, one day later was allowed).

15.3   Inspections

There are various forms of the inspection process. This section describes a general form. For a specific, and indeed most common form, please refer to [Gilb, 1993] and [Fagan, 1986].

Introduction

A formal work method is followed when executing an inspection, with products being read thoroughly by a group of experts. This can be any of the documents listed in section 15.2. The inspectors look at deviations from pre-defined criteria in these products, which must be 100% complete. In addition to determining whether the solution is adequately processed, an inspection focuses primarily on achieving consensus on the quality of a product. Aspects for evaluation are e.g. compliance of the product with certain standards, specifications, regulations, guidelines, plans and/or procedures. Often the inspection criteria are collected and recorded in a checklist. The aim of the inspection is to help the author find as many deviations as possible in the available time.

Responsibilities

Three to six participants are involved in an inspection. Possible roles are:
- Moderator
  The moderator prepares and leads the inspection process. This means

planning the process, making agreements, determining product and group size, and bearing responsibility for recording all defects detected during the inspection process.

- Author
  The author requests an inspection. During the inspection process, he explains anything that may be unclear in the product. The author must also ensure that he understands the defects found by the inspectors.

- Minutes secretary
  The minutes secretary records all defects, actions, decisions and recommendations of the inspectors during the inspection process.

- Inspector
  Prior to the inspection meeting, the inspector tries to find and document as many defects as possible. Often an inspector is asked by the moderator to do so from one specific perspective, e.g. project management, testing, development or quality (see text box "perspective-based reading"). An inspector can also be asked to check the entire product on the correct use of a certain standard.

With the exception of the author, all participants may fulfil one or more of the above roles. All participants (except the author) at least fulfil the role of inspector. None of the participants may be the superior of one of the other participants because there is a risk that participants will restrain themselves when reporting their findings.

In more detail

Perspective-based reading
Participants in an evaluation activity often assess a product with the same objective and from the same perspective. Often, a systematic approach during preparation is missing. The risk is that the various participants find the same type of defects. Using a good reading technique can result in improvement. One technique commonly used is the perspective-based reading (PBR) technique. Properties of PBR are:
- Participants evaluate a product from one specific perspective (e.g. as developer, tester, user, project manager).
- Approach based on the *what* and *how* questions. It is laid down in a procedure *what* the product parts are that must be evaluated from one specific perspective and *how* they must be evaluated. Often a procedure (scenario) is created for each perspective.

PBR is one of the 'scenario-based reading' (SBR) techniques. Defect reading, scope reading, use-based reading and horizontal/vertical reading are other SBR techniques that participants in an evaluation activity can use.
Please refer to e.g. [Laitenberger, 1995] and [Basili, 1997] for more information.

Entry criteria

The inspection process can be started when:

- The aim of the inspection and the inspection procedure are clear.
- The product is 100% complete (but not yet definitive), and spelling errors have been eliminated, it complies with the agreed standards, accompanying documentation is available, references are correct, etc.
- The checklists and inspection forms to record defects to be used during the inspection are available.
- (Possibly) a list with known defects is available.

Procedures

The inspection process can be split up into the phases planning, kick-off, preparation and execution:

Planning

When the product for inspection complies with the entry criteria, the moderator organises an inspection meeting. This means, among other things: determining date and location of the meeting, creating a team, allocating roles, distributing the products for inspection (delivered by the author) to the participants, and reaching agreements on the period within which the author must receive the defects found.

Kick-off

The kick-off meeting is held before the actual inspection. The meeting is optional and is organised by the moderator for the following reasons:

- If participants are invited that have not yet participated in an inspection before, the moderator provides a summary introduction to the technique and the method used.
- The author of the product for inspection describes the product.
- If there are improvements or changes in the work method to be used during the inspection, they are explained.

If a kick-off is held, the documents are handed out and the roles can be explained during this meeting.

Preparation

Good preparation is necessary to ensure the most efficient and effective possible inspection meeting. During the preparation, the inspectors look for defects in the products for inspection and record them on the inspection form. The moderator collects the forms, classifies the defects, and makes the result available to the author in a timely manner so that the latter can prepare.

Execution

The aim of the inspection meeting is not just recording the defects detected by the participants in the preparation phase. Detecting new defects during the meeting and the implicit exchange of knowledge are other important objectives. During the meeting, the moderator ensures that the defects are inventoried page by page in an efficient manner. The minutes secretary records the defects on a defect list. Cosmetic defects are not generally registered, but handed over to the author at the end of the meeting.

At the end of the meeting, the moderator goes through the defect list prepared by the minutes secretary with all participants to ensure that it is complete and the defects are recorded correctly. Inaccuracies are corrected immediately, but due to efficiency the idea is not to open a discussion on defects and (possible) solutions.

Finally, it is determined whether the product is accepted as is (possibly with some small changes), or if the product is accepted after changes and a check by one of the inspectors, or if the product must be submitted to re-inspection after changes.

Based on the defect list and agreements made during the meeting, the author adapts the product.

Exit criteria

The inspection process is considered complete when:
- The changes (rework) are complete (check by moderator).
- The product has been given a new version number.
- All changes made are documented in the new version of the inspected product (change history).
- Any change proposals with respect to other products, that have emerged from the inspection process, have been submitted.
- The inspection form has been completed and handed over to the quality management employee responsible, among other things for statistical purposes.

15.4   Reviews

There are various review types, such as: technical review (e.g. selecting solution direction/alternative), management review (e.g. determining project status), peer review (review by colleagues), and expert review (review by experts). This section describes the review process in general.

Introduction

A review follows a formal method, where a product (60-80% complete) is submitted to a number of reviewers with the question to assess it from a certain perspective (depending on the review type). The author collects the comments and on this basis adjusts the product.

A review focuses primarily on finding courses for a solution on the basis of the knowledge and competencies of the reviewers, and on finding and correcting defects. A review of a product often occurs earlier on in the product's lifecycle than a product inspection.

Responsibilities

The minimum number of participants in a review is three. This may be less for a peer review, e.g. when reviewing the code, which is usually done by one reviewer. Possible roles are:

- Moderator
  The moderator prepares and leads the review process. This means planning the review process, inviting the reviewers, and possibly allocating specific tasks to the reviewers.
- Author
  The author requests a review and delivers the product for reviewing.
- Minutes secretary
  The minutes secretary records all defects, actions, decisions and recommendations of the reviewers during the review process.
- Reviewer
  Prior to the review meeting, the inspector tries to find and document as many defects as possible.

All participants may fulfil one or more of the above roles. All participants (except the author) at least fulfil the role of reviewer.

Entry criteria

The review process can be started when:

- The aim of the review and the review procedure are clear.
- The product for review is available. A comprehensive "entry check" is not necessary because the product is only 60%-80% complete.
- The checklists and inspection forms to record defects to be used during the review are available.
- (Possibly) a list with known defects is available.

Procedures

The review process can be split up into the phases planning, preparation and execution:

Planning
When the product for review complies with the entry criteria, the moderator organises an review meeting. This means, among other things: determining date and location of the meeting, inviting reviewers, distributing the products for review to the participants, and reaching agreements on the period within which the author must receive the defects found.

Preparation
Good preparation is necessary to ensure the most efficient and effective review meeting. During the preparation, the reviewers look for defects in the products for review and record them on the review form. The moderator collects the forms, preferably classifies the defects, and makes the result available to the author in a timely manner so that the latter can prepare.

Execution
At the beginning of the meeting, the agenda is created or adjusted under the leadership of the moderator. The most important defects are placed at the top of the agenda. The objective is to reserve adequate time in the agenda to discuss these defects. Since the product is not yet complete, little to no attention is devoted to less important defects (contrary to the inspection process). The minutes secretary records the defects on a defect list. Often an action list is also compiled.

Finally, the moderator may recommend an additional review, determined among other things by the severity and number of defects. Based on the defect/action list made during the meeting, the author adapts the product.

Exit criteria
The review process is considered complete when:
- All actions on the action list are "closed" and all changes based on important defects are incorporated into the product (check by moderator).
- The product is approved for use in a subsequent phase/activity.

15.5　Walkthroughs

A walkthrough is a method by which the author explains the contents of a product during a meeting. Several different objectives are possible:
- Bringing all participants to the same starting point, e.g. in preparation for a review or inspection process.
- Transfer of information, e.g. to developers and testers to help them in their programming and test design work, respectively.
- Asking the participants for additional information.

- Letting the participants choose from the alternatives proposed by the author.

Introduction
A walkthrough can be held for any of the documents listed in 15.2 when they are 50-100% complete.

Responsibilities
The number of participants in a walkthrough is unlimited if the author wishes to explain his product to certain groups, e.g. by means of a presentation. For an interactive walkthrough, we recommend a group size of two to seven persons. Possible roles are:
- Moderator
  The moderator prepares the walkthrough. This means planning the walkthrough, inviting the participants, distributing both the product and a document explaining the purpose of the walkthrough.
- Author
  The author requests a walkthrough and explains the product during the walkthrough.
- Minutes secretary
  The minutes secretary records all decisions and identified actions during the walkthrough. He also records findings (such as conflicts, questions and omissions) and recommendations from the participants.
- Participant
  The participant's role depends on the purpose of the walkthrough. It can vary from listener to actively proposing certain solutions.

All participants may fulfil one or more of these roles. The author can act as the moderator. Both the moderator and the author may fulfil the role of minutes secretary.

Entry criteria
The walkthrough can be started when:
- The purpose of the walkthrough is clear.
- The subject (product) of the walkthrough is available.

Procedures
The walkthrough process can be split up into the phases planning, preparation and execution:

Planning
When the entry criteria are met, the moderator plans the walkthrough, invites participants, distributes the product and explains the purpose of the walkthrough to the participants.

Preparation

Depending on the purpose of the walkthrough, the participants may submit defects but usually this does not happen (for example because the purpose is knowledge transfer). If defects are submitted, the moderator collects them and makes them available to the author. The author determines how the product is presented, e.g. relating to any defects, sequentially, bottom up or top down.

Execution

At the beginning of the meeting, the moderator explains the purpose of the walkthrough and the procedure to be followed. The author then provides a detailed description of the product; the participants can ask questions, submit comments and criticism, etc during or after the description.

Decisions, identified actions, any defects, etc are recorded by the minutes secretary. At the end of the walkthrough, the moderator goes through the recorded decisions, actions and other important information with all those present for verification purposes.

Exit criteria

The walkthrough is considered complete when:

- The product has been described during the walkthrough.
- Decisions, actions and recommendations have been recorded
- The purpose of the walkthrough has been achieved.

15.6 Evaluation technique selection matrix

As with testing, every organisation or project organises evaluation processes in their own way. This means that there is no single uniform description of the evaluation techniques, nor can we specify in which situation a specific technique is most suitable. However, the table on the next page (also to be found at www.tmap.net) may offer some assistance in selecting a technique:

Aspect	Inspection	Review	Walkthrough
Area of application	In addition to determining whether the solution is adequately processed, focuses primarily on achieving consensus on the quality of a product.	Focuses primarily on finding courses for a solution and on finding and correcting defects. Review types include technical, management, peer and expert review.	Focuses on choosing from alternative solutions, completing missing information, or knowledge transfer.
Products to be evaluated	For example: functional/technical design, requirements document, management plan, development plan, test plan, maintenance documentation, user/installation manual, software, release note, test design, test script, prototype, and screen print.		
Group size	Three to six participants.	At least three participants.	Two to seven participants in alternative version to unlimited for presentation version.
Preparation	Strict management of the aspects to be evaluated by the inspectors. Defects (based on checklists, standards, etc) described by inspectors to be delivered to the author before the meeting.	Reviewers largely determine themselves which aspects they want to evaluate. Defects of reviewers to be delivered to the author before the meeting.	From being informed of the product to delivering defects.
Product status and size	Product is 100% complete, not yet definitive and limited in size (10-20 pages).	Product is 60%-80% complete and has a variable size.	Product is 50%-100% complete and has a variable size.
Benefits	High quality, incidental and structural quality improvement.	Limited labour intensity, early involvement of reviewers.	High learning impact, low labour intensity.
Dis-advantages	Labour-intensive (costly), relatively long lead time.	Subjective, possible disturbance of collegial relationships.	Risk of ad-hoc discussions because participants are often not prepared.

Table 15.1: Evaluation technique selection matrix

16   Test roles

16.1   Introduction

Test activities within a project or in the organisational line are named by defining the various tasks. For the execution of those tasks, particular knowledge and skills are required. A group of tasks, together with the relevant knowledge and skills that are required, is referred to as a role.

Definition

A role describes one or more tasks and the knowledge and skills required to carry them out.

There are roles that correspond, like for like, with the positions described in section 8.6.5 "Positions". There are also roles that do not occur as a position in themselves.

Difference between position and role

The significant difference between a position and a role is that the professional *holds* a position and *fulfils* a role. A role is aimed at the performance of tasks for the test project or the permanent test organisation in a specific situation. Roles are fulfilled by a test professional. A position of a test professional formally describes which tasks the individual should be able to perform and what knowledge and skills he should possess. A position says something about the suitability for a role.

Example 1

A test project wishes to fill the role of tester. To this end, an individual is sought who holds the position of tester.

Example 2

A test project seeks to fill the role of test-team leader with an individual who will also be required to carry out testing (a co-working supervisor). To this end, an individual is sought who holds the position of tester, has practical experience as a tester, possesses the capacity to manage and has the desire to become a test-team leader.

In this chapter, we will name roles that commonly exist in test projects or in permanent test organisations. Roles that correspond with test positions are named in section 16.2. In section 16.3, roles are described that do not have an explicit position description.

16.2   Roles that are described as a position

The roles below have already been described as a position in section 8.6.5 "Positions", but may be filled separately.
- Tester
- Test tool programmer
- Test method expert
- Test coordinator
- Test tool expert
- Test consultant
- Test manager
- Test tool consultant.

With UATs and PATs the role of tester may naturally be taken by a professional tester, but also by a user or administrator.

16.3   Roles not described as a position

In this section, roles are described that do not constitute positions in themselves.
Besides the roles described here, in practice other roles also arise. Roles may also be combined.
- Application integrator
- Defects administrator
- Domain knowledge expert
- Intermediary
- System expert
- Test infrastructure coordinator
- Test project administrator
- Test team leader
- Testware administrator.

For each role, we will explain the tasks and the knowledge and skills they require.

Application integrator
The application integrator is responsible for the integration of the separate system parts (programs, objects, modules, components, etc.) into a correctly

operating system, and is able to position as a quality inspector in order to monitor the agreements made. The application integrator supports the unit test and carries out the unit integration test. The application integrator delivers the system to the subsequent phase in the project.

Tasks
- Integration of the separate programs, objects, modules, components, etc. into user positions or (sub)systems
- Creation of, obtaining approval for, and maintenance of the unit integration test plan
- Creation of the entry criteria that the separate programs, objects, modules and components should meet in order to be included in the integration process
- Creation of exit criteria that an integrated part of the system should meet in order to be released to the following phase
- Facilitation and support of the programmers in the execution of the unit tests
- Execution of the unit integration test plan on time and on budget
- (Ordering) the execution of configuration management and version management
- (Ordering) the execution of internal defects management
- Functioning as contact for the client's organisation concerning later test types
- Reporting on the progress of the integration process and the quality of the test object
- Creation of release advice concerning the unit integration test
- Evaluation of the integration process
- Delivery of the system to the next phase.

Required knowledge and skills
Test-specific
- Experience in the application of the TMap life cycle and test-design techniques
- Experience as team leader and experience in support positions
IT
- Knowledge of the system development method
- Knowledge of the architecture and tools for system development
- Knowledge of the hardware, software (including programming language) and data-communication equipment used
- Knowledge of integration techniques and integration tools
General
- General knowledge of the subject and the line organisation
- Good interpersonal skills and a motivational approach
- Able to gain the respect of developers

- Good written and verbal communication skills
- Critical attitude and ability to evaluate arguments accurately
- Tactful, stress-resistant and able to take criticism
- Able to provide support with defect analysis.

Defects administrator
The defects administrator is responsible for the setup and optimum use of the defects administration and processes surrounding it.

Tasks
- Setup of the defects administration and associated processes
- Advising on the selection of a defect administration tool
- Monitoring, evaluating and improving the defect administration tool method and processes
- Managing defects registered by analysis and/or decision-making forum
- Management of access to the defect administration tool.

Required knowledge and skills
Test-specific
- Knowledge of the TMap life cycle
- Extensive knowledge of defects procedures and the relationship with the test process
IT
- General knowledge of IT, system development and the project approach
- Capable of issuing new and amended reports from the defect administration tool
General
- Able to translate procedures and project aims into adequate processes.

Domain knowledge expert
The domain knowledge expert supplies subject knowledge and insight into how this domain is specified in requirements, functional designs, business processes and user manuals.

Tasks
- Providing support and advice on functionality and business processes in:
  - Analysing product risks
  - Determining test strategy
  - Introduction of new test workers
  - Making assumptions on defects as regards consistency
  - Analysing defects
  - Prioritising defects
  - Creating and/or reviewing test cases.

Required knowledge and skills
Test-specific
- General knowledge of the TMap concepts
IT
- General IT knowledge and experience
- Knowledge of the functional architecture principles of the test object
General
- Specialist knowledge of the domain, both in terms of the business processes and the functionality
- Knowledge of the organisation in which the test object will operate
- Good interpersonal skills and a motivational approach
- Good written and verbal communication skills.

Intermediary

The intermediary maintains contact, at operational level, with the test team, developers and subject-matter experts/users concerning the defects. On the one hand, the intermediary explains the defects and supplies supplementary data, if required. On the other hand, he passes the solutions of the defects on to the test team. This role emphatically demands explicit attention if the test team is placed at another location or if there is a very formal relationship with the other parties, for example in the case of outsourcing.

Tasks
- Explaining defects to solution-finders and participants in the analysis forum
- Filtering duplicate defects
- Providing/ordering supplementary data for the defects
- Ordering evaluation of whether defects can be reproduced in other environments
- Checking solutions for completeness and project-policy fit
- Explaining defects solutions
- Monitoring the status of defects
- Reporting on the progress of solutions (also in terms of any agreements on the speed of problem-solving)
- Advising consultation bodies on defects.

Required knowledge and skills
Test-specific
- General knowledge of the TMap life cycle
IT
- General IT knowledge and experience
- Competent in interpreting test bases in any form
General
- Sound knowledge of agreements within the project in connection with

prioritisation of defects
- Excellent interpersonal skills
- Excellent written and verbal communication skills
- Competent in coping with conflict and possessing negotiation techniques
- Able to accept criticism.

System expert

The system expert has the responsibility of explaining to the testers the functionality and overall technical architecture of the system under test. He/she will provide support with the system test, functional acceptance test, user acceptance test and system integration test.

Tasks
- Explaining the functionality of the system, also in relation to the business processes
- Explaining the technical architecture of the system.

Required knowledge and skills
Test-specific
- General knowledge of the TMap life cycle
IT
- Detailed knowledge of the functionality
- Detailed knowledge of the technical architecture
- Competent in interpreting the functional specifications
General
- General knowledge of the subject matter
- Good interpersonal skills.

Test infrastructure coordinator

The test infrastructure coordinator is responsible within the test team for contact with the parties charged with the setup and maintenance of a high level of availability of test infrastructure (test environment, test tools and workplaces for the tester).
This role is preferably filled by one person, often on a part-time basis. If a suitable individual cannot be found, the tasks within the role can be distributed among several people.

Tasks
- Ensuring timely availability of the test environment
- Ensuring timely availability of test tools, with planning and controlling tools being required earlier than test execution tools
- Ensuring timely availability of workplaces
- Coordination with other parties on test infrastructure

- Advising on:
  - Solving defects/incidents in the area of test infrastructure
  - Impact of test infrastructure change proposals
  - Specifications of test infrastructure
  - Costs of using test infrastructure.

Required knowledge and skills
Test-specific
- Knowledge of the TMap life cycle
- Knowledge of test tools
IT
- General knowledge of hardware, environment software, connections and environment data
- Specific knowledge of hardware, environment software, connections and environment data necessary for the system under test
- Knowledge of the operation and administration of the system
General
- Knowledge of the processes in the organisation that provide availability of test environment, test tools and workplaces, both for structural and problem-solving issues
- Good interpersonal skills
- Good written and verbal communication skills
- Active in (management of) problem-solving.

Test project administrator
The test project administrator is responsible for the administration of the testproject information and the availability of this information, which can include information on progress and project documentation.

Tasks
- Collecting, checking and registering information on progress
- Supplying information on progress
- Collecting and administering project documentation.

Required knowledge and skills
Test-specific
- General knowledge of the TMap life cycle
IT
- Knowledge of spreadsheet and word-processing programs
General
- Excellent administration skills
- Competent in the use of project management tools
- Conscientious approach.

Test team leader

The role of test team leader includes responsibility for the day-to-day work of a test team. This role is introduced if the test team is split into several teams. Reasons for splitting may be that the test team is too big for one test manager, or the test team is operating at several locations. Each team is then led by a test team leader. In a small test team, this role is combined with the role of tester into that of co-working supervisor.

Tasks
- Creating detailed planning of the test team
- Monitoring of and reporting on the progress of the test process
- Reporting on the quality of the test object
- Managing the solving of problems concerning the test infrastructure
- Reporting on bottlenecks and, where possible, their solutions
- Day-to-day management of the test team
- Coaching of testers in the test team.

Required knowledge and skills
Test-specific
- Extensive knowledge of the TMap life cycle and the primary test activities
- Specialist skills in testability review and test design techniques
- Knowledge of the use of test tools

IT
- General knowledge of IT and general IT experience
- Knowledge of system development techniques
- Competent in the interpretation of test basis

General
- Leadership skills
- Knowledge of project-based approaches
- Able to provide coaching.

Testware administrator

The testware administrator is responsible for the administration of the testware and checking of compliance with the testing regulations in the area of testware.

Tasks
- Setting up of testware administration, procedures and regulations
- Management of the testware
- Physical configuration management of testware, also in relation to the configuration management of the test basis, test object and test infrastructure
- Checking compliance with regulations on testware.

Required knowledge and skills

Test-specific

- Knowledge of the TMap life cycle
- General knowledge of the testware types
- Knowledge of the test regulations on testware

IT

- General knowledge of the system development process and system development products
- Knowledge of management tools for testware management and configuration management

General

- Proactive approach
- Conscientious and strict approach to working in accordance with the procedures
- Creative in coming up with solutions within the set rules
- Good interpersonal skills.

Glossary

Acceptance test
A test executed by the user(s) and manager(s) in an environment simulating the operational environment to the greatest possible extent, that should demonstrate that the developed system meets the functional and quality requirements.

Adaptive
The ability to split up an element into sub-elements that, in a different combination, result in a new, valuable element for the specific situation.

Basic technique
The method of deriving test situations from the test basis to achieve the required coverage type.

BDTM
Business driven test management is aimed at enabling the client to manage the test process on rational and economic grounds. Important BDTM aspects are: result, risk, time and cost.

Boundary value analysis
Test principle based on the fact that a test around a boundary has a greater chance to detect a defect.

Business case
The business case provides the economic justification for the project and answers the questions: why do we do this project, which investments are needed, what does the client wish to achieve with the result?

Central starting point
See Starting point.

Chain test
See End-to-end test.

Checklist (coverage type)
All the situations are tested that are summed up in an unstructured list.

Code review
A method of improving the quality of written code by evaluating the work against the specifications and/or guidelines and subjecting it to peer review.

Combined test
Test approach by which the system test and the functional acceptance test are combined to a single test level.

Completeness
The certainty that *all* inputs and changes are processed by the system.

Condition coverage
The possible outcomes of ("true" or "false") for each condition are tested at least once.

Condition/decision coverage
The possible outcomes of each condition and of the decision are tested at least once. This implies both "condition coverage" and "decision coverage".

Connectivity
How easy a link with a different information system or within the information system can be made and modified.

Continuity
The certainty that the information system will continue uninterruptedly, which means that it can be resumed within a reasonable time even after serious interruptions.

Correctness
The degree to which the system processes the input and changes entered correctly, in accordance with the specifications, to produce consistent data sets.

Coverage
Coverage is the ratio between that which can be tested and that which is tested with the test set.

Coverage ratio
The percentage of test situations, as defined by the coverage type, that is covered by the test.

Coverage type
The form in which the covering of test situations deducible from the test basis, is expressed.

Data controllability
The ease with which the correctness and completeness of the information (in the course of time) can be checked.

Decision coverage
The possible outcomes of the decision are tested at least once.

Decision point
A combination of one or more conditions that define the conditions for the various possibilities in the subsequent system behaviour.

Defect (fault)
The result of an error residing in the code or document.

Degradation factor
The ease with which the core of the information system can continue after a part has failed.

Driver
A simulation program that replaces a program that should take care of the control and/or the calling of the test object.

Dynamic testing
Testing by execution of the test object and/or the running of software.

Effectivity
The degree to which the information system meets the demands of the organisation and the profile of the end users for whom it is intended, as well as the degree to which the information system contributes to the achievement of business objectives.

Efficiency
The relationship between the performance level of the system (expressed in the transaction volume and overall speed) and the amount of resources (CPU cycles, I/O time, memory and network capacity, etc.) that are used.

End-to-end test
A test type where the end-to-end functionality of one or more systems is tested with end-to-end test cases.

Equivalence class
In the application of equivalence classes, the entire value range of a parameter is partitioned into classes, in which the system behaviour is similar (equivalent).

Error
Human mistake; this action takes place prior to any faults and/or failures.

Evaluation
Evaluation is assessing the intermediary products in the system development process.

Exploration Testing
Is the simultaneous learning, designing and executing of tests, in other words every form of testing in which the tester designs his tests during test execution and the information obtained is reused to design new and improved test cases.

Fail-over possibilities
The ease with which (part of) the information system can continue elsewhere.

Failure
The result or manifestation of one or more faults. When the system is performing differently from the required behaviour, from a viewpoint outside the system. Users will see the failure.

Fault (defect)
The result of an error residing in the code or document. Fault is the view from inside the system. Fault is the state where mistake or error exists. Developers will see the fault.

Flexibility
The degree to which the user may introduce extensions or modifications to the information system without changing the program itself. Or: the degree to which the system can be modified by the controlling organisation without being dependent on the IT department for maintenance.

FPA functions
Subdivision of user functions in FPA functions: logical set of data, links, input functions, output functions, reading functions. These FPA functions are the elementary building blocks to determine the functionality of a system.

Function point
Unit to measure the functionality and/or the size of application software.

Function point analysis (FPA)
A method aiming to measure the size of the functionality of an automated system. The measurement is independent of the technology. This measurement may be used as a base for the measurement of productivity, the estimation of the needed resources, and project control.

Functional acceptance test
A test carried out by the future user(s) in an optimally simulated production environment, with the aim of demonstrating that the developed system meets the functional requirements.

Functionality
The certainty that data processing is correct and complete, in accordance with the description in the functional specifications.

Generic Test Agreements
The overall approach for the setup and organisation of test processes that applies to more than one project or release. General agreements on e.g. the test process, standard strategy, estimating method, procedures, organisation, communication, documentation, etc.

Infrastructure (suitability of)
The suitability of hardware, network, systems software and DBMS for the application concerned and the degree to which the elements of this infrastructure interrelate.

Initial situation
Everything that is needed to prepare the system for receiving the required input. This includes not only the data that are needed for the processing, but also the condition in which the system and its environment must be. For instance, one might think of setting a specific system date, or running specific week and month batches that bring the system to a specific status.

Inspection
A formal evaluation technique, with products being read thoroughly by a group of experts. In addition to determining whether the solution is adequately processed, an inspection focuses primarily on achieving consensus on the quality of a product. The aim of the inspection is to help the author find as many deviations as possible in the available time.

Known errors
Defects that have been found but have not been solved (yet).

Logical test case
Describes, *in logical terms*, the circumstances in which the system behaviour is examined by indicating which *test situations* are covered by the test case.

Maintainability
The ease with which the information system can be adapted to new demands from the user, to changing external environments, or in order to correct defects.

Manageability
The effort needed to get and keep the information system in its operational state.

Master test plan
Test plan by which the various test levels are geared to one another.

Modified condition/decision coverage
Every possible outcome of a condition is the determinant of the outcome of the decision, at least once.

Multiple condition coverage
All the possible combinations of outcomes of conditions in a decision (therefore the complete decision table) are tested at least once. This implies "modified condition/decision coverage".

Object part
A logically coherent part of the test object from the perspective of the characteristic to be tested.

Online
Function mode of an information system in which the information system immediately processes the commands and directly shows the answer (output) on the screen (or otherwise).

Orthogonal array
An orthogonal array $L_N(s^k, t)$ is a 2-dimensional array of N rows and k columns consisting of elements that can assume s values, whereby every combination of t columns contains all the combinations of the s values in equal proportion.

Pairwise testing
Tests all the possibilities of any combination of 2 factors.

Performance
The speed with which the information system processes interactive and batch transactions.

Permanent test organisation
A line organisation that offers test services.

Physical test case
The *concrete elaboration* of a logical test case, with choices having been made for the values of all required the input and settings of the environmental factors.

Portability
The diversity of the hardware and software platforms on which the information system can run, and how easy it is to transfer the system from one environment to another.

Pre-test
Testing the delivered product in such a way that it is determined whether or not the product is of sufficient quality to execute a complete test of this product.

Product risk
The chance that the product fails in relation to the expected damage if this occurs:
Product risk = Chance of failure * Damage
where Chance of failure = Chance of defects * Frequency of use

Product risk analysis
Analysing the product to be tested with the aim of achieving a joint view, for the test manager and other stakeholders, of the more or less risky characteristics and parts of the product to be tested so that the thoroughness of testing can be related to this view.

Production acceptance test
A test carried out by the future administrator(s) in an optimally simulated production environment, with the aim of demonstrating that the developed system meets the requirements set by system management.

Quality
The totality of features and characteristics of a product or service that bear on its ability to satisfy stated or implied needs.

Quality assurance
All the planned and systematic activities necessary to provide adequate confidence that a product or service meets the requirements for quality.

Quality characteristic
A quality characteristic describes a property of an information system.

Recoverability
The ease and speed with which the information system can be restored after an interruption.

Regression
Regression is the phenomenon that the quality of a system deteriorates as a whole as a result of individual amendments.

Regression test
A regression test is aimed at verifying that all the unchanged parts of a system still function correctly after the implementation of a change.

Reliability
The degree to which the information system remains free from interruptions.

Reusability
The degree to which parts of the information system, or the design, can be reused for the development of different applications.

Review
An evaluation technique where a product (60-80% complete) is submitted to a number of reviewers with the question to assess it from a certain perspective (depending on the review type). A review focuses primarily on finding courses for a solution on the basis of the knowledge and competencies of the reviewers, and on finding and correcting defects. There are various review types, such as: technical review (e.g. selecting solution direction/alternative), management review (e.g. determining project status), peer review (review by colleagues), and expert review (review by experts).

Risk reporting
A description of the extent to which the system meets the specified quality requirements and the risks associated with bringing a particular version into production, including any available alternatives.

Robustness
The degree to which the information system proceeds as usual even after an interruption.

Role
Describes one or more tasks and the knowledge and skills required to carry them out.

Security
The certainty that data can be viewed and changed only by those who are authorized to do so.

Starting point
Initial situations often contain the same data for several test cases. Such data are therefore included in a so-called starting point for the entire test and not separated for each test case. It is called a central starting point if this is intended for more tests or testers.

Static testing
Testing by examining products (such as manuals or source code) without any programs being executed.

Stub
A simulation program.

Suitability
The degree to which manual procedures match the automated information system and the fitness for use of these manual procedures for the organisation.

System integration test
A test carried out by the future user(s) in an optimally simulated production environment, with the aim of demonstrating that (sub)system interface agreements have been met, correctly interpreted and correctly implemented.

System management
System management is responsible for technical operation of the software in its intended infrastructure in production.

System test
A test carried out by the supplier in a (manageable) laboratory environment, with the aim of demonstrating that the developed system, or parts of it, meet with the functional and non-functional specifications and the technical design.

Test basis
The test basis is the information that defines the required system behaviour.

Test case
Used to examine whether the system displays the desired behaviour under specific circumstances.

Test depth level
Test depth level N = the certainty that all the combinations of N consecutive paths are covered.

Test design technique
A standardised method of deriving test cases from a particular test basis that will achieve a certain coverage.

Test environment
A composition of parts, such as hardware and software, connections, environment data, maintenance tools and management processes in which a test is carried out.

Test goal
A goal that, for the client, is relevant for testing, often formulated in terms of business processes supported by IT, realised user requirements or use cases, critical success factors, change proposals or cited risks to be covered.

Test harness
A collection of software and test data configured for a development environment with the purpose of dynamically testing one unit or a series of units, whereby the behaviour and output are checked.

Test infrastructure
Consists of the facilities and resources necessary to facilitate the satisfactory execution of the test. A distinction is made between test environments, test tools and workplaces.

Test level
A test level is a group of test activities that are managed and executed collectively.

Test line
The operational organisation to provide test services to one or more clients. A test line has a fixed team of testers, infrastructure, test tools and standardised work procedures.

Test object
The test object is the information system (or part thereof) to be tested.

Test organisation
The whole of the test functions, facilities, procedures and activities including their relationships.

Test pattern
A general solution for a specific recurring test problem.

Test plan
In a test plan the general structure and the strategic choices with respect to the test to be executed are formulated. The test plan forms the scope of reference during the execution of the test and also serves as an instrument to communicate with the client of the test. The test plan is a description of the test project, including a description of the activities and the planning; therefore it is *not* a description of the tests themselves.

Test point
Unit of measurement for the size of the high-level test to be executed.

Test point analysis (TPA)
A method with the possibility to perform a technology-independent measurement of the test depth level of an information system, on the basis of a function point analysis, and to use this measurement as a basis for a productivity measurement, an estimate of the required resources, and project management.

Test policy
Describes how an organisation deals with the people, resources and methods involved with the test process in the various situations.

Test process
The collection of tools, techniques and working methods used to perform a test.

Test script
Combines multiple physical test cases to be able to execute them in an efficient and simple manner.

Test situation
An isolated condition under which the test object displays a specific behaviour that needs to be tested.

Test strategy
The distribution of the test effort and coverage over the parts to be tested or aspects of the test object aimed at finding the most important defects as early and cheaply as possible.

Test team
A group of people who, led by a test manager, undertake test activities.

Test technique
A set of actions aimed at creating a test deliverable by a universal method.

Test tool
An automated instrument that supports one or more test activities, such as planning, control, specification and execution.

Test tool policy
Describes how an organisation handles the acquisition, implementation and use of test tools in the various situations.

Test type
A group of test activities with the intention of checking the information system in respect of a number of correlated (part aspects of) quality characteristics.

Test unit
A collection of processes, transactions and/or functions that are tested collectively.

Testability
The ease and speed with which characteristics of the system can be tested (following each adjustment).

Testability review
The detailed check of the test basis on testability.

Testing
Testing is a process that provides insight into, and advice on, quality and the related risks.

Testing (ISO)
Technical operation that consists of the determination of one or more characteristics of a given product, process or service according to a specified procedure [ISO/IEC Guide 2, 1991].

Testware
All the test documentation produced in the course of the test process that can be used for maintenance purposes and that should therefore be transferable and maintainable.

Unit integration test
A test carried out by the developer in the development environment, with the aim of demonstrating that a logical group of units meets the requirements defined in the technical specifications.

Unit test
A test carried out in the development environment by the developer, with

the aim of demonstrating that a unit meets the requirements defined in the technical specifications.

User function
A property recognized by the user which the delivered product should meet. Generally speaking the user functions may best be described as objects and processes.

User-friendliness
How easy it is for end users to use the system. This general definition is often divided into how easy it is for end users to learn to work with the information system, and how easy it is to work with for trained users.

Users acceptance test
A test carried out by the future user(s) in an optimally simulated production environment, with the aim of demonstrating that the developed system meets the requirements of the users.

Walkthrough
An evaluation technique by which the author explains the contents of a product during a meeting. Several different objectives are possible: bringing all participants to the same starting point, transfer of information, asking the participants for additional information or letting the participants choose from the alternatives proposed by the author.

References

- [Aalst, 1999]
  Aalst, L. van der, Koning, C. de, *Testing expensive? Not testing is more expensive!*, Informatie, October 1999, www.tmap.net
- [Abran, 2003]
  Abran, A. (2003), *Implementation Guide for ISO/IEC 19761:2003 (Measurement Manual)*, version 2.2, Common Software Measurement International Consortium, www.cosmicon.com
- [Bach, 2000]
  Bach, Jonathan, (2000) Session-based test management, www.satisfice.com
- [Bach, 2002]
  Bach, James, (2002) Exploratory testing explained, www.satisfice.com
- [Bach, 2003]
  Bach, J. (1996-2002), From his workshop Rapid Software Testing
- [Basili, 1994]
  Basili, V.R., Galdiera, G. and Rombach, H.D. (1994), *The Goal-Question-Metric Approach*, John Wiley & Sons, Inc., New York
- [Basili, 1997]
  Basili, V., Green, S., Laitenberger, O., Lanubile, F., Shull, F., Sorumgard, S., Zelkowitz, M., *The Empirical Investigation of Perspective-Based Reading*, also appeared in: Empirical Software Engineering, 2, 1997
- [Beck, 2002]
  Beck, Kent, Test Driven Development By Example (2002) Addison-Wesley Professional, ISBN 0321146530
- [Beizer, 1990]
  Beizer, B. (1990), *Software Testing Techniques*, International Thomson Computer Press.
- [Belbin, 2003]
  Belbin, R Meredith, Management Teams – Why They Succeed or Fail (second edition) (2003), Butterworth Heinemann, ISBN: 0 7506 5910 6
- [Bieberstein, 2005]
  Bieberstein, Norbert; Bose, Sanjay; Fiammante, Marc; Jones, Keith and Shah, Rawn, *Service-Oriented Architecture (SOA) Compass, Business Value, Planning and Enterprise Roadmap*, (2005) IBM Press, ISBN 0-13-187002-5
- [Black, 2002]
  Rex Black, keynote at Eurostar2002, Kopenhagen
- [Black, 2004]
  Black, Rex, *Critical Testing Processes* (2004) Addison Wesley, ISBN 0-201-74868-1

- [Boehm, 1981]
  Boehm, B.W. (1981), *Software Engineering Economics*, Prentice-Hall Inc., Englewood Cliffs, ISBN 0-13-822122-7
- [Broekman, 2003]
  Broekman, B., Notenboom, E. (2003), *Testing Embedded Software*, Addison-Wesley, London, ISBN 0-321-15986-1
- [Brooks, 1975/1995]
  Brooks, Frederic P., The Mythical Man-Month: Essays on Software Engineering, 20th Anniversary Edition, (1975/1995), Addison-Wesley Professional, ISBN 0201835959
- [Clifton, 2004]
  Clifton, Marc, Advanced Unit Testing (2004), http://www.codeproject.com/gen/design/autp5.asp
- [Cockburn, 2000]
  Cockburn, Alistair and Williams, Laurie, The Costs and Benefits of Pair Programming, Humans and Technology Technical Report 2000.01, Jan 2000, http://alistair.cockburn.us
- [Collard, 1999]
  Collard, R. (1999), *Test Estimation*, STAREast 1999
- [Copeland, 2003]
  Copeland, L. (2003), *A Practitioner's Guide to Software Test Design*, Artech House Publishers, ISBN 1-58053-791-X
- [Deming, 1992]
  Deming, W. Edwards (1992), *Out of the crisis*, University of Cambridge, ISBN 0-521-30553-5
- [Fagan, 1986]
  Fagan, M.E. (1986), *Advances in Software Inspections*, in: IEEE Transactions on Software Engineering, July 1986
- [Fewster, 1999]
  Fewster, M., Graham, D. (1999), *Software Test Automation*, Addison/Wesley US, ISBN 0-201-331403
- [Gilb, 1993]
  Gilb, T. & R. Graham (1993), *Software Inspection*, Addison Wesley, ISBN 0-201-63181-4
- [Hedayat, 1999]
  Hedayat, A.S., Sloane, N.J.A. and John Stufken (1999) *Orthogonal arrays: Theory and Applications*, Springer Verlag, ISBN 0-387-98766-5
- [IEEE, 1998]
  The Institute of Electrical and Electronics Engineers, Inc. (1998), *IEEE Std 1028-1997 Standard for Software Reviews*, 345 East 47th Street, New York, NY 10017-2394, USA, ISBN 1-55937-987-1
- [IFPUG, 1994]
  IFPUG (International Function Point User Group) (1994), *Function Point Counting Practices*, release 4.0, IFPUG, January 1994

- [ISO/IEC, 1991]
  ISO/IEC Guide 2 (1991), *General terms and definitions concerning standardization and related activities*, International Organization of Standardization
- [ISO 9126-1, 1999]
  ISO/IEC 9126 part 1 (1999), *Information Technology - Software Product Quality - Part 1: Quality Model*, International Organization of Standardization
- [ISO, 1994]
  ISO 8402 (1994), *Quality Management and quality assurance - vocabulary*, International Organization of Standardization
- [Jones, 1996]
  Jones, Capers, (1996), *Applied Software Measurement: Assuring Productivity & Quality*, McGraw Hill Text, ISBN 0070328269
- [Kaner, 1999]
  Kaner, C., Falk, J., Nguyen, H.Q. (1999), Testing computer software, 2nd edition, Wiley, ISBN 0-471-35846-0
- [Kaner, 2001]
  Kaner C., Bach J. (2001), *Exploratory testing in pairs*, StarEast 2001
- [Koomen, 1999]
  Koomen, T., Pol, M. (1999), *Test Process Improvement: a practical step-by-step guide to structures testing, Addison-Wesley London*, ISBN 0 210 59624 5
- [Koomen, 2005]
  Koomen, T., Baarda, R., (2005), *TMap® Test Topics* (part I), Tutein Nolthenius, 's-Hertogenbosch, ISBN 90-72194-75-6
- [Laitenberger, 1995]
  Laitenberger, O., (1995), *Perspective based Reading: Technique, Validation and Research in Future*, Student project (Projektarbeit), Department of Computer Science, University of Kaiserslautern, 67653 Kaiserslautern, Germany
- [Lyndsay, 2002]
  Lyndsay, James (2002), Adventures in session-based testing, Proceedings EuroSTAR 2002
- [McCabe, 1976]
  McCabe, T.J. (1976), *A complexity metric*, IEEE Transactions on software engineering, vol. 2, IEEE Press
- [McCall, 1977]
  McCall, J.A., P.K. Richards en G.F. Walters (1977), *Factors in software quality*, RADC-TR-77-363 Rome Air Development Center, Griffis Air Force, Rome (New York, USA)
- [Musa, 1998]
  Musa, J.D. (1998), *Software Reliability Engineering*, McGraw-Hill
- [Nielsen, 1999]
  Jakob Nielsen, Designing Web Usability: The Practice of Simplicity, (1999) New Riders Publishing, Indianapolis, ISBN 1-56205-810-X Nielsen Jakob, www.useit.com, 2006
- [Pettichord, 2000]

Pettichord, Bret, Testers and Developers Think Differently; Understanding and utilizing the diverse traits of key players on your team, Jan/Feb 2000, STQE Magazine

- [PRINCE2, 2002]
  Managing Successful Projects with PRINCE2 (2002), The Stationary Office London, ISBN 0-11-330891-4
- [Roden, 2005]
  Lloyd Roden, Choosing and Managing the Ideal Test Team, winter 2005 issue, www.methodsandtools.com
- [Rothman, 2006]
  Johanna Rothman, "Hiring The Best Knowledge Workers, Techies & Nerds: The Secrets & Science Of Hiring Technical People, (2006) Dorset House Publishing Company, ISBN 0932633595
- [Schaefer, 1996]
  Schaefer, H., (1996), *Surviving under time and budget pressure*, in Proceedings EuroSTAR Conferencce 1996, Amsterdam. Also home.c2i.net/schaefer/testing/risktest.doc
- [Splaine, 2002]
  Splaine, Steven, Testing Web Security: Assessing the Security of Web Sites and Applications (2002) Wiley, ISBN 0471232815
- [The Standish Group, 2003]
  The Standish Group, (2003), *What Are Your Requirements?*, The Standish Group International, West Yarmouth
- [Test Cube, 2006]
  The Test Cube, Expertise group Sogeti, 1.0, October 2006, www.tmap.net
- [Tufte, 2001]
  Edward Tufte, The visual display of quantitative information, 2nd edition, 2001, Graphics Press LLC, ISBN 0961392142
- [Vaaraniemi, 2003]
  Vaaraniemi, Sami, The benefits of automated unit testing, November 2003, http://www.codeproject.com
- [Whittaker, 2000]
  Whittaker, J., Jorgenson, A. (2000), *How to break software*, proceedings Eurostar 2000
- [Whittaker, 2003]
  Whittaker, James A., Thompson, Herbert H., *How to Break Software Security* (2003) Addison Wesley, ISBN 0321194330
- [www.w3c.org]
  Web Content Accessibility Guidelines 1.0 en 2.0

About Sogeti

Sogeti forms the Capgemini's Local Professional Services Division, counting over 15,000 employees. Sogeti offers a package of local services for large enterprises.

Designing, developing, implementing, testing and managing IT solutions is our core-business. One of our specializations is our testing and QA offering, Software Control Testing (SCT). Proof of this are our internationally recognized methods TMap®, the Test Management approach for structured software testing and TPI®, the Test Process Improvement model for improving test processes.

Software Control Testing

We understand the importance of getting maximum business value from your software, especially in today's challenging and increasingly competitive economic environment. Currently, organizations are under intense pressure to develop high-quality software more quickly, making the risk associated with insufficient software quality greater. Effective software testing is one of the most powerful actions that an organization can take to control and minimize these risks.

Built on practical "real-world" experience, Sogeti's SCT solution takes a proactive and structured approach to software testing. We help organizations detect and correct defects early in the development lifecycle and save on unnecessary cost escalations in the future. Using our solutions, our clients deliver more complex, high-quality software, faster and more cost effectively. At the heart of the SCT solution is the world-renowned Test Management approach (TMap), the company's methodology for structured software testing services. This methodology, built on Sogeti's global experience and expertise, is designed to address the key issues of quality, time and cost. Flexible by design, TMap offers a complete and consistent approach, which is suitable for all types of organizations, of varying size, and can be adapted for use in any development environment. Complementing the TMap approach is Sogeti's Test Process Improvement (TPI) model, a model for reviewing and improving the entire test process.

The SCT solution covers the complete spectrum of software testing and quality assurance. Examples of our TMap related services are:

- Test management
- Testing (specifying and executing tests)
- Test consultancy
- Test automation

- Training and coaching
- Assessment and improvement of the test process
- Setting up a test organization
- Outsourcing of testing (TMap Factories, with local offices in the different countries and back offices in Spain and India)
- Requirements Lifecycle Management
- Reviews and inspections
- Quality assurance.

We offer our services throughout Europe and the USA. Countries where we have local offices are Belgium/Luxembourg, Denmark, France, Germany, Ireland, Spain, Sweden, Switzerland, the Netherlands, United Kingdom, and the USA. The website www.sogeti.com offers connections to all local websites.

In order to be able to continuously follow the developments and trends in IT, Sogeti invests considerably in research & development of the SCT offering. Innovations in technology, new development methodologies, new areas of use and changes in trends of the IT-policies of the leading companies are closely followed.

The results of research & development are published in journals, international newsletters and in TMap Test Topics books, presented on TMap Test Topics seminars and the international test conferences and networks like EuroSTAR, ICSTest and STAREast. Detailed results are also published on www.tmap.net.

Index